Alexander
Chapsiadis.

£2-00

FOUNDATIONS OF MODERN ANALYSIS

This is Volume 10-I in
PURE AND APPLIED MATHEMATICS
A Series of Monographs and Textbooks
Editors: PAUL SMITH AND SAMUEL EILENBERG
A complete list of titles in this series appears at the end of this volume

Volume 10
TREATISE ON ANALYSIS
10-I. Chapters I–XI
(Foundations of Modern Analysis, enlarged and corrected printing, 1969).
10-II. Chapters XII–XV

ACADEMIC PRESS INTERNATIONAL EDITION

FOUNDATIONS OF

MODERN ANALYSIS

Enlarged and Corrected Printing

J. DIEUDONNÉ

Université de Nice
Faculté des Sciences
Parc Valrose, Nice, France

ACADEMIC PRESS **New York and London** **1969**

A Subsidiary of Harcourt Brace Jovanovich, Publishers

ACADEMIC PRESS INTERNATIONAL EDITION

This edition not for sale in the United States of America and Canada.

ACADEMIC PRESS, INC.
111 Fifth Avenue, New York, New York 10003

United Kingdom Edition published by
ACADEMIC PRESS, INC. (LONDON) LTD.
Berkeley Square House, London W1X 6BA

LIBRARY OF CONGRESS CATALOG CARD NUMBER: 60-8049
THIRD (ENLARGED AND CORRECTED) PRINTING, 1970
AMS 1968 Subject Classification 0001

PRINTED IN THE UNITED STATES OF AMERICA

PREFACE TO THE ENLARGED AND CORRECTED PRINTING

This book is the first volume of a treatise which will eventually consist of four volumes. It is also an enlarged and corrected printing, essentially without changes, of my "Foundations of Modern Analysis," published in 1960. Many readers, colleagues, and friends have urged me to write a sequel to that book, and in the end I became convinced that there was a place for a survey of modern analysis, somewhere between the "minimum tool kit" of an elementary nature which I had intended to write, and specialist monographs leading to the frontiers of research. My experience of teaching has also persuaded me that the mathematical apprentice, after taking the first step of "Foundations," needs further guidance and a kind of general bird's eye-view of his subject before he is launched onto the ocean of mathematical literature or set on the narrow path of his own topic of research.

Thus I have finally been led to attempt to write an equivalent, for the mathematicians of 1970, of what the "Cours d'Analyse" of Jordan, Picard, and Goursat were for mathematical students between 1880 and 1920.

It is manifestly out of the question to attempt encyclopedic coverage, and certainly superfluous to rewrite the works of N. Bourbaki. I have therefore been obliged to cut ruthlessly in order to keep within limits comparable to those of the classical treatises. I have opted for breadth rather than depth, in the opinion that it is better to show the reader rudiments of many branches of modern analysis rather than to provide him with a complete and detailed exposition of a small number of topics.

Experience seems to show that the student usually finds a new theory difficult to grasp at a first reading. He needs to return to it several times before he becomes really familiar with it and can distinguish for himself which are the essential ideas and which results are of minor importance, and only then will he be able to apply it intelligently. The chapters of this treatise are therefore samples rather than complete theories: indeed, I have systematically tried not to be exhaustive. The works quoted in the bibliography will always enable the reader to go deeper into any particular theory.

However, I have refused to distort the main ideas of analysis by presenting them in too specialized a form, and thereby obscuring their power and generality. It gives a false impression, for example, if differential geometry is restricted to two or three dimensions, or if integration is restricted to Lebesgue measure, on the pretext of making these subjects more accessible or "intuitive."

On the other hand I do not believe that the essential content of the ideas involved is lost, in a first study, by restricting attention to separable metrizable topological spaces. The mathematicians of my own generation were certainly right to banish hypotheses of countability wherever they were not needed: this was the only way to get a clear understanding. But now the situation is well understood: the most central parts of analysis (let us say those which turn on the notion of a finite-dimensional manifold) involve only separable metrizable spaces, in the great majority of important applications. Moreover, there exists a general technique, which is effective and usually easy to apply, for passing from a proof based on hypotheses of countability to a general proof. Broadly speaking, the recipe is to "replace sequences by filters." Often, it should be said, the result is simply to make the original proof more elegant. At the risk of being reviled as a reactionary I have therefore taken as my motto "only the countable exists at infinity": I believe that the beginner will do better to concentrate his attention on the real difficulties involved in concepts such as differential manifolds and integration, without having at the same time to worry about secondary topological problems which he will meet rather seldom in practice.†

In this text, the whole structure of analysis is built up from the foundations. The only things assumed at the outset are the rules of logic and the usual properties of the natural numbers, and with these two exceptions all the proofs in the text rest on the axioms and theorems proved earlier.‡ Nevertheless this treatise (including the first volume) is not suitable for students who have not yet covered the first two years of an undergraduate honours course in mathematics.

† In the same spirit I have abstained (sometimes at the cost of greater length) from the use of transfinite induction in separable metrizable spaces: not in the name of philosophical scruples which are no longer relevant, but because it seems to me to be unethical to ban the uncountable with one hand whilst letting it in surreptitiously with the other.

‡ This logical order is not followed so rigorously in the problems and in some of the examples, which contain definitions and results that have not up to that point appeared in the text, or will not appear at all.

A striking characteristic of the elementary parts of analysis is the small amount of algebra required. Effectively all that is needed is some elementary linear algebra (which is included in an appendix at the end of the first volume, for the reader's convenience). However, the role played by algebra increases in the subsequent volumes, and we shall finally leave the reader at the point where this role becomes preponderant, notably with the appearance of advanced commutative algebra and homological algebra. As reference books in algebra we have taken R. Godement's "Abstract Algebra,"§ and S. A. Lang's "Algebra"¶ which we shall possibly augment in certain directions by means of appendices.

As with the first volume, I have benefited greatly during the preparation of this work from access to numerous unpublished manuscripts of N. Bourbaki and his collaborators. To them alone is due any originality in the presentation of certain topics.

Nice, France
April, 1969

J. DIEUDONNÉ

§ Godement, R., "Abstract Algebra." Houghton-Mifflin, New York, 1968. (Original French edition published by Hermann, Paris, 1963.)

¶ Lang, S. A., "Algebra." Addison-Wesley, Reading, Massachusetts, 1965.

PREFACE

This volume is an outgrowth of a course intended for first year graduate students or exceptionally advanced undergraduates in their junior or senior year. The purpose of the course (taught at Northwestern University in 1956–1957) was twofold: (a) to provide the necessary elementary background for all branches of modern mathematics involving "analysis" (which in fact means everywhere, with the possible exception of logic and pure algebra); (b) to train the student in the use of the most fundamental mathematical tool of our time—the axiomatic method (with which he will have had very little contact, if any at all, during his undergraduate years).

It will be very apparent to the reader that we have everywhere emphasized the *conceptual* aspect of every notion, rather than its *computational* aspect, which was the main concern of classical analysis; this is true not only of the text, but also of most of the problems. We have included a rather large number of problems in order to supplement the text and to indicate further interesting developments. The problems will at the same time afford the student an opportunity of testing his grasp of the material presented.

Although this volume includes considerable material generally treated in more elementary courses (including what is usually called "advanced calculus") the point of view from which this material is considered is completely different from the treatment it usually receives in these courses. The fundamental concepts of function theory and of calculus have been presented within the framework of a theory which is sufficiently general to reveal the scope, the power, and the true nature of these concepts far better than it is possible under the usual restrictions of "classical analysis." It is not necessary to emphasize the well-known "economy of thought" which results from such a general treatment; but it may be pointed out that there is a corresponding "economy of notation," which does away with hordes of indices, much in the same way as "vector algebra" simplifies classical analytical geometry. This has also as a consequence the necessity of a strict adherence to axiomatic methods, with no appeal whatsoever to "geometric intuition," at least in the formal proofs: a necessity which we have emphasized by deliberately abstaining from introducing any diagram in the book. My opinion is that the graduate student of today must, as soon as possible, get a thorough training in this abstract and axiomatic way of thinking, if he is ever to understand what is currently going on in mathematical research. This volume aims to help the student to build up this "intuition of the abstract" which is so essential in the mind of a modern mathematician.

It is clear that students must have a good working knowledge of classical analysis before approaching this course. From the strictly logical point of view, however, the exposition is not based on *any* previous knowledge, with the exception of:

1. The first rules of mathematical logic, mathematical induction, and the fundamental properties of (positive and negative) integers.
2. Elementary linear algebra (over a field) for which the reader may consult Halmos [11], Jacobson [13], or Bourbaki [4]; these books, however, contain much more material than we will actually need (for instance we shall not use the theory of duality and the reader will know enough if he is familiar with the notions of vector subspace, hyperplane, direct sum, linear mapping, linear form, dimension, and codimension).

In the proof of each statement, we rely exclusively on the axioms and on theorems already proved in the text, with the two exceptions just mentioned. This rigorous sequence of logical steps is somewhat relaxed in the examples and problems, where we will often apply definitions or results which have not yet been (or ever will never be) proved in the text.

There is certainly room for a wide divergence of opinion as to what parts of analysis a student should learn during his first graduate year. Since we wanted to keep the contents of this book within the limits of what can materially be taught during a single academic year, some topics had to be eliminated. Certain topics were not included because they are too specialized, others because they may require more mathematical maturity than can usually be expected of a first-year graduate student or because the material has undoubtedly been covered in advanced calculus courses. If we were to propose a general program of graduate study for mathematicians we would recommend that *every* graduate student should be expected to be familiar with the contents of this book, whatever his future field of specialization may be.

I would like to express my gratitude to the mathematicians who have helped me in preparing these lectures, especially to H. Cartan and N. Bourbaki, who allowed me access to unpublished lecture notes and manuscripts, which greatly influenced the final form of this book. My best thanks also go to my colleagues in the Mathematics Department of Northwestern University, who made it possible for me to teach this course along the lines I had planned and greatly encouraged me with their constructive criticism.

April, 1960 J. DIEUDONNÉ

CONTENTS

NOTATIONS

In the following definitions the first digit refers to the number of the chapter in which the notation occurs and the second to the section within the chapter.

$=$	equals: 1.1
$\neq$	is different from: 1.1
$\in$	is an element of, belongs to: 1.1
$\notin$	is not an element of: 1.1
$\subset$	is a subset of, is contained in: 1.1
$\supset$	contains: 1.1
$\not\subset$	is not contained in: 1.1
$\{x \in X \mid P(x)\}$	the set of elements of X having property P: 1.1
$\emptyset$	the empty set: 1.1
$\{a\}$	the set having *a* as unique element: 1.1
$\mathfrak{P}(X)$	the set of subsets of X: 1.1
$X - Y$, $\complement_X Y$, $\complement Y$	complement of Y in X: 1.2
$\cup$	union: 1.2
$\cap$	intersection: 1.2
(a,b)	ordered pair: 1.3
$\mathrm{pr}_1\, c$, $\mathrm{pr}_2\, c$	first and second projection: 1.3
$G(x)$, $G^{-1}(y)$	cross sections of $G \subset X \times Y$: 1.3
$X \times Y$	product of two sets: 1.3
$X_1 \times X_2 \times \ldots \times X_n$	product of *n* sets: 1.3
$\mathrm{pr}_i\, z$	*i*th projection: 1.3
$\mathrm{pr}_{i_1 i_2 \ldots i_k}(z)$	partial projection: 1.3
X^n	product of *n* sets equal to X: 1.3
$F(x)$	value of the mapping F at *x*: 1.4

Y^X, $\mathscr{F}(X,Y)$	set of mappings of X into Y: 1.4
1_X	identity mapping of X: 1.4
$x \to T(x)$	mapping: 1.4
$F(A)$	direct image: 1.5
$F^{-1}(A)$	inverse image: 1.5
$F^{-1}(y)$	inverse image of a one element set $\{y\}$: 1.5
$F(.\,,y)$, $F(x,.)$	partial mappings of a mapping F of $A \subset X \times Y$ into Z: 1.5
j_A	natural injection: 1.6
F^{-1}	inverse mapping of a bijective mapping: 1.6
$G \circ F$	composed mapping: 1.7
$(x_\lambda)_{\lambda \in L}$	family: 1.8
$\mathbf{N}$	set of natural integers: 1.8
$\{x_1, \ldots, x_n\}$	set of elements of a finite sequence: 1.8
$\bigcup_{\lambda \in L} A_\lambda$, $\bigcup_\lambda A_\lambda$	union of a family of sets: 1.8
$\bigcap_{\lambda \in L} A_\lambda$, $\bigcap_\lambda A_\lambda$	intersection of a family of sets: 1.8
X/R	quotient set of a set X by an equivalence relation R: 1.8
$\prod_{\lambda \in L} X_\lambda$	product of a family of sets: 1.8
pr_J	projection on a partial product: 1.8
(u_λ)	mapping into a product of sets: 1.8
$\mathbf{R}$	set of real numbers: 2.1
$x + y$	sum of real numbers: 2.1
xy	product of real numbers: 2.1
0	element of **R**: 2.1
$-x$	opposite of a real number: 2.1
1	element of **R**: 2.1
x^{-1}, $1/x$	inverse in **R**: 2.1
$x \leqslant y$, $y \geqslant x$	order relation in **R**: 2.1
$x < y$, $y > x$	relation in **R**: 2.1
$]a,b[$, $[a,b]$, $[a,b[$, $]a,b]$	intervals in **R**: 2.1
$\mathbf{R}_+$, $\mathbf{R}_+^*$	set of real numbers $\geqslant 0$ (resp. > 0): 2.2
$\|x\|$, x^+, x^-	absolute value, positive and negative part of a real number: 2.2
$\mathbf{Q}$	set of rational numbers: 2.2
$\mathbf{Z}$	set of positive or negative integers: 2.2
l.u.b. X, sup X	least upper bound of a set: 2.3
g.l.b. X, inf X	greatest lower bound of a set: 2.3
$\sup_{x \in A} f(x)$, $\inf_{x \in A} f(x)$	supremum and infimum of f in A: 2.3
$\overline{\mathbf{R}}$	extended real line: 3.3

$+\infty, -\infty$	points at infinity in $\overline{\mathbf{R}}$: 3.3
$x \leqslant y, y \geqslant x$	order relation in $\overline{\mathbf{R}}$: 3.3
$d(\mathrm{A},\mathrm{B})$	distance of two sets: 3.4
$\mathrm{B}(a;r)$, $\mathrm{B}'(a;r)$, $\mathrm{S}(a;r)$	open ball, closed ball, sphere of center a and radius r: 3.4
$\delta(\mathrm{A})$	diameter: 3.4
$\mathring{\mathrm{A}}$	interior: 3.7
$\bar{\mathrm{A}}$	closure: 3.8
$\mathrm{fr}(\mathrm{A})$	frontier: 3.8
$\lim_{x \to a,\, x \in \mathrm{A}} f(x)$	limit of a function: 3.13
$\lim_{n \to \infty} x_n$	limit of a sequence: 3.13
$\Omega(a;f)$	oscillation of a function: 3.14
$\log_a x$	logarithm of a real number: 4.3
a^x	exponential of base a (x real): 4.3
$\mathbf{C}$	set of complex numbers: 4.4
$z + z'$, zz'	sum, product of complex numbers: 4.4
$0, 1, i$	elements of $\mathbf{C}$: 4.4
$\mathscr{R}z$, $\mathscr{I}z$	real and imaginary parts: 4.4
$\bar{z}$	conjugate of a complex number: 4.4
$\lvert z \rvert$	absolute value of a complex number: 4.4
$x + y$, λx, x	sum and product by a scalar in a vector space: 5.1
0	element of a vector space: 5.1
$\lVert x \rVert$	norm: 5.1
$\sum_{n=0}^{\infty} x_n$	sum of a series, series: 5.2
$\sum_{\alpha \in \mathrm{A}} x_\alpha$	sum of an absolutely summable family: 5.3
(c_0)	space of sequences tending to 0: 5.3, prob. 5
$\mathscr{L}(\mathrm{E};\mathrm{F})$	space of linear continuous mappings: 5.7
$\lVert u \rVert$	norm of a linear continuous mapping: 5.7
$\mathscr{L}(\mathrm{E}_1, \ldots, \mathrm{E}_n; \mathrm{F})$	space of multilinear continuous mappings: 5.7
l^1	space of absolutely convergent series: 5.7, prob. 1
l^∞	space of bounded sequences: 5.7, prob. 1
$(x \mid y)$	scalar product: 6.2
P_{F}	orthogonal projection: 6.3
l^2, $l^2_{\mathbf{R}}$, $l^2_{\mathbf{C}}$	Hilbert spaces of sequences: 6.5
$\mathscr{B}_{\mathrm{F}}(\mathrm{A})$, $\mathscr{B}_{\mathbf{R}}(\mathrm{A})$, $\mathscr{B}_{\mathbf{C}}(\mathrm{A})$	spaces of bounded mappings: 7.1
$\mathscr{C}_{\mathrm{F}}(\mathrm{E})$	space of continuous mappings: 7.2
$\mathscr{C}^{\infty}_{\mathrm{F}}(\mathrm{E})$	space of bounded continuous mappings: 7.2
$f(x+)$, $f(x-)$	limits to the right, to the left: 7.6
$f'(x_0)$, $\mathrm{D}f(x_0)$	(total) derivative at x_0: 8.1

f', $\mathrm{D}f$	derivative (as a function): 8.1
$f'(\alpha)$, $\mathrm{D}_+f(\alpha)$	derivative on the right: 8.4
$f_g'(\beta)$, $\mathrm{D}_-f(\beta)$	derivative on the left: 8.4
$\int_\alpha^\beta f(\xi)\,d\xi$	integral: 8.7
e, $\exp(x)$, $\log x$	(x real): 8.8
$\mathrm{D}_1f(a_1, a_2)$, $\mathrm{D}_2f(a_1, a_2)$	partial derivatives: 8.9
$f_{\xi_i}'(\xi_1, \ldots, \xi_n)$, $\dfrac{\partial}{\partial\xi_i} f(\xi_1, \ldots, \xi_n)$	partial derivatives: 8.10
$\dfrac{\mathrm{D}(f_1, \ldots, f_n)}{\mathrm{D}(\xi_1, \ldots, \xi_n)}$, $\dfrac{\partial(f_1, \ldots, f_n)}{\partial(\xi_1, \ldots, \xi_n)}$	jacobian: 8.10
$f''(x_0)$, $\mathrm{D}^2f(x_0)$, $f^{(p)}(x_0)$, $\mathrm{D}^pf(x_0)$	higher derivatives: 8.12
$f * \rho$	regularization: 8.12, prob. 2
$\mathscr{E}_{\mathrm{F}}^{(p)}(\mathrm{A})$	space of p times continuously differentiable mappings: 8.13.
$\lvert\alpha\rvert$, M_α, D^α, $\mathrm{D}_{\mathrm{M}_\alpha}$	(α composite index): 8.13
e^z, $\exp(z)$	(z complex): 9.5
$\sin z$, $\cos z$	sine and cosine: 9.5
π	9.5
$\log z$, $\mathrm{am}(z)$, $\dbinom{t}{n}$, $(1+z)^t$	(z, t complex numbers): 9.5, prob. 8
γ^0	opposite path: 9.6
$\gamma_1 \vee \gamma_2$	juxtaposition of paths: 9.6
$\int_\gamma f(z)\,dz$	integral along a road: 9.6
$j(a; \gamma)$	index with respect to a circuit: 9.8
$\mathrm{E}(z, p)$	primary factor: 9.12, prob. 1
$\Gamma(z)$	gamma function: 9.12, prob. 2
γ	Euler's constant: 9.12, prob. 2
$\int_\gamma f(z)\,dz$	integral along an endless road: 9.12, prob. 3
$\omega(a; f)$, $\omega(a)$	order of a function at a point: 9.15
$\mathscr{L}(\mathrm{E})$	algebra of operators: 11.1
uv	composed operator: 11.1
$\mathrm{sp}(u)$	spectrum: 11.1
$\mathrm{E}(\zeta)$, $\mathrm{E}(\zeta; u)$	eigenspace: 11.1
$\tilde{u}$	continuous extension: 11.2
$\mathrm{N}(\lambda)$, $\mathrm{N}(\lambda; u)$, $\mathrm{F}(\lambda)$, $\mathrm{F}(\lambda; u)$	subspaces attached to an eigenvalue of a compact operator: 11.4
$k(\lambda)$, $k(\lambda; u)$	order of an eigenvalue: 11.4
u^*	adjoint operator: 11.5

CHAPTER I

ELEMENTS OF THE THEORY OF SETS

We do not try in this chapter to put set theory on an axiomatic basis; this can however be done, and we refer the interested reader to Kelley [15] and Bourbaki [3] for a complete axiomatic description. Statements appearing in this chapter and which are not accompanied by a proof or a definition may be considered as axioms connecting undefined terms.

The chapter starts with some elementary definitions and formulas about sets, subsets and product sets (Sections **1.1** to **1.3**); the bulk of the chapter is devoted to the fundamental notion of *mapping*, which is the modern extension of the classical concept of a (numerical) *function* of one or several numerical "variables." Two points related to this concept deserve some comment:

1. The all-important (and characteristic) property of a mapping is that it associates to any "value" of the variable a *single* element; in other words, there is no such thing as a "multiple-valued" function, despite many books to the contrary. It is of course perfectly legitimate to define a mapping whose values are *subsets* of a given set, which may have more than one element; but such definitions are in practice useless (at least in elementary analysis), because it is impossible to define in a sensible way *algebraic operations* on the "values" of such functions. We return to this question in Chapter IX.

2. The student should as soon as possible become familiar with the idea that a function f is a single object, which may itself "vary" and is in general to be thought of as a "point" in a large "functional space"; indeed, it may be said that one of the main differences between the classical and the modern concepts of analysis is that, in classical mathematics, when one writes $f(x)$, f is visualized as "fixed" and x as "variable," whereas nowadays *both* f

and x are considered as "variables" (and sometimes it is x which is fixed, and f which becomes the "varying" object).

Section 1.9 gives the most elementary properties of denumerable sets; this is the beginning of the vast theory of "cardinal numbers" developed by Cantor and his followers, and for which the interested reader may consult Bourbaki ([3], Chapter III) or (for more details) Bachmann [2]. It turns out, however, that, with the exception of the negative result that the real numbers do not form a denumerable set (see (2.2.17)), one very seldom needs more than these elementary properties in the applications of set theory to analysis.

1. ELEMENTS AND SETS

We are dealing with objects, some of which are called *sets*. Objects are susceptible of having *properties*, or *relations* with one another. Objects are denoted by *symbols* (chiefly letters), properties or relations by combinations of the symbols of the objects which are involved in them, and of some other symbols, characteristic of the property or relation under consideration. The relation $x = y$ means that the objects denoted by the symbols x and y are the same; its negation is written $x \neq y$.

If X is a set, the relation $x \in X$ means that x is an *element* of the set X, or *belongs* to X; the negation of that relation is written $x \notin X$.

If X and Y are two sets, the relation $X \subset Y$ means that every element of X is an element of Y (in other words, it is equivalent to the relation $(\forall x)(x \in X \Rightarrow x \in Y)$); we have $X \subset X$, and the relation ($X \subset Y$ and $Y \subset Z$) implies $X \subset Z$. If $X \subset Y$ and $Y \subset X$, then $X = Y$, in other words, two sets are equal if and only if they have the same elements. If $X \subset Y$, one says that X is *contained* in Y, or that Y *contains* X, or that X is a *subset* of Y; one also writes $Y \supset X$. The negation of $X \subset Y$ is written $X \not\subset Y$.

Given a set X, and a property P, there is a unique subset of X whose elements are all elements $x \in X$ for which $P(x)$ is true; that subset is written $\{x \in X \mid P(x)\}$. The relation $\{x \in X \mid P(x)\} \subset \{x \in X \mid Q(x)\}$ is equivalent to $(\forall x \in X)(P(x) \Rightarrow Q(x))$; the relation $\{x \in X \mid P(x)\} = \{x \in X \mid Q(x)\}$ is equivalent to $(\forall x \in X)(P(x) \Leftrightarrow Q(x))$. We have, for instance, $X = \{x \in X \mid x = x\}$ and $X = \{x \in X \mid x \in X\}$. The set $\varnothing_X = \{x \in X \mid x \neq x\}$ is called the *empty set of* X; it contains no element. If P is any property, the relation $x \in \varnothing_X \Rightarrow P(x)$ is true for every x, since the negation of $x \in \varnothing_X$ is true for every x (remember that $Q \Rightarrow P$ means "not Q or P"). Therefore, if X and Y are sets, $x \in \varnothing_X$ implies $x \in \varnothing_Y$, in other words $\varnothing_X \subset \varnothing_Y$, and similarly $\varnothing_Y \subset \varnothing_X$, hence $\varnothing_X = \varnothing_Y$, all empty sets are equal, hence noted $\varnothing$.

If a is an object, the set having a as unique element is written $\{a\}$.

▲ If X is a set, there is a (unique) set the elements of which are all subsets of X; it written $\mathfrak{P}(X)$. We have $\varnothing \in \mathfrak{P}(X)$, $X \in \mathfrak{P}(X)$; the relations $x \in X$, $\{x\} \in \mathfrak{P}(X)$ are equivalent; the relations $Y \subset X$, $Y \in \mathfrak{P}(X)$ are equivalent.

PROBLEM

• Show that the set of all subsets of a finite set having n elements ($n \geqslant 0$) is a finite set having 2^n elements. By induction.

2. BOOLEAN ALGEBRA

● If X, Y are two sets such that $Y \subset X$, the set $\{x \in X \mid x \notin Y)$ is a subset of X called the *difference* of X and Y or the *complement* of Y with respect to X, and written $X - Y$ or $\complement_X Y$ (or $\complement Y$ when there is no possible confusion).

● Given two sets X, Y, there is a set whose elements are those which belong to both X and Y, namely $\{x \in X \mid x \in Y\}$; it is called the *intersection* of X and Y and written $X \cap Y$. There is also a set whose elements are those which belong to one at least of the two sets X, Y; it is called the *union* of X and Y and written $X \cup Y$.

The following propositions follow at once from the definitions:

(1.2.1) $$X - X = \varnothing, \qquad X - \varnothing = X.$$

(1.2.2) $$X \cup X = X, \qquad X \cap X = X.$$

(1.2.3) $$X \cup Y = Y \cup X, \qquad X \cap Y = Y \cap X.$$

(1.2.4) The relations $X \subset Y$, $X \cup Y = Y$, $X \cap Y = X$ are equivalent.

(1.2.5) $$X \subset X \cup Y, \qquad X \cap Y \subset X.$$

(1.2.6) The relation "$X \subset Z$ and $Y \subset Z$" is equivalent to $X \cup Y \subset Z$; the relation "$Z \subset X$ and $Z \subset Y$" is equivalent to $Z \subset X \cap Y$.

(1.2.7) $$X \cup (Y \cup Z) = (X \cup Y) \cup Z, \qquad \text{written} \quad X \cup Y \cup Z.$$
$$X \cap (Y \cap Z) = (X \cap Y) \cap Z, \qquad \text{written} \quad X \cap Y \cap Z.$$

(1.2.8) $$X \cup (Y \cap Z) = (X \cup Y) \cap (X \cup Z)$$
$$X \cap (Y \cup Z) = (X \cap Y) \cup (X \cap Z) \quad \text{(distributivity).}$$

(1.2.9) For subsets X, Y of a set E (with $\complement$ written for $\complement_E$)

$$\complement(\complement X) = X;$$

$$\complement(X \cup Y) = (\complement X) \cap (\complement Y), \qquad \complement(X \cap Y) = (\complement X) \cup (\complement Y).$$

The relations $X \subset Y$, $\complement X \supset \complement Y$ are equivalent; the relations $X \cap Y = \varnothing$, $X \subset \complement Y$, $Y \subset \complement X$ are equivalent; the relations $X \cup Y = E$, $\complement X \subset Y$, $\complement Y \subset X$ are equivalent. The union $\{x\} \cup \{y\}$ is written $\{x, y\}$; similarly, $\{x\} \cup \{y\} \cup \{z\}$ is written $\{x, y, z\}$; etc.

3. PRODUCT OF TWO SETS

▲To any two objects a, b corresponds a new object, their *ordered pair* (a, b); the relation $(a, b) = (a', b')$ is equivalent to "$a = a'$ and $b = b'$"; in particular, $(a, b) = (b, a)$ if and only if $a = b$. The first (resp. second) element of an ordered pair $c = (a, b)$ is called the *first* (resp. *second*) *projection* of c and written $a = \mathrm{pr}_1\, c$ (resp. $b = \mathrm{pr}_2\, c$).

▲Given any two sets X, Y (distinct or not), there is a (unique) set the elements of which are all ordered pairs (x, y) such that $x \in X$ and $y \in Y$; it is written $X \times Y$ and called the *cartesian product* (or simply *product*) *of* X *and* Y.

▲To a relation $R(x, y)$ between $x \in X$ and $y \in Y$ is associated the property $R(\mathrm{pr}_1\, z, \mathrm{pr}_2\, z)$ of $z \in X \times Y$; the subset of $X \times Y$ consisting of the elements for which this property is true is the set of all pairs (x, y) for which $R(x, y)$ is true; it is called the *graph* of the relation R. Any subset G of $X \times Y$ is the graph of a relation, namely the relation $(x, y) \in G$. If $X' \subset X$, $Y' \subset Y$, the graph of the relation "$x \in X'$ and $y \in Y'$" is $X' \times Y'$. For every $x \in X$, $G(x)$ is the set of all elements $y \in Y$ such that $(x, y) \in G$, and for every $y \in Y$, $G^{-1}(y)$ is the set of all elements $x \in X$ such that $(x, y) \in G$; $G(x)$ and $G^{-1}(y)$ are called the *cross sections* of G at x and y.

▲The following propositions follow at once from the definitions:

(1.3.1) The relation $X \times Y = \varnothing$ is equivalent to "$X = \varnothing$ or $Y = \varnothing$."

(1.3.2) If $X \times Y \neq \varnothing$ (which means that both X and Y are nonempty), the relation $X' \times Y' \subset X \times Y$ is equivalent to

$$\text{"}X' \subset X \quad \text{and} \quad Y' \subset Y.\text{"}$$

(1.3.3) $$(X \times Y) \cup (X' \times Y) = (X \cup X') \times Y.$$

(1.3.4) $$(X \times Y) \cap (X' \times Y') = (X \cap X') \times (Y \cap Y').$$

▲ The product of three sets X, Y, Z is defined as $X \times Y \times Z = (X \times Y) \times Z$, and the product of n sets is similarly defined by induction: $X_1 \times X_2 \times \cdots \times X_n = (X_1 \times X_2 \times \cdots \times X_{n-1}) \times X_n$. An element z of $X_1 \times \cdots \times X_n$ is written $(x_1, x_2, \ldots, x_n)$ instead of $((\cdots(x_1, x_2), x_3), \ldots, x_{n-1}), x_n)$; x_i is the ith *projection* of z, and is written $x_i = \text{pr}_i\, z$ for $1 \leqslant i \leqslant n$. More generally, if $i_1, i_2, \ldots, i_k$ are distinct indices belonging to $\{1, 2, \ldots, n\}$, one writes

$$\text{pr}_{i_1 i_2 \ldots i_k}(z) = (x_{i_1}, x_{i_2}, \ldots, x_{i_k}) \in X_{i_1} \times X_{i_2} \times \cdots \times X_{i_k}.$$

If $X_1 = X_2 = \cdots = X_n = X$ we write X^n instead of $X \times X \times \cdots \times X$ n times.

4. MAPPINGS

▲ Let X, Y be two sets, $R(x, y)$ a relation between $x \in X$ and $y \in Y$; R is said to be *functional in y*, if, for *every* $x \in X$, there is *one and only one* $y \in Y$ such that $R(x, y)$ is true. The graph of such a relation is called a *functional graph* in $X \times Y$; such a subset F of $X \times Y$ is therefore characterized by the fact that, for each $x \in X$, there is one and only one $y \in Y$ such that $(x, y) \in F$; this element y is called the *value of* F *at* x, and written $F(x)$. A functional graph in $X \times Y$ in also called a *mapping of* X *into* Y, or a *function defined in* X, *taking its values in* Y. It is customary, in the language, to talk of a mapping and a functional graph as if they were two different kinds of objects in one-to-one correspondence, and to speak therefore of "the graph of a mapping," but this is a mere psychological distinction (corresponding to whether one looks at F either "geometrically" or "analytically"). In any case, it is fundamental, in modern mathematics, to get used to considering a mapping as a *single* object, just as a point or a number, and to make a clear distinction between the mapping F and any one of its values $F(x)$; the first is an element of $\mathfrak{P}(X \times Y)$, the second an element of Y, and one has $F = \{(x, y) \in X \times Y \mid y = F(x)\}$. The subsets of $X \times Y$ which have the property of being functional graphs form a subset of $\mathfrak{P}(X \times Y)$, called the *set of mappings of* X *into* Y, and written Y^X or $\mathscr{F}(X, Y)$.

Examples of mappings

(1.4.1) If b is an element of Y, $X \times \{b\}$ is a functional graph, called the *constant mapping* of X into Y, with the value b; it is essential to distinguish it from the element b of Y.

(1.4.2) For $Y = X$, the relation $y = x$ is functional in y; its graph is the set of all pairs (x, x), and is called the *diagonal* of $X \times X$, or the *identity mapping* of X into itself and is written 1_X.

▲ If, for every $x \in X$, we have constructed an object $T(x)$ which is an element of Y, the relation $y = T(x)$ is functional in y; the corresponding mapping is written $x \to T(x)$. This is of course the usual definition of a mapping; it coincides essentially with the one given above, for if F is a functional graph, it is the mapping $x \to F(x)$. Examples (1.4.1) and (1.4.2) are written respectively $x \to b$ and $x \to x$. Other examples:

(1.4.3) The mapping $Z \to X - Z$ of $\mathfrak{P}(X)$ into itself.

(1.4.4) The mappings $z \to \mathrm{pr}_1 z$ of $X \times Y$ into X, and $z \to \mathrm{pr}_2 z$ of $X \times Y$ into Y, which are called respectively the *first* and *second projection* in $X \times Y$.

▲ From the definition of equality of sets (Section 1.1) it follows that the relation $F = G$ between two mappings of X into Y is equivalent to the relation "$F(x) = G(x)$ for every $x \in X$."

▲ If A is a subset of X, F a mapping of X into Y, the set $F \cap (A \times Y)$ is a functional graph in $A \times Y$, which, as a mapping, is called the *restriction of* F *to* A; when F and G have the same restriction to A (i.e. when $F(x) = G(x)$ for every $x \in A$) they are said to *coincide in* A. A mapping F of X into Y having a given restriction F′ to A is called an *extension of* F′ *to* X; there are in general many different extensions of F′.

▲ We will consider as an axiom (the "axiom of choice") the following proposition:

(1.4.5) *Given a mapping* F *of* X *into* $\mathfrak{P}(Y)$, *such that* $F(x) \neq \varnothing$ *for every* $x \in X$, *there exists a mapping* f *of* X *into* Y *such that* $f(x) \in F(x)$ *for every* $x \in X$.

▲ It can sometimes be shown that a theorem proved with the help of the axiom of choice can actually be proved without using that axiom. We shall never go into such questions, which properly belong to a course in logic.

5. DIRECT AND INVERSE IMAGES

Let F be a mapping of X into Y. For any subset A of X, the subset of Y defined by the property "there exists $x \in A$ such that $y = F(x)$" is called the *image* (or *direct image*) of A by F and written F(A).

We have:

(1.5.1) $$F(A) = \mathrm{pr}_2(F \cap (A \times Y)).$$

(1.5.2) The relation $A \neq \varnothing$ is equivalent to $F(A) \neq \varnothing$.

(1.5.3) $$F(\{x\}) = \{F(x)\} \quad \text{for every} \quad x \in X.$$

(1.5.4) The relation $A \subset B$ implies $F(A) \subset F(B)$.

(1.5.5) $$F(A \cap B) \subset F(A) \cap F(B).$$

(1.5.6) $$F(A \cup B) = F(A) \cup F(B).$$

For $F(A) \subset F(A \cup B)$ and $F(B) \subset F(A \cup B)$ by (1.5.4). On the other hand, if $y \in F(A \cup B)$, there is $x \in A \cup B$ such that $y = F(x)$; as $x \in A$ or $x \in B$, we have $y \in F(A)$ or $y \in F(B)$.

Examples in which $F(A \cap B) \neq F(A) \cap F(B)$ are immediate (take for instance for F the first projection pr_1 of a product).

For any subset A' of Y, the subset of X defined by the property $F(x) \in A'$ is called the *inverse image* of A' by F and written $F^{-1}(A')$. We have:

(1.5.7) $$F^{-1}(A') = pr_1(F \cap (X \times A')).$$

(1.5.8) $F^{-1}(A') = F^{-1}(A' \cap F(X))$, for $F(x) \in F(X)$ is true for every $x \in X$.

(1.5.9) $F^{-1}(\varnothing) = \varnothing$ (but here one may have $F^{-1}(A') = \varnothing$ for nonempty subsets A', namely those for which $A' \cap F(X) = \varnothing$).

(1.5.10) The relation $A' \subset B'$ implies $F^{-1}(A') \subset F^{-1}(B')$.

(1.5.11) $$F^{-1}(A' \cap B') = F^{-1}(A') \cap F^{-1}(B').$$

(1.5.12) $$F^{-1}(A' \cup B') = F^{-1}(A') \cup F^{-1}(B').$$

(1.5.13) $$F^{-1}(A' - B') = F^{-1}(A') - F^{-1}(B') \quad \text{if} \quad A' \supset B'.$$

Notice the difference between (1.5.11) and (1.5.5). If $B \subset A \subset X$, one has by (1.5.6) $F(A) = F(B) \cup F(A - B)$, hence $F(A - B) \supset F(A) - F(B)$; but there is no relation between $F(X - A)$ and $Y - F(A)$.

The set $F^{-1}(\{y\})$ is identical to the cross section $F^{-1}(y)$ defined in Section 1.3; we have:

(1.5.14) $$F(F^{-1}(A')) = A' \cap F(X) \quad \text{for} \quad A' \subset Y.$$

(1.5.15) $$F^{-1}(F(A)) \supset A \quad \text{for} \quad A \subset X.$$

Finally, we note the special relations in a product:

(1.5.16) $pr_1^{-1}(A) = A \times Y$ for any $A \subset X$; $pr_2^{-1}(A') = X \times A'$ for any $A' \subset Y$.

(1.5.17) $$C \subset pr_1(C) \times pr_2(C) \quad \text{for every} \quad C \subset X \times Y.$$

Let X, Y, Z be three sets, A a subset of $X \times Y$. For any mapping F of A into Z, and every $x \in pr_1(A)$ (resp. every $y \in pr_2(A)$), we shall write $F(x, .)$ the mapping $y \to F(x, y)$ of the cross section $A(x)$ into Z (resp. $F(\,.\,, y)$ the mapping $x \to F(x, y)$ of the cross section $A^{-1}(y)$ into Z). These mappings are called *partial mappings* of F.

PROBLEMS

1. Give an example of two subsets $A \supset B$ in X and of a mapping F such that

$$F(A - B) \neq F(A) - F(B).$$

2. Give examples of mappings $F : X \to Y$ and subsets $A \subset X$ such that:
(a) $F(X - A) \subset Y - F(A)$; (b) $F(X - A) \supset Y - F(A)$; (c) neither of the sets $F(X - A)$, $Y - F(A)$ is contained in the other (one can take for X and Y finite sets, for instance).

3. For any subset G of a product $X \times Y$, any subset $A \subset X$, any subset $A' \subset Y$, write $G(A) = pr_2(G \cap (A \times Y))$ and $G^{-1}(A') = pr_1(G \cap (X \times A'))$. For $x \in X$, $y \in Y$, write $G(x)$ (resp $G^{-1}(y)$) instead of $G(\{x\})$ and $G^{-1}(\{y\})$. Prove that the following four properties are equivalent:
(a) G is the graph of a mapping of a subset of X into Y.
(b) For any subset A′ of Y, $G(G^{-1}(A')) \subset A'$.
(c) For any pair of subsets A′, B′ of Y, $G^{-1}(A' \cap B') = G^{-1}(A') \cap G^{-1}(B')$.
(d) For any pair of subsets A′, B′ of Y such that $A' \cap B' = \varnothing$, we have

$$G^{-1}(A') \cap G^{-1}(B') = \varnothing.$$

[Hint: show that when (a) is not satisfied, (b), (c) and (d) are violated.]

6. SURJECTIVE, INJECTIVE, AND BIJECTIVE MAPPINGS

Let F be a mapping of X into Y. F is called *surjective* (or *onto*) or a *surjection* if $F(X) = Y$, i.e., if for every $y \in Y$ there is (at least) one $x \in X$ such that $y = F(x)$. F is called *injective* (or *one-to-one*) or an *injection* if the relation $F(x) = F(x')$ implies $x = x'$. F is called *bijective* (or a *bijection*) if it is both injective and surjective. Any restriction of an injective mapping is injective.

Any mapping F of X into Y can also be considered as a mapping of X into F(X); it is then surjective, and if it was injective (as a mapping of X into Y), it is bijective as a mapping of X into F(X).

Examples

(1.6.1) If A is a subset of X, the restriction to A of the identity mapping $x \to x$ is an injective mapping j_A, called the *natural injection* of A into X; for any subset B of X, $j_A^{-1}(B) = B \cap A$.

(1.6.2) If F is any mapping of X into Y, the mapping $x \to (x, F(x))$ is an injection of X into $X \times Y$.

(1.6.3) The projections pr_1 and pr_2 are surjective mappings of $X \times Y$ into X and Y respectively.

(1.6.4) The identity mapping of any set is bijective.

(1.6.5) The mapping $Z \to X - Z$ of $\mathfrak{P}(X)$ into itself is bijective.

(1.6.6) If $Y = \{b\}$ is a one element set, the mapping $x \to (x, b)$ of X into $X \times \{b\}$ is bijective.

(1.6.7) The mapping $(x, y) \to (y, x)$ of $X \times Y$ into $Y \times X$ is bijective.

If F is injective, then $F^{-1}(F(A)) = A$ for any $A \subset X$; if F is surjective, then $F(F^{-1}(A')) = A'$ for any $A' \subset Y$.

If F is *bijective*, the relation $y = F(x)$ is by definition a functional relation *in* x; the corresponding mapping of Y into X is called the *inverse* mapping of F, and written $\overset{-1}{F}$ or F^{-1} (this mapping is *not defined* if F is not bijective!). The relations $y = F(x)$ and $x = F^{-1}(y)$ are thus equivalent; F^{-1} is bijective and $(F^{-1})^{-1} = F$. For each subset A′ of Y, the direct image of A′ by F^{-1} coincides with the inverse image of A′ by F, hence the notations are consistent.

PROBLEM

Let F be a mapping $X \to Y$. Show that the following properties are equivalent: (a) F is injective; (b) for any subset A of X, $F^{-1}(F(A)) = A$; (c) for any pair of subsets A,B of X, $F(A \cap B) = F(A) \cap F(B)$; (d) for any pair of subsets A, B of X such that $A \cap B = \varnothing$, $F(A) \cap F(B) = \varnothing$; (e) for any pair of subsets A, B of X such that $B \subset A$, $F(A - B) = F(A) - F(B)$.

7. COMPOSITION OF MAPPINGS

Let X, Y, Z be three sets, F a mapping of X into Y, G a mapping of Y into Z. Then $x \to G(F(x))$ is a mapping of X into Z, which is said to be *composed* of G and F (in that order) and written $H = G \circ F$. One has

(1.7.1) $$H(A) = G(F(A)) \quad \text{for any} \quad A \subset X.$$

(1.7.2) $$H^{-1}(A'') = F^{-1}(G^{-1}(A'')) \quad \text{for any} \quad A'' \subset Z.$$

If *both* F and G are injective (resp. surjective, bijective), then $H = G \circ F$ is injective (resp. surjective, bijective); if F and G are bijections, then $H^{-1} = F^{-1} \circ G^{-1}$. If F is a bijection, then $F^{-1} \circ F$ is the identity mapping of X, and $F \circ F^{-1}$ the identity mapping of Y.

Conversely, if F is a mapping of X into Y, G a mapping of Y into X such that $G \circ F = 1_X$ and $F \circ G = 1_Y$, F and G are bijections inverse to each other, for the first relation implies that F is injective and G surjective, and the second that G is injective and F surjective.

Let T be a set, F_1 a mapping of X into Y, F_2 a mapping of Y into Z, F_3 a mapping of Z into T. Then $F_3 \circ (F_2 \circ F_1) = (F_3 \circ F_2) \circ F_1$ by definition; it is a mapping of X into T, also written $F_3 \circ F_2 \circ F_1$. Composition of any finite number of mappings is defined in the same way.

PROBLEMS

1. Let A, B, C, D be sets, f a mapping of A into B, g a mapping of B into C, h a mapping of C into D. Show that if $g \circ f$ and $h \circ g$ are bijective, f, g, h are all bijective.
2. Let A, B, C be sets, f a mapping of A into B, g a mapping of B into C, h a mapping of C into A. Show that if, among the mappings $h \circ g \circ f$, $g \circ f \circ h$, $f \circ h \circ g$, two are surjective and the third injective, or two are injective and the third surjective, then all three mappings f, g, h are bijective.
3. Let F be a subset of $X \times Y$, G a subset of $Y \times X$. With the notations of Problem 3 of Section 1.5, suppose that for any $x \in X$, $G(F(x)) = \{x\}$ and for any $y \in Y$, $F(G(y)) = \{y\}$. Show that F is the graph of a bijection of X onto Y and G the graph of the inverse of F.
4. Let X, Y be two sets, f an injection of X into Y, g an injection of Y into X. Show that there exist two subsets A, B of X such that $B = X - A$, two subsets A′, B′ of Y such that $B' = Y - A'$, and that $A' = f(A)$ and $B = g(B')$. [Let $R = X - g(Y)$, and $h = g \circ f$; take for A the intersection of all subsets M of X such that $M \supset R \cup h(M)$.]

8. FAMILIES OF ELEMENTS. UNION, INTERSECTION, AND PRODUCTS OF FAMILIES OF SETS. EQUIVALENCE RELATIONS

Let L and X be two sets. A mapping of L into X is sometimes also called a *family of elements of* X, having L as set of *indices*, and it is written $\lambda \to x_\lambda$, or $(x_\lambda)_{\lambda \in L}$, or simply (x_λ) when no confusion can arise. The most important examples are given by *sequences* (finite or infinite) which correspond to the cases in which L is a finite or infinite subset of the set **N** of integers $\geqslant 0$.

Care must be taken to distinguish a *family* $(x_\lambda)_{\lambda \in L}$ of elements of X from the *subset* of X whose elements are the elements of the family, which is the image of L by the mapping $\lambda \to x_\lambda$, and can very well consist only of one element; different families may thus have the same set of elements.

For any subset $M \subset L$, the *restriction* to M of $\lambda \to x_\lambda$ is called the *subfamily* of $(x_\lambda)_{\lambda \in L}$ having M as set of indices, and written $(x_\lambda)_{\lambda \in M}$.

For a finite sequence $(x_i)_{1 \leqslant i \leqslant n}$, the set of elements of that sequence is written $\{x_1, x_2, \ldots, x_n\}$; similar notations may be used for the set of elements of any finite or infinite sequence.

If $(A_\lambda)_{\lambda \in L}$ is a family of subsets of a set X, the set of elements $x \in X$ such that there exists a $\lambda \in L$ such that $x \in A_\lambda$ is called the *union* of the family $(A_\lambda)_{\lambda \in L}$, and written $\bigcup_{\lambda \in L} A_\lambda$ or $\bigcup_{\lambda} A_\lambda$; the set of elements $x \in X$ such that $x \in A_\lambda$ for every $\lambda \in L$ is called the *intersection* of the family $(A_\lambda)_{\lambda \in L}$ and written $\bigcap_{\lambda \in L} A_\lambda$ or $\bigcap_{\lambda} A_\lambda$. When $L = \{1, 2\}$, the union and intersection are respectively $A_1 \cup A_2$ and $A_1 \cap A_2$.

The following propositions are easily verified:

(1.8.1) $$\complement\Big(\bigcup_{\lambda \in L} A_\lambda\Big) = \bigcap_{\lambda \in L} (\complement A_\lambda)$$

(1.8.2) $$\Big(\bigcup_{\lambda \in L} A_\lambda\Big) \cap \Big(\bigcup_{\mu \in M} B_\mu\Big) = \bigcup_{(\lambda, \mu) \in L \times M} (A_\lambda \cap B_\mu)$$

(1.8.3) $$\Big(\bigcap_{\lambda \in L} A_\lambda\Big) \cup \Big(\bigcap_{\mu \in M} B_\mu\Big) = \bigcap_{(\lambda, \mu) \in L \times M} (A_\lambda \cup B_\mu)$$

(1.8.4) $F\Big(\bigcup_{\lambda \in L} A_\lambda\Big) = \bigcup_{\lambda \in L} F(A_\lambda)$ if F is a mapping of X into Y, and $(A_\lambda)_{\lambda \in L}$ is a family of subsets of X.

(1.8.5) $$F^{-1}\Big(\bigcup_{\lambda \in L} A'_\lambda\Big) = \bigcup_{\lambda \in L} F^{-1}(A'_\lambda)$$

(1.8.6) $$F^{-1}\Big(\bigcap_{\lambda \in L} A'_\lambda\Big) = \bigcap_{\lambda \in L} F^{-1}(A'_\lambda)$$

if F is a mapping of X into Y, and $(A'_\lambda)_{\lambda \in L}$ a family of subsets of Y.

If B is a subset of X, a *covering* of B is a family $(A_\lambda)_{\lambda \in L}$ of subsets of X such that $B \subset \bigcup_{\lambda \in L} A_\lambda$.

A *partition* of X is a family $(A_\lambda)_{\lambda \in L}$ of subsets of X which is a covering of X (i.e., $X = \bigcup_{\lambda \in L} A_\lambda$) such that $A_\lambda \cap A_\mu = \varnothing$ for $\lambda \neq \mu$.

An *equivalence relation* in a set X is a relation $R(x, y)$ between two elements x, y of X, satisfying the following conditions:

1. for every $x \in X$, $R(x, x)$ is true (*reflexivity*);
2. the relations $R(x, y)$ and $R(y, x)$ are equivalent (*symmetry*);
3. the relations $R(x, y)$ and $R(y, z)$ (for x, y, z in X) imply $R(x, z)$ (*transitivity*).

Suppose $(A_\lambda)_{\lambda \in L}$ is a *partition* of X; then it is clear that the relation

"there exists $\lambda \in L$ such that $x \in A_\lambda$ and $y \in A_\lambda$"

is an *equivalence relation* between x and y.

Conversely, let R be an equivalence relation in X, and let $G \subset X \times X$ be its *graph* (Section **1.3**); for each $x \in X$, the *cross section* $G(x)$ (Section **1.3**) is called the *class* (or *equivalence class*) *of* x for R (or "mod R"). The set of all subsets of X which can be written $G(x)$ for some $x \in X$ is a subset of $\mathfrak{P}(X)$ called the *quotient set of* X *by* R and written X/R; the mapping $x \to G(x)$ is called the *canonical* (or *natural*) mapping of X into X/R; it is surjective by definition. The family of subsets of X defined by the natural injection of X/R into $\mathfrak{P}(X)$ is a *partition* of X, whose elements are the *classes mod* R. Indeed, if $z \in G(x) \cap G(y)$, both relations $R(x, z)$ and $R(y, z)$ hold, hence also $R(z, y)$ (symmetry) and $R(x, y)$ (transitivity), which proves that $y \in G(x)$; this implies $G(y) \subset G(x)$ (transitivity) and exchanging x and y one gets $G(x) \subset G(y)$, hence finally $G(x) = G(y)$; as moreover $x \in G(x)$ for every $x \in X$ (reflexivity), our assertion is proved.

For every mapping f of X into a set Y, the relation $f(x) = f(x')$ is an equivalence relation between x and x'.

Let $(X_\lambda)_{\lambda \in L}$ be a family of subsets of a set Y, and for each $\lambda \in L$, let $X'_\lambda = \{\lambda\} \times X_\lambda$ (subset of $L \times Y$); it is clear that the restriction to X'_λ of the second projection $\mathrm{pr}_2 : L \times Y \to Y$ is a *bijection* p_λ of X'_λ on X_λ. The subset $S = \bigcup_{\lambda \in L} X'_\lambda \subset L \times Y$ is called the *sum* of the family (X_λ) (not to be mistaken for the *union* of that family!); it is clear that (X'_λ) is a *partition* of S. Usually, X_λ and X'_λ will be identified by the natural bijection p_λ. If, for every $\lambda \in L$, u_λ is a mapping of X'_λ into a set T, there is one and only one mapping u of S into T which coincides with u_λ in each X'_λ.

With the same notations, let us now consider the subset of the set Y^L (Section **1.4**) consisting of all mappings $\lambda \to x_\lambda$ of L into Y such that, for every $\lambda \in L$, one has $x_\lambda \in X_\lambda$; this subset is called the *product* of the family $(X_\lambda)_{\lambda \in L}$, and is written $\prod_{\lambda \in L} X_\lambda$; for each $x = (x_\lambda) \in \prod_{\lambda \in L} X_\lambda$, and every index $\mu \in L$, one writes $x_\mu = \mathrm{pr}_\mu(x)$. More generally, for each nonempty subset J of L, one writes $\mathrm{pr}_J(x) = (x_\lambda)_{\lambda \in J}$ (subfamily of $x = (x_\lambda)_{\lambda \in L}$). From the axiom of choice (**1.4.5**) it follows that if $X_\lambda \neq \varnothing$ for every $\lambda \in L$, then $\prod_{\lambda \in L} X_\lambda \neq \varnothing$, and each of the mappings pr_J is *surjective*. Furthermore, if J and $L - J$ are both nonempty, the mapping $x \to (\mathrm{pr}_J(x), \mathrm{pr}_{L-J}(x))$ is a *bijection* of $\prod_{\lambda \in L} X_\lambda$

on the product $\left(\prod_{\lambda \in L} X_\lambda\right) \times \left(\prod_{\lambda \in L - J} X_\lambda\right)$. If, for every $\lambda \in L$, u_λ is a mapping of a set T into X_λ, there exists a unique mapping u of T into $\prod_{\lambda \in L} X_\lambda$ such that $\text{pr}_\lambda \circ u = u_\lambda$ for each $\lambda \in L$: to each $t \in T$, u associates the element $u(t) = (u_\lambda(t)) \in \prod_{\lambda \in L} X_\lambda$; the mapping u is usually written (u_λ).

PROBLEM

Let $(X_i)_{1 \leqslant i \leqslant n}$ be a finite family of sets. For any subset H of the interval $[1, n]$ of **N**, let $P_H = \bigcup_{i \in H} X_i$ and $Q_H = \bigcap_{i \in H} X_i$. Let $\mathfrak{F}_k$ be the set of all subsets of $[1, n]$ having k elements; show that

$$\bigcup_{H \in \mathfrak{F}_k} Q_H \supset \bigcap_{H \in \mathfrak{F}_k} P_H \quad \text{if } 2k \leqslant n + 1$$

$$\bigcup_{H \in \mathfrak{F}_k} Q_H \subset \bigcap_{H \in \mathfrak{F}_k} P_H \quad \text{if } 2k \geqslant n + 1.$$

9. DENUMERABLE SETS

▲ A set X is said to be *equipotent* to a set Y if there exists a bijection of X onto Y. It is clear that X is equipotent to X; if X is equipotent to Y, Y is equipotent to X; if X and Y are both equipotent to Z, X is equipotent to Y. A set is called *denumerable* if it is equipotent to the set **N** of integers.

(1.9.1) *Any subset of the set* **N** *of integers is finite or denumerable.*

For suppose $A \subset \mathbf{N}$ is infinite. We define a mapping $n \to x_n$ of **N** into A by the following inductive process: x_0 is the smallest element of A, x_n is the smallest element of the set $A - \{x_0, \ldots, x_{n-1}\}$, which by assumption is not empty. This shows first that $x_i \neq x_n$ for $i < n$, hence $n \to x_n$ is injective; let us prove in addition that $x_i < x_n$ for $i < n$. We use induction on i for fixed n: we have $x_0 < x_n$ by definition of x_n, and if $x_j < x_n$ has been proved for $j < i$, then $x_i \leqslant x_n$ by definition of x_i, hence $x_i < x_n$ since $x_i \neq x_n$. Next, by induction on n, it follows at once from the relation $x_i < x_n$ for $i < n$ that $n \leqslant x_n$ for every n; hence, if $a \in A$, we have $a \leqslant x_a$. Let m be the greatest integer $< a$ such that $x_m < a$; if there existed an integer $b \in A$ such that $x_m < b < a$, we would have $x_{m+1} \leqslant b < a$ by definition, which contradicts the definition of m; hence a is the smallest element of $A - \{x_0, \ldots, x_m\}$, in other words $a = x_{m+1}$, the mapping $n \to x_n$ is surjective. Q.E.D.

▲ It follows from (1.9.1) that any subset of a denumerable set is finite or denumerable; such a set is also called *at most denumerable.*

(1.9.2) *Let* A *be a denumerable set, and f a mapping of* A *onto a set* B. *Then* B *is at most denumerable.*

▲ Let $n \to a_n$ be a bijection of **N** onto A; then $n \to f(a_n)$ is a mapping of **N** onto B, and we can therefore suppose $A = \mathbf{N}$. For each $b \in B$, $f^{-1}(b)$ is not empty by assumption; let $m(b)$ be its smallest element. Then $f(m(b)) = b$, which shows at once that m is an injective mapping of B into **N**; m can be considered as a bijection of B onto $m(B) \subset \mathbf{N}$, and by (1.9.1) $m(B)$ is at most denumerable. Q.E.D.

▲ We observe that if a set A is at most denumerable, there is always a surjection of **N** onto A; this is obvious if A is infinite; if not, there is a bijection f of an interval $0 \leqslant i \leqslant m$ onto A, and one extends f to a surjection by putting $g(n) = f(m)$ for $n > m$.

(1.9.3) *The set* $\mathbf{N} \times \mathbf{N} = \mathbf{N}^2$ *is denumerable.*

We define an injection f of $\mathbf{N} \times \mathbf{N}$ into **N** by putting

$$f(x, y) = (x + y)(x + y + 1)/2 + y$$

("diagonal enumeration"; it turns out to be a bijection, but we do not need that result). Indeed, if $x + y = a$, then $(a + 1)(a + 2)/2 = a + 1 + a(a + 1)/2$; hence if $x + y < x' + y'$, as $y \leqslant a$, $f(x, y) \leqslant a + a(a + 1)/2 < f(x', y')$; and if $x + y = x' + y'$ and $y' < y$, $f(x, y) - f(x', y') = y - y'$; hence $(x, y) \neq (x', y')$ implies $f(x, y) \neq f(x', y')$. We then apply (1.9.1).

▲ We say that a family $(x_\lambda)_{\lambda \in L}$ is *denumerable* (resp. *at most denumerable*) if the set of indices L is denumerable (resp. at most denumerable).

(1.9.4) *The union of a denumerable family of denumerable sets is denumerable.*

Let $(A_\lambda)_{\lambda \in L}$ be a denumerable family of denumerable sets; there is a bijection $n \to \lambda_n$ of **N** onto L, and for each $\lambda \in L$, a bijection $n \to f_\lambda(n)$ of **N** onto A_λ. Let $A = \bigcup_{\lambda \in L} A_\lambda$, and consider the mapping $(m, n) \to f_{\lambda_n}(m)$ of $\mathbf{N} \times \mathbf{N}$ into A; this mapping is surjective, for if $x \in A_\mu$, there is an n such that $\mu = \lambda_n$, and an m such that $x = f_\mu(m) = f_{\lambda_n}(m)$. The result now follows from (1.9.3) and (1.9.2) since A is infinite.

The result (1.9.4) is still valid if the word "denumerable" is everywhere replaced by "at most denumerable." We have only to replace bijections by surjections in the proof, using the remark which follows (1.9.2).

Finally, we consider the following result as an *axiom*:

(1.9.5) *Every infinite set contains a denumerable subset.*

PROBLEMS

1. Show that the set $\mathfrak{F}(\mathbf{N})$ of all finite subsets of **N** is denumerable (write it as a denumerable union of denumerable sets).
2. Show that the set of all finite sequences of elements of **N** is denumerable (use Problem 1; observe the distinction between a sequence and the set of elements of the sequence!).
3. Prove the result of Problem 4 in Section **1.7** by the following method: let $u = g \circ f$, $v = f \circ g$, and define by induction u_n and v_n as $u_n = u_{n-1} \circ u$, $v_n = v_{n-1} \circ v$; then consider in X (resp. Y) the decreasing sequence of the sets $u_n(X)$ (resp. $v_n(Y)$), and their images in Y (resp. X) by f (resp. g).
4. Show that in order that a set X be infinite, the following condition is necessary and sufficient: for every mapping f of X into itself, there exists a nonempty subset A of X, such that $A \neq X$ and $f(A) \subset A$. (If f did not possess that property and X was infinite, show first that X would be denumerable, and that one could suppose that $X = \mathbf{N}$ and $f(n) > n$ for $n \geqslant 0$; show that this leads to a contradiction.)
5. Let E be an infinite set, D an at most denumerable subset of E such that $E - D$ is infinite. Show that $E - D$ is equipotent to E (use **(1.9.4)** and **(1.9.5)** to define a bijection of E onto $E - D$).

CHAPTER II

REAL NUMBERS

The material in this chapter is completely classical; the main difference with most treatments of the real numbers is that their properties are here derived from a certain number of statements taken as axioms, whereas in fact these statements can be proved as consequences of the axioms of set theory (or of the axioms of natural integers, together with some part of set theory, allowing one to perform the classical constructions of the "Dedekind cuts" or the "Cantor fundamental sequences"). These proofs have great logical interest, and historically they helped a great deal in clarifying the classical (and somewhat nebulous) concept of the "continuum". But they have no bearing whatsoever on analysis, and it has not been thought necessary to burden the student with them; the interested reader may find them in practically any book on analysis; for a particularly lucid and neat description, see Landau [16].

1. AXIOMS OF THE REAL NUMBERS

The field of real numbers is a set **R** for which are defined: (1) two mappings $(x, y) \to x + y$ and $(x, y) \to xy$ from $\mathbf{R} \times \mathbf{R}$ into $\mathbf{R}$; (2) a relation $x \leqslant y$ (also written $y \geqslant x$) between elements of **R**, satisfying the four following groups of axioms:

(I) **R** *is a field*, in other words:

(I.1) $x + (y + z) = (x + y) + z$;

(I.2) $x + y = y + x$;

(I.3) there is an element $0 \in \mathbf{R}$ such that $0 + x = x$ for every $x \in \mathbf{R}$;

(I.4) for each element $x \in \mathbf{R}$, there is an element $-x \in \mathbf{R}$ such that $x + (-x) = 0$;

(I.5) $x(yz) = (xy)z$;

(I.6) $xy = yx$;

(I.7) there is an element $1 \neq 0$ in $\mathbf{R}$ such that $1 \cdot x = x$ for every $x \in \mathbf{R}$;

(I.8) for each element $x \neq 0$ in $\mathbf{R}$, there is an element $x^{-1} \in \mathbf{R}$ (also written $1/x$) such that $xx^{-1} = 1$;

(I.9) $x(y + z) = xy + xz$.

We assume that the elementary consequences of these axioms ("general theory of fields") are known.

(II) **R** *is an ordered field.* This means that the following axioms are satisfied:

(II.1) $x \leqslant y$ and $y \leqslant z$ imply $x \leqslant z$;

(II.2) "$x \leqslant y$ and $y \leqslant x$" is equivalent to $x = y$;

(II.3) for any two elements x, y of **R**, either $x \leqslant y$ or $y \leqslant x$;

(II.4) $x \leqslant y$ implies $x + z \leqslant y + z$;

(II.5) $0 \leqslant x$ and $0 \leqslant y$ imply $0 \leqslant xy$.

The relation "$x \leqslant y$ and $x \neq y$" is written $x < y$, or $y > x$. For any pair of elements a, b of **R** such that $a < b$, the set of real numbers x such that $a < x < b$ is called the *open interval of origin a and extremity b*, and written $]a, b[$; the set of real numbers x such that $a \leqslant x \leqslant b$ is called the *closed interval of origin a and extremity b*, and written $[a, b]$ (for $a = b$, the notation $[a, a]$ means the one-point set $\{a\}$); the set of real numbers x such that $a < x \leqslant b$ (resp. $a \leqslant x < b$) is called a *semi-open interval* of origin a and extremity b, open at a (resp. b), closed at b (resp. a) and written $]a, b]$ (resp. $[a, b[$). The origin and extremity of an interval are also called "the extremities" of the interval.

(III) **R** *is an archimedean ordered field* which means that it satisfies the *axiom of Archimedes*: for any pair x, y of real numbers such that $0 < x$, $0 \leqslant y$, there is an integer n such that $y \leqslant n \cdot x$.

(IV) **R** satisfies the *axiom of nested intervals*: Given a sequence $([a_n, b_n])$ of closed intervals such that $a_n \leqslant a_{n+1}$ and $b_{n+1} \leqslant b_n$ for every n, the intersection of that sequence is not empty.

2. ORDER PROPERTIES OF THE REAL NUMBERS

The relation $x \leqslant y$ is equivalent to "$x < y$ or $x = y$."

(2.2.1) *For any pair of real numbers x, y, one and only one of the three relations $x < y$, $x = y$, $x > y$ holds.*

This follows from (II.3) and (II.2), for if $x \neq y$, it is impossible that $x < y$ and $x > y$ hold simultaneously by (II.2).

(2.2.2) *The relations "$x \leqslant y$ and $y < z$" and "$x < y$ and $y \leqslant z$" both imply $x < z$.*

For by (II.1) they imply $x \leqslant z$, and if we had $x = z$, then we would have both $x \leqslant y$ and $y < x$ (or both $x < y$ and $y \leqslant x$) which is absurd.

(2.2.3) *Any finite subset* A *of* **R** *has a greatest element b and a smallest element a* (i.e., *$a \leqslant x \leqslant b$ for every $x \in$* A).

We use induction on the number n of elements of A, the property being obvious for $n = 1$. Let c be an element of A, $\mathrm{B} = \mathrm{A} - \{c\}$; B has $n - 1$ elements, hence a smallest element a' and a greatest element b'. If $a' \leqslant c \leqslant b'$, a' is the smallest and b' the greatest element of A; if $b' \leqslant c$, c is the greatest and a' the smallest element of A; if $c \leqslant a'$, c is the smallest and b' the greatest element of A.

(2.2.4) *If* A *is a finite subset of* **R** *having n elements, there is a unique bijection f of the set I_n of integers i such that $1 \leqslant i \leqslant n$, onto* A, *such that $f(i) < f(j)$ for $i < j$ (f is called the natural ordering of* A).

Use induction on n, the result being obvious for $n = 1$. Let b be the greatest element of A (2.2.3), and $\mathrm{B} = \mathrm{A} - \{b\}$; let g be the natural ordering of B. Any mapping f of I_n onto A having the properties stated above must be such that $f(n) = b$, and therefore $f(\mathrm{I}_{n-1}) = \mathrm{B}$; hence f must coincide on I_{n-1} with the natural ordering g of B, which shows f is unique; conversely, defining f as equal to g in I_{n-1} and such that $f(n) = b$, we see at once that f has the required properties.

(2.2.5) *If* (x_i) *and* (y_i) *are two finite sequences of n real numbers* $(1 \leqslant i \leqslant n)$ *such that* $x_i \leqslant y_i$ *for each i, then*

$$x_1 + x_2 + \cdots + x_n \leqslant y_1 + y_2 + \cdots + y_n.$$

If in addition $x_i < y_i$ *for one index i at least, then*

$$x_1 + x_2 + \cdots + x_n < y_1 + y_2 + \cdots + y_n.$$

For $n = 2$ the assumptions imply successively by (II.4)

$$x_1 + x_2 \leqslant y_1 + x_2 \leqslant y_1 + y_2,$$

hence the first conclusion in that case; moreover, the relation $x_1 + x_2 = y_1 + y_2$ implies $x_1 + x_2 = x_1 + y_2 = y_1 + y_2$, hence $x_2 = y_2$ and $x_1 = y_1$, from which our second statement follows. The proof is concluded by induction on n, applying the result just obtained for $n = 2$.

(2.2.6) *The relation* $x \leqslant y$ *is equivalent to* $x + z \leqslant y + z$; *same result when* $\leqslant$ *is replaced by* $<$.

We already know by (II.4) that $x \leqslant y$ implies $x + z \leqslant y + z$; conversely $x + z \leqslant y + z$ implies $x + z + (-z) \leqslant y + z + (-z)$, i.e. $x \leqslant y$. On the other hand, $x + z = y + z$ is equivalent to $x = y$.

(2.2.7) *The relations* $x \leqslant y$, $0 \leqslant y - x$, $x - y \leqslant 0$, $-y \leqslant -x$ *are equivalent*; *same result with* $<$ *replacing* $\leqslant$.

This follows from (2.2.6) by taking in succession $z = -x$, $z = -y$ and $z = -x - y$.

Real numbers such that $x \geqslant 0$ (resp. $x > 0$) are called *positive* (resp. *strictly positive*); those which are such that $x \leqslant 0$ (resp. $x < 0$) are called *negative* (resp. *strictly negative*). The set of positive (resp. strictly positive) numbers is written $\mathbf{R}_+$ (resp. $\mathbf{R}_+^*$).

(2.2.8) *If* $x_1, \ldots, x_n$ *are positive, so is* $x_1 + x_2 + \cdots + x_n$; *moreover* $x_1 + x_2 + \cdots + x_n > 0$ *unless* $x_1 = x_2 = \cdots = x_n = 0$.

This is a special case of (2.2.5).

In particular, $x \geqslant 0$ (resp. $x > 0$) is equivalent to $n \cdot x \geqslant 0$ (resp. $n \cdot x > 0$) for any integer $n > 0$.

For an interval of origin a and extremity b, the positive number $b - a$ is called the *length* of the interval.

For any real number x, we define $|x|$ as equal to x if $x \geqslant 0$, to $-x$ if $x \leqslant 0$, hence $|-x| = |x|$; $|x|$ is called the *absolute value* of x; $|x| = 0$ is equivalent to $x = 0$. We write $x^+ = (x + |x|)/2$ (positive part of x), $x^- = (|x| - x)/2$ (negative part of x) so that $x^+ = x$ if $x \geqslant 0$, $x^+ = 0$ if $x \leqslant 0$, $x^- = 0$ if $x \geqslant 0$, $x^- = -x$ if $x \leqslant 0$, and $x = x^+ - x^-$, $|x| = x^+ + x^-$.

(2.2.9) *If $a > 0$, the relation $|x| \leqslant a$ is equivalent to $-a \leqslant x \leqslant a$, the relation $|x| < a$ to $-a < x < a$.*

For if $x \geqslant 0$, $x > -a$ is always satisfied and $|x| \leqslant a$ (resp. $|x| < a$) is equivalent to $x \leqslant a$ (resp. $x < a$); and if $x \leqslant 0$, $x < a$ is always satisfied and $|x| \leqslant a$ (resp. $|x| < a$) is equivalent to $-x \leqslant a$ (resp. $-x < a$).

(2.2.10) *For any pair of real numbers x, y, $|x + y| \leqslant |x| + |y|$ and*

$$||x| - |y|| \leqslant |x - y|.$$

The first relation is evident by definition and from (2.2.8) when x, y are both positive or both negative. If for instance $x \leqslant 0 \leqslant y$, then $x + y \leqslant y \leqslant y + |x| = |y| + |x|$, and $x + y \geqslant x \geqslant x - |y| = -|x| - |y|$. From the first inequality follows $|x| = |y + (x - y)| \leqslant |y| + |x - y|$ and $|y| = |x + (y - x)| \leqslant |x| + |y - x|$ whence $-|x - y| \leqslant |x| - |y| \leqslant |x - y|$.

By induction, it follows from (2.2.10) that

$$|x_1 + x_2 + \cdots + x_n| \leqslant |x_1 + |x_2| + \cdots + |x_n|.$$

(2.2.11) *If $z \geqslant 0$, the relation $x \leqslant y$ implies $xz \leqslant yz$.*

For by (2.2.7), $x \leqslant y$ implies $0 \leqslant y - x$, hence $0 \leqslant z(y - x) = zy - zx$ from (II.5).

(2.2.12) *The relations $x \leqslant 0$ and $y \geqslant 0$ imply $xy \leqslant 0$; the relations $x \leqslant 0$ and $y \leqslant 0$ imply $xy \geqslant 0$. Same results with $\leqslant$ replaced by $<$. In particular, $x^2 \geqslant 0$ for any real number, and $x^2 > 0$ unless $x = 0$.*

The first statements follow from (II.5) and $(-x)y = -(xy), (-x)(-y) = xy$; on the other hand, $xy = 0$ implies $x = 0$ or $y = 0$.

(2.2.12) implies that $|xy| = |x| \cdot |y|$ for any pair of real numbers x, y.

From (2.2.12) and (I.7) it follows that $1 = 1^2 > 0$, hence, by (2.2.8), the real number $n \cdot 1$ (1 added n times) is >0 for $n > 0$; this shows that the mapping $n \to n \cdot 1$ of the natural integers into $\mathbf{R}$ is injective, and preserves order relations, addition and multiplication; hence natural integers are *identified* to real numbers by means of that mapping.

(2.2.13) *If* $x > 0$, $x^{-1} > 0$. *For* $z > 0$, *the relation* $x \leqslant y$ (resp. $x < y$) *is equivalent to* $xz \leqslant yz$ (resp. $xz < yz$). *The relation* $0 < x < y$ *is equivalent to* $0 < y^{-1} < x^{-1}$, *and to* $0 < x^n < y^n$ *for every integer* $n > 0$.

The first statement follows from the fact that $xx^{-1} = 1 > 0$, hence $x^{-1} > 0$ by (2.2.12); the second follows from the first and (2.2.11), since $x = (xz)z^{-1}$. The third is an obvious consequence of the second. The last follows by induction on the integer $n > 0$ from the relations $x^n < x^{n-1}y < y^n$.

Remark. An open interval $]a, b[$ of $\mathbf{R}$ (with $a < b$) is not empty, for the relation $b - a > 0$ implies, by (2.2.13), $(b - a)/2 > 0$; hence $a < (a + b)/2 < b$.

From that remark one deduces:

(2.2.14) *Let* $J_1, \dots, J_n$ *be* n *open intervals, no two of which have common points, and let* I *be an interval containing* $\bigcup_{k=1}^{n} J_k$; *then, if* l_k *is the length of* J_k $(1 \leqslant k \leqslant n)$, l *the length of* I, $l_1 + l_2 + \cdots + l_n \leqslant l$.

Let $I =]a, b[$, $J_k =]c_k, d_k[$. For each $k \neq 1$, we have either $c_k < d_k \leqslant c_1$ or $d_1 \leqslant c_k < d_k$, otherwise $J_1 \cap J_k$ would not be empty. For $n = 1$, the property is immediate as $a \leqslant c_1 < d_1 \leqslant b$, hence $-c_1 \leqslant -a$, and $d_1 - c_1 \leqslant b - a$. Use induction on n; let $J_{i_1}, \dots, J_{i_p}$ be the intervals contained in $]a, c_1[$, and $J_{j_1}, \dots, J_{j_{n-1-p}}$ the intervals contained in $]d_1, b[$; then $\sum_{h=1}^{p} l_{i_h} \leqslant c_1 - a$, $\sum_{k=1}^{n-1-p} l_{j_k} \leqslant b - d_1$ by induction, and $l_1 + l_2 + \cdots + l_n = l_1 + \sum_h l_{i_h} + \sum_k l_{j_k} \leqslant d_1 - c_1 + c_1 - a + b - d_1 = b - a$.

Real numbers of the form $\pm r/s$, where r and s are natural integers, $s \neq 0$, are called *rational numbers*. Those for which $s = 1$ are called *integers* (positive or negative) and the set of all integers is written $\mathbf{Z}$.

(2.2.15) *The set* **Q** *of rational numbers is denumerable.*

As **Q** is the union of $\mathbf{Q} \cap \mathbf{R}_+$ and $\mathbf{Q} \cap (-\mathbf{R}_+)$, it is enough to prove $\mathbf{Q} \cap \mathbf{R}_+$ denumerable. But there is a surjective mapping $(m, n) \to m/n$ of the subset of $\mathbf{N} \times \mathbf{N}$ consisting of the pairs such that $n \neq 0$, onto $\mathbf{Q} \cap \mathbf{R}_+$, hence the result by (1.9.2), (1.9.3), and (1.9.4).

(2.2.16) *Every open interval in* **R** *contains an infinite set of rational numbers.*

It is enough to prove that $]a, b[$ contains *one* rational number c, for then $]a, c[$ contains a rational number, and induction proves the final result. Let $x = b - a > 0$; by (III) there is an integer $n > 1/x$, hence $1/n < x$ by (2.2.13). We can suppose $b > 0$ (otherwise we consider the interval $]-b, -a[$ with $-a > 0$). By (III) there is an integer $k > 0$ such that $b \leqslant k/n$; let h be the smallest integer such that $b \leqslant h/n$. Then $(h-1)/n < b$; let us show that $(h-1)/n > a$; if not, we would have $b - a = x \leqslant 1/n$ by (2.2.14), contradicting the definition of n.

(2.2.17) *The set of real numbers is not denumerable.*

We argue by contradiction. Suppose we had a bijection $n \to x_n$ from **N** onto **R**. We define a subsequence $n \to p(n)$ of integers by induction in the following way: $p(0) = 0$, $p(1)$ is the smallest value of n such that $x_n > x_0$. Suppose that $p(n)$ has been defined for $n \leqslant 2m - 1$, and that $x_{p(2m-2)} < x_{p(2m-1)}$; then the set $]x_{p(2m-2)}, x_{p(2m-1)}[$ is infinite by (2.2.16), and we define $p(2m)$ to be the smallest integer $k > p(2m-1)$ such that $x_{p(2m-2)} < x_k < x_{p(2m-1)}$; then we define $p(2m+1)$ as the smallest integer $k > p(2m)$ such that $x_{p(2m)} < x_k < x_{p(2m-1)}$. It is immediate that the sequence $(p(n))$ is strictly increasing, hence $p(n) \geqslant n$ for all n. On the other hand, from the construction it follows that the closed interval $[x_{p(2m)}, x_{p(2m+1)}]$ is contained in the open interval $]x_{p(2m-2)}, x_{p(2m-1)}[$. By (IV) there is a real number y contained in all closed intervals $[x_{p(2m)}, x_{p(2m+1)}]$ and it cannot coincide with any extremity, since the extremities of an interval do not belong to the next one. Let q be the integer such that $y = x_q$, and let n be the largest integer such that $p(n) \leqslant q$, hence $q < p(n+1)$. Suppose first $n = 2m$; then, the relation $x_{p(2m)} < x_q < x_{p(2m+1)} < x_{p(2m-1)}$ contradicts the definition of $p(2m+1)$. If on the contrary $n = 2m - 1$, then the relation $x_{p(2m-2)} < x_{p(2m)} < x_q < x_{p(2m-1)}$ contradicts the definition of $p(2m)$. This ends the proof.

PROBLEMS

1. Let A be a denumerable subset of **R** having the following properties: for every pair of elements x, y of A such that $x < y$, there are elements u, v, w of A such that $u < x < v < y < w$. Show that there is a bijection f of A onto the set **Q** of rational numbers, such that $x < y$ implies $f(x) < f(y)$. [Let $n \to a_n$, $n \to b_n$ be bijections of **N** onto A and **Q**. Show by induction on n that there exist finite subsets $A_n \subset A$, $B_n \subset \mathbf{Q}$, and a bijection f_n of A_n onto B_n such that: (1) the a_i with $i \leqslant n$ belong to A_n; (2) the b_i with $i \leqslant n$ belong to B_n; (3) $x < y$ in A_n implies $f_n(x) < f_n(y)$; (4) $A_n \subset A_{n+1}$ and f_n is the restriction of f_{n+1} to A_n.]
2. Show that the set I of all irrational numbers is equipotent to **R** (cf. Section 1.9, Problem 5).

3. LEAST UPPER BOUND AND GREATEST LOWER BOUND

A real number b is said to be a *majorant* (resp. *minorant*) of a subset X of real numbers if $x \leqslant b$ (resp. $b \leqslant x$) for every $x \in X$. A set $X \subset \mathbf{R}$ is said to be *majorized*, or *bounded from above* (resp. *minorized*, or *bounded from below*) if the set of majorants (resp. minorants) of X is not empty. If X is majorized, then $-X$ (set of $-x$, where $x \in X$) is minorized, and for every majorant b of X, $-b$ is a minorant of $-X$, and vice versa. A set which is both majorized and minorized is said to be *bounded.*

(2.3.1) *In order that a set* $X \subset \mathbf{R}$ *be bounded, a necessary and sufficient condition is that there exist an integer* n *such that* $|x| \leqslant n$ *for every* $x \in X$.

For it follows from (III) that if a is a minorant and b a majorant of X, there exist integers p, q such that $-p < a$ and $b < q$; take $n = p + q$. The converse is obvious.

(2.3.2) *If a nonempty subset* X *of* **R** *is majorized, the set* M *of majorants of* X *has a smallest element.*

Let $a \in X$, $b \in M$; by (III), for every integer n, there is an integer m such that $b \leqslant a + m \cdot 2^{-n}$; on the other hand, if c is a majorant of X, so is every $y \geqslant c$, so there is a smallest p_n such that $a + p_n 2^{-n}$ is a majorant of X; this implies that, if $I_n = [a + (p_n - 1)2^{-n}, \ a + p_n 2^{-n}]$, $I_n \cap X$ is not empty. As $p_n 2^{-n} = (2p_n)2^{-n-1}$, we necessarily have $p_{n+1} = 2p_n$ or $p_{n+1} = 2p_n - 1$, since $a + (2p_n - 2)2^{-n-1}$ is not a majorant; in other words,

$I_{n+1} \subset I_n$. From (IV) it follows that the intervals I_n have a nonempty intersection J; if J contained at least two distinct elements $\alpha < \beta$, the interval $[\alpha, \beta]$ would be contained in each I_n, and therefore by (2.2.14) we should have $2^{-n} \geqslant \beta - \alpha$, or $1 \geqslant 2^n(\beta - \alpha)$ for every n, which contradicts (III) (remember that $2^n \geqslant n$, as is obvious by induction). Therefore $J = \{\gamma\}$. Let us first show that γ is a majorant of X; if not, there would be an $x \in X$ such that $x > \gamma$; but there would then be an n such that $2^{-n} < x - \gamma$, and as $\gamma \in I_n$, we would have $a + p_n 2^{-n} < x$, contrary to the definition of p_n. On the other hand, every $y \in M$ is $\geqslant \gamma$; otherwise, there would be an n such that $2^{-n} < \gamma - y$, and as $\gamma \in I_n$, we would have $a + (p_n - 1)2^{-n} > y$, and $a + (p_n - 1)2^{-n}$ would be a majorant of X; this contradicts again the definition of p_n. The number γ is thus the smallest element of M; it is called the *least upper bound* or *supremum* of X, and written l.u.b. X, or sup X.

(2.3.3) *If a nonempty subset* X *of* **R** *is minorized, the set of minorants* M′ *of* X *has a greatest element.*

Apply (2.3.2) to the set $-X$.

The greatest element of M′ is called the *greatest lower bound* or *infimum* of X and written g.l.b. X or inf X. For a nonempty bounded set X, both inf X and sup X exist, and inf X $\leqslant$ sup X.

(2.3.4.) *The l.u.b. of a majorized set* X *is the real number* γ *characterized by the following two properties*: (1) γ *is a majorant of* X; (2) *for every integer* $n > 0$, *there exists an element* $x \in X$ *such that* $\gamma - 1/n < x \leqslant \gamma$.

Both properties of $\gamma = \sup X$ follow from the definition, since the second expresses that $\gamma - 1/n$ is not a majorant of X. Conversely, if these properties are satisfied, we cannot have $\sup X = \beta < \gamma$, for there would be an n such that $1/n < \gamma - \beta$, hence $\beta < \gamma - 1/n$, and $\gamma - 1/n$ would be a majorant of X, contrary to property (2). A similar characterization holds for inf X, by applying (2.3.4) to $-X$, since $\inf X = -\sup(-X)$.

If a set $X \subset \mathbf{R}$ has a *greatest* element b (resp. a *smallest* element a), then $b = \sup X$ (resp. $a = \inf X$) and we write max X (resp. min X) instead of sup X (resp. inf X). This applies in particular to finite sets by (2.2.3). But the l.u.b. and g.l.b. of a bounded infinite set X need not belong to X; for instance, if X is the set of all numbers $1/n$, where n runs through all integers $\geqslant 1$, 0 is the g.l.b. of X.

(2.3.5) *If* $A \subset \mathbf{R}$ *is majorized and* $B \subset A$, B *is majorized and* $\sup B \leqslant \sup A$.

This follows from the definitions.

(2.3.6) *Let* $(A_\lambda)_{\lambda \in L}$ *be a family of nonempty majorized subsets of* $\mathbf{R}$; *let* $A = \bigcup_{\lambda \in L} A_\lambda$, *and let* B *be the set of elements* $\sup A_\lambda$. *In order that* A *be majorized, a necessary and sufficient condition is that* B *be majorized, and then* $\sup A = \sup B$.

▲It follows at once from the definition that any majorant of A is a majorant of B, and vice versa, hence the result.

Let f be a mapping of a set A into the set $\mathbf{R}$ of real numbers; f is said to be *majorized* (resp. *minorized, bounded*) *in* A if the subset $f(A)$ of $\mathbf{R}$ is majorized (resp. minorized, bounded); we write $\sup f(A) = \sup_{x \in A} f(x)$, $\inf f(A) = \inf_{x \in A} f(x)$ when these numbers are defined (*supremum* and *infimum of f in* A). If f is majorized, then $-f$ is minorized, and

$$\inf_{x \in A}(-f(x)) = -\sup_{x \in A} f(x).$$

(2.3.7) *Let f be a mapping of* $A_1 \times A_2$ *into* $\mathbf{R}$; *if f is majorized,*

$$\sup_{(x_1, x_2) \in A_1 \times A_2} f(x_1, x_2) = \sup_{x_1 \in A_1} \left(\sup_{x_2 \in A_2} f(x_1, x_2) \right)$$

For we can write $f(A_1 \times A_2)$ as the union of sets $f(\{x_1\} \times A_2)$, x_1 ranging through A_1, and apply (2.3.6).

(2.3.8) *Let f, g be two mappings of* A *into* $\mathbf{R}$ *such that* $f(x) \leqslant g(x)$ *for every* $x \in A$; *then if g is majorized, so is f, and* $\sup_{x \in A} f(x) \leqslant \sup_{x \in A} g(x)$.

This follows immediately from the definitions.

(2.3.9) *Let f and g be two mappings of* A *into* $\mathbf{R}$; *if f and g are both majorized, so is $f + g$* (i.e. *the mapping* $x \to f(x) + g(x)$), *and*

$$\sup_{x \in A} (f(x) + g(x)) \leqslant \sup_{x \in A} f(x) + \sup_{x \in A} g(x).$$

If in addition g is minorized then

$$\sup_{x \in A} f(x) + \inf_{x \in A} g(x) \leqslant \sup_{x \in A} (f(x) + g(x))$$

Let $a = \sup_{x \in A} f(x)$, $b = \sup_{x \in A} g(x)$; then $f(x) \leqslant a$ and $g(x) \leqslant b$ for every $x \in A$, hence $f(x) + g(x) \leqslant a + b$, and the first inequality follows. Let $c = \inf_{x \in A} g(x)$; then for every $x \in A$, $f(x) + c \leqslant f(x) + g(x) \leqslant d = \sup_{x \in A} (f(x) + g(x))$; but this yields $f(x) \leqslant d - c$ for every $x \in A$, hence $a \leqslant d - c$, or $a + c \leqslant d$, which is the second inequality.

(2.3.10) *Let f be a majorized mapping of* A *into* **R**; *then, for every real number* c, $\sup_{x \in A} (f(x) + c) = c + \sup_{x \in A} f(x)$.

Take for g the constant function equal to c in (2.3.9).

(2.3.11) *Let f_1* (resp. f_2) *be a majorized mapping of* A_1 (resp. A_2) *into* **R**; *then* $(x_1, x_2) \to f_1(x_1) + f_2(x_2)$ *is majorized, and*

$$\sup_{(x_1, x_2) \in A_1 \times A_2} (f_1(x_1) + f_2(x_2)) = \sup_{x_1 \in A_1} f_1(x_1) + \sup_{x_2 \in A_2} f_2(x_2).$$

Apply (2.3.7) and (2.3.10).

We leave to the reader the formulation of the similar properties for inf (change the signs everywhere).

PROBLEM

Let $x \to I(x)$ be a mapping of **R** into the set of open intervals of **R**, such that $I(x)$ be an open interval of center x and of length $\leqslant c$ (c being a given number > 0). Show that, for every closed interval $[a, b]$ of **R**, there exist a finite number of points x_i of $[a, b]$ such that: (1) the intervals $I(x_i)$ form a covering of $[a, b]$; (2) the sum of the lengths of the $I(x_i)$ is $\leqslant c + 2(b - a)$. (Prove that if the theorem is true for any interval $[a, x]$ such that $a \leqslant x < u < b$, then there exists v such that $u < v < b$ and that the theorem is still true for any interval $[a, y]$ such that $a \leqslant y < v$. Consider then the l.u.b. of all numbers $u < b$ such that the theorem is true for any interval $[a, x]$ such that $a \leqslant x < u$.) Show by an example that the majoration is best possible.

CHAPTER III

METRIC SPACES

▲This chapter, together with Chapter V, constitutes the core of this first volume: in them is developed the geometric language in which are now expressed the results of analysis, and which has made it possible to give to these results their full generality, as well as to supply for them the simplest and most perspicuous proofs. Most of the notions introduced in this chapter have very intuitive meanings, when specialized to "ordinary" three-dimensional space; after some experience with their use, both in problems and in the subsequent chapters, the student should be able to reach the conviction that, with proper safeguards, this intuition is on the whole an extremely reliable guide, and that it would be a pity to limit it to its classical range of application.

▲ There are almost no genuine theorems in this chapter; most results follow in a straightforward manner from the definitions, and those which require a little more elaboration never lie very deep. Sections 3.1 to 3.13 are essentially concerned with laying down the terminology; it may seem to the unprepared reader that there is a very great deal of it, especially in Sections 3.5 to 3.8, which really are only various ways of saying the same things over again; the reason for this apparent redundancy of the language is to be sought in the applications: to dispense with it (as one theoretically might) would often result in very awkward and cumbersome expressions, and it has proved worthwhile in practice to burden the memory with a few extra terms in order to achieve greater clarity.

The most important notions developed in this chapter are those of *completeness* (Section 3.14), *compactness* (Sections 3.16 to 3.18) and *connectedness* (Section 3.19), which will be repeatedly used later on, and of which the student should try to get as thorough a grasp as possible before he moves on.

Metric spaces only constitute one special kind of "topological spaces," and this chapter may therefore be visualized as introductory to the study of "general topology," as developed for instance in Kelley [15] and Bourbaki [5]; the way to this generalization is made apparent in the remarks of Section (3.12) when it is realized that in most questions, the distance defining a metric space only plays an auxiliary role, and can be replaced by "equivalent" ones without disturbing in an appreciable way the phenomena under study. In Chapter XII, we shall develop the notions of general topology which will be needed in further chapters.

1. DISTANCES AND METRIC SPACES

▲ Let E be a set. *A distance on* E is a mapping d of $E \times E$ into the set **R** of real numbers, having the following properties:

(I) $d(x, y) \geqslant 0$ for any pair of elements x, y of E.

(II) The relation $d(x, y) = 0$ is equivalent to $x = y$.

(III) $d(y, x) = d(x, y)$ for any pair of elements of E.

(IV) $d(x, z) \leqslant d(x, y) + d(y, z)$ for any three elements x, y, z of E ("*triangle inequality*").

▲ From (IV) it follows by induction that

$$d(x_1, x_n) \leqslant d(x_1, x_2) + d(x_2, x_3) + \cdots + d(x_{n-1}, x_n)$$

for any $n > 2$.

(3.1.1) *If d is a distance on* E, *then*

$$|d(x, z) - d(y, z)| \leqslant d(x, y)$$

for any three elements x, y, z of E.

For it follows from (III) and (IV) that

$$d(x, z) \leqslant d(y, z) + d(x, y)$$

and

$$d(y, z) \leqslant d(y, x) + d(x, z) = d(x, y) + d(x, z)$$

hence

$$-d(x, y) \leqslant d(x, z) - d(y, z) \leqslant d(x, y).$$

▲A *metric space* is a set E together with a given distance on E. In the general arguments of this chapter, whenever we introduce metric spaces written E, E′, E″, we will in general write d, d', d'' for the distances on E, E′, E″.

2. EXAMPLES OF DISTANCES

•(3.2.1) The function $(x, y) \to |x - y|$ is a distance on the set of real numbers, as follows at once from (2.2.10); the corresponding metric space is called the *real line*. When $\mathbf{R}$ is considered as a metric space without mentioning explicitly for what distance, it is always understood that the distance is the one just defined.

•(3.2.2) In usual three-dimensional space $\mathbf{R}^3 = \mathbf{R} \times \mathbf{R} \times \mathbf{R}$, the usual "euclidean distance" defined by

$$d(x, y) = ((x_1 - y_1)^2 + (x_2 - y_2)^2 + (x_3 - y_3)^2)^{1/2}$$

for two elements $x = (x_1, x_2, x_3)$ and $y = (y_1, y_2, y_3)$ verifies axioms (I), (II) and (III) in a trivial way; (IV) is verified by direct computation.

•(3.2.3) In the "real plane" $\mathbf{R}^2 = \mathbf{R} \times \mathbf{R}$, let us define

$$d(x, y) = |x_1 - y_1| + |x_2 - y_2|$$

for any two elements $x = (x_1, x_2)$ and $y = (y_1, y_2)$; axioms (I), (II), (III) are again trivially verified, whilst (IV) follows from (2.2.10).

•(3.2.4) Let A be any set, $E = \mathscr{B}(A)$ the set of *bounded* mappings of A into $\mathbf{R}$ (see Section 2.3). Then, for any two functions f, g belonging to E, $f - g$ also belongs to E, and the number

$$d(f, g) = \sup_{t \in A} |f(t) - g(t)|$$

is defined. The mapping $(f, g) \to d(f, g)$ is a *distance* on E; for (I) and (III) are trivial, and (IV) follows at once from (2.3.9) and (2.3.8); on the other hand, if $d(f, g) = 0$, then $f(t) - g(t)) = 0$ for all $t \in A$, which means $f = g$ (see Section 1.4), hence (II).

•(3.2.5) Let E be an arbitrary set, and let us define $d(x, y) = 1$ if $x \neq y$, $d(x, x) = 0$. Then (I), (II), (III) are verified; (IV) is immediate if two of the three elements x, y, z are equal; if not, we have $d(x, z) = 1$, $d(x, y) + d(y, z) = 2$, hence (IV) is satisfied in every case. The corresponding metric space defined on E by that distance is called *a discrete* metric space.

• (3.2.6) Let p be a prime number; for any natural integer $n > 0$, we define $v_p(n)$ as the exponent of p in the decomposition of n into prime numbers. It follows at once from that definition that

$$v_p(nn') = v_p(n) + v_p(n') \tag{3.2.6.1}$$

for any pair of integers >0. Next let $x = \pm r/s$ be any rational number $\neq 0$, with r and s integers >0; we define $v_p(x) = v_p(r) - v_p(s)$; this does not depend on the particular expression of x as a fraction, as follows at once from (3.2.6.1); the same relation also shows that

$$v_p(xy) = v_p(x) + v_p(y) \tag{3.2.6.2}$$

for any pair of rational numbers $\neq 0$. We now put, for any pair of rational numbers x, y, $d(x, y) = p^{-v_p(x-y)}$ if $x \neq y$, and $d(x, x) = 0$; we will prove this is a *distance* (the so-called "p-adic distance") on the set $\mathbf{Q}$ of rational numbers. Axioms (I), (II) and (III) follow at once from the definition; moreover, we prove the following reinforced form of axiom (IV):

$$d(x, z) \leqslant \max(d(x, y), d(y, z)). \tag{3.2.6.3}$$

As this is obvious if two of the elements x, y, z are equal, we can suppose they are all distinct, and then we have to prove that for any pair of rational numbers x, y such that $x \neq 0$, $y \neq 0$ and $x - y \neq 0$, we have

$$v_p(x - y) \geqslant \min(v_p(x), v_p(y)). \tag{3.2.6.4}$$

We may suppose $v_p(x) \geqslant v_p(y)$; using (3.2.6.2), the relation to prove reduces to

$$v_p(z - 1) \geqslant 0 \tag{3.2.6.5}$$

for any rational z such that $z \neq 0$, $z \neq 1$ and $v_p(z) \geqslant 0$. But then, by definition, $z = p \pm^h r/s$, with $h \geqslant 0$, r and s not divisible by p; as $z - 1$ has a denominator which is not divisible by p, (3.2.6.5) follows from the definition of v_p.

Other examples will be studied in detail in Chapters V, VI, and VII.

3. ISOMETRIES

Let E, E′ be two metric spaces, d, d' the distances on E and E′. A bijection f of E onto E′ is called *an isometry* if

$$d'(f(x), f(y)) = d(x, y) \tag{3.3.1}$$

for any pair of elements of E; the inverse mapping f^{-1} is then an isometry of E′ onto E. Two metric spaces E, E′ *are isometric* if there is an isometry of E onto E′. Any theorem proved in E and which involves *only distances* between elements of E immediately yields a corresponding theorem in any isometric space E′, relating the distances of the images by f of the elements of E which intervene in the theorem.

▲Let now E be a metric space, d the distance on E, and f a bijection of E onto a set E′ (where no previous distance need be defined); we can then *define* a distance d' on E′ by the formula (3.3.1), and f is then an isometry of E onto E′. The distance d' is said to have been *transported* from E to E′ by f.

Example

•(3.3.2) *The extended real line* $\overline{\mathbf{R}}$. The function f defined in $\mathbf{R}$ by $f(x) = x/(1 + |x|)$ is a bijection of $\mathbf{R}$ on the open interval $\mathrm{I} =]-1, +1[$; the inverse mapping g being defined by $g(x) = x/(1 - |x|)$ for $|x| < 1$. Let J be the closed interval $[-1, +1]$, and let $\overline{\mathbf{R}}$ be the set which is the union of $\mathbf{R}$ and of two new elements written $+\infty$ and $-\infty$ (points at infinity); we extend f to a bijection of $\overline{\mathbf{R}}$ onto J by putting $f(+\infty) = +1$, $f(-\infty) = -1$, and write again g for the inverse mapping. As J is a metric space for the distance $|x - y|$, we can apply the process described above to define $\overline{\mathbf{R}}$ as a metric space, by putting $d(x, y) = |f(x) - f(y)|$. With this distance (which, when considered for elements of $\mathbf{R}$, is *different* from the one defined in (3.2.1)), the metric space $\overline{\mathbf{R}}$ is called the extended real line; we note that for $x \geqslant 0$, $d(+\infty, x) = 1/(1 + |x|)$ and for $x \leqslant 0$, $d(-\infty, x) = 1/(1 + |x|)$.

▲We can define an order relation on $\overline{\mathbf{R}}$ by defining $x \leqslant y$ to be equivalent to $f(x) \leqslant f(y)$; it is readily verified that for x, y in $\mathbf{R}$ this is equivalent to the order relation already defined on $\mathbf{R}$, and that in addition we have $-\infty < x < +\infty$ for every $x \in \mathbf{R}$; the real numbers are also called the *finite* elements of $\overline{\mathbf{R}}$. All properties and definitions, seen in Chapter II, which relate to the order relation *only* (excluding everything which has to do with algebraic operations) can immediately be "transported" to $\overline{\mathbf{R}}$ by the mapping g. A nonempty subset A of $\overline{\mathbf{R}}$ is *always bounded* for that order relation, and therefore sup A and inf A are defined, but may be $+\infty$ or $-\infty$ as well as real numbers. The definition of $\sup_{x \in \mathrm{A}} u(x)$ and $\inf_{x \in \mathrm{A}} u(x)$ (for any mapping u of a set A into $\overline{\mathbf{R}}$) is given in the same manner, and in particular, properties (2.3.5), (2.3.6), (2.3.7), and (2.3.8) hold without change.

4. BALLS, SPHERES, DIAMETER

▲In the theory of metric spaces, it is extremely convenient to use a geometrical language inspired by classical geometry. Thus elements of a metric space will usually be called *points*. Given a metric space E, with distance d, a point $a \in \mathrm{E}$, and a real number $r > 0$, the *open ball* (resp. *closed ball, sphere*) of *center* a and *radius* r is the set $\mathrm{B}(a; r) = \{x \in \mathrm{E} \mid d(a, x) < r\}$ (resp. $\mathrm{B}'(a; r) = \{x \in \mathrm{E} \mid d(a, x) \leqslant r\}$, $\mathrm{S}(a; r) = \{x \in \mathrm{E} \mid d(a, x) = r\}$). Open and closed balls of center a always contain the point a, but a sphere of center a may be empty (for examples of strange properties which balls may possess in a general metric space, see Problem 4 of Section 3.8).

Examples

▲ In the real line, an open (resp. closed) ball of center a and radius r is the interval $]a - r, a + r[$ (resp. $[a - r, a + r]$); the sphere of center a and radius r consists of two points $a - r$, $a + r$. In the extended line $\overline{\mathbf{R}}$, an open ball of center $+\infty$ and radius $r < 1$ is the interval $](1 - r)/r, +\infty]$. In a discrete space E, a ball (open or closed) of center a and radius $r < 1$ is reduced to a and the corresponding sphere is empty; if on the contrary $r \geqslant 1$, $\mathrm{B}(a; r) = \mathrm{B}'(a; r) = \mathrm{E}$ and $\mathrm{S}(a; r) = \varnothing$ if $r > 1$, $\mathrm{S}(a; r) = \mathrm{E} - \{a\}$ if $r = 1$.

▲ Let A, B be two nonempty subsets of E; the *distance of* A *to* B is defined as the positive number $d(\mathrm{A}, \mathrm{B}) = \inf_{x \in \mathrm{A},\, y \in \mathrm{B}} d(x, y)$. When A is reduced to a single point, $d(\mathrm{A}, \mathrm{B})$ is also written $d(x, \mathrm{B})$; we have by (2.3.7), $d(\mathrm{A}, \mathrm{B}) = \inf_{x \in \mathrm{A}} d(x, \mathrm{B})$. If $\mathrm{A} \cap \mathrm{B} \neq \varnothing$, $d(\mathrm{A}, \mathrm{B}) = 0$, but the converse need not hold; more generally, if $d(\mathrm{A}, \mathrm{B}) = a$, there does not necessarily exist a pair of points $x \in \mathrm{A}$, $y \in \mathrm{B}$ such that $d(x, y) = a$. For instance, in the real line $\mathbf{R}$, let A be the set of all integers $\geqslant 1$, and let B be the set of numbers of the form $n - 1/n$ for all integers $n \geqslant 2$; A and B have no common points, but $d(n, n - 1/n) = 1/n$ is arbitrarily small, hence $d(\mathrm{A}, \mathrm{B}) = 0$ (see Section 3.17, Problem 2).

(3.4.1) *If a point* x *does not belong to a ball* $\mathrm{B}(a; r)$ (resp. $\mathrm{B}'(a; r)$), *then* $d(x, \mathrm{B}(a; r)) \geqslant d(a, x) - r$ (resp. $d(x, \mathrm{B}'(a; r)) \geqslant d(a, x) - r$).

$d(a,y) + d(x,y) \geqslant d(a,x) \Rightarrow d(x,y) + r \geqslant d(a,x), \Rightarrow d(x,y) \geqslant d(a,x) - r.$

▲ Indeed, the assumption implies $d(a, x) \geqslant r$; for any $y \in \mathrm{B}(a; r)$ (resp. $y \in \mathrm{B}'(a; r)$), $d(x, y) \geqslant d(a, x) - d(a, y) \geqslant d(a, x) - r$ by the triangle inequality.

(3.4.2) *If* A *is a nonempty subset of* E, x, y *two points of* E,

$$|d(x, \mathrm{A}) - d(y, \mathrm{A})| \leqslant d(x, y).$$

▲ For every $z \in A$, $d(x, z) \leqslant d(x, y) + d(y, z)$, hence

$$d(x, A) = \inf_{z \in A} d(x, z) \leqslant \inf_{z \in A}(d(x, y) + d(y, z)) = d(x, y) + \inf_{z \in A} d(y, z)$$
$$= d(x, y) + d(y, A)$$

by (2.3.8) and (2.3.10). Similarly one has $d(y, A) \leqslant d(x, y) + d(x, A)$.

▲ For any nonempty set A in E, *the diameter of* A is defined as $\delta(A) = \sup_{x \in A, y \in A} d(x, y)$; it is a positive real number or $+\infty$; $A \subset B$ implies $\delta(A) \leqslant \delta(B)$. The relation $\delta(A) = 0$ holds if and only if A is a one point set.

(3.4.3) *For any ball,* $\delta(B'(a; r)) \leqslant 2r$.

For if $d(a, x) \leqslant r$ and $d(a, y) \leqslant r$, $d(x, y) \leqslant 2r$ by the triangle inequality.

▲ A *bounded set* in E is a nonempty set whose diameter is finite. Any ball is bounded. The whole space E can be bounded, as the example of the extended real line $\overline{\mathbf{R}}$ shows. Any nonempty subset of a bounded set is bounded.

(3.4.4) *The union of two bounded sets* A, B *is bounded.*

▲ For if $a \in A$, $b \in B$, then, if x, y are any two points in $A \cup B$, either x and y are in A, and then $d(x, y) \leqslant \delta(A)$, or they are in B and $d(x, y) \leqslant \delta(B)$, or for instance $x \in A$ and $y \in B$, and then $d(x, y) \leqslant d(x, a) + d(a, b) + d(b, y)$ by the triangle inequality, hence

$$\delta(A \cup B) \leqslant d(a, b) + \delta(A) + \delta(B);$$

this being true for any $a \in A$, $b \in B$, we have

$$\delta(A \cup B) \leqslant d(A, B) + \delta(A) + \delta(B)$$

by definition of $d(A, B)$.

▲ It follows that if A is bounded, for any $x_0 \in E$, A is contained in the closed ball of center x_0 and radius $d(x_0, A) + \delta(A)$.

5. OPEN SETS

▲ In a metric space E, with distance d, *an open set* is a subset A of E having the following property: for every $x \in A$, there exists $r > 0$ such that $B(x; r) \subset A$. The empty set is open (see Section 1.1); the whole space E is open.

(3.5.1) *Any open ball is an open set.*

▲ For if $x \in B(a; r)$, then $d(a, x) < r$ by definition; hence the relation $d(x, y) < r - d(a, x)$ implies $d(a, y) \leqslant d(a, x) + d(x, y) < r$, which proves the inclusion $B(x; r - d(a, x)) \subset B(a; r)$.

(3.5.2) *The union of any family $(A_\lambda)_{\lambda \in L}$ of open sets is open.*

▲ For if $x \in A_\mu$ for some $\mu \in L$, then there is $r > 0$ such that

$$B(x; r) \subset A_\mu \subset A = \bigcup_{\lambda \in L} A_\lambda .$$

▲ For instance, in the real line **R**, any interval $]a, +\infty[$ is open, being the union of the open sets $]a, x[$ for all $x > a$. Similarly, $]-\infty, a[$ is open.

(3.5.3) *The intersection of a finite number of open sets is open.*

▲ It is enough to prove that the intersection of two open sets A_1, A_2 is open, and then to argue by induction. If $x \in A_1 \cap A_2$, there are $r_1 > 0$, $r_2 > 0$ such that $B(x; r_1) \subset A_1$, $B(x; r_2) \subset A_2$; clearly if $r = \min(r_1, r_2)$, $B(x; r) \subset A_1 \cap A_2$.

▲ In general, an infinite intersection of open sets is no longer open; for instance the intersection of the intervals $]-1/n, 1/n[$ in **R** is the one point set $\{0\}$, which is not open by (2.2.16). However:

(3.5.4) *In a discrete space any set is open.*

▲ Due to (3.5.2), it is enough to prove that a one point set $\{a\}$ is open. But by definition, $\{a\} = B(a; 1/2)$, and the result follows from (3.5.1).

6. NEIGHBORHOODS

▲ If A is a nonempty subset of E, an *open neighborhood* of A is an open set containing A; a *neighborhood* of A is any set containing an open neighborhood of A. When $A = \{x\}$, we speak of neighborhoods of the point x (instead of the set $\{x\}$).

(3.6.1) *For any nonempty set* $A \subset E$, *and any* $r > 0$, *the set* $V_r(A) = \{x \in E \mid d(x, A) < r\}$ *is an open neighborhood of* A.

▲For if $d(x, A) < r$ and $d(x, y) < r - d(x, A)$, it follows from (3.4.2) that $d(y, A) < d(x, A) + r - d(x, A) = r$, hence $V_r(A)$ is open, and obviously contains A.

▲When $A = \{a\}$, $V_r(A)$ is the open ball $B(a; r)$.

▲A *fundamental system of neighborhoods* of A is a family (U_λ) of neighborhoods of A such that any neighborhood of A contains one of the sets U_λ. For arbitrary sets A, the $V_r(A)$ $(r > 0)$ *do not* in general form a fundamental system of neighborhoods of A (see however (3.17.11)). It follows from the definitions that:

(3.6.2) *The balls* $B(a; 1/n)$ (n *integer* > 0) *form a fundamental system of neighborhoods of* a.

(3.6.3) *The intersection of a finite number of neighborhoods of* A *is a neighborhood of* A.

This follows from (3.5.3).

(3.6.4) *In order that a set* A *be a neighborhood of every one of its points, a necessary and sufficient condition is that* A *be open.*

▲The condition is obviously sufficient; conversely, if A is a neighborhood of every $x \in A$, there exists for each $x \in A$ an open set $U_x \subset A$ which contains x. From the relations $x \in U_x \subset A$ we deduce $A = \bigcup_{x \in A} \{x\} \subset \bigcup_{x \in A} U_x \subset A$, hence $A = \bigcup_{x \in A} U_x$ is an open set, by (3.5.2).

PROBLEM

In the real line, show that the subset **N** of all integers $\geqslant 0$ does not possess a denumerable fundamental system of neighborhoods. (Use contradiction, and apply the following remark: if (a_{mn}) is a double sequence of numbers > 0, the sequence (b_n) where $b_n = a_{nn}/2$ is such that for no integer m does the inequality $b_n \geqslant a_{mn}$ hold for all integers n.)

7. INTERIOR OF A SET

▲ A point x is said to be *interior to a set* A if A is a neighborhood of x. The set of all points interior to A is called the *interior of* A, and written $\mathring{A}$. For instance, in the real line **R**, the interior of any interval of origin a and extremity b ($a < b$) is the open interval $]a, b[$; for neither a nor b can be an interior point of the intervals $[a, b]$, $[a, b[$ and $]a, b]$, as no interval of center a or b is contained in these three intervals.

(3.7.1) *For any set* A, $\mathring{A}$ *is the largest open set contained in* A.

▲ For if $x \in \mathring{A}$, there is an open set $U_x \subset A$ containing x; for each $y \in U_x$, A is by definition a neighborhood of y, hence $y \in \mathring{A}$, and therefore $U_x \subset \mathring{A}$, which proves $\mathring{A}$ is open by (3.6.4). Conversely, if $B \subset A$ is open, it is clear by definition that $B \subset \mathring{A}$. Open sets are therefore *characterized* by the relation $A = \mathring{A}$.

(3.7.2) *If* $A \subset B$, *then* $\mathring{A} \subset \mathring{B}$.

▲ This follows at once from (3.7.1).

(3.7.3) *For any pair of sets* A, B, $\overset{\circ}{\widehat{A \cap B}} = \mathring{A} \cap \mathring{B}$.

▲ The inclusion $\overset{\circ}{\widehat{A \cap B}} \subset \mathring{A} \cap \mathring{B}$ follows from (3.7.2); on the other hand, $\mathring{A} \cap \mathring{B}$ is open by (3.5.3) and (3.7.1) and contained in $A \cap B$, hence $\mathring{A} \cap \mathring{B} \subset \overset{\circ}{\widehat{A \cap B}}$ by (3.7.1).

▲ The interior of a nonempty set can be empty; this is the case, for instance, for one point sets in **R**.

▲ An interior point of $E - A$ is said to be *exterior to* A, and the interior of $E - A$ is called the *exterior of* A.

(3.7.4) *In order that a point* $x \in E$ *be exterior to* A, *a necessary and sufficient condition is that* $d(x, A) > 0$.

▲ For that condition implies that $B(x; d(x, A)) \subset E - A$, hence x is interior to $E - A$; conversely, if x is exterior to A, there is a ball $B(x; r)$ with $r > 0$ contained in $E - A$; for any $y \in A$, we have therefore $d(x, y) \geqslant r$, hence $d(x, A) \geqslant r$.

8. CLOSED SETS, CLUSTER POINTS, CLOSURE OF A SET

▲ In a metric space E, a *closed set* is by definition the complement of an open set. The empty set is closed, and so is the whole space E. In the real line, the intervals $[a, +\infty[$ and $]-\infty, a]$ are closed sets; so is the set **Z** of integers; the intervals $[a, b[$ and $]a, b]$ are neither open sets nor closed sets.

(3.8.1) *A closed ball is a closed set; a sphere is a closed set.*

▲ For if $x \notin B'(a; r)$, then $d(x, B'(a; r)) \geqslant d(a, x) - r > 0$ by (3.4.1), hence the open ball of center x and radius $d(a, x) - r$ is in the complement of $B'(a; r)$, which proves that complement is open. The complement of the sphere $S(a; r)$ is the union of the ball $B(a; r)$ and of the complement of the ball $B'(a; r)$, hence is open by (3.5.2).

(3.8.2) *The intersection of any family of closed sets is closed.*

(3.8.3) *The union of a finite number of closed sets is closed.*

▲ This follows at once from (3.5.2) and (3.5.3) respectively, by considering complements (see formulas (1.2.9) and (1.8.1)).
▲ In particular, a one point set $\{x\}$ is closed, as intersection of the balls $B'(x; r)$ for $r > 0$.

(3.8.4) *In a discrete space every set is closed.*

▲ This follows at once from (3.5.4).

▲ A *cluster point* of a subset A of E is a point $x \in E$ such that every neighborhood of x has a nonempty intersection with A. The set of all cluster points of A is called the *closure* of A and written $\bar{A}$. To say that x *is not* a cluster point of A means therefore that it is interior to $E - A$, in other words:

(3.8.5) *The closure of a set* A *is the complement of the exterior of* A.

▲ The closure of an open ball $B(a; r)$ is contained in the closed ball $B'(a; r)$, but may be different from it. If a subset A of the real line is majorized (resp minorized), sup A (resp inf A) is a cluster point of A, as follows from (2.3.4).

▲ Due to (3.8.5), the four following properties of cluster points and closure are read off from those proved in Section 3.7 for interior points and interior, by using the formulas of boolean algebra:

(3.8.6) *For any set* A, $\bar{A}$ *is the smallest closed set containing* A.

▲ In particular, closed sets are *characterized* by the relation $A = \bar{A}$.

(3.8.7) *If* $A \subset B$, $\bar{A} \subset \bar{B}$.

(3.8.8) *For any pair of sets* A, B, $\overline{A \cup B} = \bar{A} \cup \bar{B}$.

(3.8.9) *In order that a point* x *be a cluster point of* A, *a necessary and sufficient condition is that* $d(x, A) = 0$.

(3.8.10) *The closure of a set* A *is the intersection of the open neighborhoods* $V_r(A)$ *of* A.

▲ This is only a restatement of (3.8.9).

(3.8.11) *In a metric space* E, *any closed set is the intersection of a decreasing sequence of open sets; any open set is the union of an increasing sequence of closed sets.*

▲ The first statement is proved by considering the open sets $V_{1/n}(A)$ and the second follows from the first by considering complements.

(3.8.12) *If a cluster point* x *of* A *does not belong to* A, *any neighborhood* V *of* x *is such that* $V \cap A$ *is infinite.*

▲ Suppose the contrary, and let $V \cap A = \{y_1, \ldots, y_n\}$: by assumption, $r_k = d(x, y_k) > 0$. Let $r > 0$ be such that $B(x; r) \subset V$ and $r < \min(r_1, \ldots, r_k)$; then the intersection of A and $B(x; r)$ would be empty, contrary to assumption.

▲ A point $x \in E$ is said to be a *frontier point* of a set A if it is a cluster point of both A and $\complement A$; the set fr(A) of all frontier points of A is called the *frontier* of A. It is clear that $\text{fr}(A) = \bar{A} \cap \overline{\complement A} = \text{fr}(\complement A)$; by (3.8.6), fr(A) is a closed set, which may be empty (see (3.19.9)). A frontier point x of A is characterized by the property that in any neighborhood of x there is at least one point of A *and* one point of $\complement A$. The whole space E is the union of the interior of A, the exterior of A and the frontier of A, for if a neighborhood of x is neither contained in A nor in $\complement A$, it must contain points of both; any two of these three sets have no common points.

▲The frontier of any interval of origin a and extremity b in **R** is the set $\{a, b\}$; the frontier of the set **Q** in **R** is **R** itself.

PROBLEMS

• **1.** •(a) Let A be an open set in a metric space E; show that for any subset B of E, $A \cap \bar{B} \subset \overline{A \cap B}$.

•(b) Give examples in the real line, of open sets A, B such that the four sets $A \cap \bar{B}$, $B \cap \bar{A}$, $\overline{A \cap B}$ and $\bar{A} \cap \bar{B}$ are all different.

•(c) Give an example of two intervals A, B in the real line, such that $A \cap \bar{B}$ is not contained in $\overline{A \cap B}$. (a, b] and (b, c)

•**2.** For every subset A of a metric space E, let $\alpha(A) = \mathring{\bar{A}}$ and $\beta(A) = \bar{\mathring{A}}$.

•(a) Show that if A is open, $A \subset \alpha(A)$, and if A is closed, $A \supset \beta(A)$.

•(b) Show that for every subset A of E, $\alpha(\alpha(A)) = \alpha(A)$ and $\beta(\beta(A)) = \beta(A)$ (use (a)).

•(c) Give an example, in the real line, of a set A such that the seven sets A, $\mathring{A}$, $\bar{A}$, $\alpha(A)$, $\beta(A)$, $\alpha(\mathring{A})$, $\beta(\bar{A})$ are all distinct and have no other inclusion relations than the following ones: $\mathring{A} \subset A \subset \bar{A}$; $\mathring{A} \subset \alpha(\mathring{A}) \subset \beta(A) \subset \bar{A}$, $\mathring{A} \subset \alpha(A) \subset \beta(\bar{A}) \subset \bar{A}$.

•**3.** Let E be a metric space.

•(a) Show that for every subset A of E, $\text{fr}(\bar{A}) \subset \text{fr}(A)$, $\text{fr}(\mathring{A}) \subset \text{fr}(A)$, and give examples (in the real line) in which these three sets are distinct.

•(b) Let A, B be two subsets of E. Show that $\text{fr}(A \cup B) \subset \text{fr}(A) \cup \text{fr}(B)$, and give an example (in the real line) in which these sets are distinct. If $\bar{A} \cap \bar{B} = \varnothing$, show that $\text{fr}(A \cup B) = \text{fr}(A) \cup \text{fr}(B)$. ?

•(c) If A and B are open, show that

$$(A \cap \text{fr}(B)) \cup (B \cap \text{fr}(A)) \subset \text{fr}(A \cap B) \subset (A \cap \text{fr}(B)) \cup (B \cap \text{fr}(A)) \cup (\text{fr}(A) \cap \text{fr}(B))$$

and give an example (in the real line) in which these three sets are distinct.

•**4.** Let d be a distance on a set E, satisfying the *ultrametric inequality*

$$d(x, z) \leqslant \max(d(x, y), d(y, z))$$

for x, y, z in E (see Example (3.2.6)).

•(a) Show that if $d(x, y) \neq d(y, z)$, then $d(x, z) = \max(d(x, y), d(y, z))$.

- •(b) Show that any open ball $B(x; r)$ is both an open and a closed set and that for any $y \in B(x; r)$, $B(y; r) = B(x; r)$.

•(c) Show that any closed ball $B'(x; r)$ is both an open and a closed set, and that for any $y \in B'(x; r)$, $B'(y; r) = B'(x; r)$.

• (d) If two balls in E have a common point, one of them is contained in the other.

•(e) The distance of two distinct open balls of radius r, contained in a closed ball of radius r, is equal to r.

9. DENSE SUBSETS; SEPARABLE SPACES

▲In a metric space E, a set A is said to be *dense with respect to a set* B, if any point of B is a cluster point of A, in other words if $B \subset \bar{A}$ (or, equivalently, if for every $x \in B$, any neighborhood of x contains points of A).

(3.9.1) *If* A *is dense with respect to* B, *and* B *dense with respect to* C, *then* A *is dense with respect to* C.

▲ For the relation $B \subset \bar{A}$ implies $\bar{B} \subset \bar{A}$ by (3.8.6), and as by assumption $C \subset \bar{B}$, we have $C \subset \bar{A}$.

▲ A set A dense with respect to E is called *everywhere dense*, or simply *dense* in E; such sets are characterized by the fact that $\bar{A} = E$, or equivalently that every nonempty open set contains a point of A. A metric space E is said to be *separable* if there exists in E an at most denumerable dense set.

(3.9.2) *The real line* **R** *is separable.*

▲ Indeed, by (2.2.16) the set **Q** of rational numbers is dense in **R**, and **Q** is denumerable by (2.2.15).

▲ A family $(G_\lambda)_{\lambda \in L}$ of nonempty open sets is called a *basis* for the open sets of a metric space E if every nonempty open set of E is the union of a subfamily of the family (G_λ).

(3.9.3) *In order that a family* $(G_\lambda)_{\lambda \in L}$ *be a basis, a necessary and sufficient condition is that for every* $x \in E$ *and every neighborhood* V *of* x, *there exist an index* λ *such that* $x \in G_\lambda \subset V$.

The condition is necessary, for there is by definition an open neighborhood $W \subset V$ of x, and as W is a union of sets G_λ, there is at least an index μ such that $x \in G_\mu$. The condition is sufficient, for if it is satisfied, and U is an arbitrary open set, for each $x \in U$, there is (by (1.4.5)) an index $\mu(x)$ such that $x \in G_{\mu(x)} \subset U$, hence $U \subset \bigcup_{x \in U} G_{\mu(x)} \subset U$.

(3.9.4) *In order that a metric space* E *be separable, a necessary and sufficient condition is that there exist an at most denumerable basis for the open sets of* E.

▲ The condition is sufficient, for if (G_n) is a basis, and a_n a point of G_n, every nonempty open set is a union of some G_n, hence its intersection with the at most denumerable set of the a_n is not empty. Conversely, suppose there exists a sequence (a_n) of points of E such that the set of points of that sequence is dense; then the family of open balls $B(a_n; 1/m)$, which is at most denumerable (by (1.9.3) and (1.9.2)) is a basis for the open sets of E. Indeed, for each $x \in E$ and each $r > 0$, there is an index m such that $1/m < r/2$, and an index n such that $a_n \in B(x; 1/m)$. This implies that $x \in B(a_n; 1/m)$; on the other hand, if $y \in B(a_n; 1/m)$, then $d(x, y) \leqslant d(x, a_n) + d(a_n, y) \leqslant 2/m < r$, so that $B(a_n; 1/m) \subset B(x; r)$, which ends the proof (by (3.9.3)).

PROBLEMS

• **1.** Show that in a metric space E, the union of an open subset and of its exterior is everywhere dense.

• **2.** Show that in a separable metric space E, any family $(U_\lambda)_{\lambda \in L}$ of nonempty open sets such that $U_\lambda \cap U_\mu = \varnothing$ if $\lambda \neq \mu$, is at most denumerable.

• **3.** Let A be a nonempty subset of the real line, B the set of points $x \in \bar{A}$ such that there is an interval $]x, y[$ with $y > x$ which has an empty intersection with A. Show that B is at most denumerable (prove that B is equipotent with a set of open intervals, no two of which have common points).

• **4.** Let E be a separable metric space. A *condensation point* x of a subset A of E is a point $x \in E$ such that in every neighborhood of x, there is a nondenumerable set of points of A. Show that:

•(a) If A has no condensation point, it is denumerable (consider the intersections of A with the sets of a basis for the open sets of E).

(b) If B is the set of condensation points of a set A, show that every point of B is a condensation point of B, and that $A \cap (\complement B)$ is at most denumerable. (Observe that B is closed, and use (a).)

• **5.** Show that from every open covering of a separable metric space, one can extract a denumerable open covering.

• **6.** Let E be a separable metric space, f an arbitrary mapping of E into **R**. We say that at a point $x_0 \in E$, f reaches a *relative maximum* (resp. a *strict relative maximum*) if there is a neighborhood V of x_0 such that $f(x) \leqslant f(x_0)$ (resp. $f(x) < f(x_0)$) for any point $x \in V$ distinct from x_0. Show that the set M of the points $x \in E$ where f reaches a strict relative maximum is at most denumerable. (If (U_n) is a basis for the open sets of E, consider the values of n for which there is a unique point $x \in U_n$ such that $f(x)$ is equal to its l.u.b. in U_n.)

10. SUBSPACES OF A METRIC SPACE

▲ Let F be a nonempty subset of a metric space E; the restriction to $F \times F$ of the mapping $(x, y) \to d(x, y)$ is obviously a distance on F, which is said to be *induced* on F by the distance d on E. The metric space defined by that induced distance is called the *subspace* F of the metric space E.

(3.10.1) *In order that a set* $B \subset F$ *be open in the subspace* F, *a necessary and sufficient condition is that there exist an open set* A *in* E *such that* $B = A \cap F$.

▲ If $a \in F$, $F \cap B(a; r)$ is the open ball of center a and radius r *in the subspace* F. If A is open in E and $x \in A \cap F$, there is $r > 0$ such that $B(x; r) \subset A$, hence $x \in F \cap B(x; r) \subset A \cap F$, which shows $F \cap A$ is open in F. Conversely, if B is open in the subspace F, for each $x \in B$, there is a number $r(x) > 0$ such that $F \cap B(x; r(x)) \subset B$. This shows that $B = \bigcup_{x \in B} (F \cap B(x; r(x))) = F \cap A$, with $A = \bigcup_{x \in B} B(x; r(x))$, and A is open in E by (3.5.1) and (3.5.2).

(3.10.2) *In order that every subset* B *in* F, *which is open in* F, *be open in* E, *a necessary and sufficient condition is that* F *be open in* E.

▲ The condition is seen to be necessary by taking $B = F$; it is sufficient, due to (3.10.1) and (3.5.3).

(3.10.3) *If* $x \in F$, *in order that a subset* W *of* F *be a neighborhood of* x *in* F, *a necessary and sufficient condition is that* $W = V \cap F$, *where* V *is a neighborhood of* x *in* E.

(3.10.4) *In order that every neighborhood in* F *of a point* $x \in F$ *be a neighborhood of* x *in* E, *a necessary and sufficient condition is that* F *be a neighborhood of* x *in* E.

▲ These properties follow at once from (3.10.1) and the definition of a neighborhood.

(3.10.5) *In order that a set* $B \subset F$ *be closed in the subspace* F, *a necessary and sufficient condition is that there exist a closed set* A *in* E *such that* $B = A \cap F$.

▲ To say B is closed in F means that F − B is open in F, and therefore is equivalent by (3.10.1) to the existence of an open set C in E such that $F - B = C \cap F$; but that relation is equivalent by (1.5.13) to $B = F \cap (E - C)$, hence the result.

(3.10.6) *In order that every subset* B *in* F, *which is closed in* F, *be closed in* E, *a necessary and sufficient condition is that* F *be closed in* E.

▲ Same proof as for (3.10.2), using (3.10.5) and (3.8.2).

(3.10.7) *The closure, with respect to* F, *of a subset* B *of* F, *is equal to* $\bar{B} \cap F$, *where* $\bar{B}$ *is the closure of* B *in* E.

▲ Indeed, for every neighborhood V of $x \in F$ in E, $V \cap B = (V \cap F) \cap B$, and the result therefore follows from (3.10.3) and from the definition of a cluster point.

(3.10.8) *Suppose* F *is a dense subset of* E. *For every point* $x \in F$ *and every neighborhood* W *of* x *in* F, *the closure* $\bar{W}$ *of* W *in* E *is a neighborhood of* x *in* E.

▲ By definition, there is an open neighborhood U of x in E such that $U \cap F \subset W$; it is enough to prove that $U \subset \bar{W}$. But if $y \in U$, and V is any neighborhood of y in E, $U \cap V$ is a neighborhood of y in E, hence $F \cap (U \cap V)$ is not empty, which means $(F \cap U) \cap V$ is not empty, i.e. $y \in \overline{F \cap U} \subset \bar{W}$.

(3.10.9) *Any subspace of a separable metric space is separable.*

▲ Indeed, if (G_n) is an at most denumerable basis for the open sets of E, the sets $G_n \cap F$ form a denumerable basis for the open sets of $F \subset E$, due to (3.10.1) and (1.8.2). Hence the result by (3.9.4).

(3.10.10) Let A be a subset of a metric space E; a point $x_0 \in A$ is said to be *isolated* in A if there is a neighborhood V of x_0 in E such that $V \cap A = \{x_0\}$. To say that *every* point of A is isolated in A means that in the subspace A every set is an open set (in other words the subspace A is homeomorphic to a *discrete* space: see Section 3.12). In a *separable* metric space, every subset all of whose points are isolated is therefore *at most denumerable* (3.9.4).

PROBLEMS

1. Let B, B′ be two nonempty subsets of a metric space E, and A a subset of $B \cap B'$, which is open (resp. closed) both with respect to B and with respect to B′; show that A is open (resp. closed) with respect to $B \cup B'$.
2. Let (U_α) be a covering of a metric space E, consisting of open subsets. In order that a subset A of E be closed in E, it is necessary and sufficient that each set $A \cap U_\alpha$ be closed with respect to U_α.
3. In a metric space E, a subset A is said to be *locally closed* if for every $x \in A$, there is a neighborhood V of x such that $A \cap V$ is closed with respect to V. Show that the locally closed subsets of E are the sets $U \cap F$, where U is open and F closed in E. (To prove that a locally closed set has that form, use Problem 2.)
4. Give an example of a subspace E of the plane $\mathbf{R}^2$, such that there is in E an open ball which is a closed set but not a closed ball, and a closed ball which is an open set but not an open ball. (Take E consisting of the two points (0, 1) and (0, −1) and of a suitable subset of the x-axis.)
5. Give a proof of (3.10.9) without using the notion of basis (in other words, exhibit an at most denumerable subset which is dense in the subspace).

11. CONTINUOUS MAPPINGS

▲ Let E and E′ be two metric spaces, d, d' the distances on E and E′. A mapping f of E into E′ is said to be *continuous at a point* $x_0 \in E$ if, for every neighborhood V′ of $f(x_0)$ in E′, there is a neighborhood V of x_0 in E such that $f(V) \subset V'$; f is said to be *continuous in* E (or simply "continuous") if it is continuous at *every point* of E.

▲ If we agree that the mathematical notion of neighborhood corresponds to the intuitive idea of "proximity," then we can express the preceding definition in a more intuitive way, by saying that *$f(x)$ is arbitrarily close to $f(x_0)$ as soon as x is close enough to x_0.*

(3.11.1) *In order that f be continuous at $x_0 \in E$, a necessary and sufficient condition is that for every neighborhood V' of $f(x_0)$ in E', $f^{-1}(V')$ be a neighborhood of x_0 in E.*

(3.11.2) *In order that f be continuous at $x_0 \in E$, a necessary and sufficient condition is that, for every $\varepsilon > 0$, there exist a $\delta > 0$ such that the relation $d(x_0, x) < \delta$ implies $d'(f(x_0), f(x)) < \varepsilon$.*

▲ These are mere restatements of the definition.

▲The natural injection j_F: $F \to E$ of a subspace F of E into E (1.6.1) is continuous. Any constant mapping is continuous.

(3.11.3) *If $x_0 \in E$ is a cluster point of a set $A \subset E$, and if f is continuous at the point x_0, then $f(x_0)$ is a cluster point of $f(A)$.*

▲ For if V' is a neighborhood of $f(x_0)$ in E', $f^{-1}(V')$ is a neighborhood of x_0 in E, hence there is $y \in A \cap f^{-1}(V')$, and therefore $f(y) \in f(A) \cap V'$.

(3.11.4) *Let f be a mapping of E into E′. The following properties are equivalent:*

(a) *f is continuous;*
(b) *for every open set A' in E', $f^{-1}(A')$ is an open set in E;*
(c) *for every closed set A' in E', $f^{-1}(A')$ is a closed set in E;*
(d) *for every set A in E, $f(\bar{A}) \subset \overline{f(A)}$.*

▲We have seen in (3.11.3) that (a) ⇒ (d). (d) ⇒ (c), for if A' is closed and $A = f^{-1}(A')$, then $f(\bar{A}) \subset \bar{A}' = A'$, hence $\bar{A} \subset f^{-1}(A') = A$; as $A \subset \bar{A}$, A is closed. (c) ⇒ (b) from the definition of closed sets and formula (1.5.13). Finally (b) ⇒ (a), for if V' is a neighborhood of $f(x_0)$, there is an open neighborhood $W' \subset V'$ of $f(x_0)$; $f^{-1}(W')$ is an open set containing x_0 and contained in $f^{-1}(V')$, hence f is continuous at every point x_0 by (3.11.1).

It should be observed that the *direct* image of an open (resp. closed) set by a continuous mapping is *not* in general an open (resp. closed) set; for instance, $x \to x^2$ is continuous in **R**, but the image $[0, 1[$ of the open set $]-1, +1[$ is not open; $x \to 1/x$ is continuous in the subspace $E = [1, +\infty[$ of **R**, but the image of the closed set E is the interval $]0, 1]$ which is not closed in **R** (see however (3.17.9) and (3.20.13)).

(3.11.5) *Let f be a mapping of a metric space* E *into a metric space* E′, *g a mapping of* E′ *into a metric space* E″; *if f is continuous at x_0, and g continuous at $f(x_0)$, then $h = g \circ f$ is continuous at x_0. If f is continuous in* E *and g continuous in* E′, *then h is continuous in* E.

▲ The second statement obviously follows from the first. Let W″ be a neighborhood of $h(x_0) = g(f(x_0))$; then, by (3.11.1) and the assumptions, $g^{-1}(W'')$ is a neighborhood of $f(x_0)$ in E′, and $f^{-1}(g^{-1}(W''))$ a neighborhood of x_0 in E; but $f^{-1}(g^{-1}(W'')) = h^{-1}(W'')$. In particular:

(3.11.6) *If f is a mapping of* E *into* E′, *continuous at x_0, and* F *a subspace of* E *containing x_0, then the restriction of f to* F *is continuous at x_0.*

▲ For that restriction is the mapping $f \circ j_F$, j_F being the natural injection of F into E, which is continuous.

▲ Note however that the restriction to a subspace F of a mapping f: E → E′ may be continuous without f being continuous at any point of E; an example is given by the mapping f: **R** → **R** which is equal to 0 in the set **Q** of rational points, to 1 in its complement ("Dirichlet's function"); the restriction of f to **Q** is constant, hence continuous.

▲ A *uniformly continuous* mapping of E into E′ is a mapping such that for every $\varepsilon > 0$, there exists a $\delta > 0$ such that the relation $d(x, y) < \delta$ implies $d'(f(x), f(y)) < \varepsilon$. From this definition and (3.11.2), it follows that

(3.11.7) *A uniformly continuous mapping is continuous.*

▲ The converse is not true in general: for instance, the function $x \to x^2$ is not uniformly continuous in **R**, since for given $\alpha > 0$, the difference $(x + \alpha)^2 - x^2 = \alpha(2x + \alpha)$ can take arbitrarily large values (see however (3.16.5)).

▲ The examples given above (constant mapping, natural injection) are uniformly continuous.

(3.11.8) *For any nonempty subset* A *of* E, $x \to d(x, A)$ *is uniformly continuous.*

▲ This follows from the definition and (3.4.2).

(3.11.9) *If f is a uniformly continuous mapping of* E *into* E′, *g a uniformly continuous mapping of* E′ *into* E″, *then $h = g \circ f$ is uniformly continuous.*

▲ Indeed, given any $\varepsilon > 0$, there is $\delta > 0$ such that $d'(x', y') < \delta$ implies $d''(g(x'), g(y')) < \varepsilon$; then there is $\eta > 0$ such that $d(x, y) < \eta$ implies $d'(f(x), f(y)) < \delta$; therefore $d(x, y) < \eta$ implies $d''(h(x), h(y)) < \varepsilon$.

PROBLEMS

1. Let f be a mapping of a metric space E into a metric space E′. Show that the following properties are equivalent:
   (a) f is continuous;
   (b) for every subset A′ of E′, $f^{-1}(\mathring{A}') \subset (f^{-1}(A'))^{\circ}$;
   (c) for every subset A′ of E′, $\overline{f^{-1}(A')} \subset f^{-1}(\bar{A}')$.
   Give an example of a continuous mapping f and a subset $A' \subset E'$ such that $f^{-1}(\bar{A}')$ is not the closure of $f^{-1}(A')$.
2. For any metric space E, any number $r > 0$ and any subset A of E, the set $V'_r(A)$ of points $x \in E$ such that $d(x, A) \leqslant r$ is closed (use **(3.11.8)**).
3. In a metric space E, let A, B be two nonempty subsets such that $A \cap \bar{B} = \bar{A} \cap B = \varnothing$. Show that there exists an open set $U \supset A$ and an open set $V \supset B$ such that $U \cap V = \varnothing$ (consider the function $x \to d(x, A) - d(x, B)$). implies normality.
4. Let f be a continuous mapping of **R** into itself.
   (a) Show that if f is uniformly continuous in **R**, there exist two real numbers $\alpha \geqslant 0$, $\beta \geqslant 0$ such that $|f(x)| \leqslant \alpha|x| + \beta$ for every $x \in \mathbf{R}$.
   (b) Show that if f is monotone and bounded in **R**, f is uniformly continuous in **R**.

12. HOMEOMORPHISMS, EQUIVALENT DISTANCES

▲A mapping f of a metric space E into a metric space E′ is called *a homeomorphism* if: (1) it is a bijection; (2) *both* f and its inverse mapping f^{-1} are continuous. Such a mapping is also said to be *bicontinuous*. The inverse mapping f^{-1} is then a homeomorphism of E′ onto E. If f is a homeomorphism of E onto E′, g a homeomorphism of E′ onto E″, $g \circ f$ is a homeomorphism of E onto E″ by **(3.11.5)**. A homeomorphism may fail to be uniformly continuous (for instance, the homeomorphism $x \to x^3$ of **R** onto itself). Two metric spaces E, E′ are *homeomorphic* if there exists a homeomorphism of E onto E′. Two spaces homeomorphic to a thrid one are homeomorphic. By abuse of language, a space homeomorphic to a discrete metric space (3.2.5) is called a *discrete* space, even if the distance in not defined as in (3.2.5).

▲An isometry is always uniformly continuous by definition, hence a homeomorphism. For instance, the extended real line $\overline{\mathbf{R}}$ is by definition homeomorphic to the subspace $[-1, 1]$ of $\mathbf{R}$.

▲ Let d_1, d_2 be two distances on a set E; this defines two metric spaces on E, which have to be considered as distinct (although they have the same "underlying set"); let E_1, E_2 be these spaces. If the identity mapping $x \to x$ of E_1 onto E_2 is a homeomorphism, d_1, d_2 are called *equivalent distances* (or *topologically equivalent distances*) on E; from (3.11.4), we see that this means *the families of open sets are the same* in E_1 and E_2. The family of open sets of a metric space E is often called the *topology* of E (cf. Section 12.1); equivalent distances are thus those giving rise to the same topology. It may be observed here that the definitions of *neighborhoods, closed sets, cluster point, closure, interior, exterior, dense sets, frontier, continuous function* only depend on the topologies of the spaces under consideration; they are *topological notions*; on the other hand, the notions of *balls, spheres, diameter, bounded set, uniformly continuous function* are not topological notions. Topological properties of a metric space are *invariant under homeomorphisms*.

▲With the preceding notations, it may happen that the identity mapping $x \to x$ of E_1 into E_2 is continuous but *not* bicontinuous: for instance, take $E = \mathbf{R}$, $d_2(x, y) = |x - y|$ and for $d_1(x, y)$ the distance defined in (3.2.5) taking only values 0 and 1. In such a case, the distance d_1 (resp. the topology of E_1) is said to be *finer* than the distance d_2 (resp. the topology of E_2).

PROBLEMS

• **1.** Let a be an irrational number > 0; for each rational number $x > 0$, let $f_a(x)$ be the unique real number such that $0 < f_a(x) < a$ and that $x - f_a(x)$ is an integral multiple of a. Show that f_a is an injective continuous mapping of the space $\mathbf{Q}_+^*$ of rational numbers > 0 into the interval $]0, a[$ of $\mathbf{R}$, and that $f_a(\mathbf{Q}_+^*)$ is dense in $]0, a[$. Deduce from that result and from Problem 1 in Section 2.2 that there exists a bijective continuous mapping of $\mathbf{Q}$ onto itself which is not bicontinuous (compare to (4.2.2)).

• **2.** Let f be a continuous mapping of a metric space E into a metric space F.

• (a) Let (V_λ) be a covering of F by open subsets; show that if, for each λ, the restriction of f to $f^{-1}(V_\lambda)$ is a homeomorphism of the subspace $f^{-1}(V_\lambda)$ of E onto the subspace V_λ of F, f is a homeomorphism of E onto F.

• (b) Give an example of a mapping f which is not injective, and of a covering (U_α) of E by open subsets, such that the restriction of f to each of the U_α is a homeomorphism of the subspace U_α of E onto the subspace $f(U_\alpha)$ of F (one can take both E and F discrete).

• **3.** Let E, F, G be three metric spaces, f a continuous mapping of E into F, g a continuous mapping of F into G. Show that if f is surjective and $g \circ f$ is a homeomorphism of E onto G, then f is a homeomorphism of E onto F and g is a homeomorphism of F onto G.

13. LIMITS

▲ Let E be a metric space, A a subset of E, a a cluster point of A. Suppose first that a does not belong to A. Then, if f is a mapping of A into a metric space E′, we say that *$f(x)$ has a limit $a' \in E'$ when $x \in A$ tends to a* (or also that a' is *a limit of f at the point $a \in \bar{A}$ with respect to* A), if the mapping g of $A \cup \{a\}$ into E′ defined by taking $g(x) = f(x)$ for $x \in A$, $g(a) = a'$, is *continuous at the point* a; we then write $a' = \lim_{x \to a,\, x \in A} f(x)$. If $a \in A$, we use the same language and notation to mean that f is *continuous at the point a*, with $a' = f(a)$.

(3.13.1) *In order that $a' \in E'$ be limit of $f(x)$ when $x \in A$ tends to a, a necessary and sufficient condition is that, for every neighborhood V′ of a' in E′, there exist a neighborhood V of a in E such that $f(V \cap A) \subset V'$.*

(3.13.2) *In order that $a' \in E'$ be limit of $f(x)$ when $x \in A$ tends to a, a necessary and sufficient condition is that, for every $\varepsilon > 0$, there exist a $\delta > 0$ such that the relations $x \in A$, $d(x, a) < \delta$ imply $d'(a', f(x)) < \varepsilon$.*

▲ These criteria are mere translations of the definitions.

(3.13.3) *A mapping can only have one limit with respect to A at a given point $a \in \bar{A}$.*

▲ For if a', b' were two limits of f at the point a, it follows from (3.13.2) and the triangle inequality that, for any $\varepsilon > 0$, we would have $d'(a', b') \leqslant 2\varepsilon$, which is absurd if $a' \neq b'$.

(3.13.4) *Let f be a mapping of E into E′. In order that f be continuous at a point $x_0 \in E$ such that x_0 is a cluster point of $E - \{x_0\}$* (which means x_0 is *not isolated* in E (3.10.10)), *a necessary and sufficient condition is that* $f(x_0) = \lim_{x \to x_0,\, x \in E - \{x_0\}} f(x)$.

▲ Mere restatement of definitions.

(3.13.5) *Suppose* $a' = \lim_{x \to a,\, x \in A} f(x)$. *Then, for every subset* $B \subset A$ *such that* $a \in \bar{B}$, *a' is also the limit of f at the point a, with respect to* B. *This applies in particular when* $B = V \cap A$, *where V is a neighborhood of a.*

▲ Obvious consequence of the definition and (3.11.6).

(3.13.6) *Suppose f has a limit a' at the point $a \in \bar{A}$ with respect to* A; *if g is a mapping of* E′ *into* E″, *continuous at the point a', then* $g(a') = \lim_{x \to a,\, x \in A} g(f(x))$.

▲ This follows at once from (3.11.5).

(3.13.7) *If* $a' = \lim_{x \to a,\, x \in A} f(x)$, *then* $a' \in \overline{f(A)}$.

▲ For by (3.13.1), for every neighborhood V′ of a', $V' \cap f(A)$ contains $f(V \cap A)$, which is not empty since $a \in \bar{A}$.

▲ An important case is that of *limits of sequences*: in the extended real line, we consider the point $+\infty$, which is a cluster point of the set **N** of natural integers. A mapping of **N** into a metric space E is a sequence $n \to x_n$ of points of E; if $a \in E$ is limit of that mapping at $+\infty$, with respect to **N**, we say that a is *limit of the sequence* (x_n) (or that the sequence (x_n) *converges* to a) and write $a = \lim_{n \to \infty} x_n$. The criteria (3.13.1) and (3.13.2) become here:

(3.13.8) *In order that* $a = \lim_{n \to \infty} x_n$, *a necessary and sufficient condition is that, for every neighborhood V of a, there exist an integer n_0 such that the relation* $n \geqslant n_0$ *implies* $x_n \in V$ (in other words, V contains all x_n with the exception of a finite number of indices).

(3.13.9) *In order that* $a = \lim_{n \to \infty} x_n$, *a necessary and sufficient condition is that, for every* $\varepsilon > 0$, *there exist an integer n_0 such that the relation* $n \geqslant n_0$ *implies* $d(a, x_n) < \varepsilon$.

▲ This last criterion can also be written $\lim_{n \to \infty} d(a, x_n) = 0$.

▲ A *subsequence* of an infinite sequence (x_n) is a sequence $k \to x_{n_k}$, where $k \to n_k$ is a strictly increasing infinite sequence of integers. It follows at once from (3.13.5) that:

(3.13.10) *If* $a = \lim_{n\to\infty} x_n$, *then* $a = \lim_{k\to\infty} x_{n_k}$ *for any subsequence of* (x_n).

▲ Let (x_n) be an infinite sequence of points in a metric space E; a point $b \in$ E is said to be a *cluster value* of the sequence (x_n) if there exists a subsequence (x_{n_k}) such that $b = \lim_{k\to\infty} x_{n_k}$.

▲ A cluster value of a subsequence of a sequence (x_n) is also a cluster value of (x_n). If (x_n) has a limit a, a is the *unique* cluster value of (x_n), as follows from (3.13.10); the converse does not hold in general: for instance, the sequence (x_n) of real numbers such that $x_{2n} = 1/n$ and $x_{2n+1} = n$ $(n \geqslant 1)$ has 0 as a unique cluster value, but does not converge to 0 (see however (3.16.4))

(3.13.11) *In order that* $b \in$ E *should be a cluster value of* (x_n), *a necessary and sufficient condition is that, for any neighborhood* V *of* b *and any integer* m, *there exist an integer* $n \geqslant m$ *such that* $x_n \in$ V.

▲The condition is obviously necessary. Conversely, suppose it is satisfied, and define the subsequence (x_{n_k}) by the following condition: $n_0 = 1$ and n_k is the smallest integer $> n_{k-1}$ and such that $d(b, x_{n_k}) < 1/k$. As $d(x_{n_k}, b) < 1/h$ for any $k \geqslant h$, the subsequence (x_{n_k}) converges to b.

(3.13.12) *If* b *is a cluster value of* (x_n) *in* E, *and if the mapping* g *of* E *into* E′ *is continuous at* b, *then* $g(b)$ *is a cluster value of the sequence* $(g(x_n))$.

▲ Clear from the definition and (3.13.6).

▲ From (3.13.7) it follows that if b is a cluster value (and *a fortiori* a limit) of a sequence of points x_n belonging to a subset A of E, then $b \in \bar{\text{A}}$. Conversely:

(3.13.13) *For any point* $a \in \bar{\text{A}}$, *there is a sequence* (x_n) *of points of* A *such that* $a = \lim_{n\to\infty} x_n$.

▲ For by assumption, the set A ∩ B(a; $1/n$) is not empty, hence (by the axiom of choice (1.4.5)) for each n, there is an $x_n \in$ A ∩ B(a; $1/n$), and the sequence (x_n) converges to a by (3.13.9).

(3.13.14) *Let* f *be a mapping of* A ⊂ E *into a metric space* E′ *and* $a \in \bar{\text{A}}$. *In order that* f *have a limit* $a' \in$ E′ *with respect to* A *at the point* a, *a necessary and sufficient condition is that, for every sequence* (x_n) *of points of* A *such that* $a = \lim_{n\to\infty} x_n$, *then* $a' = \lim_{n\to\infty} f(x_n)$.

▲ The necessity follows from the definitions and (3.13.6). Suppose conversely that the condition is satisfied and that a' is *not* the limit of f with respect to A at the point a. Then, by (3.13.2) and (1.4.5), there exists $\alpha > 0$ such that, for each integer n, there exists $x_n \in A$ satisfying the two conditions $d(a, x_n) < 1/n$ and $d(a', f(x_n)) \geqslant \alpha$. The sequence (x_n) converges then to a, but $(f(x_n))$ does not converge to a', which is a contradiction.

PROBLEMS

1. Let (u_n) be a sequence of real numbers $\geqslant 0$ such that $\lim_{n\to\infty} u_n = 0$. Show that there are infinitely many indices n such that $u_n \geqslant u_m$ for every $m \geqslant n$.
2. (a) Let (x_n) be a sequence in a metric space E. Show that if the three subsequences (x_{2n}), (x_{2n+1}) and (x_{3n}) are convergent, (x_n) is convergent.
   (b) Give an example of a sequence (x_n) of real numbers which is not convergent, but is such that for each $k \geqslant 2$, the subsequence (x_{kn}) is convergent (consider the subsequence (x_{p_k}), where (p_k) is the strictly increasing sequence of prime numbers).
3. Let E be a separable metric space, f an arbitrary mapping of E into **R**. Show that the set of points $a \in E$ such that $\lim_{x\to a,\, x\neq a} f(x)$ exists and is *distinct* from $f(a)$, is at most denumerable. (For every pair of rational numbers p, q such that $p < q$, consider the set of points $a \in E$ such that

$$f(a) \leqslant p < q \leqslant \lim_{x\to a,\, x\neq a} f(x)$$

and show that it is at most denumerable, using Problem 2(a) of Section 3.9. Consider similarly the set of points $a \in E$ such that

$$\lim_{x\to a,\, x\neq a} f(x) \leqslant p < q \leqslant f(a).)$$

14. CAUCHY SEQUENCES, COMPLETE SPACES

▲ In a metric space E, a *Cauchy sequence* is an infinite sequence (x_n) such that, for any $\varepsilon > 0$, there exists an integer n_0 such that the relations $p \geqslant n_0$ and $q \geqslant n_0$ imply $d(x_p, x_q) < \varepsilon$.

(3.14.1) *Any convergent sequence is a Cauchy sequence.*

▲ For if $a = \lim_{n\to\infty} x_n$, for any $\varepsilon > 0$ there exists n_0 such that $n \geqslant n_0$ implies $d(a, x_n) < \varepsilon/2$; by the triangle inequality, the relations $p \geqslant n_0$, $q \geqslant n_0$ imply $d(x_p, x_q) < \varepsilon$.

(3.14.2) *If (x_n) is a Cauchy sequence, any cluster value of (x_n) is a limit of (x_n).*

▲Indeed, if b is a cluster value of (x_n), given $\varepsilon > 0$, there is n_0 such that $p \geqslant n_0$ and $q \geqslant n_0$ imply $d(x_p, x_q) < \varepsilon/2$; on the other hand, by (3.13.11) there is a $p_0 \geqslant n_0$ such that $d(b, x_{p_0}) < \varepsilon/2$; by the triangle inequality, it follows that $d(b, x_n) \leqslant \varepsilon$ for any $n \geqslant n_0$.

▲A metric space E is called *complete* if any Cauchy sequence in E is convergent (to a point of E, of course).

(3.14.3) *The real line* **R** *is a complete metric space.*

▲ Let (x_n) be a Cauchy sequence of real numbers. Define the sequence (n_k) of integers by induction in the following way: $n_0 = 1$ and n_{k+1} is the smallest integer $> n_k$ such that, for $p \geqslant n_{k+1}$ and $q \geqslant n_{k+1}$, $|x_p - x_q| < 1/2^{k+2}$; the possibility of the definition follows from the fact that (x_n) is a Cauchy sequence. Let I_k be the closed interval $[x_{n_k} - 2^{-k}, x_{n_k} + 2^{-k}]$; we have $I_{k+1} \subset I_k$, for $|x_{n_k} - x_{n_{k+1}}| < 2^{-k-1}$; on the other hand, for $m \geqslant n_k$, $x_m \in I_k$ by definition. Now from axiom (IV) (Section 2.1) it follows that the nested intervals I_k have a nonempty intersection; let a be in I_k for all k. Then it is clear that $|a - x_m| \leqslant 2^{-k+1}$ for all $m \geqslant n_k$, hence $a = \lim_{n \to \infty} x_n$.

(3.14.4) *If a subspace* F *of a metric space* E *is complete,* F *is closed in* E.

▲Indeed, any point $a \in \bar{F}$ is the limit of a sequence (x_n) of points of F by (3.13.13). The sequence (x_n) is a Cauchy sequence by (3.14.1), hence by assumption converges to a point b *in* F; but by (3.13.3) $b = a$, hence $a \in F$; this shows $\bar{F} = F$. Q.E.D.

(3.14.5) *In a complete metric space* E, *any closed subset* F *is a complete subspace.*

▲For a Cauchy sequence (x_n) of points of F converges by assumption to a point $a \in E$, and as the x_n belong to F, $a \in \bar{F} = F$ by (3.13.7).

▲Theorems (3.14.4) and (3.14.5) immediately enable one to give examples both of complete and of noncomplete spaces, starting from the fact that the real line is complete.

▲ The fundamental importance of complete spaces lies in the fact that to prove a sequence is convergent in such a space, one needs only prove it is a Cauchy sequence (one also says that such a sequence satisfies the *Cauchy criterion*); the main difference between application of that test and of the definition of a convergent sequence is that in the Cauchy criterion *one does not need to know in advance the value of the limit.*

▲ We have already mentioned that on a same set E, two distances d_1, d_2 may be topologically equivalent, but the identity mapping of E_1 into E_2 (E_1, E_2 being the corresponding metric spaces) may fail to be uniformly continuous. This is the case, for instance, if we take $E = \mathbf{R}$, $d_2(x, y) = |x - y|$, $d_1(x, y)$ being the distance in the extended real line, restricted to $\mathbf{R}$; E_2 is then complete and not E_1 since E_1 is not closed in $\overline{\mathbf{R}}$. When two distances d_1, d_2 are such that the identity mapping of E_1 into E_2 is uniformly continuous as well as the inverse mapping, d_1 and d_2 are said to be *uniformly equivalent.* Cauchy sequences are then the same for both distances. For instance, if there exist two real numbers $\alpha > 0$, $\beta > 0$ such that, for any pair of points x, y in E, $\alpha d_1(x, y) \leqslant d_2(x, y) \leqslant \beta d_1(x, y)$, then d_1 and d_2 are uniformly equivalent distances.

▲ Let E, E′ be two metric spaces, A a subset of E, f a mapping of A into E′; the *oscillation of f in* A is by definition the diameter $\delta(f(A))$ (which may be $+\infty$). Let a be a cluster point of A; *the oscillation of f at the point a with respect to* A is $\Omega(a; f) = \inf_V \delta(f(V \cap A))$, where V runs over the set of neighborhoods of a (or merely a fundamental system of neighborhoods).

(3.14.6) *Suppose* E′ *is a complete metric space; in order that* $\lim_{x \to a,\, x \in A} f(x)$ *exist, a necessary and sufficient condition is that the oscillation of f at the point a, with respect to* A, *be* 0.

▲ The condition is necessary by (3.13.2). Suppose conversely that it is satisfied, and let (x_n) be a sequence of points of A converging to a; then it follows from the assumption that the sequence $(f(x_n))$ is a Cauchy sequence in E′, for, given any $\varepsilon > 0$, there is a neighborhood V of a such that $d'(f(x), f(y)) < \varepsilon$ for any two points x, y in $V \cap A$, and we have $x_n \in V \cap A$ except for a finite number of indices. Hence the sequence $(f(x_n))$ has a limit a'. Moreover, for any other sequence (y_n) of points of A, converging to a, the limits of $(f(x_n))$ and of $(f(y_n))$ are the same since $d'(f(x_n), f(y_n)) < \varepsilon$ as soon as x_n and y_n are both in $V \cap A$. Hence $\lim_{x \to a,\, x \in A} f(x) = a'$ from the definition of the limit and from (3.13.14).

PROBLEMS

1. (a) Let E be an *ultrametric* space (Section **3.8**, Problem 4). In order that a sequence (x_n) in E be a Cauchy sequence, show that it is necessary and sufficient that $\lim_{n\to\infty} d(x_n, x_{n+1}) = 0$.

(b) Let X be an arbitrary set, E the set of all infinite sequences $x = (x_n)$ of elements of X. For any two distinct elements $x = (x_n)$, $y = (y_n)$ of E, let $k(x, y)$ be the smallest integer n such that $x_n \neq y_n$; let $d(x, y) = 1/k(x, y)$ if $x \neq y$, $d(x, x) = 0$. Prove that d is an ultrametric distance on E, and that the metric space E defined by d is complete.

2. Let φ be an increasing real valued function defined in the interval $0 \leqslant u < +\infty$, and such that $\varphi(0) = 0$, $\varphi(u) > 0$ if $u > 0$, and $\varphi(u + v) \leqslant \varphi(u) + \varphi(v)$. Let $d(x, y)$ be a distance on a set E; then $d_1(x, y) = \varphi(d(x, y))$ is another distance on E.

(a) Show that if φ is continuous at the point $u = 0$, the distances d and d_1 are uniformly equivalent. Conversely, if, for the distance d, there is a point $x_0 \in$ E which is not isolated in E (**3.10.10**), and if d and d_1 are topologically equivalent, then φ is continuous at the point $u = 0$.

(b) Prove that the functions

$$u^r \quad (0 < r \leqslant 1), \qquad \log(1 + u), \qquad u/(1 + u), \qquad \inf(1, u)$$

satisfy the preceding conditions. Using the last two, it is thus seen that for any distance on E, there is a uniformly equivalent distance which is *bounded*.

3. On the real line, let $d(x, y) = |x - y|$ be the usual distance, $d'(x, y) = |x^3 - y^3|$; show that these two distances are topologically equivalent and that the Cauchy sequences are the same for both, but that they are not uniformly equivalent.

4. Let E be a complete metric space, d the distance on E, A the intersection of a sequence (U_n) of open subsets of E; let $F_n = E - U_n$, and for every pair of points x, y of A, write

$$f_n(x, y) = \left| \frac{1}{d(x, F_n)} - \frac{1}{d(y, F_n)} \right|,$$

$d_n(x, y) = f_n(x, y)/(1 + f_n(x, y))$, and $d'(x, y) = d(x, y) + \sum_{n=0}^{\infty} d_n(x, y)/2^n$. Show that on the subspace A of E, d' is a distance which is topologically equivalent to d, and that for the distance d', A is a *complete* metric space. (Note that a Cauchy sequence for d' is also a Cauchy sequence for d, but that its limit in E may not belong to any of the F_n.) Apply to the subspace I of **R** consisting of all irrational numbers.

15. ELEMENTARY EXTENSION THEOREMS

(**3.15.1**) *Let f and g be two continuous mappings of a metric space* E *into a metric space* E′. *The set* A *of the points $x \in$ E such that $f(x) = g(x)$ is closed in* E.

▲ It is equivalent to prove the set E − A open. Let $a \in$ E − A, then $f(a) \neq g(a)$; let $d'(f(a), g(a)) = \alpha > 0$. By continuity of f, g at a and from (**3.6.3**) it follows that there is a neighborhood V of a in E such that for

$x \in V$, $d'(f(a), f(x)) < \alpha/2$ and $d'(g(a), g(x)) < \alpha/2$. Then for $x \in V$, $f(x) \neq g(x)$, otherwise we would have $d'(f(a), g(a)) < \alpha$ by the triangle inequality.

(3.15.2) ("Principle of extension of identities") *Let f, g be two continuous mappings of a metric space E into a metric space E'; if $f(x) = g(x)$ for all points x of a dense subset A in E, then $f = g$.*

▲ For the set of points x where $f(x) = g(x)$ is closed by (3.15.1) and contains A.

(3.15.3) *Let f, g be two continuous mappings of a metric space E into the extended real line $\overline{\mathbf{R}}$. The set P of the points $x \in E$ such that $f(x) \leqslant g(x)$ is closed in E.*

▲ We prove again $E - P$ is open. Suppose $f(a) > g(a)$, and let $\beta \in \overline{\mathbf{R}}$ be such that $f(a) > \beta > g(a)$ (cf. (2.2.16) and the definition of $\overline{\mathbf{R}}$ in Section 3.3). The inverse image V by f of the open interval $]\beta, +\infty]$ is a neighborhood of a by (3.11.1); so is the inverse image W by g of the open interval $[-\infty, \beta[$. Hence $V \cap W$ is a neighborhood of a by (3.6.3), and for $x \in V \cap W, f(x) > \beta > g(x)$. Q.E.D.

(3.15.4) ("Principle of extension of inequalities") *Let f, g be two continuous mappings of a metric space E into the extended real line $\overline{\mathbf{R}}$; if $f(x) \leqslant g(x)$ for all points x of a dense subset A of E, then $f(x) \leqslant g(x)$ for all $x \in E$.*

The proof follows from (3.15.3) as (3.15.2) from (3.15.1).

(3.15.5) *Let A be a dense subset of a metric space E, and f a mapping of A into a metric space E'. In order that there exist a continuous mapping $\bar{f}$ of E into E', coinciding with f in A, a necessary and sufficient condition is that, for any $x \in E$, the limit $\lim_{y \to x, y \in A} f(y)$ exist in E'; the continuous mapping $\bar{f}$ is then unique.*

As any $x \in E$ belongs to $\bar{A}$, we must have $\bar{f}(x) = \lim_{y \to x, y \in A} \bar{f}(y)$ by (3.13.5), hence $\bar{f}(x) = \lim_{y \to x, y \in A} f(y)$; this shows the necessity of the condition and the fact that if the continuous mapping $\bar{f}$ exists, it is unique (this follows also from (3.15.2)). Conversely, suppose the condition satisfied, and let us prove that the mapping $\bar{f}$ defined by $\bar{f}(x) = \lim_{y \to x, y \in A} f(y)$ is a solution of the extension problem. First of all, if $x \in A$, the existence of the limit implies by definition $\bar{f}(x) = f(x)$, hence $\bar{f}$ extends f, and it remains to see that $\bar{f}$ is continuous. Let $x \in E$, V' a neighborhood of $\bar{f}(x)$ in E'; there is a *closed* ball B' of center $\bar{f}(x)$ contained in V'. By assumption, there is an open neighborhood V of x in E such that $f(V \cap A) \subset B'$ (by (3.13.1)). For any $y \in V$, $\bar{f}(y)$ is the limit of f at the point y with respect to A, hence also with respect to $V \cap A$, by (3.13.5); hence, it follows from (3.13.7) that $\bar{f}(y) \in \overline{f(V \cap A)}$, and therefore $\bar{f}(y) \in B'$ since B' is closed. Q.E.D.

(3.15.6) *Let A be a dense subset of a metric space E, and f a uniformly continuous mapping of A into a complete metric space E′. Then there exists a continuous mapping $\bar{f}$ of E into E′ coinciding with f in A; moreover, $\bar{f}$ is uniformly continuous.*

To prove the existence of $\bar{f}$, it follows from (3.15.5) and (3.14.6) that we have to show the oscillation of f at any point $x \in E$, with respect to A, is 0. Now, for any $\varepsilon > 0$, there is $\delta > 0$ such that $d(y, z) < \delta$ implies $d'(f(y), f(z)) < \varepsilon/3$ (y, z in A). Hence, the diameter of $f(A \cap B(x; \delta/2))$ is at most $\varepsilon/3$, which proves our assertion. Consider now any two points s, t in E such that $d(s, t) < \delta/2$. There is a $y \in A$ such that $d(s, y) < \delta/4$ and $d'(\bar{f}(s), f(y)) < \varepsilon/3$, and a $z \in A$ such that $d(t, z) < \delta/4$ and $d'(\bar{f}(t), f(z)) < \varepsilon/3$. From the triangle inequality it follows that $d(y, z) < \delta$, and as y, z are in A, $d'(f(y), f(z)) < \varepsilon/3$; hence, by the triangle inequality, $d'(\bar{f}(s), \bar{f}(t)) < \varepsilon$; this proves that $\bar{f}$ is uniformly continuous.

PROBLEM

Let $n \to r_n$ be a bijection of $\mathbf{N}$ onto the set A of all rational numbers x such that $0 \leqslant x \leqslant 1$ (2.2.15). We define a function in $E = [0, 1]$ by putting $f(x) = \sum_{r_n < x} 1/2^n$, the infinite sum being extended only to those n such that $r_n < x$. Show that the restriction of f to the set B of all irrational numbers $x \in [0, 1]$ is continuous, but cannot be extended to a function continuous in E.

16. COMPACT SPACES

A metric space E is called *compact* if it satisfies the following condition ("Borel–Lebesgue axiom"): *for every covering* $(U_\lambda)_{\lambda \in L}$ *of* E *by open sets*

Let $x \in E$. then x cannot belong to all F_n, hence for some x we have $x \in E - F_x = U_x$. Now $E = \bigcup U_n$

("open covering") *there exists a finite subfamily* $(U_\lambda)_{\lambda \in H}$ ($H \subset L$ and finite) *which is a covering of* E.

A metric space E is called *precompact* if it satisfies the following condition: *for any* $\varepsilon > 0$, *there is a finite covering of* E *by sets of diameter* $< \varepsilon$. This is immediately equivalent to the following property: *for any* $\varepsilon > 0$, *there is a finite subset* F *of* E *such that* $d(x, F) < \varepsilon$ *for every* $x \in E$.

In the theory of metric spaces, these notions are a substitute for the notion of "finiteness" in pure set theory; they express that the metric space is, so to speak, "approximately finite." Note that, from the definition, it follows that *compactness* is a topological notion, but *precompactness* is not (see remark after (3.17.6)).

(3.16.1) *For a metric space* E, *the following three conditions are equivalent*:
(a) E *is compact*;
(b) *any infinite sequence in* E *has at least a cluster value*;
(c) E *is precompact and complete.*

▲(a) ⇒ (b): Let (x_n) be an infinite sequence in the compact space E, and let F_n be the closure of the set $\{x_n, x_{n+1}, \ldots, x_{n+p}, \ldots\}$. We prove there is a point belonging to all F_n. Otherwise, the open sets $U_n = E - F_n$ would form a covering of E, hence there would exist a finite number of them, $U_{n_1}, \ldots, U_{n_k}$ forming a covering of E; this would mean that $F_{n_1} \cap F_{n_2} \cap \cdots \cap F_{n_k} = \varnothing$; but this is absurd, since if n is greater than $\max(n_1, \ldots, n_k)$, F_n (which is not empty by definition) is contained in all the F_{n_i} $(1 \leqslant i \leqslant k)$. Hence the intersection $\bigcap_{n=1}^{\infty} F_n$ contains at least a point a. By (3.13.11) and the definition of a cluster point, a is a cluster value of (x_n).

▲ (b) ⇒ (c): First any Cauchy sequence in E has a cluster value, hence is convergent by (3.14.2), and therefore E is complete. Suppose E were not precompact, i.e. there exists a number $\alpha > 0$ such that E has no finite covering by balls of radius α. Then we can define by induction a sequence (x_n) in the following way: x_1 is an arbitrary point of E; supposing that $d(x_i, x_j) \geqslant \alpha$ for $i \neq j$, $1 \leqslant i \leqslant n-1$, $1 \leqslant j \leqslant n-1$, the union of the balls of center x_i $(1 \leqslant i \leqslant n-1)$ and radius α is not the whole space, hence there is x_n such that $d(x_i, x_n) \geqslant \alpha$ for $i < n$. The sequence (x_n) cannot have a cluster value, for if a were such a value, there would be a subsequence (x_{n_k}) converging to a, hence we would have $d(a, x_{n_k}) < \alpha/2$ for $k \geqslant k_0$, and therefore $d(x_{n_h}, x_{n_k}) < \alpha$ for $h \geqslant k_0$, $k \geqslant k_0$, $h \neq k$, contrary to the definition of (x_n).

(c) ⇒ (a): Suppose we have an open covering $(U_\lambda)_{\lambda \in L}$ of E such that no finite subfamily is a covering of E. We define by induction a sequence (B_n) of balls in the following way: from the assumption it follows that the diameter of E is finite, and by multiplying the distance on E by a constant, we may assume that $\delta(E) < 1/2$, hence E is a ball B_0 of radius 1. Suppose the B_k have been defined for $0 \leqslant k \leqslant n-1$, and that for these values of k, B_k has a radius equal to $1/2^k$, and there is no finite subfamily of $(U_\lambda)_{\lambda \in L}$ which is a covering of B_k. Then we consider a finite covering $(V_k)_{1 \leqslant k \leqslant m}$ of E by balls of radius $1/2^n$; among the balls V_k which have a nonempty intersection with B_{n-1}, there is one at least B_n for which no finite subfamily of (U_λ) is a covering; otherwise, as these V_k form a covering of B_{n-1}, there would be a finite subfamily of (U_λ) which would be a covering of B_{n-1}; the induction can thus proceed indefinitely. Let x_n be the center of B_n; as B_{n-1} and B_n have a common point, the triangle inequality shows that

$$d(x_{n-1}, x_n) \leqslant 1/2^{n-1} + 1/2^n \leqslant 1/2^{n-2}$$

Hence, if $n \leqslant p < q$, we have

$$d(x_p, x_q) \leqslant d(x_p, x_{p+1}) + \cdots + d(x_{q-1}, x_q) \leqslant \frac{1}{2^{p-1}} + \cdots + \frac{1}{2^{q-2}} \leqslant \frac{1}{2^{n-2}}.$$

This proves that (x_n) is a Cauchy sequence in E, hence converges to a point a. Let λ_0 be an index such that $a \in U_{\lambda_0}$; there is an $\alpha > 0$ such that $B(a; \alpha) \subset U_{\lambda_0}$. From the definition of a, it follows there exists an integer n such that $d(a, x_n) < \alpha/2$, and $1/2^n < \alpha/2$. The triangle inequality then shows that $B_n \subset B(a; \alpha) \subset U_{\lambda_0}$. But this is a contradiction since no finite subfamily of (U_λ) is supposed to be a covering of B_n.

(3.16.2) *Any precompact metric space is separable.*

If E is precompact, for any n there is, by definition, a finite subset A_n of E such that for every $x \in E$, $d(x, A_n) < 1/n$. Let $A = \bigcup_n A_n$; A is at most denumerable, and for each $x \in E$, $d(x, A) \leqslant d(x, A_n) < 1/n$ for any n, hence $d(x, A) = 0$, $E = \bar{A}$.

(3.16.3) *Let* E *be a metric space. Any two of the following properties imply the third:*

(a) E *is compact.*
(b) E *is discrete* (more precisely, homeomorphic to a discrete space).
(c) E *is finite.*

(a) and (b) imply (c), for each one-point set $\{x\}$ is open, hence the family of sets $\{x\}$ is an open covering of E, and a finite subfamily can only be a covering of E if E is finite. On the other hand, (c) implies both (a) and (b), for each one point set being closed, every subset of E is closed as finite union of closed sets, hence every subset of E is open, and therefore E is homeomorphic to a discrete space. Finally, as there is only a finite number of open sets, E is compact.

(3.16.4) *In a compact metric space* E, *any infinite sequence* (x_n) *which has only one cluster value* a *converges to* a.

Suppose a is not the limit of (x_n); then there would exist a number $\alpha > 0$ such that there would be an infinite subsequence (x_{n_k}) of (x_n) whose points belong to $E - B(a; \alpha)$. By assumption, this subsequence has a cluster value b, and as $E - B(a; \alpha)$ is closed, b belongs to $E - B(a; \alpha)$ by (3.13.7). The sequence (x_n) would thus have two distinct cluster values, contrary to assumption.

(3.16.5) *Any continuous mapping* f *of a compact metric space* E *into a metric space* E′ *is uniformly continuous.*

Suppose the contrary; there would then be a number $\alpha > 0$ and two sequences (x_n) and (y_n) of points of E such that $d(x_n, y_n) < 1/n$ and $d'(f(x_n), f(y_n)) \geqslant \alpha$. We can find a subsequence (x_{n_k}) converging to a point a, and as $d(x_{n_k}, y_{n_k}) < 1/n_k$, it follows from the triangle inequality that the sequence (y_{n_k}) also converges to a. But f is continuous at the point a, hence there is a $\delta > 0$ such that $d'(f(a), f(x)) < \alpha/2$ for $d(a, x) < \delta$. Take k such that $d(a, x_{n_k}) < \delta$, $d(a, y_{n_k}) < \delta$; then $d'(f(x_{n_k}), f(y_{n_k})) < \alpha$ contrary to the definition of the sequences (x_n) and (y_n).

(3.16.6) *Let* E *be a compact metric space,* $(U_\lambda)_{\lambda \in L}$ *an open covering of* E. *There exists a number* $\alpha > 0$ *such that any open ball of radius* α *is contained in at least one of the* U_λ ("Lebesgue's property").

For every $x \in E$, there exists an open ball $B(x; r_x)$ contained in one of the sets U_λ. As the balls $B(x; r_x/2)$ form an open covering of E, there exist a finite number of points $x_i \in E$ such that the balls $B(x_i; r_{x_i}/2)$ form a covering of E. If $\alpha > 0$ is the smallest of the numbers $r_{x_i}/2$, it satisfies the required property: indeed, every $x \in E$ belongs to a ball $B(x_i; r_{x_i}/2)$ for some i, hence $B(x; \alpha)$ is contained in $B(x_i; r_{x_i})$ since $\alpha \leqslant r_{x_i}/2$; but by construction $B(x_i; r_{x_i})$ is contained in some U_λ.

PROBLEMS

1. Give an example of a precompact space in which the result of **(3.16.6)** fails to be true.

2. For a metric space E, show that the following properties are equivalent:

(a) E is compact;

(b) every denumerable open covering of E contains a finite subcovering;

(c) every decreasing sequence (F_n) of nonempty closed sets of E has a nonempty intersection;

(d) for any infinite open covering $(U_\lambda)_{\lambda \in L}$ of E, there is a subset $H \subset L$, distinct from L and such that $(U_\lambda)_{\lambda \in H}$ is still a covering of E;

(e) every *pointwise finite* open covering (U_λ) of E (i.e. such that for any point $x \in E$, $x \in U_\lambda$ only for a finite subset of indices) contains a finite subcovering;

(f) every infinite subspace of E which is discrete is not closed.

(Using **(3.16.1)**, show that (f) implies (a), and that (d) and (e) imply (f).)

3. Let E be a metric space, d the distance on E, $\mathfrak{F}(E) \subset \mathfrak{P}(E)$ the set of all closed nonempty subsets of E. We may suppose that the distance on E is bounded (Section **3.14**, Problem 2). For any two elements A, B of $\mathfrak{F}(E)$, let $\rho(A, B) = \sup_{x \in A} d(x, B)$, $h(A, B) = \sup(\rho(A, B), \rho(B, A))$.

(a) Show that, on $\mathfrak{F}(E)$, h is a distance (the "Hausdorff distance").

(b) Show that for any four elements A, B, C, D of $\mathfrak{F}(E)$, one has

$$h(A \cup B, C \cup D) \leqslant \max(h(A, C), h(B, D)).$$

(c) Show that if E is complete, $\mathfrak{F}(E)$ is complete. (Let (X_n) be a Cauchy sequence in $\mathfrak{F}(E)$; for each n, let Y_n be the closure of the union of the sets X_{n+p} such that $p \geqslant 0$; consider the intersection of the decreasing sequence (Y_n) in E.)

(d) Show that if E is precompact, $\mathfrak{F}(E)$ is precompact (use the problem in Section **1.1**). Therefore, if E is compact, $\mathfrak{F}(E)$ is compact.

4. Let E be a compact metric space. For every $\varepsilon > 0$, let $N_\varepsilon(E)$ be the smallest integer n such that there exists a covering of E by n sets of diameter $\leqslant 2\varepsilon$; let $M_\varepsilon(E)$ be the largest integer m such that there exists a finite sequence of m points of E for which the distance of any two (distinct) of these points is $> \varepsilon$. The number $H_\varepsilon(E) = \log N_\varepsilon(E)$ is called the *ε-entropy* of E, the number $C_\varepsilon(E) = \log M_\varepsilon(E)$ the *ε-capacity* of E.

(a) Show that $M_{2\varepsilon}(E) \leqslant N_\varepsilon(E) \leqslant M_\varepsilon(E)$, hence $C_{2\varepsilon}(E) \leqslant H_\varepsilon(E) \leqslant C_\varepsilon(E)$.

(b) Show that the functions $N_\varepsilon(E)$ and $M_\varepsilon(E)$ of ε, defined for $\varepsilon > 0$, are decreasing and continuous on the right (to prove the continuity of $N_\varepsilon(E)$ on the right, use contradiction, and apply problem 3(d)).

(c) If A and B are closed nonempty subsets of E, show that

$$N_\varepsilon(A \cup B) \leqslant N_\varepsilon(A) + N_\varepsilon(B), \qquad M_\varepsilon(A \cup B) \leqslant M_\varepsilon(A) + M_\varepsilon(B)$$

$$H_\varepsilon(A \cup B) \leqslant H_\varepsilon(A) + H_\varepsilon(B), \qquad C_\varepsilon(A \cup B) \leqslant C_\varepsilon(A) + C_\varepsilon(B).$$

(d) If E is a closed interval of **R** of length l, show that $N_\varepsilon(E) = M_{2\varepsilon}(E) = l/2\varepsilon$ if $l/2\varepsilon$ is an integer, and $N_\varepsilon(E) = M_{2\varepsilon}(E) = [l/2\varepsilon] + 1$ (where $[t]$ is the largest integer $\leqslant t$ for $t > 0$) if $l/2\varepsilon$ is not an integer.

17. COMPACT SETS

A *compact* (resp. *precompact*) *set* in a metric space E is a subset A such that the *subspace* A of E be compact (resp. precompact).

(3.17.1) *Any precompact set is bounded.*

This follows from the fact that a finite union of bounded sets is bounded (3.4.4).

The converse of (3.17.1) does not hold in general, for any distance is equivalent to a bounded distance (Section 3.14, Problem 2) (but see (3.17.6)).

(3.17.2) *Any compact set in a metric space is closed.*

Indeed, such a subspace is complete by (3.16.1), and we need only apply (3.14.4).

(3.17.3) *In a compact space* E, *every closed subset is compact.*

For such a set is obviously precompact, and it is a complete subspace by (3.14.5).

A *relatively compact set* in a metric space E is a subset A such that the closure $\bar{A}$ is compact.

(3.17.4) *Any subset of a relatively compact* (resp. *precompact*) *set is relatively compact* (resp. *precompact*).

This follows at once from the definitions and (3.17.3).

(3.17.5) *A relatively compact set is precompact. In a complete space, a precompact set is relatively compact.*

The first assertion is immediate by (3.17.4). Suppose next E is complete and $A \subset E$ precompact. For any $\varepsilon > 0$, there is a covering of A by a finite number of sets C_k of A having a diameter $< \varepsilon/2$; each C_k is contained in a closed ball D_k (in E) of radius $\varepsilon/2$. We have therefore $\bar{A} \subset \bigcup_k D_k$, the set $\bigcup_k D_k$ being closed, and each D_k has a diameter $\leqslant \varepsilon$. On the other hand, $\bar{A}$ is a complete subspace by (3.14.5), whence the result.

A precompact space E which is not complete gives an example of a precompact set which is not relatively compact in E.

(3.17.6) (Borel–Lebesgue theorem). *In order that a subset of the real line be relatively compact, a necessary and sufficient condition is that it be bounded.*

In view of (3.17.1), (3.17.4), and (3.17.5), all we have to do is to prove any closed interval $[a, b]$ is precompact. For each integer n, let $x_k = a + k(b - a)/n$ $(0 \leqslant k \leqslant n)$; then the open intervals of center x_k and length $2/n$ form a covering of $[a, b]$. Q.E.D.

Remark. If, on the real line, we consider the two distances d_1, d_2 defined in Section 3.14, it follows from (3.17.1) that E_2 is not precompact, whereas E_1 is precompact, since the extended real line $\overline{\mathbf{R}}$, being homeomorphic to the closed interval $[-1, +1]$ of $\mathbf{R}$ (3.12), is compact by (3.17.6).

(3.17.7) *A necessary and sufficient condition that a subset* A *of a metric space* E *be relatively compact is that every sequence of points of* A *have a cluster value in* E.

The condition is obviously necessary, by (3.16.1). Conversely, let us suppose it is satisfied, and let us prove that every sequence (x_n) of points of $\bar{A}$ has a cluster value in E (which will therefore be in $\bar{A}$ by (3.13.7)), and hence that $\bar{A}$ is compact by (3.16.1). For each n, it follows from the definition of closure that there exists $y_n \in A$ such that $d(x_n, y_n) \leqslant 1/n$. By assumption, there is a subsequence (y_{n_k}) which converges to a point a; from the triangle inequality it follows that (x_{n_k}) converges also to a. Q.E.D.

(3.17.8) *The union of two relatively compact sets is relatively compact.*

From (3.8.8) it follows that we need only prove that the union of two compact sets A, B is compact. Let $(U_\lambda)_{\lambda \in L}$ be an open covering of the subspace $A \cup B$; each U_λ can be written $(A \cup B) \cap V_\lambda$, where V_λ is open in E, by (3.10.1). By assumption, there is a finite subset H (resp. K) of L such that the subfamily $(A \cap V_\lambda)_{\lambda \in H}$ (resp. $(B \cap V_\lambda)_{\lambda \in K}$) is a covering of A (resp. B). It is then clear that the family $((A \cap B) \cap V_\lambda)_{\lambda \in H \cup K}$ is a covering of $A \cup B$.

(3.17.9) *Let* f *be a continuous mapping of a metric space* E *into a metric space* E′. *For every compact* (resp. *relatively compact*) *subset* A *of* E, $f(A)$ *is compact, hence closed in* E′ (resp. *relatively compact in* E′).

It is enough to prove that $f(A)$ is compact when A is compact. Let $(U_\lambda)_{\lambda \in L}$ be an open covering of the subspace $f(A)$ of E'; then the sets $A \cap f^{-1}(U_\lambda)$ form an open covering of the subspace A by (3.11.4); by assumption, there is a finite subset H of L such that the sets $A \cap f^{-1}(U_\lambda)$ for $\lambda \in H$ still form a covering of A; then the sets $U_\lambda = f(A \cap f^{-1}(U_\lambda))$ for $\lambda \in H$ will form a covering of $f(A)$. Q.E.D.

(3.17.10) *Let* E *be a nonempty compact metric space, f a continuous mapping of* E *into* **R**; *then* $f(E)$ *is bounded, and there exist two points a, b in* E *such that* $f(a) = \inf_{x \in E} f(x), f(b) = \sup_{x \in E} f(x)$.

The first assertion follows from (3.17.9) and (3.17.1). On the other hand, $f(E)$ is closed in **R** by (3.17.2), hence $\sup f(E)$ and $\inf f(E)$, which are cluster points of $f(E)$, belong to $f(E)$.

(3.17.11) *Let* A *be a compact subset in a metric space* E. *Then the sets* $V_r(A)$ (see Section 3.6) *form a fundamental system of neighborhoods of* A.

Let U be a neighborhood of A; the real function $x \to d(x, E - U)$ is > 0 and continuous in A by (3.11.8), hence there is a point $x_0 \in A$ such that $d(x_0, E - U) = \inf_{x \in A} d(x, E - U)$ by (3.17.10). But $d(x_0, E - U) = r > 0$; hence $V_r(A) \subset U$.

(3.17.12) *If* E *is a compact metric space, f a continuous injective mapping of* E *into a metric space* E', *then f is a homeomorphism of* E *onto* $f(E)$.

All we need to prove is that for every closed set $A \subset E$, $f(A)$ is closed in $f(E)$ (by (3.11.4)); but this follows from (3.17.3) and (3.17.9).

PROBLEMS

1. Let f be a uniformly continuous mapping of a metric space E into a metric space E'. Show that for any precompact subset A of E, $f(A)$ is precompact.
3. In a metric space E, let A be a compact subset, B a closed subset such that $A \cap B = \varnothing$. Show that $d(A, B) > 0$.

3. Let E be a compact ultrametric space (Section 3.8, Problem 4), d the distance on E. Show that for every $x_0 \in E$, the image of E by the mapping $x \to d(x_0, x)$ is an at most denumerable subset of the interval $[0, +\infty[$ in which every point (with the possible exception of 0) is isolated (3.10.10). (For any $r = d(x_0, x) > 0$, consider the l.u.b. of $d(x_0, y)$ on the set of points y such that $d(x_0, y) < r$, and the g.l.b. of $d(x_0, z)$ on the set of points z such that $d(x_0, z) > r$; use Section 3.8, Problem 4).
4. Let E be a compact metric space, d the distance on E, f a mapping of E into E such that, for any pair (x, y) of points of E, $d(f(x), f(y)) \geqslant d(x, y)$. Show that f is an *isometry of* E *onto* E. (Let a, b be any two points of E; put $f_n = f_{n-1} \circ f$, $a_n = f_n(a)$, $b_n = f_n(b)$; show that for any $\varepsilon > 0$ there exists an index k such that $d(a, a_k) \leqslant \varepsilon$ and $d(b, b_k) \leqslant \varepsilon$ (consider a cluster value of the sequence (a_n)), and conclude that $f(E)$ is dense in E and that $d(f(a), f(b)) = d(a, b)$.)
5. Let E, E′ be two metric spaces, f a mapping of E into E′. Show that if the restriction of f to any compact subspace of E is continuous, then f is continuous in E (use (3.13.14)).
6. Let E, E′ be two metric spaces, f a continuous mapping of E into E′, K a compact subset of E. Suppose the restriction $f \mid K$ of f is injective and that for every $x \in K$, there is a neighborhood V_x of x in E such that the restriction $f \mid V_x$ of f is injective. Show that there exists a neighborhood U of K in E such that the restriction $f \mid U$ is injective (use contradiction and (3.17.11)).

18. LOCALLY COMPACT SPACES

A metric space E is said to be *locally compact* if for every point $x \in E$, there exists a compact neighborhood of x in E. Any discrete space is locally compact, but not compact unless it is finite (3.16.3).

(3.18.1) *The real line* **R** *is locally compact but not compact.*

This follows immediately from the Borel–Lebesgue theorem (3.17.6).

(3.18.2) *Let* A *be a compact set in a locally compact metric space* E. *Then there exists an* $r > 0$ *such that* $V_r(A)$ (*see Section* 3.6) *is relatively compact in* E.

For each $x \in A$, there is a compact neighborhood V_x of x; the $\mathring{V}_x$ form an open covering of A, hence there is a finite subset $\{x_1, \ldots, x_n\}$ in A such that the $\mathring{V}_{x_i}$ $(1 \leqslant i \leqslant n)$ form an open covering of A. The set $U = \bigcup_{i=1}^{n} V_{x_i}$ is compact by (3.17.8) and is a neighborhood of A; hence the result, by applying (3.17.11).

(3.18.3) *Let* E *be a locally compact metric space. The following properties are equivalent*:

(a) *there exists an increasing sequence* (U_n) *of open relatively compact sets in* E *such that* $\overline{U}_n \subset U_{n+1}$ *for every* n, *and* $E = \bigcup_n U_n$;

(b) E *is a denumerable union of compact subsets*;

(c) E *is separable.*

It is clear that (a) implies (b), since $\overline{U}_n$ is compact. If E is the union of a sequence (K_n) of compact sets, each subspace K_n is separable (by (3.16.2)); if D_n is an at most denumerable set in K_n, dense with respect to K_n, then $D = \bigcup_n D_n$ is at most denumerable, and dense in E, since $E = \bigcup_n K_n \subset \bigcup_n \bar{D}_n \subset \bar{D}$; hence (b) implies (c). Let us suppose finally that E is separable, and let (T_n) be an at most denumerable basis for the open sets of E (see (3.9.4)). For every $x \in E$, there is a compact neighborhood W_x of x, hence, by (3.9.3), an index $n(x)$ such that $x \in T_{n(x)} \subset W_x$. It follows that those of the T_n which are relatively compact already constitute a basis for the open sets of E. We can therefore suppose that all the T_n are relatively compact. We then define U_n by induction in the following way: $U_1 = T_1$, U_{n+1} is the union of T_{n+1} and of $V_r(\overline{U}_n)$, where $r > 0$ has been taken such that $V_r(\overline{U}_n)$ is relatively compact (which is possible by (3.18.2)); it is then clear that the sequence (U_n) verifies property (a).

(3.18.4) *In a locally compact metric space* E, *every open subspace and every closed subspace is locally compact.*

Suppose A is open in E; for every $a \in E$, there is a closed ball $B'(a; r)$ which is compact (from the definition of a locally compact space and (3.17.3)). On the other hand, there is $r' \leqslant r$ such that the ball $B'(a; r')$ is contained in A; as it is compact by (3.17.3), A is locally compact.

Suppose A is closed in E, and let $a \in A$; then, if V is a compact neighborhood of a in E, $V \cap A$ is a neighborhood of a in A by (3.10.4), and is compact by (3.17.3); this proves A is locally compact.

PROBLEMS

1. If A is a locally compact subspace of a metric space E, show that A is locally closed (Section 3.10, Problem 3) in E. The converse is true if E is locally compact (use (3.18.4)).
2. (a) Show that in a locally compact metric space, the intersection of two locally compact subspaces is locally compact (cf. Problem 1).

(b) In the real line, give an example of two locally compact subspaces whose union is not locally compact, and an example of a locally compact subspace whose complement is not locally compact.

3. (a) Give an example of a locally compact metric space which is not complete.

(b) Let E be a metric space such that there exists a number $r > 0$ having the property that each closed ball $B'(x; r)$ $(x \in E)$ is compact. Show that E is complete and that for any relatively compact subset A of E, the set $V'_{r/2}(A)$ of the points $x \in E$ such that $d(x, A) \leqslant r/2$ is compact.

19. CONNECTED SPACES AND CONNECTED SETS

▲ A metric space E is said to be *connected* if the only subsets of E which are both open and closed are the empty set $\varnothing$ and the set E itself. An equivalent formulation is that there does not exist a pair of open nonempty subsets A, B of E such that $A \cup B = E$, $A \cap B = \varnothing$. A space reduced to a single point is connected. A subset F of a metric space E is *connected* if the *subspace* F of E is connected. A metric space E is said to be *locally connected* if, for every $x \in E$, there is a fundamental system of *connected neighborhoods* of x.

(3.19.1) *In order that a subset* A *of the real line* **R** *be connected, a necessary and sufficient condition is that* A *be an interval (bounded or not). The real line is a connected and locally connected space.*

The second assertion obviously follows from the first. Suppose A is connected; if A is reduced to a single point, A is an interval. Suppose A contains two distinct points $a < b$. We prove every x such that $a < x < b$ belongs to A. Otherwise, A would be the union of the nonempty sets $B = A \cap]-\infty, x[$ and $C = A \cap]x, +\infty[$, both of which are open in A and such that $B \cap C = \varnothing$. From this property, we deduce that A is necessarily an interval. Indeed, let $c \in A$, and let p, q be the g.l.b. and l.u.b. of A in $\overline{\mathbf{R}}$; if $p = -\infty$, then for every $x < c$, there is $y < x$ belonging to A; hence $x \in A$, so $]-\infty, c]$ is contained in A; if p is finite and $p < c$, for every x such that $p < x < c$ there is $y \in A$ such that $p < y < x$, hence again $x \in A$, so that A contains the interval $]p, c]$. Similarly, one shows that A contains $[c, q[$ if $q > c$; it follows that in any case A contains the interval $]p, q[$, and therefore must be one of the four intervals in $\overline{\mathbf{R}}$ of extremities p, q (of course, if $p = -\infty$ (resp. $q = +\infty$) p (resp. q) does not belong to A).

▲ Conversely, suppose A is a nonempty interval of origin a and extremity b in $\overline{\mathbf{R}}$ (the possibilities $a = -\infty$, $a \notin A$, $b = +\infty$, $b \notin A$ being included).

Suppose $A = B \cup C$, with B, C nonempty open sets in A and $B \cap C = \varnothing$; suppose for instance $x \in B$, $y \in C$, and $x < y$. Let z be the l.u.b. of the bounded set $B \cap [x, y]$; if $z \in B$, then $z < y$ and there is by assumption an interval $[z, z+h[$ contained in $[x, y]$ and in B, which contradicts the definition of z; if on the other hand $z \in C$, then $x < z$, and there is similarly an interval $]z-h, z] \subset C \cap [x, y]$, which again contradicts the definition of z (see (2.3.4)); hence z cannot belong to B nor to C, which is absurd since the closed set $[x, y]$ is contained in A. Hence A is connected.

(3.19.2) *If* A *is a connected set in a metric space* E, *then any set* B *such that* $A \subset B \subset \bar{A}$ *is connected.*

For suppose X, Y are two nonempty open sets in B such that $X \cup Y = B$, $X \cap Y = \varnothing$; as A is dense in B, $X \cap A$ and $Y \cap A$ are not empty, open in A, and we would have $(X \cap A) \cup (Y \cap A) = A$, $(X \cap A) \cap (Y \cap A) = \varnothing$, a contradiction.

(3.19.3) *In a metric space* E, *let* $(A_\lambda)_{\lambda \in L}$ *be a family of connected sets having a nonempty intersection; then* $A = \bigcup_{\lambda \in L} A_\lambda$ *is connected.*

Let a be a point of $\bigcap_{\lambda \in L} A_\lambda$, and suppose $A = B \cup C$, where B, C are nonempty open sets in A such that $B \cap C = \varnothing$. Suppose for instance $a \in B$; by assumption there is at least one λ such that $C \cap A_\lambda \neq \varnothing$; then $B \cap A_\lambda$ and $C \cap A_\lambda$ are open in A_λ and such that $(B \cap A_\lambda) \cup (C \cap A_\lambda) = A_\lambda$, $(B \cap A_\lambda) \cap (C \cap A_\lambda) = \varnothing$, a contradiction since $B \cap A_\lambda \neq \varnothing$.

(3.19.4) *Let* $(A_i)_{1 \leqslant i \leqslant n}$ *be a sequence of connected sets such that* $A_i \cap A_{i+1} \neq \varnothing$ *for* $1 \leqslant i \leqslant n-1$; *then* $\bigcup_{i=1}^{n} A_i$ *is connected.*

This follows at once from (3.19.3) by induction on n.

From (3.19.3) it follows that the union $C(x)$ of *all* connected subsets of E containing a point $x \in E$ is connected, hence the largest connected set containing x; it is called the *connected component of* x *in* E. It is clear that for any $y \in C(x)$, we have $C(y) = C(x)$, and if $y \notin C(x)$, then $C(x) \cap C(y) = \varnothing$; moreover, it follows from (3.19.2) that $C(x)$ is *closed* in E. For any subset A of E, the connected components (in the subspace A) of the points of the subspace A are called the *connected components of* A; if every connected component of A is reduced to a single point, A is said to be *totally disconnected.*

A discrete space is totally disconnected; the set of rational numbers and the set of irrational numbers are totally disconnected, by (2.2.16) and (3.19.1).

(3.19.5) *In order that a metric space* E *be locally connected, a necessary and sufficient condition is that the connected components of the open sets in* E *be open.*

The condition is sufficient, for if V is any open neighborhood of a point $x \in$ E, the connected component of x in the subspace V is a connected neighborhood of x contained in V, hence E is locally connected. The condition is necessary, for if E is locally connected and A is an open set in E, B a connected component of A, then for any $x \in$ B, there is by assumption a connected neighborhood V of x contained in A, hence V $\subset$ B by definition of B, and therefore B is a neighborhood of every one of its points, hence an open set.

(3.19.6) *Any nonempty open set* A *in the real line* **R** *is the union of an at most denumerable family of open intervals, no two of which have common points.*

From (3.19.1) and (3.19.5) it follows that the connected components of A are intervals and open sets, hence open intervals. The intersection A $\cap$ **Q** of A with the set **Q** of rational numbers is denumerable, and each component of A contains points of A $\cap$ **Q** by (2.2.16); the mapping $r \to$ C(r) of A $\cap$ **Q** into the set $\mathfrak{C}$ of the connected components of A is thus surjective, and therefore, by (1.9.2), $\mathfrak{C}$ is at most denumerable.

(3.19.7) *Let f be a continuous mapping of* E *into* E'*; for any connected subset* A *of* E, f(A) *is connected.*

▲ Suppose f(A) = M $\cup$ N, where M and N are nonempty subsets of f(A), open in f(A) and such that M $\cap$ N = $\varnothing$; then, by (3.11.4), A $\cap f^{-1}$(M) and A $\cap f^{-1}$(N) would be nonempty sets, open in A and such that A = (A $\cap f^{-1}$(M)) $\cup$ (A $\cap f^{-1}$(N)) and (A $\cap f^{-1}$(M)) $\cap$ (A $\cap f^{-1}$(N)) = $\varnothing$, contrary to assumption.

(3.19.8) (Bolzano's theorem) *Let* E *be a connected space, f a continuous mapping of* E *into the real line* **R**. *Suppose a, b are two points of f*(E) *such* *that $a < b$. Then, for any c such that $a < c < b$ there exists $x \in E$ such that $f(x) = c$.*

For $f(E)$ is connected in $\mathbf{R}$ by (3.19.7), hence an interval by (3.19.1).

(3.19.9) *Let A be a subset of a metric space E. If B is a connected subset of E such that both $A \cap B$ and $(E - A) \cap B$ are not empty, then $(\mathrm{fr}(A)) \cap B$ is not empty. In particular, if E is connected, any subset A of E distinct from E and $\varnothing$ has at least one frontier point.*

Suppose $(\mathrm{fr}(A)) \cap B = \varnothing$; let $A' = E - A$; as E is the union of $\mathring{A}$, $\mathring{A}'$ and $\mathrm{fr}(A)$, B would be the union of $U = \mathring{A} \cap B$ and $V = \mathring{A}' \cap B$, both of which are open in B and not empty by assumption (for a point of $A \cap B$ must belong to $\mathring{A} \cap B$ since $\mathrm{fr}(A) \cap B = \varnothing$, and similarly for $A' \cap B$); as $U \cap V \varnothing$, $=$this would be contrary to the assumption that B is connected.

Remark. If we agree to call "curve" the image of an interval of $\mathbf{R}$ by a continuous mapping (see Section 4.2, Problem 5), (3.19.7) shows that a "curve" is connected, and (3.19.9) that a "curve" linking a point of A and a point of $E - A$ meets $\mathrm{fr}(A)$, which corresponds to the intuitive idea of "connectedness" (see Problem 3 and Section 5.1, Problem 4).

PROBLEMS

1. Let E be a connected metric space, in which the distance is not bounded. Show that in E every sphere is nonempty.
2. (a) Let E be a compact metric space such that in E, the closure of any open ball $B(a; r)$ is the closed ball $B'(a; r)$. Show that in E any open ball $B(a; r)$ is connected. (Suppose $B(a; r)$ is the union $C \cup D$ of two nonempty sets which are open in $B(a; r)$ and such that $C \cap D = \varnothing$; if $a \in C$, consider a point $x \in D$ such that the distance $d(a, x)$ is minimum (3.17.10).)
   (b) Give an example of a totally disconnected metric space in which the closure of any open ball $B(a; r)$ is the closed ball $B'(a; r)$.
   (c) In the plane $\mathbf{R}^2$ with the distance $d(x, y) = \max(|x_1 - y_1|, |x_2 - y_2|)$, let E be the compact subspace consisting of the points (x_1, x_2) such that $x_1 = 0$ and $0 \leqslant x_2 \leqslant 1$, or $0 \leqslant x_1 \leqslant 1$ and $x_2 = 0$. Show that in E every ball is connected, but the closure of an open ball $B(a; r)$ is not necessarily $B'(a; r)$.
3. In the plane $\mathbf{R}^2$, let E be the subspace consisting of the points (x, y) such that either x is irrational and $0 \leqslant y \leqslant 1$, or x is rational and $-1 \leqslant y < 0$.
   (a) Show that E is connected and not locally connected (use (3.19.1) and (3.19.6) to study the structure of a subset of E which is both open and closed).

(b) Let $t \to (f(t), g(t))$ be a continuous mapping of the interval [0, 1] into E (f and g being continuous). Show that f is constant. (If there exist points $t_0 \in [0, 1]$ such that $g(t_0) < 0$, consider the open subset $U \subset [0, 1]$ consisting of all t such that $g(t) < 0$, and use **(3.19.6)**.) In other words, there are pairs of distinct points in E which "cannot be joined by a curve in E."

4. In a metric space E, let A and B be two connected sets such that $\bar{A} \cap B \neq \varnothing$; show that $A \cup B$ is connected.

5. Let A and B be two nonempty subsets of a metric space E. Show that if A and B are closed, $A \cup B$ and $A \cap B$ connected, then A and B are connected. Show by an example in the real line that the assumption that both A and B are closed cannot be deleted.

6. Let E be a connected metric space having at least two points.

(a) Let A be a connected subset of E, B a subset of $\complement A$, which is open and closed with respect to $\complement A$; show that $A \cup B$ is connected (apply Problem 1 of Section **3.10** to the two sets $A \cup B$ and $\complement A$).

(b) Let A be a connected subset of E, B a connected component of $\complement A$; show that $\complement B$ is connected (apply (a), using an indirect proof).

(c) Show that there are in E two nonempty connected subsets M, N such that $M \cup N = E$, $M \cap N = \varnothing$ (use (b)).

7. In a denumerable metric space E, show that each point has a fundamental system of neighborhoods which are both open and closed.

8. (a) In a metric space E, the connected component of a point x is contained in every open and closed set containing x.

(b) In the plane $\mathbf{R}^2$, let A_n be the set of pairs $(1/n, y)$ such that $-1 \leqslant y \leqslant 1$, B the set of pairs $(0, y)$ such that $0 < y \leqslant 1$, C the set of pairs $(0, y)$ such that $-1 \leqslant y < 0$; let E be the subspace of $\mathbf{R}^2$, union of B, C and the A_n for $n \geqslant 1$. Show that E is a locally compact subspace of E, which is not locally connected; the connected components of E are B, C and the A_n ($n \geqslant 1$), but the intersection of all open and closed sets containing a point of B is $B \cup C$.

9. Let E be a locally compact metric space.

(a) Let C be a connected component of E which is *compact*. Show that C is the intersection of all open and closed neighborhoods of C. (Reduce the problem to the case in which E is compact, using **(3.18.2)**. Suppose the intersection B of all open and closed neighborhoods of C is different from C; B is the union of two closed sets $M \supset C$ and N without common points. Consider in E two open sets $U \supset M$ and $V \supset N$ without common points (Section **3.11**, Problem 3), and take the intersections of $E - (M \cup N)$ with the complements of the open and closed neighborhoods of C.)

(b) Suppose E is connected, and let A be a relatively compact open subset of E. Show that every connected component of A has at least a cluster point in $\complement A$ (if not, apply (a) to such a component, and get a contradiction).

(c) Deduce from (b) that for every compact subset K of E, the intersection of a connected component of K with $\overline{E - K}$ is not empty.

20. PRODUCT OF TWO METRIC SPACES

▲ Let E_1, E_2 be two metric spaces, d_1, d_2 the distances on E_1 and E_2. For any pair of points $x = (x_1, x_2)$, $y = (y_1, y_2)$ in $E = E_1 \times E_2$, let

$$d(x, y) = \max(d_1(x_1, y_1), d_2(x_2, y_2)).$$

It is immediately verified that this function satisfies the axioms (I) to (IV) in Section 3.1, in other words, it is a *distance* on E; the metric space obtained by taking d as a distance on E is called the *product* of the two metric spaces E_1, E_2. The mapping $(x_1, x_2) \to (x_2, x_1)$ of $E_1 \times E_2$ onto $E_2 \times E_1$ is an isometry.

▲We observe that the two functions d', d'' defined by

$$d'(x, y) = d_1(x_1, y_1) + d_2(x_2, y_2)$$
$$d''(x, y) = ((d_1(x_1, y_1))^2 + (d_2(x_2, y_2))^2)^{1/2}$$

are also distances on E, as is easily verified, and are *uniformly equivalent* to d (see Section 3.14), for we have

$$d(x, y) \leqslant d''(x, y) \leqslant d'(x, y) \leqslant 2d(x, y).$$

▲ For all questions dealing with topological properties (or Cauchy sequences and uniformly continuous functions) it is therefore equivalent to take on E any one of the distances d, d', d''. When nothing is said to the contrary, we will consider on E the distance d. Open (resp. closed) balls for the distances d, d_1, d_2 will be respectively written B, B_1, B_2 (resp. B', B'_1, B'_2) instead of the uniform notation B (resp. B') used up to now.

(3.20.1) *For any point* $a = (a_1, a_2) \in E$ *and any* $r > 0$, *we have* $B(a; r) = B_1(a_1; r) \times B_2(a_2; r)$ *and* $B'(a; r) = B'_1(a_1; r) \times B'_2(a_2; r)$.

This follows at once from the definition of d.

(3.20.2) *If* A_1 *is an open set in* E_1, A_2 *an open set in* E_2, *then* $A_1 \times A_2$ *is open in* $E_1 \times E_2$.

For if $a = (a_1, a_2) \in A_1 \times A_2$, there exists $r_1 > 0$ and $r_2 > 0$ such that $B_1(a_1; r_1) \subset A_1$, $B_2(a_2; r_2) \subset A_2$; take $r = \min(r_1, r_2)$; then by (3.20.1), $B(a; r) \subset A_1 \times A_2$.

(3.20.3) *For any pair of sets* $A_1 \subset E_1$, $A_2 \subset E_2$, $\overline{A_1 \times A_2} = \bar{A}_1 \times \bar{A}_2$; *in particular, in order that* $A_1 \times A_2$ *be closed in* E, *a necessary and sufficient condition is that* A_1 *be closed in* E_1 *and* A_2 *closed in* E_2.

If $a = (a_1, a_2) \in \bar{A}_1 \times \bar{A}_2$, for any $\varepsilon > 0$ there is, by assumption, an $x_1 \in A_1$ and an $x_2 \in A_2$ such that $d_1(a_1, x_1) < \varepsilon$, $d_2(a_2, x_2) < \varepsilon$; hence if $x = (x_1, x_2)$,

$d(a, x) < \varepsilon$. On the other hand, if $(a_1, a_2) \notin \bar{A}_1 \times \bar{A}_2$ then either $a_1 \notin \bar{A}_1$ or $a_2 \notin \bar{A}_2$; in the first case, the set $(E_1 - \bar{A}_1) \times E_2$ is open in E by (3.20.2), contains a and has an empty intersection with $A_1 \times A_2$, hence $a \notin \overline{A_1 \times A_2}$; the other case is treated similarly.

(3.20.4) *Let $z \to f(z) = (f_1(z), f_2(z))$ be a mapping of a metric space* F *into* $E = E_1 \times E_2$*; in order that f be continuous at a point z_0, it is necessary and sufficient that both f_1 and f_2 be continuous at z_0.*

Let $x_0 = (f_1(z_0), f_2(z_0))$; then we have

$$f^{-1}(B(x_0; r)) = f_1^{-1}(B_1(f_1(z_0); r)) \cap f_2^{-1}(B_2(f_2(z_0); r))$$

by (3.20.1), and the result follows from (3.11.1) and (3.6.3).

(3.20.5) *Let $f = (f_1, f_2)$ be a mapping of a subspace* A *of a metric space* F *into* $E_1 \times E_2$, *and let $a \in \bar{A}$; in order that f have a limit at the point a with respect to* A, *a necessary and sufficient condition is that both limits* $b_1 = \lim_{z \to a,\, z \in A} f_1(z)$, $b_2 = \lim_{z \to a,\, z \in A} f_2(z)$ *exist, and then the limit of f is* $b = (b_1, b_2)$.

This follows at once from (3.20.4) and the definition of a limit.
In particular:

(3.20.6) *In order that a sequence of points $z_n = (x_n, y_n)$ in $E = E_1 \times E_2$ be convergent, a necessary and sufficient condition is that both limits* $a = \lim_{n \to \infty} x_n$, $b = \lim_{n \to \infty} y_n$ *exist and then* $\lim_{n \to \infty} z_n = (a, b)$.

Note that for cluster values of sequences, if (a, b) is a cluster value of $((x_n, y_n))$, a is a cluster value of (x_n) and b a cluster value of (y_n), as follows from (3.20.6) and the definition of cluster values; but it may happen that $((x_n, y_n))$ has no cluster value, although both (x_n) and (y_n) have one: for instance, in the plane $\mathbf{R}^2$, take $x_{2n} = 1/n$, $y_{2n} = n$, $x_{2n+1} = n$, $y_{2n+1} = 1/n$. However, if (x_n) has a limit a, and b is a cluster value of (y_n), then (a, b) is a cluster value of $((x_n, y_n))$, as follows from (3.20.6).

(3.20.7) *In order that a sequence of points* $z_n = (x_n, y_n)$ *in* $E_1 \times E_2$ *be a Cauchy sequence, a necessary and sufficient condition is that each of the sequences* (x_n), (y_n) *be a Cauchy sequence.*

This follows at once from the definition of the distance in $E_1 \times E_2$ and the definition of a Cauchy sequence.

(3.20.8) *Let* $z \to f(z) = (f_1(z), f_2(z))$ *be a mapping of a metric space* F *into* $E_1 \times E_2$*; in order that* f *be uniformly continuous, it is necessary and sufficient that both* f_1 *and* f_2 *be uniformly continuous.*

This follows immediately from the definitions.

(3.20.9) *If* E *is a metric space,* d *the distance on* E, *the mapping* d *of* $E \times E$ *into* **R** *is uniformly continuous.*

For $|d(x, y) - d(x', y')| \leqslant d(x, x') + d(y, y')$ by the triangle inequality.

(3.20.10) *The projections* pr_1 *and* pr_2 *are uniformly continuous in* $E = E_1 \times E_2$.

Apply (3.20.8) to the identity mapping of E.

(3.20.11) *For any* $a_2 \in E_2$ (resp. $a_1 \in E_1$), *the mapping* $x_1 \to (x_1, a_2)$ (resp. $x_2 \to (a_1, x_2)$) *is an isometry of* E_1 (resp. E_2) *on the closed subspace* $E_1 \times \{a_2\}$ (resp. $\{a_1\} \times E_2$) *of* $E_1 \times E_2$.

This is an obvious consequence of the definition of the distance in $E_1 \times E_2$, and of (3.20.3).

(3.20.12) *For any open* (resp. *closed*) *set* A *in* $E_1 \times E_2$, *and any point* $a_1 \in E_1$, *the cross section* $A(a_1) = \mathrm{pr}_2(A \cap (\{a_1\} \times E_2))$ *is open* (resp. *closed*) *in* E_2.

By (3.20.11) it is enough to prove that the set $A \cap (\{a_1\} \times E_2)$ is open (resp. closed) in $\{a_1\} \times E_2$, which follows from (3.10.1) and (3.10.5).

(3.20.13) *For any open set* A *in* $E_1 \times E_2$, $\mathrm{pr}_1 A$ (resp. $\mathrm{pr}_2 A$) *is open in* E_1 (resp. E_2).

Indeed, we can write $\mathrm{pr}_2\, A = \bigcup_{x_1 \in E_1} A(x_1)$, and the result follows from (3.20.12) and (3.5.2).

Note that if A is closed in $E_1 \times E_2$, $\mathrm{pr}_1\, A$ needs not be closed in E_1. For instance, in the plane $\mathbf{R}^2$, the hyperbola of equation $xy = 1$ is a closed set, but its projections are both equal to the complement of $\{0\}$ in $\mathbf{R}$, which is not closed.

(3.20.14) *Let f be a mapping of* $E = E_1 \times E_2$ *into a metric space* F. *If f is continuous at a point* (a_1, a_2) (resp. *uniformly continuous*), *then the mapping* $f(.\,, a_2): x_1 \to f(x_1, a_2)$ *is continuous at* a_1 (resp. *uniformly continuous*).

That mapping can be written $x_1 \to (x_1, a_2) \to f(x_1, a_2)$, hence the result follows from (3.20.11), (3.11.5), and (3.11.9).

The converse to (3.20.14) does not hold in general. A classical counter-example is the function f defined in $\mathbf{R}^2$ by $f(x, y) = xy/(x^2 + y^2)$ if $(x, y) \neq (0, 0)$ and $f(0, 0) = 0$; f is not continuous at $(0, 0)$, for $f(x, x) = 1/2$ for $x \neq 0$.

(3.20.15) *Let* E_1, E_2, F_1, F_2 *be four metric spaces*, f_1 (resp. f_2) *a mapping of* E_1 *into* F_1 (resp. *of* E_2 *into* F_2). *In order that the mapping* $f: (x_1, x_2) \to (f_1(x_1), f_2(x_2))$ *of* $E_1 \times E_2$ *into* $F_1 \times F_2$ *be continuous at a point* (a_1, a_2) (resp. *uniformly continuous*), *it is necessary and sufficient that* f_1 *be continuous at* a_1 *and* f_2 *at* a_2 (resp. *that both* f_1 *and* f_2 *be uniformly continuous*).

The mapping $(x_1, x_2) \to f_1(x_1)$ can be written $f_1 \circ \mathrm{pr}_1$, hence the sufficiency of the conditions follow from (3.20.4), (3.20.8), and (3.20.10). On the other hand, the mapping f_1 can be written $x_1 \to \mathrm{pr}_1(f(x_1, a_2))$ and the necessity of the conditions follows from (3.20.14) and (3.20.10).

(3.20.16) *Let* E_1, E_2 *be two nonempty metric spaces. In order that* $E = E_1 \times E_2$ *be a space of one of the following types:*

(i) *discrete;*
(ii) *bounded;*
(iii) *separable;*
(iv) *complete;*
(v) *compact;*
(vi) *precompact;*
(vii) *locally compact;*
(viii) *connected;*
(ix) *locally connected;*

it is necessary and sufficient that both E_1 *and* E_2 *be of the same type.*

The *necessity* part of the proofs follows a general pattern for properties (i) to (vii): from (3.20.11) it follows that E_1 and E_2 are isometric to closed subspaces of $E_1 \times E_2$; and then we remark that properties (i) to (vii) are "inherited" by closed subspaces (obvious for (i) and (ii), and proved for properties (iii) to (vii) in (3.10.9), (3.14.5), (3.17.3), (3.17.4), (3.18.4)). For property (viii), the necessity follows from (3.19.7) applied to the projections pr_1 and pr_2; similarly, if E is locally connected, for any $(a_1, a_2) \in E$ and any neighborhood V_1 of a_1 in E_1, $V_1 \times E_2$ is a neighborhood of (a_1, a_2), hence contains a connected neighborhood W of (a_1, a_2); but then $\text{pr}_1 W$ is a connected neighborhood of a_1 contained in V_1, by (3.19.7) and (3.20.13).

The *sufficiency* of the condition for (i) and (ii) is an obvious consequence of the definition of the distance in $E_1 \times E_2$. For (iii), if D_1, D_2 are at most denumerable and dense in E_1, E_2 respectively, then $D_1 \times D_2$ is at most denumerable by (1.9.3), and is dense in E by (3.20.3). For (iv), if (z_n) is a Cauchy sequence in E, then $(\text{pr}_1 z_n)$ and $(\text{pr}_2 z_n)$ are Cauchy sequences in E_1 and E_2 respectively by (3.20.7), hence they converge to a_1, a_2 respectively, and therefore (z_n) converges to (a_1, a_2) by (3.20.6). For (vi), if (A_i) (resp. (B_j)) is a finite covering of E_1 (resp. E_2) by sets of diameter $< \varepsilon$, then $(A_i \times B_j)$ is a finite covering of $E_1 \times E_2$ by sets of diameter $< \varepsilon$; and by (3.16.1), the sufficiency of the condition for (iv) and (vi) proves it also for (v). The proof for (v) yields a proof for (vii) if one remembers the definition of neighborhoods in $E_1 \times E_2$. For (viii), let (a_1, a_2), (b_1, b_2) be any two points of E; by (3.20.11) and the assumption, the sets $\{a_1\} \times E_2$ and $E_1 \times \{b_2\}$ are connected and have a common point (a_1, b_2). Hence their union is connected by (3.19.3), and it contains both (a_1, a_2) and (b_1, b_2); therefore, the connected component of (a_1, a_2) in E is E itself. The same argument proves the sufficiency of the condition for (ix), remembering the definition of the neighborhoods in E.

(3.20.17) *In order that a subset* A *of* $E_1 \times E_2$ *be relatively compact, a necessary and sufficient condition is that* $\text{pr}_1 A$ *and* $\text{pr}_2 A$ *be relatively compact in* E_1 *and* E_2 *respectively.*

The necessity follows from (3.17.9) applied to pr_1 and pr_2; the sufficiency follows from (3.20.16), (3.20.3) and (3.17.4).

All definitions and theorems discussed in this section are extended at once to a finite product of metric spaces.

PROBLEMS

1. Let E, F be two metric spaces, A a subset of E, B a subset of F; show that $\mathrm{fr}(A \times B) = (\mathrm{fr}(A) \times \bar{B}) \cup (\bar{A} \times \mathrm{fr}(B))$.
2. Let E, F be two connected metric spaces, $A \neq E$ a subset of E, $B \neq F$ a subset of F; show that in $E \times F$ the complement of $A \times B$ is connected.
3. (a) Let E, F be two metric spaces, A (resp. B) a compact subset of E (resp. F). If W is any neighborhood of $A \times B$ in $E \times F$, show that there exists a neighborhood U of A in E and a neighborhood V of B in F such that $U \times V \subset W$ (consider first the case in which B is reduced to one point).
(b) Let E be a compact metric space, F a metric space, A a closed subset of $E \times F$. Show that the projection of A into F is a closed set (use (a) to prove the complement of $\mathrm{pr}_2 A$ is open).
(c) Conversely, let E be a metric space such that for every metric space F and every closed subset A of $E \times F$, the projection of A into F is closed in F. Show that E is compact. (If not, there would exist in E a sequence (x_n) without a cluster value. Take for F the subspace of **R** consisting of 0 and of the points $1/n$ (n integer $\geqslant 1$) and consider in $E \times F$ the set of the points $(x_n, 1/n)$.)
4. Let E be a compact metric space, F a metric space, A a closed subset of $E \times F$, B the (closed) projection of A into F. Let $y_0 \in B$ and let C be the cross section $A^{-1}(y_0) = \{x \in E \mid (x, y_0) \in A\}$. Show that for any neighborhood V of C in E, there is a neighborhood W of y_0 in F such that the relation $y \in W$ implies $A^{-1}(y) \subset V$ ("continuity of the "roots" of an equation depending on a parameter"). (Use Problem 3(a).)
5. (a) Let f be a mapping of a metric space E into a metric space F, and let G be the graph of f in $E \times F$. Show that if f is continuous, G is closed in $E \times F$, and the restriction of pr_1 to G is a homeomorphism of G onto E.
(b) Conversely, if F is compact and G is closed in $E \times F$, then f is continuous (use Problem 3(b)).
(c) Let F be a metric space such that for any metric space E, any mapping of E into F whose graph is closed in $E \times F$ is continuous. Show that F is compact (use the construction of Problem 3(c)).
6. Let E, F, G be three metric spaces, A a subset of $E \times F$, B a subset of $F \times G$, $C = B \circ A = \{(x, z) \in E \times G \mid \exists y \in F \text{ such that } (x, y) \in A \text{ and } (y, z) \in B\}$. Suppose both A and B are closed and the projection of A into F is relatively compact; show that C is closed in $E \times G$ (use Problem 3(b)).
7. Let (E_n) ($n \geqslant 1$) be an infinite sequence of nonempty metric spaces, and suppose that for each n, the distance d_n on E_n is such that the diameter of E_n is $\leqslant 1$ (see Section **3.14**, Problem 2(b)). Let E be the infinite product $\prod_{n=1}^{\infty} E_n$.
(a) Show that on E the function $d((x_n), (y_n)) = \sum_{n=1}^{\infty} d_n(x_n, y_n)/2^n$ is a distance.
(b) For any $x = (x_n) \in E$, any integer $m \geqslant 1$ and any number $r > 0$, let $V_m(x; r)$ be the set of all $y = (y_n) \in E$ such that $d_k(x_k, y_k) < r$ for $k \leqslant m$. Show that the sets $V_m(x; r)$ (for all m and r) form a fundamental system of neighborhoods of x in E.
(c) Let $(x^{(m)})$ be a sequence of points $x^{(m)} = (x_n^{(m)})_{n \geqslant 1}$ of E; in order that $(x^{(m)})$ converge to $a = (a_n)$ in E (resp. be a Cauchy sequence in E), it is necessary and sufficient that for each n the sequence $(x_n^{(m)})_{m \geqslant 1}$ converge to a_n in E_n (resp. be a Cauchy sequence in E_n). In order that E be a complete space, it is necessary and sufficient that each E_n be complete.

(d) For each n, let A_n be a subset of E_n; show that the closure in E of $A = \prod_{n=1}^{\infty} A_n$ is equal to $\prod_{n=1}^{\infty} \bar{A}_n$.
(e) In order that E be precompact (resp. compact), it is necessary and sufficient that each E_n be precompact (resp. compact).
(f) In order that E be locally compact, it is necessary and sufficient that each E_n be locally compact, and that all E_n, with the exception of a finite number at most, be compact.
(g) In order that E be connected, it is necessary and sufficient that each E_n be connected.
(h) In order that E be locally connected, it is necessary and sufficient that each E_n be locally connected and that all E_n, with the exception of a finite number at most, be connected.

Let $a=(x,y)$, $b=(x',y') \in R \times R$. If $d(a,b)=\max\{d(x,y),(x',y')\} < \varepsilon/2$ i.e $\max\{|x-x'|,|y-y'|\} < \varepsilon/2$
then $|x-x'|+|y-y'| < \varepsilon$ i.e $|(x+y)-(x'+y')| < \varepsilon$.

CHAPTER IV

ADDITIONAL PROPERTIES OF THE REAL LINE

▲Many of the properties of the real line have been mentioned in Chapter III, in connection with the various topological notions developed in that chapter. The properties gathered under Chapter IV, most of which are elementary and classical, have no such direct connection, and are really those which give to the real line its unique status among more general spaces. The introduction of the logarithm and exponential functions has been made in a slightly unorthodox way, starting with the logarithm instead of the exponential; this has the technical advantage of making it unnecessary to define first $a^{m/n}$ (m, n integers > 0) as a separate stepping stone toward the definition of a^x for any x.

▲The Tietze–Urysohn theorem (Section 4.5) now occupies a very central position both in functional analysis and in algebraic topology. It can be considered as the first step in the study of the general problem of *extending* a continuous mapping of a closed subset A of a space E into a space F, to a continuous mapping of the *whole* space E into F; this general problem naturally leads to the most important and most actively studied questions of modern algebraic topology.

1. CONTINUITY OF ALGEBRAIC OPERATIONS

(4.1.1) *The mapping $(x, y) \to x + y$ of* **R** × **R** *into* **R** *is uniformly continuous.*

This follows at once from the inequality

$$|(x' + y') - (x + y)| \leqslant |x' - x| + |y' - y|$$

and the definitions.

(4.1.2) *The mapping* $(x, y) \to xy$ *of* $\mathbf{R} \times \mathbf{R}$ *into* $\mathbf{R}$ *is continuous; for any* $a \in \mathbf{R}$, *the mapping* $x \to ax$ *of* $\mathbf{R}$ *into* $\mathbf{R}$ *is uniformly continuous.*

Continuity of xy at a point (x_0, y_0) follows from the identity

$$xy - x_0 y_0 = x_0(y - y_0) + (x - x_0)y_0 + (x - x_0)(y - y_0).$$

Given any $\varepsilon > 0$, take δ such that $0 < \delta < 1$ and $\delta(|x_0| + |y_0| + 1) < \varepsilon$; then the relations $|x - x_0| < \delta$, $|y - y_0| < \delta$ imply $|xy - x_0 y_0| < \varepsilon$. Uniform continuity of $x \to ax$ is immediate, since $|ax' - ax| = |a| \cdot |x' - x|$.

(4.1.3) *Any continuous mapping* f *of* $\mathbf{R}$ *into itself such that* $f(x + y) = f(x) + f(y)$ *is of type* $x \to cx$, *with* $c \in \mathbf{R}$.

Indeed, for each integer $n > 0$, we have, by induction on n, $f(nx) = nf(x)$; on the other hand $f(0 + x) = f(0) + f(x)$, hence $f(0) = 0$, and $f(x + (-x)) = f(x) + f(-x) = f(0) = 0$, hence $f(-x) = -f(x)$. From that it follows that for any integer $n > 0$, $f(x/n) = f(x)/n$, hence for any pair of integers p, q such that $q > 0$, $f(px/q) = pf(x)/q$; in other words, $f(rx) = rf(x)$ for any rational number r. But any real number t is limit of a sequence (r_n) of rational numbers (by (2.2.16) and (3.13.13)), hence, from the assumption on f and (4.1.2) $f(tx) = f(\lim_{n\to\infty} r_n x) = \lim_{n\to\infty} f(r_n x) = \lim_{n\to\infty} r_n f(x) = f(x) \cdot \lim_{n\to\infty} r_n = tf(x)$. Let then, $c = f(1)$, and we obtain $f(x) = cx$ for every $x \in \mathbf{R}$.

(4.1.4) *The mapping* $x \to 1/x$ *is continuous at every point* $x_0 \neq 0$ *in* $\mathbf{R}$.

For given any $\varepsilon > 0$, take $\delta > 0$ such that $\delta < \min(|x_0|/2, \varepsilon|x_0|^2/2)$; then the relation $|x - x_0| < \delta$ first implies $|x| > |x_0| - \delta > |x_0|/2$, and then $|1/x - 1/x_0| = |x_0 - x|/|xx_0| \leqslant 2|x_0 - x|/|x_0|^2 < \varepsilon$.

(4.1.5) *Any rational function* $(x_1, \ldots, x_n) \to \mathrm{P}(x_1, \ldots, x_n)/\mathrm{Q}(x_1, \ldots, x_n)$ *where* P *and* Q *are polynomials with real coefficients, is continuous at each point* $(a_1, \ldots, a_n)$ *of* $\mathbf{R}^n$ *where* $\mathrm{Q}(a_1, \ldots, a_n) \neq 0$.

The continuity of a monomial in $\mathbf{R}^n$ is proved from (4.1.2) by induction on its degree, then the continuity of P and Q is proved from (4.1.1) by induction on their numbers of terms; the final result follows from (4.1.4).

$\delta(|x_0|+|y_0|+1)<\varepsilon \Rightarrow \delta(|x_0|+|y_0|+\delta)<\varepsilon \Rightarrow |x-x_0||x_0|+|y-y_0||y_0|+|x-x_0||y-y_0|<\varepsilon \Rightarrow |xy-x_0y_0|<\varepsilon.$

(4.1.6) *The mappings* $(x, y) \to \sup(x, y)$ *and* $(x, y) \to \inf(x, y)$ *are uniformly continuous in* $\mathbf{R} \times \mathbf{R}$.

As $\sup(x, y) = (x + y + |x - y|)/2$ and $\inf(x, y) = (x + y - |x - y|)/2$, the result follows from (4.1.1) and (3.20.9).

(4.1.7) *All open intervals in* $\mathbf{R}$ *are homeomorphic to* $\mathbf{R}$.

From (4.1.1.) and (4.1.2) it follows that any linear function $x \to ax + b$, with $a \neq 0$, is a homeomorphism of $\mathbf{R}$ onto itself, for the inverse mapping $x \to a^{-1}x - a^{-1}b$ has the same form. Any two bounded open intervals $]\alpha, \beta[$, $]\gamma, \delta[$ are images of one another by a mapping $x \to ax + b$, hence are homeomorphic. Consider now the mapping $x \to x/(1 + |x|)$ of $\mathbf{R}$ onto $]-1, +1[$; the inverse mapping is $x \to x/(1 - |x|)$ and both are continuous, since $x \to |x|$ is. This proves $\mathbf{R}$ is homeomorphic to any bounded open interval; finally, under the preceding homeomorphism of $\mathbf{R}$ onto $]-1, +1[$, any unbounded open interval $]a, +\infty[$ or $]-\infty, a[$ of $\mathbf{R}$ is mapped onto a bounded open interval contained in $]-1, +1[$, hence these intervals are also homeomorphic to $\mathbf{R}$.

(4.1.8) *With respect to* $\mathbf{R} \times \mathbf{R}$, *the function* $(x, y) \to x + y$ *has a limit at every point* (a, b) *of* $\overline{\mathbf{R}} \times \overline{\mathbf{R}}$, *except at the points* $(-\infty, +\infty)$ *and* $(+\infty, -\infty)$; *that limit is equal to* $+\infty$ (resp. $-\infty$) *if one at least of the coordinates* a, b *is* $+\infty$ (resp. $-\infty$).

Let us prove for instance that if $a \neq -\infty$, $x + y$ has a limit equal to $+\infty$ at the point $(a, +\infty)$. Given $c \in \mathbf{R}$, the relations $x > b$, $y > c - b$ imply $x + y > c$, and the intervals $]b, +\infty]$ and $]c - b, +\infty]$ are respectively neighborhoods of a and $+\infty$ if b is taken finite and $<a$; hence our assertion. The other cases are treated similarly.

(4.1.9) *With respect to* $\mathbf{R} \times \mathbf{R}$, *the function* $(x, y) \to xy$ *has a limit at every point* (a, b) *of* $\overline{\mathbf{R}} \times \overline{\mathbf{R}}$, *except at the points* $(0, +\infty)$, $(0, -\infty)$, $(+\infty, 0)$, $(-\infty, 0)$; *that limit is equal to* $+\infty$ (resp. $-\infty$) *if one at least of the coordinates* a, b *is infinite, and if they have the same sign* (resp. *opposite signs*).

Let us show for instance that if $a > 0$, xy has the limit $+\infty$ at the point $(a, +\infty)$. Given $c \in \mathbf{R}$, the relations $x > b$, $y > c/b$, for $b > 0$, imply $xy > c$, and the intervals $]b, +\infty]$ and $]c/b, +\infty]$ are neighborhoods of a and $+\infty$, if b is taken finite and $<a$. Similar proofs for the other cases.

We omit the proofs of the following two properties:

(4.1.10) $\lim_{x \to \pm\infty} 1/x = 0, \qquad \lim_{x \to 0,\, x>0} 1/x = +\infty, \qquad \lim_{x \to 0,\, x<0} 1/x = -\infty.$

(4.1.11) *The mappings* $(x, y) \to \sup(x, y)$ *and* $(x, y) \to \inf(x, y)$ *are continuous in* $\overline{\mathbf{R}} \times \overline{\mathbf{R}}$.

2. MONOTONE FUNCTIONS

Let E be a nonempty subset of the extended real line $\overline{\mathbf{R}}$. A mapping f of E into $\overline{\mathbf{R}}$ is called *increasing* (resp. *strictly increasing*, *decreasing*, *strictly decreasing*) if the relation $x < y$ (in E) implies $f(x) \leqslant f(y)$ (resp. $f(x) < f(y)$, $f(x) \geqslant f(y)$, $f(x) > f(y)$); a function which is either increasing or decreasing (resp. either strictly increasing or strictly decreasing) is called *monotone* (resp. *strictly monotone*); a strictly monotone mapping is *injective*. If f is increasing (resp. strictly increasing), $-f$ is decreasing (resp. strictly decreasing). If f, g are increasing, and $f + g$ is defined, $f + g$ is increasing; if in addition f and g are both finite and one of them is strictly increasing, then $f + g$ is strictly increasing.

(4.2.1) *Let* E *be a nonempty subset of* $\overline{\mathbf{R}}$, *and* $a = \sup \mathrm{E}$; *if* $a \notin \mathrm{E}$, *then, for any monotone mapping* f *of* E *into* $\overline{\mathbf{R}}$, $\lim_{x \to a,\, x \in \mathrm{E}} f(x)$ *exists and is equal to* $\sup_{x \in \mathrm{E}} f(x)$ *if* f *is increasing, to* $\inf_{x \in \mathrm{E}} f(x)$ *if* f *is decreasing.* (Theorem of the monotone limit.)

Suppose for instance f is increasing, and let $c = \sup_{x \in \mathrm{E}} f(x)$. If $c = -\infty$, f is constant (equal to $-\infty$) in E and the result is trivial; if $c > -\infty$, for any $b < c$, there is $x \in \mathrm{E}$ such that $b < f(x) \leqslant c$; hence, for $y \in \mathrm{E}$ and $x \leqslant y < a$, we have by assumption $b < f(x) \leqslant f(y) \leqslant c$, whence our conclusion.

(4.2.2) *Let* I *be an interval in* $\overline{\mathbf{R}}$; *any continuous injective mapping* f *of* I *into* $\overline{\mathbf{R}}$ *is strictly monotone*; *any continuous strictly monotone mapping* f *of* I *into* $\overline{\mathbf{R}}$ *is a homeomorphism of* I *onto an interval* f (I).

1. Suppose f continuous and injective; let a, b be two points of I such that $a < b$, and suppose for instance $f(a) < f(b)$. Then, for $a < c < b$, we must have $f(a) < f(c) < f(b)$; for our assumptions imply $f(c) \neq f(b)$ and

$f(c) \neq f(a)$, and if we had for instance $f(c) > f(b)$, there would then be an x such that $a < x < c$ and $f(x) = f(x) = f(b)$ by Bolzano's theorem (3.19.8), contrary to our assumption. Similarly one sees that $f(c) < f(a)$ is impossible. If now $b < c$, we must have $f(b) < f(c)$, for the preceding argument shows $f(b)$ must be in the interval of extremities $f(a)$ and $f(c)$. Similarly if $c < a$, $f(c) < f(a)$. Finally, if x, y are any two points of I such that $x < y$, we have $f(x) < f(y)$, by repeating the preceding argument on a, x, y instead of a, b, c.

2. If f is continuous and strictly monotone, it is a bijection of I onto $f(\mathrm{I})$, and $f(\mathrm{I})$, being connected, must be an interval ((3.19.1) and (3.19.7)). For any $x \in \mathrm{I}$, the image by f of any interval J containing x and contained in I is then an interval containing $f(x)$ and contained in $f(\mathrm{I})$ and $f(x)$ can only be an extremity of $f(\mathrm{J})$ if x is an extremity of J; this proves the image by f of any neighborhood of x in I is a neighborhood of $f(x)$ in $f(\mathrm{I})$, hence f is a homeomorphism (see (3.11.1)).

PROBLEMS

1. Let f be a mapping of **R** into **R** such that $f(x+y) = f(x) + f(y)$.
Show that if, in an interval $]a, b[$, f is majorized, then f is also minorized in $]a, b[$ (if c is a fixed point in the interval $]a, b[$, consider pairs of points x, y in that interval such that $x < c < y$ and $(y-c)/(c-x)$ is rational). Under the same assumption, f is bounded in *any* compact interval, and continuous in **R**, hence of the form $f(x) = cx$ (same method).
(It can be proved, using the axiom of choice, that there exist solutions of $f(x+y) = f(x) + f(y)$ which are unbounded in every interval.)

• **2.** Let b be an integer >1.
•(a) Show that for any infinite sequence (c_n) of integers such that $0 \leqslant c_n \leqslant b-1$, the series $\sum_{n=0}^{\infty} c_n/b^n$ converges to a number $x \in [0, 1]$. Conversely, for any $x \in [0, 1]$ there exists a sequence (c_n) such that $0 \leqslant c_n \leqslant b-1$ for every n and $x = \sum_{n=0}^{\infty} c_n/b^n$; that sequence is unique if x has not the form k/b^m (k and m natural integers); otherwise, there are exactly two sequences (c_n) having the required properties. (Use the fact that for any integer $m \geqslant 0$, and any $x \in [0, 1]$, there is a unique integer k such that $k/b^m \leqslant x < (k+1)/b^m$.)
(b) Using the case $b = 2$ of (a), and Problem 5 of Section 1.9, show that [0, 1] (hence **R** itself, see (4.1.7)) is equipotent to the set $\mathfrak{P}(\mathbf{N})$.
(c) Let K be the subset of [0, 1] consisting of all numbers of the form $\sum_{n=0}^{\infty} c_n/3^n$, with $c_n = 0$ or $c_n = 2$ ("triadic Cantor set"). Show that K is compact; its complement in [0, 1] is a denumerable union of open nonoverlapping intervals (3.19.6); describe these intervals, and show that the (infinite) sum of their lengths is 1.
(d) For each $x \in \mathrm{K}$, with $x = \sum_{n=0}^{\infty} c_n/3^n$, let $f(x)$ be the real number $\sum_{n=0}^{\infty} b_n/2^n$, where

$b_n = c_n/2$ (when x can be written in two different ways as $\sum_{n=0}^{\infty} c_n/3^n$, show that the two corresponding numbers $\sum_{n=0}^{\infty} b_n/2^n$ are equal). Prove that f is a surjective continuous mapping of K onto the interval [0, 1] of **R**, and show that K and **R** are equipotent. Furthermore it is possible to extend f to a continuous mapping of I = [0, 1] onto itself, which is *constant* in each of the connected components (**3.19.6**) of I − K.

3. (a) Let E be a metric space satisfying the following condition: for each finite sequence $s = (\varepsilon_i)_{1 \leqslant i \leqslant n}$ whose terms are equal to 0 or 1, there is a nonempty subset A_s such that:
(i) E is the union of the two subsets $A_{(0)}$, $A_{(1)}$, and for each finite sequence s of n terms, if s', s'' are the two sequences of $n+1$ terms whose first n terms are those of s, $A_s = A_{s'} \cup A_{s''}$;
(ii) for each infinite sequence $(\varepsilon_n)_{n \geqslant 1}$ whose terms are equal to 0 or 1, if $s_n = (\varepsilon_i)_{1 \leqslant i < n}$, the diameter of A_{s_n} tends to 0 when n tends to $+\infty$, and the intersection of the A_{s_n} is not empty.
Under these conditions, show that there exists a continuous mapping of the triadic Cantor set K (Problem 2) *onto* E, and in particular E is compact.
(b) Conversely, let E be an arbitrary compact metric space. Show that there exists a continuous mapping of K onto E. (Apply the method of (a), and the definition of precompact spaces (Section **3.16**); observe that properties (i) and (ii) do not imply that the two sets $A_{s'}$ and $A_{s''}$ need be different from A_s for all sequences s.)
(c) If in addition E is totally disconnected, and has no isolated points (**3.10.10**), then E is *homeomorphic* to K. (First prove that for every $\varepsilon > 0$ there is a covering of E by a finite number of sets A_i which are both open and closed and have a diameter $\leqslant \varepsilon$; to that purpose use Problem 9(a) of Section **3.19**. Then apply the method of (a).)

4. (a) Let E (resp. F) be the set of even (resp. odd) natural integers; if, to each subset X of **N**, one associates the pair $(X \cap E, X \cap F)$, show that one defines a bijection of $\mathfrak{P}(\mathbf{N})$ onto $\mathfrak{P}(E) \times \mathfrak{P}(F)$.
(b) Deduce from (a) and from Problem 2(b) that $\mathbf{R}^n$ and **R** are equipotent for all $n > 1$ (but see Section **5.1**, Problem 6).

5. Let I be the interval [0, 1] in **R**. Show that there exists a *continuous* mapping f of I *onto* the "square" I × I (a "Peano curve"). (First show that there is a continuous mapping of the Cantor set K onto I × I (Problem 3), and then extend the mapping by linearity to the connected components of the complement of K in I.)

6. Let g be a mapping of the interval]0, 1] into the interval [−1, 1], and suppose that $\lim_{x \to 0,\, x > 0} g(x) = 0$. Show that there exist a continuous decreasing mapping g_1 and a continuous increasing mapping g_2 of [0, 1] into [−1, 1], such that $g_1(0) = g_2(0) = 0$, and $g_1(x) \leqslant g(x) \leqslant g_2(x)$ for $0 < x \leqslant 1$. (For each integer n, consider the g.l.b. x_n of the set of points x such that $g(x) \geqslant 1/n$.)

3. LOGARITHMS AND EXPONENTIALS

(**4.3.1**) *For any number $a > 1$, there is a unique increasing mapping f of $\mathbf{R}_+^* =]0, +\infty[$ into* **R** *such that $f(xy) = f(x) + f(y)$ and $f(a) = 1$; moreover, f is a homeomorphism of $\mathbf{R}_+^*$ onto* **R**.

Since $a>1$ we have $a=1+b$ with $b>0$. Hence $a^n=(1+b)^n \geqslant 1+nb$. Choose $n > \frac{x-1}{b}$ if $x \geqslant 1$.

▲ We first prove a lemma:

(4.3.1.1) *For any $x > 0$, there is an integer m (positive or negative) such that $a^m \leqslant x \leqslant a^{m+1}$.*

▲ Suppose first $x \geqslant 1$. The sequence (a^n) is strictly increasing. If we had $a^n \leqslant x$ for all integers $n > 0$, then (by (4.2.1) and (3.15.4)) $b = \lim_{n\to\infty} a^n = \sup_n a^n$ would be finite, >1 and $\leqslant x$; but we can write $b = \lim_{n\to\infty} a^{n+1} = a \cdot \lim_{n\to\infty} a^n$ by (4.1.2), hence $b = ab$, which contradicts the assumption $a > 1$. Therefore there is an integer n such that $x > a^n$; take $m + 1$ as the smallest of these integers. If on the contrary $0 < x < 1$, then $x^{-1} > 1$, and if $a^m \leqslant x^{-1} \leqslant a^{m+1}$, we have $a^{-(m+1)} \leqslant x \leqslant a^{-(m+1)+1}$ (2.2.13).

▲ Suppose there exists a function f having the properties listed in (4.3.1); then f is a homomorphism of the multiplicative group $\mathbf{R}_+^*$ into the additive group $\mathbf{R}$, and therefore we must have $f(1) = 0$, $f(x^n) = n \cdot f(x)$ for any $x > 0$ and any integer n (positive or negative), and in particular $f(a^n) = n$. Moreover, if $a^m \leqslant x^n \leqslant a^{m+1}$, we must have $f(a^m) \leqslant f(x^n) \leqslant f(a^{m+1})$, in other words $m \leqslant n \cdot f(x) \leqslant m + 1$, hence $m/n \leqslant f(x)$ and $|f(x) - m/n| \leqslant 1/n$. This shows that if we denote by A_x the set of rational numbers m/n (m positive or negative, $n \geqslant 1$) such that $a^m \leqslant x^n$, (note that $a^m \leqslant x^n$ and $a^{mq} \leqslant x^{nq}$, where q is an integer >0, are equivalent relations (2.2.13)), we must have $f(x) = \sup \mathrm{A}_x$, which shows f is unique.

▲ To prove the existence of f, it remains to prove that the mapping f: $x \to \sup \mathrm{A}_x$ verifies all our conditions. Let x and y be any two elements of $\mathbf{R}_+^*$; for any integer $n \geqslant 1$, let m, m' be such that $a^m \leqslant x^n \leqslant a^{m+1}$ and $a^{m'} \leqslant y^n \leqslant a^{m'+1}$; from these relations it follows that $a^{m+m'} \leqslant (xy)^n \leqslant a^{m+m'+2}$; hence we have

$$\frac{m}{n} \leqslant f(x) \leqslant \frac{m+1}{n}, \qquad \frac{m'}{n} \leqslant f(y) \leqslant \frac{m'+1}{n},$$

$$\frac{m+m'}{n} \leqslant f(xy) \leqslant \frac{m+m'+2}{n},$$

and also

$$\frac{m+m'}{n} \leqslant f(x) + f(y) \leqslant \frac{m+m'+2}{n}.$$

We conclude that

$$|f(xy) - f(x) - f(y)| \leqslant 2/n,$$

and as n is arbitrary,

$$f(xy) = f(x) + f(y).$$

▲ From (4.3.1.1) it follows that for any $z > 1$, there is an integer $n \geqslant 1$ such that $a < z^n$, hence $f(z) \geqslant 1/n > 0$; from which it follows that f is *strictly increasing*, since if $x < y$, then $y = zx$ with $z > 1$ and $f(y) = f(x) + f(z) > f(x)$. On the other hand, we have the following lemma:

(4.3.1.2) *For any integer $n \geqslant 1$, there is a $z > 1$ such that $z^n \leqslant a$.*

▲ Remark that there is an x such that $1 < x < a$, hence $a = xy$ with $y > 1$; if $z_1 = \min(x, y)$, we have $z_1^2 \leqslant xy = a$ and $z_1 > 1$. By induction define $z_n > 1$ such that $z_1^2 \leqslant z_{n-1}$, hence $z_1^{2^n} \leqslant a$, and a fortiori $z_1^n \leqslant a$.

▲ The lemma shows that $0 < f(z) \leqslant 1/n$. For any $x \in \mathbf{R}_+^*$, take δ such that

$$\frac{x+\delta}{x} < z \quad \text{and} \quad \frac{x-\delta}{x} > \frac{1}{z}:$$

then $|f(y) - f(x)| < f(z) \leqslant 1/n$ for $|y - x| \leqslant \delta$, which proves f is continuous. By (4.2.2), f is thus a homeomorphism of $\mathbf{R}_+^*$ onto an interval I of $\mathbf{R}$; but that interval is necessarily $\mathbf{R}$ itself, since $f(a^n) = n$ is an arbitrary integer.

(4.3.2) *For any number $a > 0$ and $\neq 1$, there exists one and only one continuous mapping f of $\mathbf{R}_+^*$ into $\mathbf{R}$ such that $f(xy) = f(x) + f(y)$ and $f(a) = 1$.*

▲ Let $b > 1$; from (4.3.1) we have a homeomorphism f_0 of $\mathbf{R}_+^*$ onto $\mathbf{R}$ such that $f_0(xy) = f_0(x) + f_0(y)$ and $f_0(b) = 1$; let g_0 be the inverse homeomorphism, such that $g_0(x + y) = g_0(x)g_0(y)$ and $g_0(1) = b$. If f verifies the conditions of (4.3.2), then $h = f \circ g_0$ is a continuous mapping of $\mathbf{R}$ into itself, such that $h(x + y) = h(x) + h(y)$; by (4.1.3), we have $h(x) = cx$, and therefore $f(x) = cf_0(x)$, and there is only one value of c for which $f(a) = 1$, namely $c = 1/f_0(a)$ (as $a \neq 1$, we have $f_0(a) \neq 0 = f_0(1)$).

▲ The mapping characterized in (4.3.2) is called the *logarithm of base a*, and $f(x)$ is written $\log_a x$. From the proof of (4.3.2) it follows at once that if a, b are >0 and $\neq 1$, $\log_a x$ and $\log_b x$ are proportional, and making $x = a$ yields

(4.3.3) $$\log_b x = \log_b a \cdot \log_a x.$$

From (4.3.1) and (4.2.1) it follows that if $a > 1$, $\lim_{x \to 0} \log_a x = -\infty$, $\lim_{x \to +\infty} \log_a x = +\infty$; if $a < 1$, $\lim_{x \to 0} \log_a x = +\infty$, $\lim_{x \to +\infty} \log_a x = -\infty$. For any $a > 0$ and $\neq 1$, the inverse mapping of $x \to \log_a x$ is called the *exponential of base a* and written $x \to a^x$ (which is a coherent notation, since $\log_a(a^n) = n$, and therefore for integral values of x, the new notation has the same meaning as the algebraic one). In addition, we define 1^x to be 1 for all real numbers x. Then, for $a > 0$, x, y arbitrary real numbers, we have by definition $a^{x+y} = a^x a^y$, $a^{-x} = 1/a^x$, $a^0 = 1$. Replacing x by b^x in (4.3.3) yields

(4.3.4) $$\log_a(b^x) = x \log_a b \qquad (b > 0,\ x \text{ real})$$

and replacing b by a^y in that formula gives

(4.3.5) $$(a^x)^y = a^{xy} \qquad (x, y \text{ real}, a > 0).$$

For $a > 1$, $x \to a^x$ is strictly increasing and such that $\lim_{x \to -\infty} a^x = 0$, $\lim_{x \to +\infty} a^x = +\infty$; for $a < 1$, $x \to a^x$ is strictly decreasing, and such that $\lim_{x \to -\infty} a^x = +\infty$, $\lim_{x \to -\infty} a^x = 0$.

(4.3.6) *The mapping* $(x, y) \to x^y$ *is continuous in* $\mathbf{R}_+^* \times \mathbf{R}$, *and tends to a limit at each point of* $\overline{\mathbf{R}} \times \overline{\mathbf{R}}$ *in the closure of* $\mathbf{R}_+^* \times \mathbf{R}$ *and distinct from* $(0, 0)$, $(+\infty, 0)$, $(1, +\infty)$, $(1, -\infty)$.

From (4.3.4), we have $x^y = a^{y \cdot \log_a x}$ (a fixed number > 1), hence the result by (4.1.2) and (4.1.9).

(4.3.7) *Any continuous mapping* g *of* $\mathbf{R}_+^*$ *into itself such that* $g(xy) = g(x)g(y)$ *has the form* $x \to x^a$, *with* a *real.*

Indeed, if $b > 1$, $f(x) = \log_b g(b^x)$ is such that $f(x + y) = f(x) + f(y)$, for real x, y, and is continuous, hence $f(x) = c \cdot x$ by (4.1.3), therefore $g(b^x) = b^{cx} = (b^x)^c$, which proves the result.

As $\log_b(x^a) = a \cdot \log_b x$, we see that if $a > 0$, $x \to x^a$ is strictly increasing, and strictly decreasing if $a < 0$; moreover if $a > 0$, $\lim_{x \to 0} x^a = 0$, $\lim_{x \to +\infty} x^a = +\infty$; if $a < 0$, $\lim_{x \to 0} x^a = +\infty$, $\lim_{x \to +\infty} x^a = 0$. For $a \neq 0$, $x \to x^a$ is therefore a homeomorphism of $\mathbf{R}_+^*$ onto itself, by (4.2.2); the inverse homeomorphism is $x \to x^{1/a}$.

PROBLEM

Let f be a mapping of $\mathbf{R}$ into itself such that $f(x + y) = f(x) + f(y)$ and $f(xy) = f(x)f(y)$. Show that either $f(x) = 0$ for every $x \in \mathbf{R}$, or $f(x) = x$ for every $x \in \mathbf{R}$. (If $f(1) \neq 0$, then $f(1) = 1$; in the second case, show that $f(x) = x$ for rational x, and using the fact that every real number $z > 0$ is a square, show that f is strictly increasing.)

4. COMPLEX NUMBERS

We define two mappings of the set $\mathbf{R}^2 \times \mathbf{R}^2$ into $\mathbf{R}^2$ by

$$((x, y), (x', y')) \to (x + x', y + y')$$
$$((x, y), (x', y')) \to (xx' - yy', xy' + yx').$$

They are called respectively addition and multiplication, and written

$$(z, z') \to z + z' \text{ and } (z, z') \to zz'.$$

For these two mappings, axioms (I) (Section 2.1) of a field are satisfied, by taking $0 = (0, 0)$, $1 = (1, 0)$, and

$$z^{-1} = \left(\frac{x}{x^2 + y^2}, \frac{-y}{x^2 + y^2}\right)$$

if $z = (x, y) \neq 0$ (which, by (2.2.8) and (2.2.12), implies $x^2 + y^2 \neq 0$). The field thus defined is written $\mathbf{C}$ and called the *field of complex numbers*, its elements being called complex numbers. The mapping $x \to (x, 0)$ of $\mathbf{R}$ into $\mathbf{C}$ is injective and preserves addition and multiplication, hence we identify $\mathbf{R}$ with the subfield of $\mathbf{C}$ consisting of the elements $(x, 0)$. The element $i = (0, 1)$ is such that $i^2 = (-1, 0) = -1$, and we can write $(x, y) = x + iy$ for any $(x, y) \in \mathbf{C}$; if $z = x + iy$, x, y being real, x is written $\mathscr{R}z$ and called the *real part* of z, y is written $\mathscr{I}z$ and called the *imaginary part* of z.

(4.4.1) *Any rational function* $(z_1, \ldots, z_n) \to \mathrm{P}(z_1, \ldots, z_n)/\mathrm{Q}(z_1, \ldots, z_n)$ *where* P *and* Q *are polynomials with complex coefficients, is continuous at each point* $(a_1, \ldots, a_n)$ *of* $\mathbf{C}^n$ *such that* $\mathrm{Q}(a_1, \ldots, a_n) \neq 0$.

This is proved as (4.1.5) by using the analogs of (4.1.1), (4.1.2) and (4.1.4), which follow at once from the formulas given above for sum, product and inverse of complex numbers, and from (3.20.4) and (4.1.5).

For any complex number $z = x + iy$, the number $\bar{z} = x - iy$ is called the *conjugate* of z. We have $\bar{\bar{z}} = z$, $\overline{z + z'} = \bar{z} + \bar{z}'$, $\overline{zz'} = \bar{z} \cdot \bar{z}'$, in other words $z \to \bar{z}$ is an *automorphism* of the field $\mathbf{C}$, which is bicontinuous by (3.20.4) and (4.1.2); real numbers are characterized by $\bar{z} = z$, numbers of the form ix (x real, also called *purely imaginary* numbers) by $\bar{z} = -z$. We have $z\bar{z} = x^2 + y^2 \geqslant 0$ if $z = x + iy$; the positive real number $|z| = (z\bar{z})^{1/2}$ is called the *absolute value* of z, and coincides with the absolute value defined in Section 2.2 when z is real. The relation $|z| = 0$ is equivalent to $z = 0$. We have $|zz'|^2 = zz'\overline{zz'} = z\bar{z}z'\bar{z}' = |z|^2|z'|^2$, hence $|zz'| = |z| \cdot |z'|$, from which it follows that if $z \neq 0$, $|1/z| = 1/|z|$. Finally, by direct computation, we check the triangle inequality

$$|z + z'| \leqslant |z| + |z'|$$

which shows that $|z - z'| = d(z, z')$ is a *distance* defined on $\mathbf{C} = \mathbf{R} \times \mathbf{R}$, which is uniformly equivalent to the distance considered in Section 3.20. The balls for that distance are called *discs*. Any complex number $z \neq 0$ can be written in one and only one way as a product $r\zeta$, with $r > 0$ and $|\zeta| = 1$, namely by taking $r = |z|$ and $\zeta = z/|z|$.

PROBLEM

Let f be a continuous mapping of $\mathbf{C}$ into itself such that $f(z + z') = f(z) + f(z')$ and $f(zz') = f(z)f(z')$. Show that either $f(z) = 0$ for every $z \in \mathbf{C}$, or f is one of the mappings $z \to z$, $z \to \bar{z}$ (use (4.1.3)). (It can be proved, using the axiom of choice, that there are injective, nonsurjective and noncontinuous mappings f of $\mathbf{C}$ into itself, such that $f(z + z') = f(z) + f(z')$ and $f(zz') = f(z)f(z')$. Compare to the problem in Section 4.2.)

5. THE TIETZE–URYSOHN EXTENSION THEOREM

(4.5.1) (Tietze–Urysohn extension theorem) *Let* E *be a metric space,* A *a closed subset of* E, *f a continuous bounded mapping of* A *into* $\mathbf{R}$. *Then there exists a continuous mapping g of* E *into* $\mathbf{R}$ *which coincides with f in* A *and is such that*

$$\sup_{x \in A} g(x) = \sup_{y \in A} f(y), \qquad \inf_{x \in E} g(x) = \inf_{y \in A} f(y).$$

▲ We may suppose that $\inf_{y \in A} f(y) = 1$, $\sup_{y \in A} f(y) = 2$ by replacing eventually f by a mapping $y \to \alpha f(y) + \beta$, $\alpha \neq 0$ (the case in which f is constant is trivial). Define $g(x)$ as equal to $f(x)$ for $x \in A$, and given by the formula

$$g(x) = (\inf_{y \in A} (f(y)\, d(x, y)))/d(x, A)$$

for $x \in E - A$. From the inequalities $1 \leqslant f(y) \leqslant 2$ for $y \in A$ and the definition of $d(x, A)$, it follows that $1 \leqslant g(x) \leqslant 2$ for $x \in E - A$. We need therefore only prove the continuity of g at every point $x \in E$. If $x \in \mathring{A}$, the continuity follows from the assumption on f. In the open set $E - A$, we can write $g(x) = h(x)/d(x, A)$ with $h(x) = \inf_{y \in A} (f(y)\, d(x, y))$, and as $d(x, A)$ is continuous and $\neq 0$ (by (3.8.9) and (3.11.8)), all we have to prove then (by (4.1.2) and (4.1.4)) is that h is continuous at every $x \in E - A$. Let $r = d(x, A)$; for $d(x, x') \leqslant \varepsilon < r$, we have $d(x, y) \leqslant d(x', y) + \varepsilon$, hence $h(x) \leqslant h(x') + 2\varepsilon$ (since $f(y) \leqslant 2$), and similarly $h(x') \leqslant h(x) + 2\varepsilon$, which proves the continuity of h. Finally, let us suppose x is a frontier point of A; given $\varepsilon > 0$, let $r > 0$

be such that for $y \in A \cap B(x; r)$, $|f(y) - f(x)| \leqslant \varepsilon$. Let $C = A \cap B(x; r)$, $D = A - C$; if $x' \in E - A$ and $d(x, x') \leqslant r/4$, we have, for each $y \in D$, $d(x', y) \geqslant d(x, y) - d(x, x') \geqslant 3r/4$, hence

$$\inf_{y \in D} (f(y)\, d(x', y)) \geqslant 3r/4;$$

on the other hand, $f(x)\, d(x', x) \leqslant 2d(x', x) \leqslant r/2$, and therefore

$$\inf_{y \in A} (f(y)\, d(x', y)) = \inf_{y \in C} f(y)\, d(x', y)).$$

But, as $f(x) - \varepsilon \leqslant f(y) \leqslant f(x) + \varepsilon$ for $y \in C$, and $\inf_{y \in C} d(x', y) = d(x', A)$, we have

$$(f(x) - \varepsilon)\, d(x', A) \leqslant \inf_{y \in A}(f(y)\, d(x', y)) \leqslant (f(x) + \varepsilon)\, d(x', A)$$

which proves that $|g(x') - f(x)| \leqslant \varepsilon$ for $x' \in E - A$ and $d(x, x') \leqslant r/4$; on the other hand, if $x' \in A$ and $d(x, x') \leqslant r/4$, $|g(x') - f(x)| = |f(x') - f(x)| \leqslant \varepsilon$, and this ends the proof.

(4.5.2) *Let* A, B *be two nonempty closed sets in a metric space* E, *such that* $A \cap B = \varnothing$. *Then there is a continuous function* f *defined in* E, *with values in* $[0, 1]$, *such that* $f(x) = 1$ *in* A *and* $f(x) = 0$ *in* B.

Apply **(4.5.1)** to the mapping of $A \cup B$ in **R**, equal to 0 in B and to 1 in A, which is continuous in $A \cup B$.

PROBLEMS

1. In a metric space E, let (F_n) be a sequence of closed sets, A the union of the F_n; if $x \notin A$, show that there exists a bounded continuous function $f \geqslant 0$ defined in E, such that $f(x) = 0$ and $f(y) > 0$ for each $y \in A$ (use **(4.5.2)** and **(7.2.1)**).

2. (a) Let E be a metric space such that every bounded set in E is relatively compact; show that E is locally compact and separable (use **(3.16.2)**).

(b) Conversely, let E be a locally compact, noncompact separable metric space, d the distance on E; let (U_n) be a sequence of relatively compact open subsets of E such that $\bar{U}_n \subset U_{n+1}$ and E is the union of the sequence (U_n) **(3.18.3)**. Show that there exists a continuous real-valued function f in E such that $f(x) \leqslant n$ for $x \in \bar{U}_n$ and $f(x) \geqslant n$ for $x \in E - \bar{U}_n$ (use **(4.5.2)**); the distance $d'(x, y) = d(x, y) + |f(x) - f(y)|$ is then topologically equivalent to d, and for d', any bounded set is relatively compact.

CHAPTER V

NORMED SPACES

▲ The language described in Chapter III corresponded to that part of our geometric intuition covering the notions which intuitively remain unaltered by "deformations"; here we get much closer to classical geometry, as lines, planes, etc. are studied from the topological point of view (we recall that the purely algebraic aspects of these notions constitute linear algebra, with which we assume the reader is familiar). It is in this context that the notion of series gets its natural definition; we have particularly emphasized the fact that for the most important type of convergent series (Section 5.3), the usual rules of commutativity and associativity of finite sums are still valid, which naturally leads to the conclusion that in that case, the ordering of the terms is completely irrelevant. This, for instance, enables one to formulate in a reasonable way the theorem on the product of two such series of real numbers (see (5.5.3)), in contrast to the nonsensical so-called "Cauchy multiplication" still taught in some textbooks, and which has no meaning for series other than power series of one variable.

▲ The fundamental results of this chapter are the continuity criterion (5.5.1), and F. Riesz's theorem characterizing finite dimensional spaces (5.9.4), which is the key to the elementary spectral theory developed in Chapter XI.

▲ Of course, this chapter is only an introduction to the general theory of Banach spaces and linear topological spaces, which will be further developed in Chapter XII, and which is fundamental for modern functional analysis.

1. NORMED SPACES AND BANACH SPACES

▲ In this and the following chapters, when we speak of a *vector space*, we always mean a vector space (of finite or infinite dimension) over the field of real numbers *or* over the field of complex numbers (such a space being respectively called *real* and *complex* vector space); when the field of scalars is not specified, it is understood that the definitions and results are valid in both cases.* When several vector spaces intervene in the same statement, it is understood (unless the contrary is specified) that they have the same field of scalars. A complex vector space E can also be considered as a real vector space by restricting the scalars to **R**; when it is necessary to make the distinction, we say that this real vector space E_0 is *underlying* the complex vector space E; if E has finite dimension n over **C**, E_0 has dimension $2n$ over **R**.

▲ A *norm* in a vector space E is a mapping (usually written $x \to \|x\|$, with eventual indices to the $\|..\|$) of E into the set **R** of real numbers, having the following properties:

• (I) $\|x\| \geqslant 0$ for every $x \in E$.

• (II) The relation $\|x\| = 0$ is equivalent to $x = 0$.

• (III) $\|\lambda x\| = |\lambda| \cdot \|x\|$ for any $x \in E$ and any scalar λ.

• (IV) $\|x + y\| \leqslant \|x\| + \|y\|$ for any pair of elements of E ("*triangle inequality*").

(5.1.1) *If* $x \to \|x\|$ *is a norm on the vector space* E, *then* $d(x, y) = \|x - y\|$ *is a distance on* E *such that* $d(x + z, y + z) = d(x, y)$ *and* $d(\lambda x, \lambda y) = |\lambda|\, d(x, y)$ *for any scalar* λ.

▲ The verification of the axioms of Section 3.1 is trivial.

▲ A *normed space* is a vector space E with a given norm on E; such a space is always considered as a metric space for the distance $\|x - y\|$. A *Banach space* is a normed space which is *complete*.

▲ If E is a complex normed vector space, $x \to \|x\|$ is also a norm on the underlying real vector space E_0, and the metric spaces E and E_0 are identical; hence if E is a Banach space, so is E_0.

Examples of Norms

(5.1.2) The examples given in (3.2.1), (3.2.2), (3.2.3), and (3.2.4) are real vector spaces, and the distances introduced in those examples are deduced from norms by the process of (5.1.1). The normed spaces thus defined in examples (3.2.1) to (3.2.3) are complete by (3.20.16) and (3.14.3), hence

* The product of a scalar λ and a vector x is indifferently written λx or $x\lambda$; 0 is the neutral element of the additive group of the vector space.

Banach spaces. Example (3.2.4) will be the object of a special study in Chapter VII, and we shall see it is also a Banach space.

(5.1.3) Examples corresponding to the preceding ones are obtained by replacing everywhere real numbers by complex numbers (and in example (3.2.2), squares $(x_i - y_i)^2$ by $|x_i - y_i|^2$).

(5.1.4) Let $\mathrm{I} = [a, b]$ be a closed bounded interval in $\mathbf{R}$, and $\mathrm{E} = \mathscr{C}_{\mathbf{R}}(\mathrm{I})$ the set of all real-valued continuous functions in I; E is a vector space ($f + g$ and λf being respectively the mappings $t \to f(t) + g(t)$ and $t \to \lambda f(t)$). If we write

$$\|f\|_1 = \int_a^b |f(t)|\, dt,$$

$\|f\|_1$ is a norm on E. The only axiom which is not trivially verified is (II), which follows from the mean value theorem (see Chapter VIII). It can be proved that E is *not* complete (see Problem 1).

For other important examples of norms, see Section 5.7 and Chapter VI.

(5.1.5) *If* E *is a real* (resp. *complex*) *normed space, the mapping* $(x, y) \to x + y$ *is uniformly continuous in* $\mathrm{E} \times \mathrm{E}$; *the mapping* $(\lambda, x) \to \lambda x$ *is continuous in* $\mathbf{R} \times \mathrm{E}$ (resp. $\mathbf{C} \times \mathrm{E}$); *the mapping* $x \to \lambda x$ *is uniformly continuous in* E.

The proofs follow the same pattern as those of (4.1.1) and (4.1.2); to prove for instance the continuity of $(\lambda, x) \to \lambda x$ at a point (λ_0, x_0), we use the formula $\|\lambda x - \lambda_0 x_0\| = \|\lambda_0(x - x_0) + (\lambda - \lambda_0)x_0 + (\lambda - \lambda_0)(x - x_0)\| \leqslant |\lambda_0| \cdot \|x - x_0\| + |\lambda - \lambda_0| \cdot \|x_0\| + |\lambda - \lambda_0| \cdot \|x - x_0\|$.

As a corollary of (5.1.5), it follows that any translation $x \to a + x$ and any homothetic mapping $x \to \lambda x$ ($\lambda \neq 0$) is a *homeomorphism* of E onto itself, for the inverse mapping is again a translation (resp. a homothetic mapping).

PROBLEMS

1. Let $\mathrm{I} = [0, 1]$, and let E be the normed space defined in (5.1.4).
(a) For any $n \geqslant 3$, let f_n be the continuous function defined in I, such that $f_n(t) = 1$ for $0 \leqslant t \leqslant 1/2$, $f_n(t) = 0$ for $1/2 + 1/n \leqslant t \leqslant 1$, and that $f_n(t)$ has the form $\alpha_n t + \beta_n$ in the interval $[1/2, 1/2 + 1/n]$ (with constants α_n and β_n to be determined). Show that in E,

(f_n) is a Cauchy sequence which does not converge (if there existed a limit g of (f_n) in E, show that one would necessarily have $g(t) = 1$ for $0 \leqslant t \leqslant \frac{1}{2}$ and $g(t) = 0$ for $\frac{1}{2} < t \leqslant 1$, which would violate the continuity of g).

(b) Show that the distance on E defined in **(5.1.4)** is not topologically equivalent to the distance defined in **(3.2.4)**. (Give an example of a sequence in E which tends to 0 for $\|f - g\|_1$, but has no limit for the distance defined in **(3.2.4)**.)

2. If A, B are two subsets of a normed space E, we denote by $A + B$ the set of all sums $a + b$, where $a \in A$, $b \in B$.

(a) Show that if one of the sets A, B is open, $A + B$ is open.

(b) Show that if both A and B are compact, $A + B$ is compact (use **(3.17.9)** and **(3.20.16)**).

(c) Show that if A is compact and B is closed, then $A + B$ is closed.

(d) Give an example of two closed subsets A, B of **R** such that $A + B$ is not closed (cf. the example given before **(3.4.1)**).

3. Let E be a normed space.

(a) Show that in E the closure of an open ball is the closed ball of same center and same radius, the interior of a closed ball is the open ball of same center and same radius, and the frontier of an open ball (or of a closed ball) is the sphere of same center and same radius (compare to Section **3.8**, Problem 4).

(b) Show that the open ball $B(0; r)$ is homeomorphic to E (consider the mapping $x \to rx/(1 + \|x\|)$).

4. In a normed space E, a *segment* is the image of the interval [0, 1] of **R** by the continuous mapping $t \to ta + (1 - t)b$, where $a \in E$ and $b \in E$; a and b are called the *extremities* of the segment. A segment is compact and connected. A *broken line* in E is a subset L of E such that there exists a finite sequence $(x_i)_{0 \leqslant i \leqslant n}$ of points of E having the property that if S_i is the segment of extremities x_i and x_{i+1} for $0 \leqslant i \leqslant n - 1$, L is the union of the S_i; the sequence (x_i) is said to *define* the broken line L (a given broken line may be defined in general by infinitely many finite sequences). If A is a subset of E, a, b two points of A, one says that a and b are *linked by a broken line in* A, if there is a sequence $(x_i)_{0 \leq i \leq n}$ such that $a = x_0$, $b = x_n$ and that the broken line L defined by that sequence is contained in A.

If any two points of A can be linked by a broken line in A, A is connected. Conversely, if $A \subset E$ is a connected open set, show that any two points of A can be linked by a broken line in A (prove that the set of points $y \in A$ which can be linked to a given point $a \in A$ by a broken line in A is both open and closed in A).

5. In a real vector space E, a *linear variety* V is a set of the form $a + M$, where M is a linear subspace of E; the *dimension* (resp. *codimension*) of V is by definition the dimension (resp. codimension) of M. If $b \notin V$ and if V has finite dimension p (resp. finite codimension q), the smallest linear variety W containing both b and V has finite dimension $p + 1$ (resp. finite codimension $q - 1$).

Let A be an open connected subset of a real normed space E, and let (V_n) be a denumerable sequence of linear varieties in E, each of which has codimension $\geqslant 2$; show that if B is the union of the V_n, $A \cap (E - B)$ is connected. (Hint: Use Problem 4; if L is a broken line linking two points a, b of $A \cap (E - B)$ *in* A, prove that there exists another broken line L′ "close" to L, contained in $A \cap (E - B)$. To do that, observe that if $x \in E - B$, the set of points $y \in E$ such that the segment of extremities x, y does not meet any V_n, is dense in E, using **(2.2.17)**.)

In particular, if the dimension of E is $\geqslant 2$, and if D is a denumerable subset of E, $A \cap (E - D)$ is connected.

6. If E is a real normed space of dimension $\geqslant 2$, show that an open nonempty subset of E cannot be homeomorphic to any subset of **R** (use Problem 5).

7. (a) Show that in a normed space E, a ball cannot contain a linear variety (Problem 5) of dimension >0.

(b) Let (E_n) be an infinite sequence of normed spaces having dimension >0; show that in the metric space $E = \prod_{n=0}^{\infty} E_n$, there is no norm such that the distance $\|x - y\|$ is topologically equivalent to the distance defined in Problem 7 of Section 3.20 (where d_n is taken as a bounded distance on E_n equivalent to the distance defined on E_n by the norm on that space). (Use (a).)

2. SERIES IN A NORMED SPACE

▲Let E be a normed space. A pair of sequences $(x_n)_{n \geqslant 0}$, $(s_n)_{n \geqslant 0}$ is called a *series* if the elements x_n, s_n are linked by the relations $s_n = x_0 + x_1 + \cdots + x_n$ for any n, or, what is equivalent, by $x_0 = s_0$, $x_n = s_n - s_{n-1}$ for $n \geqslant 1$; x_n is called the *n*th *term* and s_n the *n*th *partial sum* of the series; the series will often be called the *series of general term* x_n, or simply the *series* (x_n) (and even sometimes, by abuse of language, *the series* $\sum_{n=0}^{\infty} x_n$). The series is said to *converge to s* if $\lim_{n \to \infty} s_n = s$; s is then called the *sum* of the series and written $s = x_0 + \cdots + x_n + \cdots$ or $s = \sum_{n=0}^{\infty} x_n$; $r_n = s - s_n$ is called the *n*th *remainder* of the series; it is the sum of the series having as kth term x_{n+k}; by definition $\lim_{n \to \infty} r_n = 0$. If $r_p = s - s_p$ then $\forall \varepsilon > 0$ $\exists n_0$ $\forall n \geqslant n_0$ $|s_n - s| < \varepsilon$. but $s_n = s_p + s'_n$ or $|s'_n - (s - s_p)| < \varepsilon$

(5.2.1) (Cauchy's criterion) *If the series of general term x_n is convergent, then for any $\varepsilon > 0$ there is an integer n_0 such that, for $n \geqslant n_0$ and $p \geqslant 0$, $\|s_{n+p} - s_n\| = \|x_{n+1} + \cdots + x_{n+p}\| \leqslant \varepsilon$. Conversely, if that condition is satisfied and if the space* E *is complete, then the series of general term x_n is convergent.*

▲This is merely the application of Cauchy's criterion to the sequence (s_n) (see Section 3.14).

▲As an obvious consequence of (5.2.1) it follows that if the series (x_n) is convergent, $\lim_{n \to \infty} x_n = \lim_{n \to \infty} (s_n - s_{n-1}) = 0$; but that necessary condition is by no means sufficient.

(5.2.2) *If the series* (x_n) *and* (x'_n) *are convergent and have sums* s, s', *then the series* $(x_n + x'_n)$ *converges to the sum* $s + s'$ *and the series* (λx_n) *to the sum* λs *for any scalar* λ.

Follows at once from the definition and from (5.1.5).

(5.2.3) *If* (x_n) *and* (x'_n) *are two series such that* $x'_n = x_n$ *except for a finite number of indices, they are both convergent or both nonconvergent.*

For the series $(x'_n - x_n)$ is convergent, since all its terms are 0 except for a finite number of indices.

(5.2.4) *Let* (k_n) *be a strictly increasing sequence of integers* $\geqslant 0$ *with* $k_0 = 0$; *if the series* (x_n) *converges to* s, *and if* $y_n = \sum_{p=k_n}^{k_{n+1}-1} x_p$, *then the series* (y_n) *converges also to* s.

This follows at once from the relation $\sum_{i=0}^{n} y_i = \sum_{j=0}^{k_{n+1}-1} x_j$ and from (3.13.10).

PROBLEMS

1. Let (a_n) be an arbitrary sequence in a normed space E; show that there exists a sequence (x_n) of points of E such that $\lim_{n\to 0} x_n = 0$, and a strictly increasing sequence (k_n) of integers such that $a_n = x_0 + x_1 + \cdots + x_{k_n}$ for every n.
2. Let σ be a bijection of **N** onto itself, and for each n, let $\varphi(n)$ be the smallest number of intervals $[a, b]$ in **N** such that the union of these intervals is $\sigma([0, n])$
   (a) Suppose φ is *bounded* in **N**. Let (x_n) be a convergent series in a normed space E; show that the series $(x_{\sigma(n)})$ is convergent in E and that $\sum_{n=0}^{\infty} x_n = \sum_{n=0}^{\infty} x_{\sigma(n)}$.
   (b) Suppose φ is unbounded in **N**. Define a series (x_n) of real numbers which is convergent, but such that the series $(x_{\sigma(n)})$ is not convergent in **R**. (Define by induction on k a strictly increasing sequence (m_k) of integers having the following properties:
      (1) If n_k is the largest element of $\sigma([0, m_k])$, then $[0, n_k]$ is contained in $\sigma([0, m_{k+1}])$.
      (2) $\varphi(m_k) \geqslant k + 1$.
   Define then x_n for $n_k < n \leqslant n_{k+1}$ such that $x_n = 0$ except for $2k$ conveniently chosen values of n, at each of which x_n is alternately equal to $1/k$ or to $-1/k$.)
3. Let (x_n) be a convergent series in a normed space E; let σ be a bijection of **N** onto itself, and let

$$r(n) = |\sigma(n) - n| \cdot \sup_{m \geqslant n} \|x_m\|.$$

Show that if $\lim_{n\to\infty} r(n) = 0$, the series $(x_{\sigma(n)})$ is convergent in E and that $\sum_{n=0}^{\infty} x_n = \sum_{n=0}^{\infty} x_{\sigma(n)}$.

(Evaluate the difference $\sum_{k=0}^{n} x_{\sigma(n)}) - \sum_{k=0}^{n} x_k$ for large n.)

4. Let (x_{mn}) $(m \geqslant 0, n \geqslant 0)$ be a double sequence of points of a normed space E. Suppose that: (1) for each $m \geqslant 0$, the series $x_{m0} + x_{m1} + \cdots + x_{mn} + \cdots$ is convergent in E; let y_m be its sum, and let $r_{mn} = x_{mn} + x_{m,n+1} + \cdots$; (2) for each $n \geqslant 0$, the series $r_{0n} + r_{1n} + \cdots + r_{mn} + \cdots$ is convergent in E; let t_n be its sum.

(a) Show that for each $n \geqslant 0$, the series $x_{0n} + x_{1n} + \cdots + x_{mn} + \cdots$ is convergent; let z_n be its sum.

(b) In order that $\sum_{m=0}^{\infty} y_m = \sum_{n=0}^{\infty} z_n$, it is necessary and sufficient that $\lim_{n\to\infty} t_n = 0$.

5. (a) Show that the series $\sum_{n\geqslant 1,\, n\neq m} \frac{1}{m^2 - n^2}$ is convergent and has a sum equal to $-3/4m^2$ (decompose the rational fraction $1/(m^2 - x^2)$).

(b) Let $u_{mn} = \frac{1}{m^2 - n^2}$ if $m \neq n$, and $u_{nn} = 0$; show that

$$\sum_{m=0}^{\infty}\left(\sum_{n=0}^{\infty} u_{mn}\right) = -\sum_{n=0}^{\infty}\left(\sum_{m=0}^{\infty} u_{mn}\right) \neq 0.$$

6. If f is a function defined in $\mathbf{N} \times \mathbf{N}$, with values in a metric space, we denote by $\lim_{m\to\infty,\, n\to\infty} f(m, n)$ the limit of f (when it exists) at the point $(+\infty, +\infty)$ of $\bar{\mathbf{R}} \times \bar{\mathbf{R}}$, with respect to the subspace $\mathbf{N} \times \mathbf{N}$ (Section 3.13). Let (x_{mn}) be a double sequence of real numbers, and let $s_{mn} = \sum_{h\leqslant m,\, k\leqslant n} x_{hk}$.

(a) If $\lim_{m\to\infty,\, n\to\infty} s_{mn}$ exists, then $\lim_{m\to\infty,\, n\to\infty} x_{mn} = 0$. Give an example in which $x_{nm} = x_{mn}$, $x_{m,\,2n} = -x_{m,\,2n+1} = -x_{m+1,2n}$ for $m \geqslant 2n+1$, $x_{2n,\,2n} = 0$, such that $\lim_{m\to\infty,\, n\to\infty} s_{mn} = 0$, and none of the series $x_{m0} + x_{m1} + \cdots + x_{mn} + \cdots$, $x_{0n} + x_{1n} + \cdots + x_{mn} + \cdots$ is convergent.

(b) Give an example in which $x_{mn} = 0$ except if $m = n+1$, $m = n$ or $n = m+1$ (hence all series $\sum_{n=0}^{\infty} x_{mn}$, $\sum_{m=0}^{\infty} x_{mn}$ are convergent), $\sum_{n=0}^{\infty} x_{mn} = \sum_{m=0}^{\infty} x_{mn} = 0$ for all indices m, n, but $\lim_{m\to\infty,\, n\to\infty} s_{mn}$ does not exist.

3. ABSOLUTELY CONVERGENT SERIES

(5.3.1) *In order that a series (x_n) of positive numbers be convergent it is necessary and sufficient that for a strictly increasing sequence (k_n) of integers $\geqslant 0$, the sequence (s_{k_n}) of partial sums be majorized, and then the sum $s = \sum_{n=0}^{\infty} x_n$ is equal to $\sup_n s_{k_n}$.*

▲ The assumption $x_n \geqslant 0$ is equivalent to $s_{n-1} \leqslant s_n$, and then the result follows at once from (4.2.1).

▲ In a Banach space E, an *absolutely convergent series* (x_n) is a series such that the series of general term $\|x_n\|$ is convergent.

(5.3.2) *In a Banach space* E, *an absolutely convergent series* (x_n) *is convergent, and* $\left\|\sum_{n=0}^{\infty} x_n\right\| \leqslant \sum_{n=0}^{\infty} \|x_n\|$.

▲ By assumption, for any $\varepsilon > 0$, there is an integer n_0 such that for $n \geqslant n_0$ and any $p \geqslant 0$, $\|x_{n+1}\| + \cdots + \|x_{n+p}\| \leqslant \varepsilon$; hence

$$\|x_{n+1} + \cdots + x_{n+p}\| \leqslant \varepsilon,$$

which proves the convergence of (x_n) by (5.2.1). Moreover, for any n, $\|x_0 + \cdots + x_n\| \leqslant \|x_0\| + \cdots + \|x_n\|$; the inequality $\left\|\sum_{n=0}^{\infty} x_n\right\| \leqslant \sum_{n=0}^{\infty} \|x_n\|$ then follows from the principle of extension of inequalities (3.15.4).

(5.3.3) *If* (x_n) *is an absolutely convergent series and* σ *a bijection of* **N** *onto itself, then* (y_n), *with* $y_n = x_{\sigma(n)}$, *is an absolutely convergent series, and* $\sum_{n=0}^{\infty} x_n = \sum_{n=0}^{\infty} y_n$ ("commutativity" of absolutely convergent series).

▲ Let $s_n = \sum_{k=0}^{n} x_k$, $s'_n = \sum_{k=0}^{n} y_k$; for each n, let m be the largest integer in the set $\sigma([0, n])$; then by definition $\sum_{k=0}^{n} \|y_k\| \leqslant \sum_{i=0}^{m} \|x_i\|$, and (5.3.1) shows that (y_n) is absolutely convergent. Moreover, for any $\varepsilon > 0$, let n_0 be such that $\|x_{n-1}\| + \cdots + \|x_{n+p}\| \leqslant \varepsilon$ for $n \geqslant n_0$ and $p \geqslant 0$; then if m_0 is the largest integer in $\sigma^{-1}([0, n_0])$, we have $\|y_{n+1}\| + \cdots + \|y_{n+p}\| \leqslant \varepsilon$ for $n \geqslant m_0$, $p \geqslant 0$; furthermore the difference $s'_{m_0} - s_{n_0}$ is the sum of terms x_j with $j > n_0$, hence $\|s'_{m_0} - s_{n_0}\| \leqslant \varepsilon$; therefore, for $n \geqslant n_0$ and $n \geqslant m_0$, $\|s'_n - s_n\| \leqslant 3\varepsilon$, which proves that $\sum_{n=0}^{\infty} x_n = \sum_{n=0}^{\infty} y_n$.

▲ Let A be any denumerable set. We say that a family $(x_\alpha)_{\alpha \in A}$ of elements of a Banach space E *is absolutely summable* if, for a bijection φ of **N** onto A, the series $(x_{\varphi(n)})$ is absolutely convergent; it follows from (5.3.3) that this property is independent of the particular bijection φ, and that we can define the *sum* of the family $(x_\alpha)_{\alpha \in A}$ as $\sum_{n=0}^{\infty} x_{\varphi(n)}$, which we also write $\sum_{\alpha \in A} x_\alpha$. As any denumerable set $S \subset E$ can be considered as a family (with S as the set of indices) we can also speak of an *absolutely summable (denumerable) subset* of E and of its *sum*.

(5.3.4) *In order that a denumerable family* $(x_\alpha)_{\alpha\in A}$ *of elements of a Banach space* E *be absolutely summable, a necessary and sufficient condition is that the finite sums* $\sum_{\alpha\in J} \|x_\alpha\|$ (J $\subset$ A *and finite*) *be bounded. Then, for any* $\varepsilon > 0$, *there exists a finite subset* H *of* A *such that, for any finite subset* K *of* A *for which* $H \cap K = \varnothing$, $\sum_{\alpha\in K} \|x_\alpha\| \leqslant \varepsilon$, *and for any finite subset* $L \supset H$ *of* A, $\|\sum_{\alpha\in A} x_\alpha - \sum_{\alpha\in L} x_\alpha\| \leqslant 2\varepsilon$.

The first two assertions follow at once from the definition and from (5.3.1). Then, for any finite subset $L \supset H$, we can write $L = H \cup K$ with $H \cap K = \varnothing$, hence $\|\sum_{\alpha\in L} x_\alpha - \sum_{\alpha\in H} x_\alpha\| \leqslant \varepsilon$; from the definition of the sum $\sum_{\alpha\in A} x_\alpha$ it follows (after ordering A by an arbitrary bijection of **N** onto A) that $\|\sum_{\alpha\in A} x_\alpha - \sum_{\alpha\in H} x_\alpha\| \leqslant \varepsilon$, hence $\|\sum_{\alpha\in A} x_\alpha - \sum_{\alpha\in L} x_\alpha\| \leqslant 2\varepsilon$.

(5.3.5) *Let* $(x_\alpha)_{\alpha\in A}$ *be an absolutely summable family of elements of a Banach space* E. *Then, for every subset* B *of* A, *the family* $(x_\alpha)_{\alpha\in B}$ *is absolutely summable, and* $\sum_{\alpha\in B} \|x_\alpha\| \leqslant \sum_{\alpha\in A} \|x_\alpha\|$.

If B is finite, the result immediately follows from the definition. If B is infinite, then $\sum_{\alpha\in J} \|x_\alpha\| \leqslant \sum_{\alpha\in A} \|x_\alpha\|$ for each finite subset J of B, and the result follows from (5.3.4).

(5.3.6) *Let* $(x_\alpha)_{\alpha\in A}$ *be an absolutely summable family of elements of a Banach space* E. *Let* (B_n) *be an infinite sequence of nonempty subsets of* A, *such that* $A = \bigcup_n B_n$, *and* $B_p \cap B_q = \varnothing$ *for* $p \neq q$; *then, if* $z_n = \sum_{\alpha\in B_n} x_\alpha$, *the series* (z_n) *is absolutely convergent, and* $\sum_{n=0}^{\infty} z_n = \sum_{\alpha\in A} x_\alpha$ ("associativity" of absolutely convergent series).

Given any $\varepsilon > 0$ and any integer n, there exists, by (5.3.2), for each $k \leqslant n$, a finite subset J_k of B_k such that $\|z_k\| \leqslant \sum_{\alpha\in J_k} \|x_\alpha\| + \varepsilon/(n+1)$; if $J = \bigcup_{k=0}^{n} J_k$, we have therefore $\sum_{k=0}^{n} \|z_k\| \leqslant \sum_{\alpha\in J} \|x_\alpha\| + \varepsilon \leqslant \sum_{\alpha\in A} \|x_\alpha\| + \varepsilon$; (5.3.1) then proves that the series (z_n) is absolutely convergent. Moreover, let H be a finite subset of A such that, for any finite subset K of A such that $H \cap K = \varnothing$, $\sum_{\alpha\in K} \|x_\alpha\| \leqslant \varepsilon$, whence, for any finite subset L of A containing H, $\|\sum_{\alpha\in A} x_\alpha - \sum_{\alpha\in L} x_\alpha\| \leqslant 2\varepsilon$ (see (5.3.4)). Let n_0 be the largest integer such that $H \cap B_{n_0} \neq \varnothing$, and let n be an arbitrary integer $\geqslant n_0$. For each $k \leqslant n$, let J_k be a finite subset of B_k containing $H \cap B_k$, and such that for any finite subset L_k of B_k containing J_k, we have $\|z_k - \sum_{\alpha \in L_k} x_\alpha\| \leqslant \varepsilon/(n+1)$ (5.3.4). Then, if $L = \bigcup_{k=0}^{n} L_k$, we have $\left\|\sum_{k=0}^{n} z_k - \sum_{\alpha \in L} x_\alpha\right\| \leqslant \varepsilon$, and as $L \supset H$, it follows from the definition of H that $\left\|\sum_{k=0}^{n} z_k - \sum_{\alpha \in A} x_\alpha\right\| \leqslant 3\varepsilon$, which ends the proof.

There is a similar (and easier) result when A is decomposed in a *finite* number of subsets B_k $(1 \leqslant k \leqslant n)$; moreover, in that case, there is a converse to (5.3.6), namely, if each of the families $(x_\alpha)_{\alpha \in B_k}$ is absolutely summable, so is $(x_\alpha)_{\alpha \in A}$; the proof follows, by induction on n, from the criterion (5.3.4).

PROBLEMS

1. Let (d_n) be a sequence of real numbers $d_n \geqslant 0$, such that the series (d_n) is not convergent (i.e., $\lim_{n\to\infty} \sum_{k=0}^{n} d_k = +\infty$). What can be said of the convergence of the following series:

$$\frac{d_n}{1+d_n}; \qquad \frac{d_n}{1+nd_n}; \qquad \frac{d_n}{1+n^2 d_n}; \qquad \frac{d_n}{1+d_n^2}?$$

2. Let (u_n) be a convergent series of real numbers, which is not absolutely convergent, and let $s = \sum_{n=0}^{\infty} u_n$. For each number $s' \geqslant s$, show that there exists a bijection σ of **N** onto itself such that $\sigma(n) = n$ for all n such that $u_n \geqslant 0$, and that $\sum_{n=0}^{\infty} u_{\sigma(n)} = s'$. (Show by induction that for each n there is a bijection σ_n of **N** onto itself such that $\sigma_n(k) = k$ for all k such that $u_k \geqslant 0$ and that, if $u_k^{(n)} = u_{\sigma_n(k)}$, there is an index p_n having the property that, for $k \geqslant p_n$

$$\left|s' - \sum_{i=0}^{k} u_i^{(n)}\right| \leqslant 1/n;$$

furthermore, σ_{n+1} is such that $\sigma_{n+1}(k) = \sigma_n(k)$ for all k such that $\sigma_n(k) < p_n$ and all k such that $u_k \leqslant -1/n$.)

3. Show that for every finite family $(x_i)_{i \in I}$ of points of the product space $\mathbf{R}^n$ (with the norm $\|x\| = \sup |\xi_k|$ for $x = (\xi_k)_{1 \leqslant k \leqslant n}$), one has $\sum_{i \in I} \|x_i\| \leqslant 2n \cdot \sup_{J \subset I} \|\sum_{i \in J} x_i\|$ (consider first the case $n = 1$).

4. In a normed space E, a series (x_n) is said to be *commutatively convergent* if, for every bijection σ of **N** onto itself, the series $(x_{\sigma(n)})$ is convergent.

   (a) In order that a convergent series (x_n) be commutatively convergent, it is necessary and sufficient that for every $\varepsilon > 0$, there exist a finite subset J of **N** such that, for any subset H of **N** for which $J \cap H = \varnothing$, $\|\sum_{n \in H} x_n\| \leqslant \varepsilon$. When that condition is satisfied, the sum $\sum_{n=0}^{\infty} x_{\sigma(n)}$ is independent of σ. (To prove the last assertion, and the sufficiency of the condition, proceed as in (5.3.3). To show that the condition is necessary, use contradiction: there would exist an $\alpha > 0$ and an infinity of finite subsets H_k ($k = 1, 2, \ldots$) of $\mathbf{N}$, no two of which have common points, and such that $\|\sum_{n \in H_k} x_n\| \geqslant \alpha$ for each k; starting from the existence of these subsets, define σ for which the series $(x_{\sigma(n)})$ is not convergent.)

(b) Suppose the series (x_n) is such that, for any strictly increasing sequence (n_k) of integers, the series (x_{n_k}) is convergent. Show that the series (x_n) is commutatively convergent (use the same argument as in (a)). Prove the converse when E is complete (use the criterion proved in (a)).

(c) If $E = \mathbf{R}^n$, show that any commutatively convergent series in E is absolutely convergent (use Problem 3 and the criterion of (a)).

(d) Extend the associativity property (5.3.6) to commutatively convergent series.

5. Let E be the real vector space consisting of all infinite sequences $x = (\xi_n)_{n \geqslant 0}$ of real numbers, such that $\lim_{n \to \infty} \xi_n = 0$. For any $x \in E$, let $\|x\| = \sup_n |\xi_n|$.

(a) Show that $\|x\|$ is a norm on E, and that E, with that norm, is a Banach space (the "space (c_0)" of Banach).

(b) Let e_m be the sequence $(\delta_{mn})_{n \geqslant 0}$, with $\delta_{mn} = 0$ if $m \neq n$, $\delta_{mm} = 1$. Show that for every point $x = (\xi_n) \in E$, the series $\sum_{n=0}^{\infty} \xi_n e_n$ is commutatively convergent in E, and that its sum is x; give examples in which the series is *not* absolutely convergent.

6. (a) Let (s_n) an increasing sequence of numbers >0 which tends to $+\infty$. Show that the series of general term $(s_n - s_{n-1})/s_n$ has an infinite sum. For each number $\rho > 0$, show that the series of general term $(s_n - s_{n-1})/s_n s_{n-1}^{\rho}$ is convergent; compare to the series of general term

$$\frac{1}{s_{n-1}^{\rho}} - \frac{1}{s_n^{\rho}}$$

(b) Let $(u_n)_{n \geqslant 0}$ be a sequence of numbers $\geqslant 0$ such that $u_0 > 0$, and let $s_n = \sum_{k=0}^{\infty} u_k$ for each $n \geqslant 0$. Show that a necessary and sufficient condition for the series of general term u_n to be convergent is that the series of general term u_n/s_n be convergent (use (a)).

7. Let (u_n) be a convergent series of numbers $\geqslant 0$. Show that there exists an increasing sequence (c_n) of numbers >0, such that $\lim_{n \to \infty} c_n = +\infty$, and that the series $(c_n u_n)$ is convergent.

8. Let (u_n) be a convergent series of numbers $\geqslant 0$. Show that

$$\lim_{n \to \infty} \frac{u_1 + 2n_2 + \cdots + nu_n}{n} = 0$$

and

$$\sum_{n=1}^{\infty} \frac{u_1 + 2u_2 + \cdots + nu_n}{n(n+1)} = \sum_{n=1}^{\infty} u_n$$

$$\left(\text{write } \frac{1}{n(n+1)} = \frac{1}{n} - \frac{1}{n+1}\right).$$

4. SUBSPACES AND FINITE PRODUCTS OF NORMED SPACES

▲ Let E be a normed space, F a *vector subspace* of E (i.e. a subset such that $x \in \mathrm{F}$ and $y \in \mathrm{F}$ imply $\alpha x + \beta y \in \mathrm{F}$ for any pair of scalars α, β); the restriction to F of the norm of E is clearly a norm on F, which defines on F the distance and topology induced by those of E. When talking of a "subspace" of E, we will in general mean a *vector* subspace with the induced norm. If E is a Banach space, any closed subspace F of E is a Banach space by (3.14.5); conversely, if a subspace F of a normed space E is a Banach space, F is closed in E by (3.14.4).

(5.4.1) *If* F *is a vector subspace of a normed space* E, *its closure* $\bar{\mathrm{F}}$ *in* E *is a vector subspace.*

▲ By assumption, the mapping $(x, y) \to x + y$ of E × E into E maps F × F into F, hence maps $\overline{\mathrm{F} \times \mathrm{F}}$ into $\bar{\mathrm{F}}$, by (3.11.4); as $\overline{\mathrm{F} \times \mathrm{F}} = \bar{\mathrm{F}} \times \bar{\mathrm{F}}$ by (3.20.3), the relations $x \in \bar{\mathrm{F}}$, $y \in \bar{\mathrm{F}}$ imply $x + y \in \bar{\mathrm{F}}$. Using the continuity of $(\lambda, x) \to \lambda x$, we similarly show that $x \in \bar{\mathrm{F}}$ implies $\lambda x \in \bar{\mathrm{F}}$ for any scalar λ.

▲ We say that a subset A of a normed space E is *total* if the (finite) linear combinations of vectors of A form a *dense* subspace of E; we say that a family (x_α) is *total* if the set of its elements is total.

▲ Let $\mathrm{E}_1, \mathrm{E}_2$ be two normed spaces, and consider the product vector space $\mathrm{E} = \mathrm{E}_1 \times \mathrm{E}_2$ (with $(x_1, x_2) + (y_1, y_2) = (x_1 + y_1, x_2 + y_2)$ and $\lambda(x_1, x_2) = (\lambda x_1, \lambda x_2)$). It is immediately verified that the mapping $(x_1, x_2) \to \sup(\|x_1\|, \|x_2\|)$ is a *norm* on E, which defines on E the distance corresponding to the distances on $\mathrm{E}_1, \mathrm{E}_2$, and therefore the topology of the product space $\mathrm{E}_1 \times \mathrm{E}_2$ as defined in Section 3.20. The "natural" injections $x_1 \to (x_1, 0)$, $x_2 \to (0, x_2)$ are linear isometries of E_1 and E_2 respectively onto the closed subspaces $\mathrm{E}_1' = \mathrm{E}_1 \times \{0\}$, $\mathrm{E}_2' = \{0\} \times \mathrm{E}_2$ of E (3.20.11), and E is the direct sum of its subspaces $\mathrm{E}_1', \mathrm{E}_2'$, which are often identified to $\mathrm{E}_1, \mathrm{E}_2$ respectively.

▲ Conversely, suppose a normed space E is a *direct sum* of two vector subspaces $\mathrm{F}_1, \mathrm{F}_2$; each $x \in \mathrm{E}$ can be written in a unique way $x = p_1(x) + p_2(x)$, with $p_1(x) \in \mathrm{F}_1$, $p_2(x) \in \mathrm{F}_2$, and p_1, p_2 are linear mappings of E into $\mathrm{F}_1, \mathrm{F}_2$ respectively (the "projections" of E onto $\mathrm{F}_1, \mathrm{F}_2$). The "natural" mapping $(y_1, y_2) \to y_1 + y_2$ is a linear bijection of the product space $\mathrm{F}_1 \times \mathrm{F}_2$ onto E, which is continuous (by (5.1.5)), but *not necessarily bicontinuous* (see Section 6.5, Problem 2).

(5.4.2) *In order that the mapping* $(y_1, y_2) \to y_1 + y_2$ *be a homeomorphism of* $F_1 \times F_2$ *onto* E, *a necessary and sufficient condition is that one of the linear mappings* p_1, p_2 *be continuous.*

▲ Observe that as $x = p_1(x) + p_2(x)$, if one of the mappings p_1, p_2 is continuous, so is the other. The mapping $x \to (p_1(x), p_2(x))$ of E onto $F_1 \times F_2$ being the inverse mapping to $(y_1, y_2) \to y_1 + y_2$, the conclusion follows from (3.20.4).

When the condition of (5.4.2) is satisfied, E is called the *topological direct sum* of F_1, F_2; a subspace F of E such that there exists another subspace G for which E is the topological direct sum of F and G is called a *topological direct summand* of E, and any subspace G having the preceding property is called a *topological supplement* to F. Any topological direct summand is necessarily closed (by (3.20.11)), but there may exist closed subspaces which are not topological direct summands (although any subspace always has an *algebraic* supplement in E); for examples of such spaces see Bourbaki [6], Chapter IV, p. 119, Exercise 5c, and p. 122, Exercise 17b.

The definitions and results relative to the product of two normed spaces are immediately extended to the product of a finite number n of normed spaces (by induction on n).

5. CONDITION OF CONTINUITY OF A MULTILINEAR MAPPING

(5.5.1) *Let* $E_1, \dots, E_n$ *be n normed spaces,* F *a normed space, u a multilinear mapping of* $E_1 \times \cdots \times E_n$ *into* F. *In order that u be continuous, a necessary and sufficient condition is the existence of a number* $a > 0$ *such that, for any* $(x_1, \dots, x_n) \in E_1 \times E_2 \times \cdots \times E_n$,

$$\|u(x_1, x_2, \dots, x_n)\| \leqslant a \cdot \|x_1\| \cdot \|x_2\| \cdots \|x_n\|.$$

We write the proof for $n = 2$.

▲ 1. *Sufficiency.* To prove u is continuous at any point (c_1, c_2), we write $u(x_1, x_2) - u(c_1, c_2) = u(x_1 - c_1, x_2) + u(c_1, x_2 - c_2)$, hence $\|u(x_1, x_2) - u(c_1, c_2)\| \leqslant a(\|x_1 - c_1\| \cdot \|x_2\| + \|c_1\| \cdot \|x_2 - c_2\|)$. For any δ such that $0 < \delta < 1$, suppose $\|x_1 - c_1\| \leqslant \delta$, $\|x_2 - c_2\| \leqslant \delta$, hence $\|x_2\| \leqslant \|c_2\| + 1$. We therefore have

$$\|u(x_1, x_2) - u(c_1, c_2)\| \leqslant a(\|c_1\| + \|c_2\| + 1)\delta,$$

which is arbitrarily small with δ.

▲ 2. *Necessity.* If u is continuous at the point $(0, 0)$, there exists a ball B: $\sup(\|x_1\|, \|x_2\|) \leqslant r$ in $E_1 \times E_2$ such that the relation $(x_1, x_2) \in B$ implies $\|u(x_1, x_2)\| \leqslant 1$. Let now (x_1, x_2) be arbitrary; suppose first $x_1 \neq 0$, $x_2 \neq 0$; then if $z_1 = rx_1/\|x_1\|$, $z_2 = rx_2/\|x_2\|$, we have $\|z_1\| = \|z_2\| = r$, and therefore $\|u(z_1, z_2)\| \leqslant 1$. But $u(z_1, z_2) = r^2 u(x_1, x_2)/\|x_1\| \cdot \|x_2\|$, and therefore $\|u(x_1, x_2)\| \leqslant a \cdot \|x_1\| \cdot \|x_2\|$ with $a = 1/r^2$. If $x_1 = 0$ or $x_2 = 0$, $u(x_1, x_2) = 0$, hence the preceding inequality still holds.

(5.5.2) *Let u be a continuous linear mapping of a Banach space* E *into a Banach space* F. *If (x_n) is a convergent* (resp. *absolutely convergent*) *series in* E, *$(u(x_n))$ is a convergent* (resp. *absolutely convergent*) *series in* F, *and* $\sum_n u(x_n) = u(\sum_n x_n)$.

The convergence of the series $(u(x_n))$ and the relation $\sum_n u(x_n) = u(\sum_n x_n)$ follow at once from the definition of a continuous linear mapping (see (3.13.4)). From (5.5.1) it follows that there is a constant $a > 0$ such that $\|u(x_n)\| \leqslant a \cdot \|x_n\|$ for every n, hence the series $(u(x_n))$ is absolutely convergent by (5.3.1) if the series (x_n) is absolutely convergent.

(5.5.3) *Let* E, F, G *be three Banach spaces, u a continuous bilinear mapping of* E × F *into* G. *If (x_n) is an absolutely convergent series in* E, *(y_n) an absolutely convergent series in* F, *then the family $(u(x_m, y_n))$ is absolutely summable and*

$$\sum_{m,n} u(x_m, y_n) = u\Big(\sum_n x_n, \sum_n y_n\Big).$$

Using the criterion (5.3.4), we have to prove that for any p, the sums $\sum_{m \leqslant p,\, n \leqslant p} \|u(x_m, y_n)\|$ are bounded. But from (5.5.1), there is an $a > 0$ such that $\|u(x_m, y_n)\| \leqslant a\|x_m\| \cdot \|y_n\|$, hence

$$\sum_{m \leqslant p,\, n \leqslant p} \|u(x_m, y_n)\| \leqslant a \sum_{m \leqslant p,\, n \leqslant p} \|x_m\| \cdot \|y_n\| = a\Big(\sum_{n=0}^{p} \|x_n\|\Big)\Big(\sum_{n=0}^{p} \|y_n\|\Big)$$

which is bounded, due to the assumptions on (x_n) and (y_n). Moreover from (5.3.6) and (5.5.2) it follows that, if $s = \sum_n x_n$, $s' = \sum_n y_n$,

$$\sum_{m,n} u(x_m, y_n) = \sum_{m=0}^{\infty}\Big(\sum_{n=0}^{\infty} u(x_m, y_n)\Big) = \sum_{m=0}^{\infty} u(x_m, s') = u(s, s').$$

(5.5.4) *Let* E *be a normed space,* F *a Banach space,* G *a dense subspace of* E, f *a continuous linear mapping of* G *into* F. *Then there is a unique continuous linear mapping* $\bar{f}$ *of* E *into* F *which is an extension of* f.

From (5.5.1) it follows that f is *uniformly continuous in* G, since $\|f(x)-f(y)\| = \|f(x-y)\| \leqslant a \cdot \|x-y\|$; hence by (3.15.6) there is a unique continuous extension $\bar{f}$ of f to E. The fact that $\bar{f}$ is linear follows from (5.1.5) and the principle of extension of identities (3.15.2).

PROBLEMS

1. Let u be a mapping of a normed space E into a normed space F such that $u(x+y) = u(x)+u(y)$ for any pair of points x, y of E and that u is bounded in the ball B(0; 1) in E; show that u is linear and continuous. (Observe that $u(rx) = ru(x)$ for rational r, and that for $y \in \mathrm{B}(0; 1)$, $\left\|u\left(x+\frac{1}{n}y\right) - u(x)\right\| \leqslant \frac{1}{n}\|u(y)\|$ for every integer $n \geqslant 1$; conclude that $u(\lambda x) = \lambda u(x)$ for every real λ, by taking $y = n(r-\lambda)x$, where r is rational.)
2. Let E, F be two normed spaces, u a linear mapping of E into F. Show that if for every sequence (x_n) in E such that $\lim_{n\to\infty} x_n = 0$, the sequence $(u(x_n))$ is bounded in F, then u is continuous. (Give an indirect proof.)
3. (a) Let a, b be two points of a normed space E. Let B_1 be the set of all $x \in \mathrm{E}$ such that $\|x-a\| = \|x-b\| = \|a-b\|/2$; for $n > 1$, let B_n be the set of $x \in \mathrm{B}_{n-1}$ such that $\|x-y\| \leqslant \delta(\mathrm{B}_{n-1})/2$ for all $y \in \mathrm{B}_{n-1}$ ($\delta(\mathrm{A})$ being the diameter of a set A). Show that $\delta(\mathrm{B}_n) \leqslant \delta(\mathrm{B}_{n-1})/2$, and that the intersection of all the B_n is reduced to $(a+b)/2$.
   (b) Deduce from (a) that if f is an isometry of a real normed space E onto a real normed space F, then $f(x) = u(x) + c$, where u is a *linear* isometry, and $c \in \mathrm{F}$.
4. Let us call *rectangle* in $\mathbf{N}\times\mathbf{N}$ a product of two intervals of $\mathbf{N}$; for any finite subset H of $\mathbf{N}\times\mathbf{N}$, let $\psi(\mathrm{H})$ be the smallest number of rectangles whose union is H. Let (H_n) be an increasing sequence of finite subsets of $\mathbf{N}\times\mathbf{N}$, whose union is $\mathbf{N}\times\mathbf{N}$ and such that the sequence $(\psi(\mathrm{H}_n))$ is bounded. Let E, F, G be three normed spaces, (x_n) (resp. (y_n)) a convergent series in E (resp. F), f a continuous bilinear mapping of E × F into G. Show that

$$(*)\qquad \lim_{n\to\infty} \sum_{(h,k)\in \mathrm{H}_n} f(x_h, y_k) = f\left(\sum_{n=0}^{\infty} x_n, \sum_{n=0}^{\infty} y_n\right).$$

5. Let (H_n) be an increasing sequence of finite subsets of $\mathbf{N}\times\mathbf{N}$, whose union is $\mathbf{N}\times\mathbf{N}$; for each $j \in \mathbf{N}$ and each $n \in \mathbf{N}$, let $\varphi(j, n)$ be the smallest number of intervals of $\mathbf{N}$ whose union is the set $\mathrm{H}_n^{-1}(j)$ of all integers i such that $(i, j) \in \mathrm{H}_n$. Suppose $\varphi(j, n)$ is *bounded* in $\mathbf{N}\times\mathbf{N}$. Let (x_n) be a convergent series in a normed space E, (y_n) an absolutely convergent series in a normed space F, u a continuous bilinear mapping of E × F into a normed space G. Show that formula (∗) of Problem 4 still holds (use (5.5.1), and remark that the sums $\sum_{(i,j)\in \mathrm{H}_n} x_i$ are bounded in E for all j, n) (cf. Section 12.16, Problem 12).
6. Let E, F be two real normed spaces. A mapping f of E into F is said to be *linear in a neighborhood of* 0 if there exists a $\delta > 0$ such that: (1) the relations $\|x\| \leqslant \delta$, $\|x'\| \leqslant \delta$, $\|x+x'\| \leqslant \delta$ in E imply $f(x+x') = f(x) + f(x')$; (2) the relations $\|x\| \leqslant \delta$, $\|\lambda x\| \leqslant \delta$ in E (with $\lambda \in \mathbf{R}$) imply $f(\lambda x) = \lambda f(x)$.

(a) Show that if f satisfies condition (1) and is continuous at the point 0, it is continuous in a neighborhood of 0 and is linear in a neighborhood of 0 (cf. Problem 1).
(b) Let g be a mapping of E into F; in order that g be continuous at the point 0 and linear in a neighborhood of 0, a necessary and sufficient condition is that for any convergent series (x_n) in E, the partial sums of the series $(g(x_n))$ be bounded in F. (To prove sufficiency, first observe that one must have $g(0) = 0$; if, for every n, there exist three elements u_n, v_n, w_n of E such that $\|u_n\| \leqslant 2^{-n}$, $\|v_n\| \leqslant 2^{-n}$, $\|w_n\| \leqslant 2^{-n}$, $u_n + v_n + w_n = 0$ and $g(u_n) + g(v_n) + g(w_n) \neq 0$, form a series (x_n) violating the assumption. If there are no such sequences u_n, v_n, w_n, g verifies condition (1); show that it is necessarily continuous at 0.)

6. EQUIVALENT NORMS

▲ Let E be a vector space (over the real or the complex field), $\|x\|_1$ and $\|x\|_2$ two norms on E; we say that $\|x\|_1$ is *finer* than $\|x\|_2$ if the topology defined by $\|x\|_1$ is finer than the topology defined by $\|x\|_2$ (see Section 3.12); if we note E_1 (resp. E_2) the normed space determined by $\|x\|_1$ (resp. $\|x\|_2$), this means that the identity mapping $x \to x$ of E_1 into E_2 is continuous, hence, by (5.5.1), that condition is equivalent to the existence of a number $a > 0$ such that $\|x\|_2 \leqslant a \cdot \|x\|_1$. We say that the two norms $\|x\|_1$, $\|x\|_2$ are *equivalent* if they define the *same* topology on E. The preceding remark yields at once:

(5.6.1) *In order that the two norms $\|x\|_1$, $\|x\|_2$ on a vector space* E *be equivalent a necessary and sufficient condition is that there exist two constants $a > 0$, $b > 0$, such that*

$$a\|x\|_1 \leqslant \|x\|_2 \leqslant b\|x\|_1$$

for any $x \in$ E.

▲ The corresponding distances are then *uniformly equivalent* (Section 3.14).
▲ For instance, on the product $E_1 \times E_2$ of two normed spaces, the norms $\sup(\|x_1\|, \|x_2\|)$, $\|x_1\| + \|x_2\|$, $(\|x_1\|^2 + \|x_2\|^2)^{1/2}$ are equivalent. On the space $E = \mathscr{C}_{\mathbf{R}}(I)$, the norm $\|f\|_1$ defined in (5.1.4) is *not* equivalent to the norm $\|f\|_\infty = \sup_{t \in I} |f(t)|$ (see Section 5.1, Problem 1).

7. SPACES OF CONTINUOUS MULTILINEAR MAPPINGS

Let E, F, be two normed spaces; the set $\mathscr{L}(E; F)$ of all continuous linear mappings of E into F is a vector space, as follows from (5.1.5), (3.20.4), and (3.11.5).

For each $u \in \mathscr{L}(\mathrm{E}; \mathrm{F})$, let $\|u\|$ be the g.l.b. of all constants $a > 0$ which satisfy the relation $\|u(x)\| \leqslant a \cdot \|x\|$ (see (5.5.1)) for all x. We can also write

(5.7.1) $$\|u\| = \sup_{\|x\| \leqslant 1} \|u(x)\|.$$

For by definition, for each $a > \|u\|$, and $\|x\| \leqslant 1$, $\|u(x)\| \leqslant a$, hence $\sup_{\|x\| \leqslant 1} \|u(x)\| \leqslant \|u\|$; this already proves (5.7.1) for $\|u\| = 0$. If $\|u\| > 0$, for any b such that $0 < b < \|u\|$, there is an $x \in \mathrm{E}$ such that $\|u(x)\| > b\|x\|$; this implies $x \neq 0$, hence if $z = x/\|x\|$, we still have $\|u(z)\| > b \cdot \|z\| = b$, and as $\|z\| = 1$, this proves that $b \leqslant \sup_{\|x\| \leqslant 1} \|u(x)\|$, hence $\|u\| \leqslant \sup_{\|x\| \leqslant 1} \|u(x)\|$, and (5.7.1) is proved. The same argument also shows that if $\mathrm{E} \neq \{0\}$

(5.7.2) $$\|u\| = \sup_{\|z\| = 1} \|u(z)\|.$$

We now show that $\|u\|$ is a *norm* on the vector space $\mathscr{L}(\mathrm{E}; \mathrm{F})$. For if $u = 0$, then $\|u\| = 0$ by (5.7.1), and conversely if $\|u\| = 0$, then $u(x) = 0$ for $\|x\| \leqslant 1$, hence, for *any* $x \neq 0$ in E, $u(x) = \|x\| u(x/\|x\|) = 0$. It also follows from (5.7.1) that $\|\lambda u\| = |\lambda| \cdot \|u\|$; finally, if $w = u + v$, we have $\|w(x)\| \leqslant \|u(x)\| + \|v(x)\|$, hence $\|w\| \leqslant \|u\| + \|v\|$ from (5.7.1).

(5.7.3) *If* F *is complete, so is the normed space* $\mathscr{L}(\mathrm{E}; \mathrm{F})$.

For let (u_n) be a Cauchy sequence in $\mathscr{L}(\mathrm{E}; \mathrm{F})$; for any $\varepsilon > 0$, there is therefore an n_0 such that $\|u_m - u_n\| \leqslant \varepsilon$ for $m \geqslant n_0$, $n \geqslant n_0$. By (5.7.1), for any x such that $\|x\| \leqslant 1$, we therefore have $\|u_m(x) - u_n(x)\| \leqslant \varepsilon$ for $m \geqslant n_0$, $n \geqslant n_0$; this shows that the sequence $(u_n(x))$ is a Cauchy sequence in F, hence converges to an element $v(x) \in \mathrm{F}$. This is also true for any $x \in \mathrm{E}$, since we can write $x = \lambda z$ with $\|z\| \leqslant 1$, hence $u_n(x) = \lambda u_n(z)$ tends to a limit $v(x) = \lambda v(z)$. From the relation $u_n(x + y) = u_n(x) + u_n(y)$ and from (5.1.5) it follows that $v(x + y) = v(x) + v(y)$, and one shows similarly that $v(\lambda x) = \lambda v(x)$, in other words v in linear. Finally, from $\|u_m(x) - u_n(x)\| \leqslant \varepsilon$ for $m \geqslant n_0$, $n \geqslant n_0$, we deduce $\|v(x) - u_n(x)\| \leqslant \varepsilon$ for $\|x\| \leqslant 1$, hence $\|v(x)\| \leqslant \|u_n\| + \varepsilon$, which proves (by (5.5.1)) that v is continuous, hence in $\mathscr{L}(\mathrm{E}; \mathrm{F})$; furthermore $\|v - u_n\| \leqslant \varepsilon$ for $n \geqslant n_0$ (by (5.7.1)), which proves the sequence (u_n) converges to v.

From the definition it follows that, for every $x \in \mathrm{E}$ and every $u \in \mathscr{L}(\mathrm{E}; \mathrm{F})$,

(5.7.4) $$\|u(x)\| \leq \|u\| \cdot \|x\|$$

which proves that the bilinear mapping $(x, u) \to u(x)$ of $\mathrm{E} \times \mathscr{L}(\mathrm{E}; \mathrm{F})$ into F is *continuous* (by (5.5.1)).

The definition of the norm in $\mathscr{L}(\mathrm{E};\mathrm{F})$ depends on the norms in E and in F; but it is readily seen that, when the norms in E and F are replaced by equivalent norms (Section 5.6) the new norm in $\mathscr{L}(\mathrm{E};\mathrm{F})$ is equivalent to the old one.

(5.7.5) *Let u be a continuous linear mapping of a normed space* E *into a normed space* F, *and v a continuous linear mapping of* F *into a normed space* G. *Then* $\|v \circ u\| \leqslant \|v\| \cdot \|u\|$.

For if $\|x\| \leqslant 1$, then by (5.7.4) $\|v(u(x))\| \leqslant \|v\| \cdot \|u(x)\| \leqslant \|v\| \cdot \|u\|$, and the result follows from (5.7.1).

(5.7.6) *If* F *is a real* (resp. *complex*) *normed space, the mapping which to each* $a \in \mathrm{F}$ *associates the element* $\theta_a\colon \xi \to \xi a$ *of* $\mathscr{L}(\mathbf{R};\mathrm{F})$ (resp. $\mathscr{L}(\mathbf{C};\mathrm{F})$) *is a linear isometry of* F *onto* $\mathscr{L}(\mathbf{R};\mathrm{F})$ (resp. $\mathscr{L}(\mathbf{C};\mathrm{F})$).

The mapping $a \to \theta_a$ is obviously linear; it is surjective, for every linear mapping f of **R** (resp. **C**) into F is such that $f(\xi) = f(\xi \cdot 1) = \xi f(1) = \xi a$ with $a = f(1)$. Finally $\|\theta_a\| = \sup_{|\xi| \leqslant 1} \|\xi a\| = \| a \|$ by axiom (III) of Section 5.1.

Let now $\mathrm{E}_1, \ldots, \mathrm{E}_n, \mathrm{F}$ be $n+1$ normed spaces, and define $\mathscr{L}(\mathrm{E}_1, \ldots, \mathrm{E}_n;\mathrm{F})$ as the vector space of all continuous multilinear mappings of $\mathrm{E}_1 \times \cdots \times \mathrm{E}_n$ into F. Then for $u \in \mathscr{L}(\mathrm{E}_1, \ldots, \mathrm{E}_n;\mathrm{F})$, the same argument as above shows that the g.l.b. $\|u\|$ of all constants $a > 0$ such that

$$\|u(x_1, \ldots, x_n)\| \leqslant a\|x_1\| \cdots \|x_n\|$$

is also given by

$$\|u\| = \sup_{\|x_1\| \leqslant 1, \ldots, \|x_n\| \leqslant 1} \|u(x_1, \ldots, x_n)\|. \tag{5.7.7}$$

We also see that $\|u\|$ is a norm on $\mathscr{L}(\mathrm{E}_1, \ldots, \mathrm{E}_n;\mathrm{F})$; but in fact these vector spaces can be reduced to spaces $\mathscr{L}(\mathrm{X};\mathrm{Y})$:

(5.7.8) *For each* $u \in \mathscr{L}(\mathrm{E}, \mathrm{F};\mathrm{G})$ *and each* $x \in \mathrm{E}$, *let* u_x *be the linear mapping* $y \to u(x, y)$. *Then* $\tilde{u}\colon x \to u_x$ *is a linear continuous mapping of* E *into* $\mathscr{L}(\mathrm{F};\mathrm{G})$, *and the mapping* $u \to \tilde{u}$ *is a linear isometry of* $\mathscr{L}(\mathrm{E}, \mathrm{F};\mathrm{G})$ *onto* $\mathscr{L}(\mathrm{E};\mathscr{L}(\mathrm{F};\mathrm{G}))$.

We have $\|u_x(y)\| = \|u(x, y)\| \leqslant \|u\| \cdot \|x\| \cdot \|y\|$, hence u_x is continuous by (5.5.1); moreover $\|u_x\| = \sup_{\|y\| \leqslant 1} \|u(x, y)\|$, hence (2.3.7)

$$\sup_{\|x\| \leqslant 1} \|u_x\| = \sup_{\|x\| \leqslant 1,\ \|y\| \leqslant 1} \|u(x, y)\| = \|u\|$$

which proves that $x \to u_x$ (which is obviously linear) is continuous, and $u \to \tilde{u}$ is an isometry of $\mathscr{L}(\mathrm{E}, \mathrm{F}; \mathrm{G})$ into $\mathscr{L}(\mathrm{E}; \mathscr{L}(\mathrm{F}; \mathrm{G}))$. Finally $u \to \tilde{u}$ is surjective, for if $v \in \mathscr{L}(\mathrm{E}; \mathscr{L}(\mathrm{F}; \mathrm{G}))$, then $u: (x, y) \to (v(x))(y)$ is obviously bilinear, and as $\|(v(x))(y)\| \leqslant \|v(x)\| \cdot \|y\| \leqslant \|v\| \cdot \|x\| \cdot \|y\|$ by (5.7.4), u is continuous, and $v(x) = u_x$, which ends the proof.

By induction on n, it follows that $\mathscr{L}(\mathrm{E}_1, \mathrm{E}_2, \ldots, \mathrm{E}_n; \mathrm{F})$ can be naturally identified (with conservation of the norm) to

$$\mathscr{L}(\mathrm{E}_1; \mathscr{L}(\mathrm{E}_2; \ldots, \mathscr{L}(\mathrm{E}_n; \mathrm{F})) \ldots).$$

PROBLEMS

1. Let E be the space (c_0) of Banach, defined in Section 5.3, Problem 5; we keep the notations of that problem. Let u be a continuous linear mapping of E into $\mathbf{R}$; if $u(e_n) = \eta_n$, show that the series $\sum_n \eta_n$ is absolutely convergent, and that, in the Banach space $\mathrm{E}' = \mathscr{L}(\mathrm{E}; \mathbf{R})$, $\|u\| = \sum_{n=0}^{\infty} |\eta_n|$ (apply (5.5.1) for suitable values of $x \in \mathrm{E}$). Conversely, for any absolutely convergent series (η_n) of real numbers, there is one and only one continuous linear mapping u of E into $\mathbf{R}$ such that $u(e_n) = \eta_n$ for every n; and if $x = \sum_{n=0}^{\infty} \xi_n e_n \in \mathrm{E}$, then $u(x) = \sum_{n=0}^{\infty} \eta_n \xi_n$ (the space E′, with the norm defined above, is the "space l^1" of Banach).

(b) As a vector space (without a norm) E′ can be considered as a subspace of E; show that the norm on E′ is strictly finer (Section 5.6) than the restriction to E′ of the norm of E.

(c) Show that the space $\mathrm{E}'' = \mathscr{L}(\mathrm{E}'; \mathbf{R})$ of the continuous linear mappings of E′ into $\mathbf{R}$ can be identified with the space of all bounded sequences $x = (\zeta_n)$ of real numbers, with norm $\|x\| = \sup_n |\zeta_n|$ ("space l^∞" of Banach; use the same method as in (a)). E can be considered as a closed subspace of E″.

(d) In the space E′, let P be the subset of all absolutely convergent series $u = (\eta_n)$ with terms $\eta_n \geqslant 0$; any element of E′ can be written $u - v$, where both u and v are in P; yet show that the interior of the set P is empty.

2. (a) Let E be the space (c_0) of Banach, and let U be a continuous linear mapping of E into itself. With the notations of Problem 1, let $U(e_n) = \sum_{m=0}^{\infty} \alpha_{mn} e_m$; show that: (1) $\lim_{m \to \infty} \alpha_{mn} = 0$; (2) the series $\sum_{n=0}^{\infty} |\alpha_{mn}|$ is convergent for every m; (3) $\sup_m \sum_{n=0}^{\infty} |\alpha_{mn}|$ is finite. (Same method as in Problem 1(a).) Prove the converse, and show that the Banach space $\mathscr{L}(\mathrm{E}; \mathrm{E})$ can be identified with the space of double sequences $U = (\alpha_{mn})$ satisfying the preceding conditions, with the norm $\|U\| = \sup_m \sum_{n=0}^{\infty} |\alpha_{mn}|$.

(b) Let E′ be the space l^1 of Banach (Problem 1). Show similarly that the Banach space $\mathscr{L}(\mathrm{E}'; \mathrm{E}')$ can be identified with the space of double sequences $U = (\alpha_{mn})$ such that: (1) the series $\sum_{m=0}^{\infty} |\alpha_{mn}|$ is convergent for every n; (2) $\sup_n \sum_{m=0}^{\infty} |\alpha_{mn}|$ is finite; the norm is then equal to $\|U\| = \sup_n \sum_{m=0}^{\infty} |\alpha_{mn}|$.

3. Let $E \neq \{0\}$ be a normed space; show that there cannot exist two continuous linear mappings u, v of E into itself such that $u \circ v - v \circ u = 1_E$. (Prove that this would imply $u \circ v^{n+1} - v^{n+1} \circ u = (n+1)v^n$, and therefore the inequality $(n+1)\|v^n\| \leqslant 2\|u\| \cdot \|v\| \cdot \|v^n\|$, which leads to $v^n = 0$ as soon as n is large enough, hence $v = 0$, which is a contradiction.)

8. CLOSED HYPERPLANES AND CONTINUOUS LINEAR FORMS

We recall that a *linear form* on a real (resp. complex) vector space E is a linear mapping f of E into **R** (resp. **C**); its kernel $H = f^{-1}(0)$ is then a vector subspace such that for any $a \notin H$, E is the algebraic direct sum of H and $\mathbf{R}a$ (resp. $\mathbf{C}a$). A subspace having this last property is called a *hyperplane*; if H is a hyperplane, $a \notin H$, and if for any $x \in E$ we write $x = f(x)a + y$ with $f(x)$ a scalar and $y \in H$, then f is a linear form and $H = f^{-1}(0)$. The relation $f(x) = 0$ is called an *equation* of H; if f_1 is another linear form such that $H = f_1^{-1}(0)$, then $f_1 = \alpha f$ (α scalar). We also recall that a hyperplane is *maximal*: any vector subspace of E containing a hyperplane H is either H or E itself.

(5.8.1) *In a real* (resp. *complex*) *normed space* E, *let* H *be a hyperplane of equation* $f(x) = 0$. *In order that* H *be closed in* E, *a necessary and sufficient condition is that* f *be continuous. For any* $b \notin H$, E *is then the topological direct sum* (see Section 5.4) *of* H *and of the one-dimensional subspace* $D = \mathbf{R}b$ (resp. $D = \mathbf{C}b$).

It is clear that if f is continuous, $H = f^{-1}(0)$ is closed (see (3.15.1)). To prove the converse, let $a \notin H$ be such that $f(a) = 1$. As H is closed, so is $a + H$ (by (5.1.5)), and as $0 \notin a + H$, there is a ball V: $\|x\| \leqslant r$ which does not meet $a + H$; therefore $x \in V$ implies $f(x) \neq 1$. We prove $x \in V$ implies $|f(x)| \leqslant 1$. Suppose the contrary, and let $\alpha = f(x)$, with $|\alpha| > 1$; then $\|x/\alpha\| = (1/|\alpha|)\|x\| < r$, and $f(x/\alpha) = 1$, which contradicts the definition of V. By homogeneity and (5.5.1) it follows that f is continuous. If $b \notin H$, we have $x = g(x)b + y$ with $y \in H$ for each $x \in E$, and $g(x) = 0$ is another equation of H; hence g is continuous, and the mapping $x \to g(x)b$ of E into $D = \mathbf{R}b$ (resp. $\mathbf{C}b$) is therefore continuous, which proves the last part of (5.8.1) by (5.4.2).

(5.8.2) *In a normed space* E, *a hyperplane* H *is either closed or dense.*

For $\overline{H}$ is a vector subspace (by (5.4.1)) which can only be E or H.

PROBLEMS

1. Let E be the (noncomplete) subspace of the space (c_0) of Banach, consisting of the sequences $x = (\xi_n)$ of real numbers, having only a *finite* number of terms different from 0. For *any* sequence (α_n) of real numbers, the mapping $x \to u(x) = \sum_{n=0}^{\infty} \alpha_n \xi_n$ is a linear form on E, and all linear forms on E are obtained in that way; which of them are continuous (see (5.5.4) and Problem 1 of Section 5.7)?
2. (a) In a real normed space E, let H be the closed hyperplane of equation $u(x) = 0$, where u is a continuous linear form. Show that for any point $a \in E$, the distance $d(a, \sum) = |u(a)| / \|u\|$.
(b) In the space (c_0) of Banach, let H be the closed hyperplane of equation $u(x) = \sum_{n=0}^{\infty} 2^{-n}\xi_n = 0$; if $a \notin H$, show that there is no point $b \in H$ such that $d(a, H) = d(a, b)$.
3. In a real vector space E, the linear varieties of codimension 1 (Section 5.1, Problem 5) are again called *hyperplanes*; they are the sets defined by an equation of the type $u(x) = \alpha$, where u is a linear form, α any real number; the hyperplanes considered in the text are those which contain 0, and are also called *homogeneous* hyperplanes; any hyperplane defined by an equation $u(x) = \alpha$ is said to be *parallel* to the homogeneous hyperplane defined by $u(x) = 0$. If A is a nonempty subset of E, a *hyperplane of support* of A is a hyperplane H defined by an equation $u(x) = \alpha$, such that $u(x) - \alpha \geqslant 0$ for all $x \in A$, or $u(x) - \alpha \leqslant 0$ for all $x \in A$, and $u(x_0) = \alpha$ for at least one point $x_0 \in A$.
(a) In a real normed space E, a hyperplane of support of a set containing an interior point is closed (see (5.8.2)).
(b) Let A be a compact subset of a real normed space E; show that for any homogeneous closed hyperplane H_0 defined by the equation $u(x) = 0$, there are two hyperplanes of support of A which are defined by equations of the form $u(x) = \alpha$, and may eventually coincide; their distance is at most equal to the diameter of A.
(c) In the space (c_0) of Banach, consider the continuous linear form $x \to u(x) = \sum_{n=0}^{\infty} 2^{-n}\xi_n$; show that the closed ball $B'(0; 1)$ has no hyperplane of support having an equation of the form $u(x) = \alpha$ (cf. Problem 2(b)).

9. FINITE DIMENSIONAL NORMED SPACES

(5.9.1) *Let* E *be an n-dimensional real* (resp. *complex*) *normed vector space; if* $(a_1, \ldots, a_n)$ *is a basis of* E, *the mapping*

$$(\xi_1, \ldots, \xi_n) \to \xi_1 a_1 + \cdots + \xi_n a_n$$

of $\mathbf{R}^n$ (resp. $\mathbf{C}^n$) *onto* E *is bicontinuous.*

We use induction on n, and prove first the result for $n = 1$. We know by (5.1.5) that $\xi \to \xi a_1$ is continuous; as $a_1 \neq 0$ and $\|\xi a_1\| = \|a_1\| \cdot |\xi|$, we have $|\xi| \leqslant (1/\|a_1\|) \cdot \|\xi a_1\|$, which proves the continuity of $\xi a_1 \to \xi$, by (5.5.1).

Suppose the theorem is proved for $n-1$, and let H be the hyperplane in E generated by $a_1, \ldots, a_{n-1}$; the inductive assumption implies that the norm on H (induced by that of E) is equivalent to the norm $\sup_{1 \leq i \leq n-1} |\xi_i|$; hence H is *complete* (for both norms) and therefore *closed* in E (by (3.14.4)). It follows from (5.8.1) that the mapping $(\xi_1 a_1 + \cdots + \xi_n a_n) \to \xi_n$ is continuous, and this, together with the inductive assumption, ends the proof (by (3.20.4) and (5.4.2)).

(5.9.2) *In a normed space* E, *let* V *be a closed subspace,* W *a finite dimensional subspace; then* V + W *is closed in* E. *In particular, any finite dimensional subspace is closed in* E.

We can use induction on the dimension n of W, and therefore reduce the proof to the case $n = 1$. Let $\mathrm{W} = \mathbf{R}a$ (resp. $\mathrm{W} = \mathbf{C}a$); if $a \in \mathrm{V}$, V + W = V and there is nothing to prove. If not, we can write any $x \in \mathrm{V} + \mathrm{W}$ in the form $x = f(x)a + y$ with $y \in \mathrm{V}$, and as V is a closed hyperplane in V + W, f is continuous in V + W, by (5.8.1). Let (x_n) be a sequence of points of V + W tending to a cluster point b of V + W (see (3.13.13)); write $x_n = f(x_n)a + y_n$. By (5.5.1), the sequence $(f(x_n))$ is a Cauchy sequence in $\mathbf{R}$ (resp. $\mathbf{C}$), hence tends to a limit λ; therefore $y_n = x_n - f(x_n)a$ tends to $b - \lambda a$; but as V is closed, the limit of (y_n) is in V, hence $b \in \mathrm{V} + \mathrm{W}$. Q.E.D. (See Section 6.5, Problem 2.)

(5.9.3) *In a normed space* E, *let* V *be a closed subspace of finite codimension* (i.e. *having a finite dimensional algebraic supplement*); *then any algebraic supplement of* V *is also a topological supplement.*

Let W be an algebraic supplement of V in E; we use induction on the dimension n of W, the result having been proved for $n = 1$ in (5.8.1). We can write W = D + U where D is one-dimensional and U is $(n-1)$-dimensional (direct sum); by (5.9.2), V + D is closed in E, hence U is a topological supplement to V + D by the inductive assumption. In other words, E is naturally homeomorphic to (V + D) × U; by (5.8.1), V + D is naturally homeomorphic to V × D, hence E is naturally homeomorphic to V × D × U. Finally, as D × U is naturally homeomorphic to W, E is naturally homeomorphic to V × W. Q.E.D.

(5.9.4) (F. Riesz's theorem) *A locally compact normed space* E *is finite dimensional.*

Replacing the norm by an equivalent one, we may suppose the ball B: $\|x\| \leqslant 1$ is compact. Therefore **(3.16.1)** there exists a finite sequence of points a_i $(1 \leqslant i \leqslant n)$ such that B is contained in the union of the balls of center a_i and radius 1/2. Let V be the finite dimensional subspace generated by the a_i. We prove by contradiction that V = E. Suppose indeed there is an $x \in E$ which is not in V. As V is closed (by **(5.9.2)**) $d(x, V) = \alpha > 0$; by definition of $d(x, V)$, there is in V a point y such that $\alpha \leqslant \|x - y\| \leqslant \frac{3}{2}\alpha$. Let $z = (x - y)/\|x - y\|$; we have $\|z\| = 1$, hence there is an index i such that $\|z - a_i\| \leqslant 1/2$. Let us write

$$x = y + \|x - y\|z = y + \|x - y\|a_i + \|x - y\|(z - a_i)$$

and note that $y + \|x - y\|a_i \in V$. By definition of $d(x, V)$, we have therefore $\|x - y\| \cdot \|z - a_i\| \geqslant \alpha$, hence $\|x - y\| \geqslant 2\alpha$, which contradicts the choice of y, since $\alpha \neq 0$.

PROBLEMS

1. Show that if E is a finite dimensional normed space, every linear mapping of E into a normed space F is continuous (use **(5.9.1)** and **(5.1.5)**).
2. We recall that a *vector basis* of a vector space E is a family $(a_\lambda)_{\lambda \in L}$ such that any element of E can be written in a *unique* way as a linear combination of a finite number of a_λ; this implies in particular that the a_λ are linearly independent.
(a) Let (a_n) be a sequence of linearly independent elements in a Banach space E. Define inductively a sequence (μ_n) of real numbers >0 in the following way: if d_n is the distance of the point $\mu_n a_n$ to the subspace V_{n-1} generated by $a_1, \ldots, a_{n-1}$ (note that $d_n > 0$ by **(5.9.2)**), take μ_{n+1} such that $|\mu_{n+1}| \cdot \|a_{n+1}\| \leqslant d_n/3$. Show that the series $\sum_{n=1}^{\infty} \mu_n a_n$ is absolutely convergent, and that its sum x does not belong to any of the subspaces V_n.
(b) Deduce from (a) that a Banach space of infinite dimension cannot have a denumerable vector basis.
3. Show that a normed space in which there is a sphere which is compact is finite dimensional. (Observe that the set of points in a normed space E such that $a \leqslant \|x\| \leqslant b$ (with $a > 0$) is homeomorphic to the product space of the interval $[a, b]$ and of the sphere S: $\|x\| = 1$; use then Riesz's theorem **(5.9.4)**.)
4. Let E be a real normed space of finite dimension n, and let A be a compact subset of E. With the notations of Section **3.16**, Problem 4, show that there exists a constant $a > 0$ such that $N_\varepsilon(A) \leqslant a \cdot (1/\varepsilon)^n$; if in addition A has an interior point, show that there exists a constant $b > 0$ such that $M_{2\varepsilon}(A) \geqslant b \cdot (1/\varepsilon)^n$; in that case, one has $H_\varepsilon(A) \sim C_\varepsilon(A) \sim n \log 1/\varepsilon$.
5. Let E be a real normed space of infinite dimension, and let (E_n) be a strictly increasing sequence of vector subspaces of E of finite dimension. Show that there exists a sequence (x_n) of points of E such that $x_n \in E_n$, $\|x_n\| = 1$ and $d(x_n, E_{n-1}) = 1$. Let φ be a function >0 defined for $t \geqslant 1$, strictly decreasing and such that $\lim_{t \to +\infty} (\varphi t) = 0$, and let $z_n = 2\varphi(n)x_n$. If K is the compact subset of E consisting of 0 and the z_n, show that $M_\varepsilon(K) \geqslant \psi(\varepsilon)$, where ψ is the inverse function of φ (defined in a neighborhood of 0); $M_\varepsilon(K)$ can thus increase arbitrarily fast when $1/\varepsilon$ tend to $+\infty$.

10. SEPARABLE NORMED SPACES

(5.10.1) *If in a normed space* E *there exists a total sequence* (Section 5.4), E *is separable. Conversely, in a separable normed space* E, *there exists a total sequence consisting of linearly independent vectors.*

Suppose (a_n) is a total sequence, and let D be the set of all (finite) linear combinations $r_1 a_1 + \cdots + r_n a_n$ with *rational* coefficients (when E is a complex vector space, by a "rational" scalar we mean a complex number $\alpha + i\beta$, with both α and β rational). D is a denumerable set by (1.9.3) and (1.9.4). As by definition the set L of *all* linear combinations of the a_n is dense in E, all we have to prove is that D is dense in L, and as

$$\|(\lambda_1 a_1 + \cdots + \lambda_n a_n) - (r_1 a_1 + \cdots + r_n a_n)\| \leqslant \sum_{j=1}^{n} |\lambda_j - r_j| \cdot \|a_j\|,$$

this follows from (2.2.16).

Suppose conversely E is separable; we can of course suppose E is infinite dimensional (otherwise any basis of E is already a *finite* total subset). Let (a_n) be an infinite dense sequence of vectors of E. We define by induction a subsequence (a_{k_n}) having the property that it consists of linearly independent vectors and that for any $m \leqslant k_n$, a_m is a linear combination of $a_{k_1}, \ldots, a_{k_n}$. To do this, we merely take for k_1 the first index for which $a_n \neq 0$, and for k_{n+1} the smallest index $m > k_n$ such that a_m is not in the subspace V_n generated by $a_{k_1}, \ldots, a_{k_n}$; such an index exists, otherwise, as V_n is closed by (5.9.2), V_n would contain the closure E of the set of all the a_n, contrary to assumption. It is then clear that (a_{k_n}) has the required properties, and is obviously by construction a total sequence.

PROBLEM

Show that the spaces (c_0) and l^1 of Banach (Section 5.3, Problem 5, and Section 5.7, Problem 1) are separable, but that the space l^∞ (Section 5.7, Problem 1) is not separable. (Show that in l^∞ there exists a nondenumerable family (x_λ) of points such that $\|x_\lambda - x_\mu\| = 1$ for $\lambda \neq \mu$, using Problem 2(b) of Section 4.2, and (2.2.17).)

CHAPTER VI

HILBERT SPACES

▲ Hilbert spaces constitute at present the most important examples of Banach spaces, not only because they are the most natural and closest generalization, in the realm of "infinite dimensions," of our classical euclidean geometry, but chiefly for the fact that they have been, up to now, the most useful spaces in the applications to functional analysis. With the exception of (6.3.1), all the results easily follow from the definitions and from the fundamental Cauchy–Schwarz inequality (6.2.4).

1. HERMITIAN FORMS

▲ For any real or complex number λ, we write $\bar{\lambda}$ for its complex conjugate (equal to λ if λ is real). A *hermitian form* on a real (resp. complex) vector space E is a mapping f of $E \times E$ into **R** (resp. **C**) which has the following properties:

$$f(x + x', y) = f(x, y) + f(x', y), \tag{I}$$

$$f(x, y + y') = f(x, y) + f(x, y'), \tag{II}$$

$$f(\lambda x, y) = \lambda f(x, y), \tag{III}$$

$$f(x, \lambda y) = \bar{\lambda} f(x, y), \tag{IV}$$

$$f(y, x) = \overline{f(x, y)}. \tag{V}$$

(Observe that (II) and (IV) follow from the other identities; (V) implies that $f(x, x)$ is *real*.) When E is a *real* vector space, conditions (I) to (IV) express that *f is bilinear* and (V) boils down to $f(y, x) = f(x, y)$, which expresses that *f is symmetric.* For any finite systems (x_i), (y_j), (α_i), (β_j), we have

(6.1.1) $$f\Big(\sum_i \alpha_i x_i, \sum_j \beta_j y_j\Big) = \sum_{i,j} \alpha_i \bar{\beta}_j f(x_i, y_j)$$

by induction on the number of elements of these systems.

▲ From (6.1.1) it follows that if E is finite dimensional and (a_i) is a basis of E, f is entirely determined by its values $\alpha_{ij} = f(a_i, a_j)$, which are such that (by V))

(6.1.2) $$\alpha_{ji} = \bar{\alpha}_{ij}.$$

Indeed we have then, for $x = \sum_i \xi_i a_i$, $y = \sum_i \eta_i a_i$

(6.1.3) $$f(x, y) = \sum_{i,j} \alpha_{ij} \xi_i \bar{\eta}_j.$$

Conversely, for any system (α_{ij}) of real (resp. complex) numbers satisfying (6.1.2), the right hand side of (6.1.3) defines on the real (resp. complex) finite dimensional vector space E a hermitian form.

Example

(6.1.4) Let D be a relatively compact open set in $\mathbf{R}^2$, and let E be the real (resp. complex) vector space of all real-valued (resp. complex-valued) bounded continuous functions in D, which have bounded continuous first derivatives in D. Then the mapping

$$(f, g) \to \varphi(f, g) = \iint_D \Big(a(x, y) f(x, y) \overline{g(x, y)} + b(x, y) \frac{\partial f}{\partial x} \overline{\frac{\partial g}{\partial x}} + c(x, y) \frac{\partial f}{\partial y} \overline{\frac{\partial g}{\partial y}}\Big)\, dx\, dy$$

(where a, b, c are continuous, bounded and real-valued in D) is a hermitian form on E.

▲ A pair of vectors x, y of a vector space E is *orthogonal with respect to a hermitian form f on* E if $f(x, y) = 0$ (it follows from (V) that the relation is symmetric in x, y); a vector x which is orthogonal to itself (i.e. $f(x, x) = 0$) is *isotropic* with respect to f. For any subset M of E, the set of vectors y which are orthogonal to *all* vectors $x \in$ M is a vector subspace of E, which is said to be *orthogonal to* M (with respect to f). It may happen that there exists a vector $a \neq 0$ which is orthogonal to the whole space E, in which case we say the form *f* is *degenerate*. On a finite dimensional space E, non-degenerate hermitian forms f defined by (6.1.3) are those for which the matrix (α_{ij}) is invertible.

PROBLEMS

1. (a) Let f be a hermitian form on a vector space E. Show that if E is a real vector space, then

$$4f(x, y) = f(x + y, x + y) - f(x - y, x - y)$$

and if E is a complex vector space

$$4f(x, y) = f(x + y, x + y) - f(x - y, x - y) + if(x + iy, x + iy) - if(x - iy, x - iy).$$

(b) Deduce from (a) that if $f(x, x) = 0$ for every vector in a subspace M of E, then $f(x, y) = 0$ for any pair of vectors x, y of M.

(c) Give a proof of (b) without using the identities proved in (a). (Write that $f(x + \lambda y, x + \lambda y) = 0$ for any λ.)

2. Let E be a complex vector space. Show that if f is a mapping of $E \times E$ into **C** satisfying conditions (I), (II), (III), (IV), and such that $f(x, x) \in \mathbf{R}$ for every $x \in E$, then f is a hermitian form on E.

2. POSITIVE HERMITIAN FORMS

We say a hermitian form f on a vector space E is *positive* if $f(x, x) \geqslant 0$ for any $x \in E$. For instance, the form φ defined in example **(6.1.4)** is positive if a, b, c are $\geqslant 0$ in D.

(6.2.1) (Cauchy–Schwarz inequality) *If f is a positive hermitian form, then*

$$|f(x, y)|^2 \leqslant f(x, x)f(y, y)$$

for any pair of vectors x, y in E.

Write $a = f(x, x)$, $b = f(x, y)$, $c = f(y, y)$ and recall a and c are real and $\geqslant 0$. Suppose first $c \neq 0$ and write that $f(x + \lambda y, x + \lambda y) \geqslant 0$ for any scalar λ, which gives $a + b\bar{\lambda} + \bar{b}\lambda + c\lambda\bar{\lambda} \geqslant 0$; substituting $\lambda = -b/c$ yields the inequality. A similar argument applies when $c = 0$, $a \neq 0$; finally if $a = c = 0$, the substitution $\lambda = -b$ yields $-2b\bar{b} \geqslant 0$, i.e. $b = 0$.

(6.2.2) *In order that a positive hermitian form f on* E *be nondegenerate a necessary and sufficient condition is that there exist no isotropic vector for f other than* 0, i.e. *that $f(x, x) > 0$ for any $x \neq 0$ in* E.

Indeed, $f(x, x) = 0$ implies, by Cauchy–Schwarz, that $f(x, y) = 0$ for all $y \in E$.

(6.2.3) (Minkowski's inequality) *If f is a positive hermitian form, then*

$$(f(x+y, x+y))^{1/2} \leqslant (f(x, x))^{1/2} + (f(y, y))^{1/2}$$

for any pair of vectors x, y in E.

▲ As $f(x+y, x+y) = f(x, x) + f(x, y) + \overline{f(x, y)} + f(y, y)$, the inequality is equivalent to

$$2\mathscr{R}f(x, y) = f(x, y) + \overline{f(x, y)} \leqslant 2(f(x, x)f(y, y))^{1/2}$$

which follows from Cauchy–Schwarz.

▲ The function $x \to (f(x, x))^{1/2}$ therefore satisfies the conditions (I), (III), and (IV) of (Section 5.1); by (6.2.2), condition (II) of Section 5.1 is equivalent to the fact that the form f is nondegenerate. Therefore, when f is a nondegenerate positive hermitian form (also called a *positive definite form*), $(f(x, x))^{1/2}$ is *a norm* on E. A *prehilbert space* is a vector space E with a given nondegenerate positive hermitian form on E; when no confusion arises, that form is written $(x \mid y)$ and its value is called the *scalar product* of x and y; we always consider a prehilbert space E as a normed space, with the norm $\|x\| = (x \mid x)^{1/2}$, and of course, such a space is always considered as a metric space for the corresponding distance $\|x - y\|$. With these notations, the Cauchy–Schwarz inequality is written

(6.2.4) $$|(x|y)| \leqslant \|x\| \cdot \|y\|$$

and this proves, by (5.5.1), that for a real prehilbert space E, $(x, y) \to (x \mid y)$ is a *continuous* bilinear form on E × E (the argument of (5.5.1) can also be applied when E is a complex prehilbert space and proves again the continuity of $(x, y) \to (x \mid y)$, although this is not a bilinear form any more). We also have, as a particular case of (6.1.1):

(6.2.5) (Pythagoras' theorem) *In a prehilbert space* E, *if x, y are orthogonal vectors,*

$$\|x + y\|^2 = \|x\|^2 + \|y\|^2.$$

▲ An *isomorphism* of a prehilbert space E onto a prehilbert space E′ is a linear bijection of E onto E′ such that $(f(x) \mid f(y)) = (x \mid y)$ for any pair of vectors x, y of E. It is clear that an isomorphism is a linear *isometry* of E onto E′.

▲ Let E be a prehilbert space; then, on any vector subspace F of E, the restriction of the scalar product is a positive nondegenerate hermitian form; unless the contrary is stated, it is always that restriction which is meant when F is considered as a prehilbert space.

▲ A *Hilbert space* is a prehilbert space which is *complete*. Any finite dimensional prehilbert space is a Hilbert space by (5.9.1); other examples of Hilbert spaces will be constructed in Section 6.4.

If in example (6.1.4) we take $a > 0$, $b \geqslant 0$, $c \geqslant 0$, it can be shown that the prehilbert space thus defined is *not complete*.

PROBLEMS

1. Prove the last statement in the case $a = 1$, $b = c = 0$ (see Section 5.1, Problem 1).
2. (a) Let E be a real normed space such that, for any two points x, y of E,

$$\|x+y\|^2 + \|x-y\|^2 = 2(\|x\|^2 + \|y\|^2).$$

Show that $f(x, y) = \|x+y\|^2 - \|x\|^2 - \|y\|^2$ is a positive nondegenerate hermitian form on E. (In order to prove that $f(\lambda x, y) = \lambda f(x, y)$, use Problem 1 of Section 5.5.)

(b) Let E be a complex normed space, E_0 the underlying real vector space. Suppose there exists on E_0 a symmetric bilinear form $f(x, y)$ such that $f(x, x) = \|x\|^2$ for every $x \in E_0$. Show that there exists a hermitian form $g(x, y)$ on E such that $f(x, y) = \mathscr{R}(g(x, y))$, hence $g(x, x) = \|x\|^2$ for $x \in E$. (Using the first formula of Problem 1 of Section 6.1, prove that $f(ix, y) = -f(x, iy)$.)

(c) Let E be a complex normed space such that

$$\|x-y\|^2 + \|x+y\|^2 \leqslant 2(\|x\|^2 + \|y\|^2)$$

for any pair of points x, y of E. Show that there exists a nondegenerate positive hermitian form $f(x, y)$ on E such that $f(x, x) = \|x\|^2$. (Use (a) and (b)).

3. Let f be a positive nondegenerate hermitian form. In order that both sides of (6.2.1) be equal, it is necessary and sufficient that x and y be linearly dependent. In order that both sides of (6.2.3) be equal, it is necessary and sufficient that x and y be linearly dependent, and, if both are $\neq 0$, that $y = \lambda x$, with λ real and $\geqslant 0$.
4. Let a, b, c, d be four points in a prehilbert space E. Show that

$$\|a-c\| \cdot \|b-d\| \leqslant \|a-b\| \cdot \|c-d\| + \|b-c\| \cdot \|a-d\|.$$

(Reduce the problem to the case $a = 0$, and consider in E the transformation $x \to x/\|x\|^2$, defined for $x \neq 0$.) When are both sides of the inequality equal?

5. Let $(x_i)_{1 \leqslant i \leqslant n}$ be a finite sequence of points in a prehilbert space E. Show that

$$\sum_{i<j} \|x_i - x_j\|^2 = n\sum_{i=1}^{n} \|x_i\|^2 - \|\sum_{i=1}^{n} x_i\|^2.$$

If $\|x_i - x_j\| \geqslant 2$ for $i \neq j$, show that a ball containing all the x_i has a radius $\geqslant (2(n-1)/n)^{1/2}$.

3. ORTHOGONAL PROJECTION ON A COMPLETE SUBSPACE

(6.3.1) *Let* E *be a prehilbert space,* F *a complete vector subspace of* E *(i.e. a Hilbert space). For any $x \in E$, there is one and only one point $y = P_F(x) \in F$*

such that $\|x - y\| = d(x, \mathrm{F})$. *The point* $y = P_{\mathrm{F}}(x)$ *is also the only point* $z \in \mathrm{F}$ *such that* $x - z$ *is orthogonal to* F. *The mapping* $x \to P_{\mathrm{F}}(x)$ *of* E *onto* F *is linear, continuous, and of norm* 1 *if* $\mathrm{F} \neq \{0\}$; *its kernel* $\mathrm{F}' = P_{\mathrm{F}}^{-1}(0)$ *is the subspace orthogonal to* F, *and* E *is the topological direct sum* (see Section (5.4)) *of* F *and* F'. *Finally,* F *is the subspace orthogonal to* F'.

Let $\alpha = d(x, \mathrm{F})$; by definition, there exists a sequence (y_n) of points of F such that $\lim_{n \to \infty} \|x - y_n\| = \alpha$; we prove (y_n) is a *Cauchy sequence.* Indeed, for any two points u, v of E, it follows from (6.1.1) that

(6.3.1.1) $$\|u + v\|^2 + \|u - v\|^2 = 2(\|u\|^2 + \|v\|^2)$$

hence $\|y_m - y_n\|^2 = 2(\|x - y_m\|^2 + \|x - y_n\|^2) - 4\|x - \frac{1}{2}(y_m + y_n)\|^2$. But $\frac{1}{2}(y_m + y_n) \in \mathrm{F}$, hence $\|x - \frac{1}{2}(y_m + y_n)\|^2 \geqslant \alpha^2$; therefore, if n_0 is such that for $n \geqslant n_0$, $\|x - y_n\|^2 \leqslant \alpha^2 + \varepsilon$, we have, for $m \geqslant n_0$ and $n \geqslant n_0$, $\|y_m - y_n\|^2 \leqslant 4\varepsilon$, which proves our contention. As F is complete, the sequence (y_n) tends to a limit $y \in \mathrm{F}$, for which $\|x - y\| = d(x, \mathrm{F})$. Suppose $y' \in \mathrm{F}$ is also such that $\|x - y'\| = d(x, \mathrm{F})$; using again (6.3.11), we obtain $\|y - y'\|^2 = 4\alpha^2 - 4\|x - \frac{1}{2}(y + y')\|^2$, and as $\frac{1}{2}(y + y') \in \mathrm{F}$, this implies $\|y - y'\|^2 \leqslant 0$, i.e. $y' = y$. Let now $z \neq 0$ be any point of F, and write that $\|x - (y + \lambda z)\|^2 > \alpha^2$ for any real scalar $\lambda \neq 0$; this, by (6.1.1), gives

$$2\lambda \mathscr{R}(x - y \mid z) + \lambda^2 \|z\|^2 > 0$$

and this would yield a contradiction if we had $\mathscr{R}(x - y \mid z) \neq 0$, by a suitable choice of λ. Hence $\mathscr{R}(x - y \mid z) = 0$, and replacing z by iz (if E is a complex prehilbert space) shows that $\mathscr{I}(x - y \mid z) = 0$, hence $(x - y \mid z) = 0$ in every case; in other words $x - y$ is orthogonal to F. Let $y' \in \mathrm{F}$ be such that $x - y'$ is orthogonal to F; then, for any $z \neq 0$ in F, we have $\|x - (y' + z)\|^2 = \|x - y'\|^2 + \|z\|^2$ by Pythagoras' theorem, and this proves that $y' = y$ by the previous characterization of y.

▲ This last characterization of $y = P_{\mathrm{F}}(x)$ proves that P_{F} is linear, for if $x - y$ and $x' - y'$ are orthogonal to F, then $\lambda x - \lambda y$ is orthogonal to F and so is $(x + x') - (y + y') = (x - y) + (x' - y')$; as $y + y' \in \mathrm{F}$ and $\lambda y \in \mathrm{F}$, this shows that $y + y' = P_{\mathrm{F}}(x + x')$ and $\lambda y = P_{\mathrm{F}}(\lambda x)$. By Pythagoras' theorem, we have

(6.3.1.2) $$\|x\|^2 = \|P_{\mathrm{F}}(x)\|^2 + \|x - P_{\mathrm{F}}(x)\|^2$$

and this proves that $\|P_{\mathrm{F}}(x)\| \leqslant \|x\|$, hence (5.5.1) P_{F} is continuous and has norm $\leqslant 1$; but as $P_{\mathrm{F}}(x) = x$ for $x \in \mathrm{F}$, we have $\|P_{\mathrm{F}}\| = 1$ if F is not reduced to 0. The definition of P_{F} implies that $\mathrm{F}' = P_{\mathrm{F}}^{-1}(0)$ consists of the vectors x orthogonal to F; as $x = P_{\mathrm{F}}(x) + (x - P_{\mathrm{F}}(x))$ and $x - P_{\mathrm{F}}(x) \in \mathrm{F}'$ for any $x \in \mathrm{E}$, we have $\mathrm{E} = \mathrm{F} + \mathrm{F}'$; moreover, if $x \in \mathrm{F} \cap \mathrm{F}'$, x is isotropic, hence

$x = 0$, and this shows that the sum F + F′ is direct. Furthermore, the mapping $x \to P_F(x)$ being continuous, E is the topological direct sum of F and F′ (5.4.2). Finally, if $x \in$ E is orthogonal to F′, we have in particular $(x \mid x - P_F(x)) = 0$; but we also have $(P_F(x) \mid x - P_F(x)) = 0$, hence $\|x - P_F(x)\|^2 = 0$, i.e. $x = P_F(x) \in$ F. Q.E.D.

The linear mapping P_F is called the *orthogonal projection* of E onto F, and its kernel F′ the *orthogonal supplement* of F in E. Theorem (6.3.1) can be applied to any closed subspace F of a *Hilbert space* E (by (3.14.5)), or to any *finite dimensional* subspace F of a prehilbert space, by (5.9.1).

(6.3.2) *Let* E *be a prehilbert space; then, for any* $a \in$ E, $x \to (x \mid a)$ *is a continuous linear form of norm* $\|a\|$. *Conversely, if* E *is a Hilbert space, for any continuous linear form* u *on* E, *there is a unique vector* $a \in$ E *such that* $u(x) = (x \mid a)$ *for any* $x \in$ E.

By Cauchy–Schwarz, $|(x \mid a)| \leqslant \|a\| \cdot \|x\|$, which shows (by 5.5.1)) $x \to (x \mid a)$ is continuous and has a norm $\leqslant \|a\|$; on the other hand, if $a \neq 0$, then for $x_0 = a/\|a\|$, we have $(x_0 \mid a) = \|a\|$; as $\|x_0\| = 1$, this shows the norm of $x \to (x \mid a)$ is at least $\|a\|$. Suppose now E is a Hilbert space; the existence of the vector a $(=0)$ being obvious if $u = 0$, we can suppose $u \neq 0$. Then $\text{H} = u^{-1}(0)$ is a closed hyperplane in E; the orthogonal supplement H′ of H is a one-dimensional subspace; let $b \neq 0$ be a point of H′. Then we have $(x \mid b) = 0$ for any $x \in$ H. But any two equations of a hyperplane are proportional, hence there is a scalar λ such that $u(x) = \lambda(x \mid b) = (x \mid a)$ with $a = \bar{\lambda} b$ (see Appendix) for all $x \in$ E. The uniqueness of a follows from the fact that the form $(x \mid y)$ is nondegenerate.

PROBLEMS

1. Let B be the closed ball of center 0 and radius 1 in a prehilbert space E. Show that for each point x of the sphere of center 0 and radius 1, there exists a unique hyperplane of support of B (Section 5.8, Problem 3) containing x.
2. Let E be a prehilbert space, A a compact subset of E, δ its diameter. Show that there exist two points a, b of A such that $\|a - b\| = \delta$ and that there are two parallel hyperplanes of support of A (Section 5.8, Problem 3) containing a and b respectively, and such that their distance is equal to δ. (Consider the ball of center a and radius δ and apply the result of Problem 1.)
3. Let E be a Hilbert space, F a dense linear subspace of E, distinct from E (Section 5.9, Problem 2). Show that there exists in the prehilbert space F a closed hyperplane H such that there is no vector $\neq 0$ *in* F which is orthogonal to H.

4. Let X be a set, E a vector subspace of $\mathbf{C}^X$, on which is given a structure of complex *Hilbert* space. A mapping $(x, y) \to K(x, y)$ of $X \times X$ into $\mathbf{C}$ is called a *reproducing kernel* for E if it satisfies the two following conditions: (1) for every $y \in X$, the function $K(., y)$: $x \to K(x, y)$ belongs to E; (2) for any function $f \in E$, and any $y \in X$, $f(y) = (f \mid K(., y))$.

(a) Show that K is a *mapping of positive type* of $X \times X$ into $\mathbf{C}$, i.e., for any integer $n \geqslant 1$ and any finite sequence $(x_i)_{1 \leqslant i \leqslant n}$ of points of X, the mapping

$$((\lambda_i), (\mu_i)) \to \sum_{i,\,j} K(x_i, x_j)\lambda_i \bar{\mu}_j$$

of $\mathbf{C}^{2n}$ into $\mathbf{C}$ is a *positive hermitian form.* This in particular implies $K(x, x) \geqslant 0$ for every $x \in X$, $K(y, x) = \overline{K(x, y)}$ and $|K(x, y)|^2 \leqslant K(x, x)K(y, y)$ for x, y in X. Show that for $f \in E$, one has $|f(y)| \leqslant \|f\| \cdot (K(y, y))^{1/2}$ for $y \in X$.

(b) Show that if (f_n) is a sequence of functions of E which converges (for the Hilbert space structure) to $f \in E$, then, for every $x \in X$, the sequence $(f_n(x))$ converges to $f(x)$ in $\mathbf{C}$; the convergence is uniform in any subset of X where the function $x \to K(x, x)$ is bounded.

(c) Let $(x_i)_{1 \leqslant i \leqslant n}$ be a finite sequence of points of X, $(a_i)_{1 \leqslant i \leqslant n}$ a sequence of n complex numbers. Suppose $\det(K(x_i, x_j)) \neq 0$, so that the system of linear equations $\sum_{j=1}^{n} c_j K(x_i, x_j) = a_i$ $(1 \leqslant i \leqslant n)$ has a unique solution (c_j). Show that among the functions $f \in E$ such that $f(x_i) = a_i$ for $1 \leqslant i \leqslant n$, the function $f_0 = \sum_{j=1}^{n} c_j K(., x_j)$ has the smallest norm. In particular, among all functions $f \in E$ such that $f(x) = 1$ for a point $x \in X$ where $K(x, x) \neq 0$, the function $K(., x)/K(x, x)$ has the smallest norm.

(d) If X is a topological space and if all the functions $f \in E$ are *continuous* in X, then the functions $K(., x)$ (where x takes all values in X, or in a dense subset of X) form a *total* subset of E (show that there is no element $h \neq 0$ in E which is orthogonal to all the elements $K(., x)$). In particular, if X is a separable metric space, E is a separable Hilbert space.

5. (a) The notations being those of Problem 4, in order that there exist a reproducing kernel for E, a necessary and sufficient condition is that for every $x \in X$, the linear form $f \to f(x)$ be continuous in E. The reproducing kernel is then unique.

(b) Deduce from (a) that if there exists a reproducing kernel for E, there also exists a reproducing kernel for every closed vector subspace E_1 of E. If K_1 is the reproducing kernel for E_1, show that for every function $f \in E$, the function $y \to (f \mid K_1(., y))$ is the orthogonal projection of f in E_1. If E_2 is the orthogonal supplement of E_1 and K_2 the reproducing kernel for E_2, then $K_1 + K_2$ is the reproducing kernel for E.

6. Let X be a set, E a vector subspace of $\mathbf{C}^X$, on which is given a structure of complex *prehilbert* space. In order that there should exist a Hilbert space $\hat{E} \subset \mathbf{C}^X$ containing E, such that the scalar product on E is the restriction of the scalar product on $\hat{E}$, and that there exists a reproducing kernel for $\hat{E}$, it is necessary and sufficient that E satisfy the two following conditions: (1) for every $x \in X$, the linear form $f \to f(x)$ is continuous in E; (2) for any Cauchy sequence (f_n) in E such that, for every $x \in X$, $\lim_{n \to \infty} f_n(x) = 0$, one has $\lim_{n \to \infty} \|f_n\| = 0$. (To prove the conditions are sufficient, consider the subspace $\hat{E}$ of $\mathbf{C}^X$ whose elements are the functions f for which there exists a Cauchy sequence (f_n) in E such that $\lim_{n \to \infty} f_n(x) = f(x)$ for every $x \in X$. Show that, for all Cauchy sequences (f_n) having that property, the number $\lim_{n \to \infty} \|f_n\|$ is the same, and if $\|f\|$ is that number, this defines on $\hat{E}$ a structure of normed space which is deduced from a structure of prehilbert space which induces on E the given prehilbert structure; finally show that E is dense in Ê and that Ê is complete, hence a Hilbert space, and apply Problem 5(a) to Ê.)

7. Let X be a set, f a mapping of X into a prehilbert space H; show that the mapping $(x, y) \to (f(x) \mid f(y))$ of X × X into **C** is of positive type (Problem 4(a)).

8. Let X be a set, K a mapping of positive type of X × X into **C** (Problem 4(a)).

(a) Let E be the set of mappings $u : X \to \mathbf{C}$ such that there exists a real number $a \geqslant 0$ having the property that the mapping

$$(x, y) \to a\mathrm{K}(x, y) - u(x)\overline{u(y)}$$

is of positive type; let $m(u)$ be the smallest of all real numbers $a \geqslant 0$ having that property. Show that $m(u)$ is also the smallest number c such that, for every finite sequence (x_i) of elements of X, the inequality

$$\sum_{i,j} \mathrm{K}(x_i, x_j)\lambda_i\bar{\lambda}_j + c\mu\bar{\mu} + \sum_i (u(x_i)\lambda_i\bar{\mu} + \overline{u(x_i)\lambda_i\bar{\mu}}) \geqslant 0$$

holds for all complex numbers λ_i, μ (use the Cauchy–Schwarz inequality). For every $x \in \mathrm{X}$, show that $|u(x)|^2 \leqslant \mathrm{K}(x, x)m(u)$.

(b) Show that E is a vector subspace of $\mathbf{C}^{\mathrm{X}}$, that $(m(u))^{1/2}$ is a norm on E and that $m(u+v) + m(u-v) \geqslant 2(m(u) + m(v))$. Conclude that there is a nondegenerate positive hermitian form $g(u, v)$ on E × E such that $g(u, u) = m(u)$, and that for this form E is a *Hilbert* space; one writes $g(u, v) = (u \mid v)$. (Use Problem 2(c) of Section **6.2** to prove the existence of g; to show that E is complete, use the last inequality proved in (a)).

(c) For every $x \in \mathrm{X}$, show that the function $\mathrm{K}(., x)$ belongs to E and that $(\mathrm{K}(., x) \mid \mathrm{K}(., y)) = \mathrm{K}(x, y)$ for all $(x, y) \in \mathrm{X} \times \mathrm{X}$ (use Cauchy–Schwarz inequality). Prove that if X is a topological space and if K is continuous in X × X, the mapping $x \to \mathrm{K}(., x)$ of X into E is continuous.

(d) Deduce from (a) that the Hilbert space E defined in (b) has a reproducing kernel, and if F is the closed vector subspace of E generated by the functions $\mathrm{K}(., x)$, the reproducing kernel for F (Problem 5(b)) is equal to K.

9. Let E be a prehilbert space, N a *finite* dimensional vector subspace of E, M a vector subspace of E having infinite dimension, or finite dimension $>\dim(\mathrm{N})$. Show that there exists in M a point $x \neq 0$ such that $\|x\| = d(x, \mathrm{N})$. (Consider the intersection of M and of the orthogonal supplement of N.)

4. HILBERT SUM OF HILBERT SPACES

▲ Let (E_n) be a sequence of Hilbert spaces; on each of the E_n, we write the scalar product as $(x_n \mid y_n)$. Let E be the set of all sequences $x = (x_1, x_2, \ldots, x_n, \ldots)$ such that $x_n \in \mathrm{E}_n$ for each n, and the series $(\|x_n\|^2)$ is *convergent*. We first define on E a structure of *vector space*: it is clear that if $x = (x_n) \in \mathrm{E}$, then the sequence $(\lambda x_1, \ldots, \lambda x_n, \ldots)$ also belong to E. On the other hand, if $y = (y_n)$ is a second sequence belonging to E, we observe that $\|x_n + y_n\|^2 \leqslant 2(\|x_n\|^2 + \|y_n\|^2)$ by (6.3.1.1), hence the series $(\|x_n + y_n\|^2)$ is convergent by (5.3.1), and therefore the sequence $(x_1 + y_1, \ldots, x_n + y_n, \ldots)$ belongs to E. We define $x + y = (x_n + y_n)$,

$\lambda x = (\lambda x_n)$, and the verification of the axioms of vector spaces is trivial. On the other hand, from the Cauchy–Schwarz inequality, we have

$$|(x_n \mid y_n)| \leqslant \|x_n\| \cdot \|y_n\| \leqslant \tfrac{1}{2}(\|x_n\|^2 + \|y_n\|^2).$$

▲ Therefore, if $x = (x_n)$ and $y = (y_n)$ are in E, the series (of real or complex numbers) $((x_n \mid y_n))$ is *absolutely convergent.* We define, for $x = (x_n)$ and $y = (y_n)$ in E, the number $(x \mid y) = \sum_{n=1}^{\infty} (x_n \mid y_n)$; it is immediately verified that the mapping $(x, y) \to (x \mid y)$ is a Hermitian form on E. Moreover we have $(x \mid x) = \sum_{n=1}^{\infty} \|x_n\|^2$, hence $(x \mid y)$ is a positive nondegenerate hermitian form and defines on E a structure of prehilbert space. We finally prove E is in fact a *Hilbert space,* in other words it is *complete.* Indeed, let $(x^{(m)})$, where $x^{(m)} = (x_n^{(m)})$, be a Cauchy sequence in E: this means that for any $\varepsilon > 0$ there is an m_0 such that for $p \geqslant m_0$ and $q \geqslant m_0$, we have

$$\sum_{n=1}^{\infty} \|x_n^{(p)} - x_n^{(q)}\|^2 \leqslant \varepsilon. \tag{6.4.1}$$

For each fixed n, this implies first $\|x_n^{(p)} - x_n^{(q)}\|^2 \leqslant \varepsilon$, hence the sequence $(x_n^{(m)})_{m=1,2,\ldots}$ is a Cauchy sequence in E_n, and therefore converges to a limit y_n. From (6.4.1) we deduce that for any given N

$$\sum_{n=1}^{N} \|x_n^{(p)} - x_n^{(q)}\|^2 \leqslant \varepsilon$$

as soon as p and q are $\geqslant m_0$, hence, from the continuity of the norm, we deduce that $\sum_{n=1}^{N} \|x_n^{(p)} - y_n\|^2 \leqslant \varepsilon$ for $p \geqslant m_0$, and as this is true for all integers N, we have $\sum_{n=1}^{\infty} \|x_n^{(p)} - y_n\|^2 \leqslant \varepsilon$. This proves first that the sequence $(x_n^{(p)} - y_n)$ belongs to E, hence $y = (y_n)$ also belongs to E, and we have $\|x^{(p)} - y\|^2 \leqslant \varepsilon$ for $p \geqslant m_0$, which ends the proof by showing that the sequence $(x^{(m)})$ converges to y in E.

▲ We say that the Hilbert space E thus defined is the *Hilbert sum* of the sequence of Hilbert spaces (E_n). We observe that we can map each of the E_n into E by associating to each $x_n \in E_n$ the sequence $j_n(x_n) \in E$ equal to $(0, \ldots, 0, x_n, 0, \ldots)$ (all terms 0 except the nth equal to x_n); it is readily verified that j_n is an *isomorphism* of E_n onto a (necessarily closed) subspace E_n' of E; j_n is called the *natural injection* of E_n into E. From the definition of the scalar product in E, it follows that for $m \neq n$, any vector in E_m' is orthogonal to any vector in E_n'; furthermore, from the definition of the norm in E, it follows that for any $x = (x_n) \in E$, the series $(j_n(x_n))$ is *convergent* in E, and $x = \sum_{n=1}^{\infty} j_n(x_n)$ (observe that the series $(j_n(x_n))$ is *not* absolutely convergent in general). This proves that the (algebraic) sum of the subspaces E'_n of E (which is obviously *direct*) is *dense* in E, in other words that the smallest closed vector subspace containing all the E'_n is E itself. Conversely:

(6.4.2) *Let* F *be a Hilbert space,* (F_n) *a sequence of closed subspaces such that*: (1) *for* $m \neq n$, *any vector of* F_m *is orthogonal to any vector of* F_n; (2) *the algebraic sum* H *of the subspaces* F_n *is dense in* F. *Then, if* E *is the Hilbert sum of the* F_n, *there is a unique isomorphism of* F *onto* E *which on each* F_n *coincides with the natural injection* j_n *of* F_n *into* E.

▲ Let $F'_n = j_n(F_n)$, and let h_n be the mapping of F'_n onto F_n, inverse to j_n. Let G be the algebraic sum of the F'_n in E; that sum being direct, we can define a linear mapping h of G into F by the condition that it coincides with h_n on each F'_n. I claim that h is an isomorphism of G onto the prehilbert space H (which, incidentally, will prove that the (algebraic) sum of the F_n is *direct* in F); from the definition of the scalar product in E, we have to check that

$$\left(\sum_{k=1}^{n} x_k \,\middle|\, \sum_{k=1}^{n} y_k\right) = \sum_{k=1}^{n} (j_k(x_k) \mid j_k(y_k))$$

for $x_k \in F_k$, $y_k \in F_k$; but by assumption $(x_h \mid y_k) = 0$ if $h \neq k$, and the result follows from the fact that each j_k is an isomorphism. There is now a unique continuous extension $\bar{h}$ of h which is a linear mapping of $\bar{G} = E$ into $\bar{H} = F$, by (5.5.4); the principle of extension of identities (3.15.2) and the continuity of the scalar product show that $\bar{h}$ is an *isomorphism* of E onto a subspace of F, which, being complete and dense, must be F itself; the inverse of $\bar{h}$ satisfies the conditions of (6.4.2). Its uniqueness follows from the fact that it is completely determined in G and continuous in E (3.15.2). Under the condition of (6.4.2), the Hilbert space F is often identified with the Hilbert sum of its subspaces F_n.

Remark

(6.4.3) We can also prove (6.4.2) by establishing first that the sum of the F_n is *direct*; indeed, if $\sum_{i=1}^{n} x_i = 0$ with $x_i \in F_i$ $(1 \leqslant i \leqslant n)$ we also have $\left(x_j \,\middle|\, \sum_{i=1}^{n} x_i\right) = 0$ for any $j \leqslant n$, and as $(x_j \mid x_i) = 0$ for $i \neq j$, this boils down to $\|x_j\|^2 = 0$, hence $x_j = 0$ for $1 \leqslant j \leqslant n$. Then we define the inverse mapping g of h by the condition that it coincides with j_n on each F_n: we at once verify, as above, that g is an isomorphism of H onto G, and then (5.5.4) is applied in the same way. We observe that this argument still applies when F is a *prehilbert* space and the F_n are *complete* subspaces of F; it proves the existence of an isomorphism of F onto a *dense* subspace of the Hilbert sum E of the F_n, which coincides with j_n on each F_n.

PROBLEM

Let X be a set, E_1, E_2 two vector subspaces of $\mathbf{C}^X$, possessing reproducing kernels K_1, K_2 (Section 6.3, Problem 4). Let $E = E_1 + E_2 \subset \mathbf{C}^X$, and let F be the Hilbert sum of the Hilbert spaces E_1, E_2; the kernel of the surjective mapping u: $(f_1, f_2) \to f_1 + f_2$ of F into E is the subspace N of F consisting of the pairs $(f, -f)$ where $f \in E_1 \cap E_2$. Show that N is closed in F; if H is the orthogonal supplement of N in F, the restriction v of u to H is a bijection of H onto E; transporting by v the Hilbert structure of H, E is defined as a Hilbert space. Show that for that Hilbert space structure, E has a reproducing kernel equal to $K_1 + K_2$; the norm $\|f\|$ in E is equal to $\inf(\|f_1\|_1^2 + \|f_2\|_2^2)^{1/2}$ when (f_1, f_2) takes all values in F such that $f = f_1 + f_2$ ($\|f_1\|_1$ and $\|f_2\|_2$ being the norms in E_1 and E_2, respectively).

5. ORTHONORMAL SYSTEMS

If (with the notations of Section 6.4) we take for each E_n a *one-dimensional* space (identified to the field of scalars with the scalar product $(\xi \mid \eta) = \xi\bar{\eta}$), the Hilbert sum yields an example of an infinite dimensional Hilbert space E, which is usually written l^2 (with index **R** or **C** to indicate if necessary what the scalars are); the space $l^2_{\mathbf{R}}$ (resp. $l^2_{\mathbf{C}}$) is therefore the space of all sequences $x = (\xi_n)$ of real (resp. complex) numbers, such that $\sum_{n=1}^{\infty} |\xi_n|^2$ is convergent, with the scalar product $(x \mid y) = \sum_{n=1}^{\infty} \xi_n \bar{\eta}_n$.

In l^2, let e_n be the sequence having all its terms equal to 0 except the nth term equal to 1; we then have $(e_m \mid e_n) = 0$ for $m \neq n$, and $\|e_n\| = 1$ for each n, and we have seen in Section 6.4 that for every $x = (\xi_n)$ in l^2, we can write $x = \sum_{n=1}^{\infty} \xi_n e_n$, the series being *convergent* in l^2. We observe that this shows the sequence (e_n) is *total* in l^2, hence (5.10.1) l^2 is *separable.*

Let us now consider an arbitrary prehilbert space F; we say that a (finite or infinite) sequence (a_n) in F is an *orthogonal system* if $(a_m \mid a_n) = 0$ for $m \neq n$ and $a_n \neq 0$ for every n; we say that (a_n) is an *orthonormal system* if in addition $\|a_n\| = 1$ for each n. From any orthogonal system (a_n) we deduce at once an orthonormal system by "normalizing" (a_n), i.e. considering the sequence of the $b_n = a_n/\|a_n\|$. We have just seen an example of an orthonormal system in l^2; another fundamental example is the following:

(6.5.1) Let I be the interval $[-1, 1]$ of **R**, and let $F = \mathscr{C}_C(I)$ be the vector space of all continuous complex-valued functions defined on I. We define on F a scalar product by

$$(f \mid g) = \int_{-1}^{1} f(t)\overline{g(t)}\, dt$$

(the fact that this is a nondegenerate positive hermitian form is readily verified). For each positive or negative integer n, let

$$\varphi_n(t) = e^{\pi n i t}.$$

It is readily verified that $(\varphi_n/\sqrt{2})$ is an *orthonormal* system in F, called the *trigonometric system.*

Let now (a_n) be an arbitrary orthonormal system in a Hilbert space F; for each $x \in F$, we say that the number $c_n(x) = (x \mid a_n)$ is the nth *coefficient* (or nth *coordinate*) of x with respect to the system (a_n) ("nth *Fourier coefficient*" of x for the system **(6.5.1)**).

(6.5.2) *In a Hilbert space* F, *let* (a_n) *be an orthonormal system,* V *the closed subspace of* F *generated by the* a_n. *Then, for any* $x \in F$:

1. *the series* $\sum_{n=1}^{\infty} |(x \mid a_n)|^2$ *is convergent, and we have*

$$\sum_{n=1}^{\infty} |(x \mid a_n)|^2 = \|P_V(x)\|^2 \leqslant \|x\|^2 \qquad \textit{(Bessel's inequality)},$$

and

$$\sum_{n=1}^{\infty} (x \mid a_n)\overline{(y \mid a_n)} = (P_V(x) \mid P_V(y));$$

2. *the series of general term* $(x \mid a_n)a_n$ *is convergent in* F *and we have*

$$\sum_{n=1}^{\infty} (x \mid a_n)a_n = P_V(x).$$

Conversely, let (λ_n) *be a sequence of scalars such that* $\sum_{n=1}^{\infty} |\lambda_n|^2$ *is convergent. Then, there exists a unique vector* $y \in V$ *such that* $(y \mid a_n) = \lambda_n$ *for every* n; *any other vector* $x \in F$ *such that* $(x \mid a_n) = \lambda_n$ *for every* n *is such that* $x = y + z$, *with* z *orthogonal to* V, *and conversley.*

For any $x \in F$, we can write $x = P_V(x) + z$, with z orthogonal to V (6.3.1) and we have therefore $(x \mid a_n) = (P_V(x) \mid a_n)$. To prove the theorem, we may therefore assume $V = F$; but then, the one-dimensional subspaces F_n generated by the vectors a_n satisfy the assumptions of (6.4.2), and the results are mere restatements of (6.4.2) for that particular case (taking into account the definition of a Hilbert sum).

The most interesting case is that in which $V = F$, i.e., the orthogonal system (a_n) is *total*. It is then called a *Hilbert basis* for F; (e_n) is such a basis for l^2. It will be proved in (7.4.3) that the trigonometric system (6.5.1) is total. For a *Hilbert* space F and a *total* orthonormal system (a_n), we can replace everywhere P_V by the identity in (6.5.2); the relations

$$\sum_{n=1}^{\infty} |(x \mid a_n)|^2 = \|x\|^2$$

$$\sum_{n=1}^{\infty} (x \mid a_n)\overline{(y \mid a_n)} = (x \mid y)$$

are then called *Parseval's identities*. It follows at once from (6.5.2) that these identities represent not only necessary but *sufficient* conditions for (a_n) to be a total system in a Hilbert space.

(6.5.3) *In a Hilbert space* F, *a necessary and sufficient condition for an orthogonal system* (a_n) *to be total is that the relations* $(x \mid a_n) = 0$ *for every* n *imply* $x = 0$.

Indeed, by (6.5.2) this means that the relation $P_V(x) = 0$ implies $x = 0$, and this is equivalent to the relation $V = F$, since $P_V(x - P_V(x)) = 0$.

Remark

(6.5.4) Suppose E is a *prehilbert* space and the orthonormal system (a_n) in E is *total*. Then the results (1) and (2) of (6.5.2) are still valid, with $P_V(x)$ replaced by x; this follows by the same argument as in (6.5.2), using the *Remark* (6.4.3).

PROBLEMS

1. Let E be a Hilbert space with a Hilbert basis $(e_n)_{n \geq 1}$. Let A be the subset of E consisting of the linear combinations $x = \sum_{k=1}^{\infty} \lambda_k \left(1 - \frac{1}{k}\right) e_k$ with $\lambda_k \geq 0$ and $\sum_{k=1}^{n} \lambda_k = 1$ (n arbitrary).

(a) Show that the closure $\bar{A}$ is the set of all the sums of the series $\sum_{n=1}^{\infty} \lambda_n \left(1 - \frac{1}{n}\right) e_n$, where $\lambda_n \geqslant 0$, the series $\sum_{n=1}^{\infty} \lambda_n$ is convergent and has a sum equal to 1.

(b) Prove that the diameter of $\bar{A}$ is equal to $\sqrt{2}$ but that there is no pair of points a, b of $\bar{A}$ such that $\|a - b\| = \sqrt{2}$ (compare to Section **6.3**, Problem 2).

2. Let E be a Hilbert space with a Hilbert basis $(e_n)_{n \geqslant 0}$. Let $a_n = e_{2n}$ and $b_n = e_{2n} + \frac{1}{n+1} e_{2n+1}$ for every $n \geqslant 0$; let A (resp. B) be the closed vector subspace of E generated by the a_n (resp. b_n). Show that:

(a) $A \cap B = \{0\}$, hence the sum $A + B$ is direct (algebraically).

(b) The direct sum $A + B$ is *not* a topological direct sum (consider in that subspace the sequence of points $b_n - a_n$ and apply **(5.4.2.)**).

(c) The subspace $A + B$ of E is dense but not closed in E (show that the point $\sum_{n=0}^{\infty} (b_n - a_n)$ does not belong to $A + B$).

3. Show that the Banach space $\mathscr{L}(l^1; l^2)$ can be identified with the space of double sequences $U = (\alpha_{mn})$ such that: (1) the series $\sum_{m=0}^{\infty} |\alpha_{mn}|^2$ is convergent for every n: (2) $\sup_n \sum_{m=0}^{\infty} |\alpha_{mn}|^2$ is finite. The norm is then equal to $\|U\| = \sup_n \left(\sum_{m=0}^{\infty} |\alpha_{mn}|^2 \right)^{1/2}$ (same method as in Section **5.7**, Problem 2(b)).

4. (a) Let u be a continuous linear mapping of l^2 into itself, and let $u(e_n) = \sum_{m=0}^{\infty} \alpha_{mn} e_m$; show that the series $\sum_{n=0}^{\infty} |\alpha_{mn}|^2$ and $\sum_{m=0}^{\infty} |\alpha_{mn}|^2$ are convergent for all values of m and n, and that their sums are $\leqslant \|u\|^2$. (Observe that $x \to (u(x) \mid e_m)$ is a continuous linear form on E and use **(6.3.2)**.)

(b) Give an example of a double sequence (α_{mn}) such that $\sum_{n=0}^{\infty} |\alpha_{mn}|^2 \leqslant 1$ and $\sum_{m=0}^{\infty} |\alpha_{mn}|^2 \leqslant 1$ for all values of m and n, but such that there is *no* continuous linear mapping u of l^2 into itself satisfying the relations $(u(e_n) \mid e_m) = \alpha_{mn}$ for all pairs (m, n). (If V is a subspace of l^2 generated by the vectors e_n with $n \in H$, where H is a set of p integers, show that there is a linear mapping u_p of V into itself such that $(u_p(e_n) \mid e_m) = 1/\sqrt{p}$ for all indices m, n of the set H, but $\|u_p\| \geqslant \sqrt{p}$.)

6. ORTHONORMALIZATION

(6.6.1) *Let E be a separable prehilbert space, (b_n) a total sequence of linearly independent vectors in E (see* **(5.10.1)**), *and let V_n be the n-dimensional subspace of E generated by $b_1, \ldots, b_n$. Then if we define $c_n = b_n - P_{V_{n-1}}(b_n)$, (c_n) is a total orthogonal system, such that $c_1, \ldots, c_n$ generate V_n for each n.*

We use induction on n, assuming that $c_1, \ldots, c_{n-1}$ is an orthogonal system generating V_{n-1}; then, by definition of $P_{V_{n-1}}$ **(6.3.1)**, c_n is orthogonal to V_{n-1}, which proves that $(c_i \mid c_j) = 0$ for $1 \leqslant i < j \leqslant n$; moreover, as $b_n \notin V_{n-1}$ by assumption, $c_n \neq 0$, hence $c_1, \ldots, c_{n-1}, c_n$ is an orthogonal system; moreover, $b_n - c_n \in V_{n-1}$, hence $c_1, \ldots, c_n$ generate the same subspace as the union of V_{n-1} and $\{b_n\}$, i.e. V_n. This completes the proof.

If we normalize the system (c_n), by putting $a_n = c_n / \|c_n\|$, the system (a_n) is said to be deduced from (b_n) by the *orthonormalization process*. For instance, in the space $F = \mathscr{C}_C(I)$ considered in (6.5.1), the sequence (t^n) is total (as will be proved in (7.4.1)) and obviously consists of linearly independent vectors. If we denote by (Q_n) the orthonormal system deduced from (t^n) by orthonormalization, it is clear that $Q_n(t) = a_n t^n + \cdots$, polynomial of degree n (with $a_n \neq 0$) with real coefficients; the Q_n are (up to a constant factor) the *Legendre polynomials* (see Section 8.14, Problem 1).

(6.6.2) *Any separable prehilbert space* (resp. *Hilbert space*) *is isomorphic to a dense subspace of* l^2 (resp. *to* l^2).

As there exists in a separable prehilbert space a total orthonormal system by (6.6.1), the result follows at once from (6.5.2).

PROBLEMS

1. Let E be a separable noncomplete prehilbert space. Show that there exists in E an orthonormal system which is not total, but which is not properly contained in any orthonormal system (imbed E as a dense subspace of a Hilbert space, and use problem 3 of Section 6.3).
2. Let E be an infinite dimensional separable Hilbert space, V a closed vector subspace of E. Show that if V is infinite dimensional, there exists an isometry of E onto V (write E as the direct sum of V and its orthogonal supplement V′, and take Hilbert bases in V and V′.
3. Let $(x_i)_{1 \leqslant i \leqslant n}$ be a finite sequence of points in a prehilbert space E. The *Gram determinant* of that sequence is the determinant $G(x_1, x_2, \ldots, x_n) = \det((x_i \mid x_j))$.
   (a) Show that $G(x_1, \ldots, x_n) \geqslant 0$ and that $G(x_1, \ldots, x_n) = 0$ if and only if the x_i are linearly dependent. (Consider a Hilbert basis of the sub space generated by the x_i, and express the x_i as linear combinations of that basis.)
   (b) Suppose the x_i are linearly independent, and let V be the n-dimensional subspace which they generate. Show that the distance of a point x to V is equal to
   $$(G(x, x_1, \ldots, x_n)/G(x_1, \ldots, x_n))^{1/2}$$
   (find the projection of x on V, writing it as a linear combination of the x_i).
4. Let M be a compact subset of a Hilbert space E; if E_1 is the smallest closed vector subspace of E containing M, show that E_1 is separable.

5. Let $E \subset \mathbf{C}^X$ a *separable* Hilbert space having a reproducing kernel (Section 6.3, Problem 4).

(a) Let (f_n) be a Hilbert basis for E. Show that for every $(x, y) \in X \times X$ one has $K(x, y) = \sum_n f_n(x)\overline{f_n(y)}$, where the series converges in $\mathbf{C}$. For any function $g \in E$, if $c_n = (g \mid f_n)$, one has, for every $x \in X$, $g(x) = \sum_n c_n f_n(x)$, where the series converges in $\mathbf{C}$; in addition, that series is uniformly convergent in every subset of X where $K(x, x)$ is bounded.

(b) Conversely, let (f_n) be a sequence of complex functions defined in a set X, such that for every $x \in X$, $\sum_n |f_n(x)|^2 < +\infty$. For every sequence $(c_n) \in l^2_{\mathbf{C}}$, the series $\sum_n c_n f_n(x)$ is then convergent in $\mathbf{C}$ for every $x \in X$. The functions which are the sums of such series form a vector subspace $E \subset \mathbf{C}^X$, on which one defines a structure of separable Hilbert space by taking as scalar product, for $u = \sum_n c_n f_n$, $v = \sum_n d_n f_n$, the number $(u \mid v) = \sum_n c_n \bar{d}_n$. This space has a reproducing kernel $K(x, y) = \sum_n f_n(x)\overline{f_n(y)}$.

CHAPTER VII

SPACES OF CONTINUOUS FUNCTIONS

▲ Spaces of continuous functions are second only to Hilbert spaces as to their importance in functional analysis. Their definition makes it possible to give a much more intuitive meaning to the classical notion of uniform convergence. The most important results of the chapter are: 1. the Stone–Weierstrass approximation theorem (7.3.1), which is a very powerful tool for the proof of general results on continuous functions, by the device which consists in proving these results first for functions of a special type, and then extending them to all continuous functions by a density argument; 2. the Ascoli theorem (7.5.7), which lies at the root of most proofs of compactness in function spaces, and, together with (7.5.6), gives the motivation for the introduction of the concept of *equicontinuity*.

▲ The last section of Chapter VII introduces, as a useful technical tool in the development of calculus, a category of functions which are classically described as "functions with discontinuities of the first kind"; in an effort towards a more concise expression, and to avoid one more use of the overworked term "regular," the author has tentatively introduced the neologism "regulated functions" (corresponding to the French "fonctions réglées"), which he hopes will not sound too barbaric to English-speaking readers.

1. SPACES OF BOUNDED FUNCTIONS

▲ Let A be any set, F a real (resp. complex) normed space; a mapping f of A into F is *bounded* if $f(\mathrm{A})$ is bounded in F, or equivalently if $\sup_{t \in \mathrm{A}} \|f(t)\|$ is finite. The set $\mathscr{B}_{\mathrm{F}}(\mathrm{A})$ of all bounded mappings of A into F is a real (resp. complex) vector space, since $\|f(t) + g(t)\| \leqslant \|f(t)\| + \|g(t)\|$. Moreover, on this space,

(7.1.1)
$$\|f\| = \sup_{t \in A} \|f(t)\|$$

is a *norm*, as can be trivially verified. If F has finite dimension, and $(a_i)_{1 \leqslant i \leqslant n}$ is a basis for F such that $\|a_i\| = 1$, any mapping of A into F can be written in one and only one way

(7.1.1.1)
$$t \to f(t) = f_1(t)a_1 + \cdots + f_n(t)a_n$$

and f is bounded if and only if the scalar mappings f_i $(1 \leqslant i \leqslant n)$ are bounded. Moreover the norm of the mapping $t \to f_i(t)a_i$ is $\|f_i\| \cdot \|a_i\| = \|f_i\|$ (the norm of f_i being taken in $\mathscr{B}_{\mathbf{R}}(A)$, resp. $\mathscr{B}_{\mathbf{C}}(A)$). From (5.9.1), (5.4.2), and (5.5.1) it follows that there is a constant c such that for each $t \in A$, $|f_i(t)| \leqslant c \cdot \|f(t)\|$, hence $\|f_i\| \leqslant c \cdot \|f\|$. Let L_i be the subspace of $\mathscr{B}_F(A)$ consisting of all bounded mappings of the form $t \to f(t)a_i$ (f scalar). Then, using again (5.4.2) and (5.5.1), the preceding remarks prove that

(7.1.2) *If* F *has finite dimension, then* $\mathscr{B}_F(A)$ *is the topological direct sum of the* L_i, *each of which is isometric to* $\mathscr{B}_{\mathbf{R}}(A)$ (resp. $\mathscr{B}_{\mathbf{C}}(A)$).

In particular, if we consider the *real* normed vector space underlying $\mathscr{B}_{\mathbf{C}}(A)$, we see that it is the topological direct sum $\mathscr{B}_{\mathbf{R}}(A) + i\mathscr{B}_{\mathbf{R}}(A)$.

(7.1.3) *If* F *is a Banach space,* $\mathscr{B}_F(A)$ *is a Banach space.*

Let (f_n) be a Cauchy sequence in $\mathscr{B}_F(A)$; this means that for any $\varepsilon > 0$ there is n_0 such that $\|f_m - f_n\| \leqslant \varepsilon$ for $m \geqslant n_0$, $n \geqslant n_0$. From (7.1.1) it follows that for any $t \in A$ we have $\|f_m(t) - f_n(t)\| \leqslant \varepsilon$ for $m \geqslant n_0$, $n \geqslant n_0$, hence, as F is complete, the sequence $(f_n(t))$ converges to an element $g(t) \in F$. Furthermore we have, by the principle of extension of inequalities, $\|f_m(t) - g(t)\| \leqslant \varepsilon$ for any $t \in A$ and all $m \geqslant n_0$. From this we first deduce that $\|g(t)\| \leqslant \|f_m\| + \varepsilon$ for all $t \in A$, hence g is bounded. Moreover we have $\|f_m - g\| \leqslant \varepsilon$ for all $m \geqslant n_0$, and this means the sequence (f_n) converges to g in the space $\mathscr{B}_F(A)$.

In general, if (f_n) is a sequence of mappings of A into a metric space F, we say that the sequence (f_n) *converges simply in* A to a mapping g of A into F if, for each $t \in A$, the sequence $(f_n(t))$ converges in F to $g(t)$; we say that (f_n) *converges uniformly in* A to g if the sequence of numbers $\left(\sup_{t \in A} d(f_n(t), g(t))\right)$ tends to 0. It is clear that uniform convergence implies simple convergence; the converse is not true. If F is a normed space, convergence of a sequence of elements of $\mathscr{B}_F(A)$ therefore means, by definition, *uniform convergence* of the sequence in A. Similarly, we say that a series (u_n) which *converges in* $\mathscr{B}_F(A)$ to a sum s is *uniformly convergent in* A to the sum s. If F is a Banach space, it follows from (7.1.3) that in order that a series (u_n) in $\mathscr{B}_F(A)$ be uniformly convergent, a necessary and sufficient condition is that, for any $\varepsilon > 0$, there exist an integer n_0 such that, for $n \geqslant n_0, p \geqslant 0$ *and any* $t \in A$, we have

$$\|u_n(t) + u_{n+1}(t) + \cdots + u_{n+p}(t)\| \leqslant \varepsilon.$$

From (7.1.3) and (5.3.2) it follows that if F is a Banach space and if a series (u_n) of bounded functions is such that the series $(\|u_n\|)$ converges in **R**, then the series (u_n) is uniformly convergent; moreover, for each $t \in A$, since $\|u_n(t)\| \leqslant \|u_n\|$ the series $(u_n(t))$ is absolutely convergent in F. However, these two properties *do not* imply that the series $(\|u_n\|)$ is convergent; to avoid misunderstandings, we therefore say that the series (u_n) is *normally convergent* in $\mathscr{B}_F(A)$ if the series $(\|u_n\|)$ converges. We define similarly a *normally summable* family $(u_\lambda)_{\lambda \in L}$ in $\mathscr{B}_F(A)$ (L denumerable, cf. Section 5.3).

PROBLEMS

1. In the space $\mathscr{B}_{\mathbf{R}}(\mathbf{R})$, let u_n be the function equal to $1/n$ for $n \leqslant t < n+1$, to 0 for other values of t. Show that the series (u_n) is uniformly and commutatively convergent (Section 5.3, Problem 4) and that for every $t \in \mathbf{R}$, the series $(u_n(t))$ is absolutely convergent, but that (u_n) is not normally convergent.
2. Let A be any set; show that the mapping $u \to \sup_{t \in A} u(t)$ of $\mathscr{B}_{\mathbf{R}}(A)$ into **R** is continuous.
3. Let E be a metric space, F a normed space; show that the set of all mappings $f \in \mathscr{B}_F(E)$ whose oscillation (Section 3.14) at every point of E is at most equal to a given number $\alpha > 0$, is closed in the space $\mathscr{B}_F(E)$.

2. SPACES OF BOUNDED CONTINUOUS FUNCTIONS

Let E now be a metric space; we denote by $\mathscr{C}_F(E)$ the vector space of all *continuous* mappings of E into the normed space F, by $\mathscr{C}_F^\infty(E)$ the set of all *bounded continuous* mappings of E into F. We note that if E is compact, $\mathscr{C}_F^\infty(E) = \mathscr{C}_F(E)$ by (3.17.10). In general we have $\mathscr{C}_F^\infty(E) = \mathscr{C}_F(E) \cap \mathscr{B}_F(E)$. We will consider $\mathscr{C}_F^\infty(E)$ as a *normed* subspace of $\mathscr{B}_F(E)$, unless the contrary is explicitly stated. If F is finite dimensional, in the decomposition (7.1.2.1) f is continuous if and only if each of the f_i is continuous (see (3.20.4) and (5.4.2)). The remarks preceding (7.1.2) then show that in such a case, $\mathscr{C}_F^\infty(E)$ is a topological direct sum of a finite number of subspaces, each of which is isometric to $\mathscr{C}_{\mathbf{R}}^{\infty}(\mathrm{E})$ (resp $\mathscr{C}_{\mathbf{C}}^{\infty}(\mathrm{E})$). In particular, the real normed space underlying $\mathscr{C}_{\mathbf{C}}^{\infty}(\mathrm{E})$ is the topological direct sum $\mathscr{C}_{\mathbf{R}}^{\infty}(\mathrm{E}) + i\mathscr{C}_{\mathbf{R}}^{\infty}(\mathrm{E})$.

(7.2.1) *The subspace $\mathscr{C}_{\mathrm{F}}^{\infty}(\mathrm{E})$ is closed in $\mathscr{B}_{\mathrm{F}}(\mathrm{E})$; in other words, a uniform limit of bounded continuous functions is continuous.*

Indeed, let (f_n) be a sequence of bounded continuous mappings of E into F, which converges to g in $\mathscr{B}_{\mathrm{F}}(\mathrm{E})$; for any $\varepsilon > 0$, there is therefore an integer n_0 such that $\|f_n - g\| \leqslant \varepsilon/3$ for $n \geqslant n_0$. For any $t_0 \in \mathrm{E}$, let V be a neighborhood of t_0 such that $\|f_{n_0}(t) - f_{n_0}(t_0)\| \leqslant \varepsilon/3$ for any $t \in \mathrm{V}$. Then, as $\|f_{n_0}(t) - g(t)\| \leqslant \varepsilon/3$ for any $t \in \mathrm{E}$, we have $\|g(t) - g(t_0)\| \leqslant \varepsilon$ for any $t \in \mathrm{V}$, which proves the continuity of g.

Well-known examples (e.g. the functions $x \to x^n$ in $[0, 1]$) show that a limit of a *simply* convergent sequence of continuous functions need not be continuous. On the other hand, examples are easily given of sequences of continuous functions which converge *nonuniformly* to a continuous function (see Problem 2). However (see also (7.5.6)):

(7.2.2) (Dini's theorem) *Let* E *be a compact metric space. If an increasing (resp. decreasing) sequence (f_n) of real-valued continuous functions converges simply to a continuous function g, it converges uniformly to g.*

▲ Suppose the sequence is increasing. For each $\varepsilon > 0$ and each $t \in \mathrm{E}$, there is an index $n(t)$ such that for $m \geqslant n(t)$, $g(t) - f_m(t) \leqslant \varepsilon/3$. As g and $f_{n(t)}$ are continuous, there is a neighborhood $\mathrm{V}(t)$ of t such that the relation $t' \in \mathrm{V}(t)$ implies $|g(t) - g(t')| \leqslant \varepsilon/3$ and $|f_{n(t)}(t) - f_{n(t)}(t')| \leqslant \varepsilon/3$; hence, for any $t' \in \mathrm{V}(t)$ we have $g(t') - f_{n(t)}(t') \leqslant \varepsilon$. Take now a finite number of points t_i in E such that the $\mathrm{V}(t_i)$ cover E, and let n_0 be the largest of the integers $n(t_i)$. Then for any $t \in \mathrm{E}$, t belongs to one of the $\mathrm{V}(t_i)$, hence, for $n \geqslant n_0$, $g(t) - f_n(t) \leqslant g(t) - f_{n_0}(t) \leqslant g(t) - f_{n(t_i)}(t) \leqslant \varepsilon$. Q.E.D.

PROBLEMS

1. Let E be a metric space, F a normed space, (u_n) a sequence of bounded continuous mappings of E into F which converges simply in E to a bounded function v.
(a) In order that v be continuous at a point $x_0 \in \mathrm{E}$, it is necessary and sufficient that for any $\varepsilon > 0$ and any integer m, there exist a neighborhood V of x_0 and an index $n > m$ such that $\|v(x) - u_n(x)\| \leqslant \varepsilon$ for every $x \in \mathrm{V}$.
(b) Suppose in addition E is compact. Then, in order that v be continuous in E, it is necessary and sufficient that for any $\varepsilon > 0$ and any integer m, there exist a finite number

of indices $n_i > m$ such that, for every $x \in \mathrm{E}$, there is at least one index i for which $\|v(x) - u_{n_i}(x)\| \leqslant \varepsilon$ (use (a) and the Borel–Lebesgue axiom).

2. For any integer $n > 0$, let g_n be the continuous function defined in $\mathbf{R}$ by the conditions that $g_n(t) = 0$ for $t \leqslant 0$ and $t \geqslant 2/n$, $g_n(1/n) = 1$, and $g_n(t)$ has the form $\alpha t + \beta$ (with suitable constants α, β) in each of the intervals $[0, 1/n]$ and $[1/n, 2/n]$. The sequence (g_n) converges simply to 0 in $\mathbf{R}$, but the convergence is not uniform in any interval containing $t = 0$.

Let $m \to r_m$ be a bijection of $\mathbf{N}$ onto the set $\mathbf{Q}$ of rational numbers, and let $f_n(t) = \sum_{m=0}^{\infty} 2^{-m} g_n(t - r_m)$. The functions f_n are continuous (**7.2.1**), and the sequence (f_n) converges simply to 0 in $\mathbf{R}$, but the convergence is not uniform in *any* interval of $\mathbf{R}$.

3. Let I be a compact interval of $\mathbf{R}$, and (f_n) a sequence of monotone real functions defined in I, which converge simply in I to a continuous function f. Show that f is monotone, and that the sequence (f_n) converges uniformly to f in I.

4. Let E be a metric space, F a Banach space, A a dense subset of E. Let (f_n) be a sequence of bounded continuous mappings of E into F such that the restrictions of the functions f_n to A form a uniformly convergent sequence; show that (f_n) is uniformly convergent in E.

5. Let E be a metric space, F a normed space. Show that the mapping $(x, u) \to u(x)$ of $\mathrm{E} \times \mathscr{C}_{\mathrm{F}}^{\infty}(\mathrm{E})$ into F is continuous.

6. Let E, E′ be two metric spaces, F a normed space. For each mapping f of $\mathrm{E} \times \mathrm{E}'$ into F and each $y \in \mathrm{E}'$, let f_y be the mapping $x \to f(x, y)$ of E into F.

(a) Show that if f is bounded, if each f_y is continuous in E and if the mapping $y \to f_y$ of E′ into $\mathscr{C}_{\mathrm{F}}^{\infty}(\mathrm{E})$ is continuous, then f is continuous. Prove the converse if in addition E is compact (use Problem 3(a) in Section **3.20**).

(b) Take $\mathrm{E} = \mathrm{E}' = \mathrm{F} = \mathbf{R}$, and let $f(x, y) = \sin xy$, which is continuous and bounded in $\mathrm{E} \times \mathrm{E}'$; show that the mapping $y \to f_y$ of E′ into $\mathscr{C}_{\mathrm{F}}^{\infty}(\mathrm{E})$ is not continuous at any point of E′.

(c) Suppose both E and E′ are compact, and for any $f \in \mathscr{C}_{\mathrm{F}}(\mathrm{E} \times \mathrm{E}')$, let $\tilde{f}$ be the mapping $y \to f_y$ of E′ into $\mathscr{C}_{\mathrm{F}}(\mathrm{E})$; show that the mapping $f \to \tilde{f}$ is a linear isometry of $\mathscr{C}_{\mathrm{F}}(\mathrm{E} \times \mathrm{E}')$ onto $\mathscr{C}_{\mathscr{C}_{\mathrm{F}}(\mathrm{E})}(\mathrm{E}')$.

7. Let E be a metric space, F a normed space. For each bounded continuous mapping f of E into F, let $\mathrm{G}(f)$ be the graph of f in the space $\mathrm{E} \times \mathrm{F}$.

(a) Show that $f \to \mathrm{G}(f)$ is a uniformly continuous injective mapping of the normed space $\mathscr{C}_{\mathrm{F}}^{\infty}(\mathrm{E})$ into the space $\mathfrak{F}(\mathrm{E} \times \mathrm{F})$ of closed sets in $\mathrm{E} \times \mathrm{F}$, which is made into a metric space by the Hausdorff distance (see Section **3.16**, Problem 3). Let Γ be the image of $\mathscr{C}_{\mathrm{F}}^{\infty}(\mathrm{E})$ by the mapping $f \to \mathrm{G}(f)$.

(b) Show that if E is compact, the inverse mapping G^{-1} of Γ onto $\mathscr{C}_{\mathrm{F}}^{\infty}(\mathrm{E})$ is continuous (give an indirect proof).

(c) Show that if $\mathrm{E} = [0, 1]$ and $\mathrm{F} = \mathbf{R}$, G^{-1} is not uniformly continuous.

8. Let E be a metric space with a bounded distance d. For each $x \in \mathrm{E}$ let d_x be the bounded continuous mapping $y \to d(x, y)$ of E into $\mathbf{R}$. Show that $x \to d_x$ is an isometry of E onto a subspace of the Banach space $\mathscr{C}_{\mathbf{R}}^{\infty}(\mathrm{E})$.

3. THE STONE–WEIERSTRASS APPROXIMATION THEOREM

▲ For any metric space E, the vector space $\mathscr{C}_{\mathbf{R}}^{\infty}(\mathrm{E})$ (resp. $\mathscr{C}_{\mathbf{C}}^{\infty}(\mathrm{E})$) is an *algebra* over the real (resp. complex) field; from (**7.1.1**) it follows that we have in that algebra $\|fg\| \leqslant \|f\| \cdot \|g\|$, hence, by (**5.5.1**), the bilinear mapping $(f, g) \to fg$

is continuous. From that remark, it easily follows that for any subalgebra A of $\mathscr{C}_{\mathbf{R}}^{\infty}(\mathrm{E})$ (resp. $\mathscr{C}_{\mathbf{C}}^{\infty}(\mathrm{E})$), the closure m of A in $\mathscr{C}_{\mathbf{R}}^{\infty}(\mathrm{E})$ (resp. $\mathscr{C}_{\mathbf{C}}^{\infty}(\mathrm{E})$) is again a subalgebra (see the proof of (5.4.1)).

▲ We say that a subset A of $\mathscr{B}_{\mathbf{R}}(\mathrm{E})$ (resp. $\mathscr{B}_{\mathbf{C}}(\mathrm{E})$) *separates points of* E if for any pair of distinct points x, y in E, there is a function $f \in \mathrm{A}$ such that $f(x) \neq f(y)$.

(7.3.1) (Stone–Weierstrass theorem) *Let* E *be a compact metric space. If a subalgebra* A *of* $\mathscr{C}_{\mathbf{R}}(\mathrm{E})$ *contains the constant functions and separates points of* E, A *is dense in the Banach space* $\mathscr{C}_{\mathbf{R}}(\mathrm{E})$.

▲ In other words, if S is a subset of $\mathscr{C}_{\mathbf{R}}(\mathrm{E})$ which separates points, for any continuous real-valued function f on E, there is a sequence (g_n) of functions converging *uniformly* to f, such that each g_n can be expressed as a *polynomial* in the functions of S, with real coefficients.

▲ The proof is divided in several steps.

(7.3.1.1) *There exists a sequence of real polynomials* (u_n) *which in the interval* $[0, 1]$ *is increasing and converges uniformly to* $\sqrt{t}$.

▲ Define u_n by induction, taking $u_1 = 0$, and putting

(7.3.1.2) $$u_{n+1}(t) = u_n(t) + \tfrac{1}{2}(t - u_n^2(t)) \qquad \text{for} \quad n \geqslant 1.$$

We prove by induction that $u_{n+1} \geqslant u_n$ and $u_n(t) \leqslant \sqrt{t}$ in $[0, 1]$. From (7.3.1.2), we see the first result follows from the second. On the other hand

$$\begin{aligned}\sqrt{t} - u_{n+1}(t) &= \sqrt{t} - u_n(t) - \tfrac{1}{2}(t - u_n^2(t))\\ &= (\sqrt{t} - u_n(t))(1 - \tfrac{1}{2}(\sqrt{t} + u_n(t)))\end{aligned}$$

and from $u_n(t) \leqslant \sqrt{t}$ we deduce $\tfrac{1}{2}(\sqrt{t} + u_n(t)) \leqslant \sqrt{t} \leqslant 1$. For each $t \in [0, 1]$, the sequence $(u_n(t))$ is thus increasing and bounded, hence converges to a limit $v(t)$ (4.2.1); but (7.3.1.2) yields $t - v^2(t) = 0$ and as $v(t) \geqslant 0$, $v(t) = \sqrt{t}$. As v is continuous and the sequence (u_n) is increasing, Dini's theorem (7.2.2) proves that (u_n) converges uniformly to v.

(7.3.1.3) *For any function* $f \in \mathrm{A}$, $|f|$ *belongs to the closure* $\bar{\mathrm{A}}$ *of* A *on* $\mathscr{C}_{\mathbf{R}}(\mathrm{E})$.

▲ Let $a = \|f\|$. By (7.3.1.1), the sequence of functions $u_n(f^2/a^2)$, which belong to A (by definition of an algebra), converges uniformly to $(f^2/a^2)^{1/2} = |f|/a$ in E.

•(7.3.1.4) *For any pair of functions f, g in $\bar{A}$,* $\inf(f, g)$ *and* $\sup(f, g)$ *belong to* $\bar{A}$.

▲ For we can write $\sup(f, g) = \frac{1}{2}(f + g + |f - g|)$ and $\inf(f, g) = \frac{1}{2}(f + g - |f - g|)$; the result therefore follows from (7.3.1.3) applied to the algebra $\bar{A}$.

(7.3.1.5) *For any pair of distinct points x, y in E and any pair of real numbers α, β, there is a function $f \in \bar{A}$ such that $f(x) = \alpha, f(y) = \beta$.*

▲ By assumption, there is a function $g \in A$ such that $g(x) \neq g(y)$. As A contains the constant functions, take $f = \alpha + (\beta - \alpha)(g - \gamma)/(\delta - \gamma)$, where $\gamma = g(x), \delta = g(y)$.

(7.3.1.6) *For any function $f \in \mathscr{C}_{\mathbf{R}}(E)$, any point $x \in E$, and any $\varepsilon > 0$, there is a function $g \in \bar{A}$ such that $g(x) = f(x)$ and $g(y) \leqslant f(y) + \varepsilon$ for any $y \in E$.*

▲ For any point $z \in E$, let h_z be a function of $\bar{A}$ such that $h_z(x) = f(x)$ and $h_z(z) \leqslant f(z) + \varepsilon/2$; the existence of such a function is obvious for $z = x$ and follows from (7.3.1.5) for $z \neq x$. There exists a neighborhood $V(z)$ of z such that for $y \in V(z)$, $h_z(y) \leqslant f(y) + \varepsilon$, due to the continuity of f and h_z. Cover E with a finite number of neighborhoods $V(z_i)$. Then, by (7.3.1.4), the function $g = \inf_i(h_{z_i})$ belongs to $\bar{A}$ and satisfies the required conditions, since every $y \in E$ belongs to some $V(z_i)$.

(7.3.1.7) $\bar{A} = \mathscr{C}_{\mathbf{R}}(E)$.

▲ Let f be any function of $\mathscr{C}_{\mathbf{R}}(E)$; for any $\varepsilon > 0$ and for each $x \in E$, let $g_x \in \bar{A}$ be such that $g_x(x) = f(x)$ and $g_x(y) \leqslant f(y) + \varepsilon$ for all $y \in E$ (7.3.1.6). Then, there is a neighborhood $U(x)$ of x such that, for $y \in U(x)$, $g_x(y) \geqslant f(y) - \varepsilon$, due to the continuity of f and g_x. Cover E with a finite number of neighborhoods $U(x_i)$. Then, by (7.3.1.4), the function $\varphi = \sup_i(g_{x_i})$ belongs to $\bar{A}$ and is such that, for any $y \in E$, $f(y) - \varepsilon \leqslant \varphi(y) \leqslant f(y) + \varepsilon$ (since every $y \in E$ belongs to some $U(x_i)$); in other words $\|f - \varphi\| \leqslant \varepsilon$, and this shows that f belongs to the closure of $\bar{A}$, i.e. to $\bar{A}$ itself.

The corresponding theorem for $\mathscr{C}_{\mathbf{C}}(E)$ is *false* (see Chapter IX); there is only the weaker result:

(7.3.2) *Let* E *be a compact metric space. If a subalgebra* A *of* $\mathscr{C}_{\mathbf{C}}(E)$ *contains the constant functions, separates points of* E, *and is such that for each* $f \in A$ *the conjugate function* $\bar{f}$ *also belongs to* A, *then* A *is dense in* $\mathscr{C}_{\mathbf{C}}(E)$.

▲ We remark that for any $f \in A$, $\mathscr{R}f = \frac{1}{2}(f + \bar{f})$ and $\mathscr{I}f = (f - \bar{f})/2i$ also belong to A; hence, if A_0 is the (real) subalgebra of A consisting of real-valued functions, it follows at once from the definition that A_0 separates points of E and contains the (real) constant functions. Therefore A_0 is dense in $\mathscr{C}_{\mathbf{R}}(E)$, and the density of A in $\mathscr{C}_{\mathbf{C}}(E) = \mathscr{C}_{\mathbf{R}}(E) + i\mathscr{C}_{\mathbf{R}}(E)$ follows at once, since $A = A_0 + iA_0$.

4. APPLICATIONS

In the Stone–Weierstrass theorem, take for E any compact subset of $\mathbf{R}^n$, and for A the algebra of the restrictions to E of the *polynomials* in the n coordinates. The separation condition is satisfied, since for two distinct points of E, at least one of the coordinates has distinct values. Hence we have the original Weierstrass approximation theorem:

(7.4.1) *Any real-valued continuous function on a compact subset* E *of* $\mathbf{R}^n$ *is the limit of a sequence of polynomials which converges uniformly in* E.

Take now for E the unit circle $x^2 + y^2 = 1$ in $\mathbf{R}^2$, parametrized by the angle πt, so that continuous functions on E can be identified with continuous functions on $\mathbf{R}$ having the period 2 (see Chapter IX). Take for A the (complex) algebra generated by the constants and the functions $e^{\pi i t}$ and $e^{-\pi i t}$; it is immediate that the elements of A are the *trigonometric polynomials* $\sum_{n=-N}^{N} c_n e^{\pi n i t}$. As the function $e^{\pi i t}$ separates the points of E, all the conditions of (7.3.2) are satisfied, hence:

(7.4.2) *Any continuous complex-valued function on* $\mathbf{R}$, *which is periodic of period* 2, *is the limit of a sequence of trigonometric polynomials, which converges uniformly in* $\mathbf{R}$.

This last result enables us to give a proof of the following fact, which was announced in Section 6.5:

(7.4.3) *The trigonometric system is total in the prehilbert space* $\mathrm{F} = \mathscr{C}_{\mathbf{C}}(\mathrm{I})$ (as defined in (6.5.1); note that here we do not put on $\mathscr{C}_{\mathbf{C}}(\mathrm{I})$ the norm (7.1.1)).

Indeed, for any function $f \in \mathscr{C}_{\mathbf{C}}(\mathrm{I})$ and any integer $n > 0$, let g be the function equal to f for $-1 + 1/n \leqslant t \leqslant 1$, equal to $f(1)$ for $t = -1$, and linear between -1 and $-1 + 1/n$; then $f(t) - g(t) = 0$ if $t \geqslant -1 + 1/n$, and $|f(t) - g(t)| \leqslant 4\|f\|_\infty$ for the other values of t (we write $\|\,..\,\|_\infty$ for the norm defined by (7.1.1) and $\|\,..\,\|_2$ for the prehilbert norm). Therefore, we have

$$\|f - g\|_2^2 = \int_{-1}^{1} |f(t) - g(t)|^2 \, dt \leqslant 16 \|f\|_\infty^2 / n;$$

in other words, $\|f - g\|_2$ is arbitrarily small. As g is continuous and can be extended by periodicity since $g(1) = g(-1)$, there is, by (7.4.2), a trigonometric polynomial h such that $\|g - h\|_2 \leqslant \sqrt{2}\,\|g - h\|_\infty$ is arbitrarily small, and this ends the proof.

(7.4.4) *If* E *is a compact metric space, the spaces* $\mathscr{C}_{\mathbf{R}}(\mathrm{E})$ *and* $\mathscr{C}_{\mathbf{C}}(\mathrm{E})$ *are separable.*

As $\mathscr{C}_{\mathbf{C}}(\mathrm{E})$ is the topological direct sum of $\mathscr{C}_{\mathbf{R}}(\mathrm{E})$ and $i\mathscr{C}_{\mathbf{R}}(\mathrm{E})$, we need only give the proof for $\mathscr{C}_{\mathbf{R}}(\mathrm{E})$. Let (U_n) be a denumerable basis for the topology of E (3.16.2), and let $g_n(t) = d(t, \mathrm{E} - \mathrm{U}_n)$. The monomials $g_1^{\alpha_1} \cdots g_n^{\alpha_n}$ in the g_n also form a denumerable set (h_n) (by (1.9.3) and (1.9.4)), and the vector space A generated by the h_n is the subalgebra of $\mathscr{C}_{\mathbf{R}}(\mathrm{E})$ generated by the g_n. If we prove that A is dense in $\mathscr{C}_{\mathbf{R}}(\mathrm{E})$, our proof will be complete (5.10.1); but we only have to apply the Stone–Weierstrass theorem, and therefore check that the family (g_n) separates points of E. But if $x \neq y$, there is a U_n such that $x \in \mathrm{U}_n$, $y \notin \mathrm{U}_n$, hence by definition $g_n(x) \neq 0$, $g_n(y) = 0$. Q.E.D.

PROBLEMS

1. Let E, F be two compact metric spaces, f a continuous mapping of $\mathrm{E} \times \mathrm{F}$ into **R**. Show that for any $\varepsilon > 0$ there exists a finite system $(u_i)_{1 \leqslant i \leqslant n}$ of continuous mappings of E into **R** and a finite system $(v_i)_{1 \leqslant i \leqslant n}$ of continuous mappings of F into **R** such that, for any $(x, y) \in \mathrm{E} \times \mathrm{F}$, $|f(x, y) - \sum_{i=1}^{n} u_i(x) v_i(y)| \leqslant \varepsilon$. (Apply the Stone–Weierstrass theorem to the algebra generated by the continuous mappings $(x, y) \to u(x)$ and $(x, y) \to v(y)$, where $u \in \mathscr{C}_{\mathbf{R}}(\mathrm{E})$ and $v \in \mathscr{C}_{\mathbf{R}}(\mathrm{F})$.)

2. Let $n \to r_n$ be a bijection of $\mathbf{N}$ onto the set of rational numbers in the interval $[0, 1] = \mathrm{I}$. Define by induction a sequence (I_n) of closed intervals contained in I, such that: (1) the center of I_n is r_{kn}, where k_n is the smallest index p such that r_p is not in the union of the intervals I with $h < n$; (2) the length of I_n is $\leqslant 1/4^n$, and I_n does not meet any of the I_h with $h < n$. In the product space $\mathrm{I} \times \mathbf{R}$, define a bounded real continuous function u having the following properties: (1) for each integer $n \geqslant 0$, $x \to u(x, n)$ takes the value 1 for $x = r_{kn}$, is equal to 0 for $x \notin \mathrm{I}_n$, and $0 \leqslant u(x, n) \leqslant 1$ for all $x \in \mathrm{I}$; (2) for each $x \in \mathrm{I}$, the function $y \to u(x, y)$ has the form $\alpha y + \beta$ in each of the intervals $]-\infty, 0[$ and $[n, n+1]$ $(n \in \mathbf{N})$. Show that there is no finite system of functions $v_i \in \mathscr{C}_{\mathbf{R}}(\mathrm{I})$, $w_i \in \mathscr{C}_{\mathbf{R}}(\mathbf{R})$ $(1 \leqslant i \leqslant n)$ such that $\left| u(x, y) - \sum_{i=1}^{n} v_i(x) w_i(y) \right| \leqslant 1/4$ in $\mathrm{I} \times \mathbf{R}$. (Suppose the contrary; consider the functions $u_n : x \to u(x, n)$ in $\mathscr{C}_{\mathbf{R}}(\mathrm{I})$, and observe that $\|u_n\| = 1$, $\|u_n - u_m\| = 1$ for $m \neq n$. If there existed a finite dimensional subspace E of $\mathscr{C}_{\mathbf{R}}(\mathrm{I})$ such that $d(u_n, \mathrm{E}) \leqslant 1/4$ for each n, there would exist in E an infinite sequence (h_n) such that $\|h_n\| = 2$ and $\|h_n - h_m\| \geqslant 1/2$ for $m \neq n$, contradicting **(5.10.1)**.)

3. Let E be the interval $[0, 1]$ in $\mathbf{R}$.
(a) Show that if a_k $(1 \leqslant k \leqslant n)$ are n distinct points of E, the functions $x \to |x - a_k|$ are linearly independent in $\mathscr{C}_{\mathbf{R}}(\mathrm{E})$.
(b) Deduce from (a) that the function $(x, y) \to |x - y|$ in $\mathrm{E} \times \mathrm{E}$ cannot be written as a *finite* sum $\sum_{i=1}^{n} v_i(x) w_i(y)$, where v_i and w_i are continuous in E.

4. Show that the Banach space $\mathscr{C}_{\mathbf{R}}^{\infty}(\mathbf{R})$ is not separable. (Use a similar method as the one applied in the Problem of Section **5.10**.)

5. EQUICONTINUOUS SETS

Let H be a subset of the space $\mathscr{B}_{\mathrm{F}}(\mathrm{E})$ (E metric space, F normed space); we say that H is *equicontinuous at a point* $x_0 \in \mathrm{E}$ if, for any $\varepsilon > 0$, there is a $\delta > 0$ such that the relation $d(x_0, x) \leqslant \delta$ implies $\|f(x) - f(x_0)\| \leqslant \varepsilon$ *for every* $f \in \mathrm{H}$ (the important thing here being that δ is *independent of* f). We say that H is *equicontinuous* if it is equicontinuous at every point of E.

Examples

(7.5.1) Suppose there exist two constants $c, \alpha > 0$ such that $\|f(x) - f(y)\| \leqslant c \cdot (d(x, y))^{\alpha}$ for *any* $f \in \mathrm{H}$, and any pair of points x, y of E; then H is equicontinuous.

(7.5.2) Any *finite* set of functions which are continuous at a point x_0 (resp. in E) is equicontinuous at x_0 (resp. equicontinuous). More generally any finite union of sets of functions which are equicontinuous at x_0 (resp. equicontinuous) is equicontinuous at x_0 (resp. equicontinuous).

(7.5.3) *Let (f_n) be a sequence of functions in $\mathscr{B}_F(E)$ which converges simply to a function g and is equicontinuous at x_0* (resp. *equicontinuous*). *Then g is continuous at x_0* (resp. *continuous*).

Indeed, suppose $\|f_n(x_0) - f_n(x)\| \leqslant \varepsilon$ for any x such that $d(x, x_0) \leqslant \delta$ and any n; then, by the principle of extension of inequalities, we have $\|g(x) - g(x_0)\| \leqslant \varepsilon$ for any x such that $d(x, x_0) \leqslant \delta$. Q.E.D.

(7.5.4) *In the space $\mathscr{C}_F^\infty(E)$, the closure of any equicontinuous subset is equicontinuous.*

This follows at once from **(3.13.13)** and from the proof of **(7.5.3)**.

(7.5.5) *Suppose* F *is a Banach space,* (f_n) *an equicontinuous sequence in* $\mathscr{C}_F^\infty(E)$, *and that for any point x of a dense subset* D *of* E, *the sequence* $(f_n(x))$ *is convergent in* F. *Then the sequence* (f_n) *converges simply to a* (*continuous*) *limit* g.

As F is complete, we have to prove that for each $x \in E$, $(f_n(x))$ is a Cauchy sequence in F. Now for any $\varepsilon > 0$, there is a $\delta > 0$ such that the relation $d(x, y) \leqslant \delta$ implies $\|f_n(x) - f_n(y)\| \leqslant \varepsilon/3$ for *every* n. On the other hand, there exists $y \in D$ such that $d(x, y) \leqslant \delta$, and by assumption, there is an n_0 such that $\|f_m(y) - f_n(y)\| \leqslant \varepsilon/3$ for $m \geqslant n_0$, $n \geqslant n_0$. It follows that for $m \geqslant n_0$, $n \geqslant n_0$, $\|f_m(x) - f_n(x)\| \leqslant \varepsilon$. Q.E.D.

(7.5.6) *Suppose* E *is a compact metric space,* (f_n) *an equicontinuous sequence in* $\mathscr{C}_F(E)$. *If* (f_n) *converges simply to* g *in* E, *it converges uniformly to* g *in* E.

Given $\varepsilon > 0$, for each $x \in E$ there is a neighborhood $V(x)$ such that the relation $y \in V(x)$ implies $\|f_n(x) - f_n(y)\| \leqslant \varepsilon/3$ for *every* n. Cover E by a finite number of neighborhoods $V(x_i)$; there exists an n_0 such that for $n \geqslant n_0$, we have $\|g(x_i) - f_n(x_i)\| \leqslant \varepsilon/3$ for all the indices i. But for any $x \in E$, x belongs to one of the $V(x_i)$, hence we have $\|f_n(x) - f_n(x_i)\| \leqslant \varepsilon/3$ for all n, and letting n tend to $+\infty$, this yields $\|g(x) - g(x_i)\| \leqslant \varepsilon/3$. Hence we have $\|g(x) - f_n(x)\| \leqslant \varepsilon$ for any $n \geqslant n_0$ and every $x \in E$. Q.E.D.

(7.5.7) (Ascoli's theorem) *Suppose* F *is a Banach space and* E *a compact metric space. In order that a subset* H *of the Banach space* $\mathscr{C}_F(E)$ *be relatively* *compact, necessary and sufficient conditions are that* H *be equicontinuous and that, for each* $x \in E$, *the set* $H(x)$ *of all* $f(x)$ *such that* $f \in H$ *be relatively compact in* F.

(a) *Necessity.* If H is relatively compact for every $\varepsilon > 0$, there exists a finite number of functions $f_i \in H$ such that for every $f \in H$, there is an index i such that $\|f - f_i\| \leqslant \varepsilon/3$ (3.17.5). From this it follows first that for every $x \in E$ we have $\|f(x) - f_i(x)\| \leqslant \varepsilon/3$, and as F is complete, this shows by (3.17.5) that $H(x)$ is relatively compact. On the other hand, let V be a neighborhood of x such that $y \in V$ implies $\|f_i(y) - f_i(x)\| \leqslant \varepsilon/3$ for every index i; then, for any $f \in H$, $y \in V$ implies $\|f(y) - f(x)\| \leqslant \varepsilon$, which proves H is equicontinuous.

(b) *Sufficiency.* As $\mathscr{C}_F(E)$ is complete by (7.1.3) and (7.2.1), we need only prove H is precompact (3.17.5). Given any $\varepsilon > 0$, for each $x \in E$, let $V(x)$ be a neighborhood of x such that $y \in V(x)$ implies $\|f(y) - f(x)\| \leqslant \varepsilon/4$ for every $f \in H$. Cover E with a finite number of neighborhoods $V(x_i)$ $(1 \leqslant i \leqslant m)$. On the other hand each of the sets $H(x_i)$ is relatively compact in F by assumption; so is therefore their union K; let $(c_j)_{1 \leqslant j \leqslant n}$ be a finite subset of K such that every point of K is in a ball of center one of the c_j and radius $\varepsilon/4$. Let Φ now be the (finite) set of all mappings $i \to \varphi(i)$ of $[1, m]$ into $[1, n]$ (intervals in **N**); for each $\varphi \in \Phi$, denote by L_φ the set of all functions $f \in H$ such that, for every index i in $[1, m]$, we have $\|f(x_i) - c_{\varphi(i)}\| \leqslant \varepsilon/4$. Some of the L_φ may be empty, but from the definition of the c_j it follows that H is covered by the union of the L_φ. To end the proof we need only show that the diameter of each L_φ is $\leqslant \varepsilon$. Now if f, g are both in L_φ, for each $y \in E$ there is an i such that $y \in V(x_i)$, hence $\|f(y) - f(x_i)\| \leqslant \varepsilon/4$ and $\|g(y) - g(x_i)\| \leqslant \varepsilon/4$; as $\|f(x_i) - g(x_i)\| \leqslant \varepsilon/2$ by definition, we have $\|f(y) - g(y)\| \leqslant \varepsilon$ for every $y \in E$, i.e. $\|f - g\| \leqslant \varepsilon$. Q.E.D.

PROBLEMS

1. Let E be a metric space, F a normed space, H a bounded subset of $\mathscr{C}_F^\infty(E)$. For each $x \in E$, let $\tilde{x}$ be the mapping $u \to u(x)$ of H into F, which is continuous and bounded. Show that in order that H be equicontinuous at x_0, it is necessary and sufficient that the mapping $x \to \tilde{x}$ of E into $\mathscr{C}_F^\infty(H)$ be continuous at x_0.
2. Let E be a metric space, F a normed space, (f_n) an equicontinuous sequence in $\mathscr{C}_F^\infty(E)$. Show that the set of points $x \in E$, such that $(f_n(x))$ is a Cauchy sequence in F, is closed in E.
3. Let E be the interval $[0, +\infty[$ in **R**, and for any n, let

$$f_n(t) = \sin((t + 4n^2\pi^2)^{1/2})$$

in E. Show that the sequence (f_n) is equicontinuous in E and converges simply to 0 in E, but that it is not relatively compact in the space $\mathscr{C}_{\mathbf{R}}^{\infty}(E)$ (show that if it were, it would converge *uniformly* to 0).

4. Let E be a metric space, F a normed space, (f_n) a sequence of functions in $\mathscr{C}_F^{\infty}(E)$, which is equicontinuous at a point $a \in E$. Show that if the sequence $(f_n(a))$ is convergent to $b \in F$, then for any sequence (x_n) in E such that $\lim_{n \to \infty} x_n = a$, the sequence $(f_n(x_n))$ converges to b in F.

5. Let E be a metric space, F a normed space. We say that a subset H of $\mathscr{C}_F^{\infty}(E)$ is *uniformly equicontinuous* if for any $\varepsilon > 0$, there is a $\delta > 0$ such that the relation $d(x, y) \leqslant \delta$ implies $\|f(x) - f(y)\| \leqslant \varepsilon$ for every $f \in H$. Any function $f \in H$ is uniformly continuous; conversely a finite set of uniformly continuous functions is uniformly equicontinuous. Show that for a bounded subset H of $\mathscr{C}_F^{\infty}(E)$, the following properties are equivalent:

(a) H is uniformly equicontinuous.

(b) The mapping $x \to \tilde{x}$ of E into $\mathscr{C}_F^{\infty}(H)$ (Problem 1) is uniformly continuous.

(c) The mapping $(u, x) \to u(x)$ of $H \times E$ into F (H being considered as a subspace of $\mathscr{C}_F^{\infty}(E)$) is uniformly continuous.

6. Let E be a metric space, F a normed space, H a uniformly equicontinuous subset of $\mathscr{C}_F^{\infty}(E)$ (Problem 5); show that the closure of H in $\mathscr{C}_F^{\infty}(E)$ is uniformly equicontinuous.

7. Let E be a compact metric space, F a normed space. Show that any equicontinuous subset of $\mathscr{C}_F(E)$ is uniformly equicontinuous.

8. Let E be a compact metric space, F a Banach space. Show that if a subset H of $\mathscr{C}_F(E)$ is relatively compact, the union of all the sets $H(x)$, where $x \in E$, is relatively compact in F (use Problem 5 of Section 7.2).

9. Show that the conclusion of Ascoli's theorem **(7.5.7)** is still valid if instead of supposing $H(x)$ relatively compact in F for every $x \in E$, one only supposes $H(x)$ relatively compact for all $x \in D$, where D is a dense subset of E.

10. Let E be a metric space, H an equicontinuous subset of $\mathscr{C}_{\mathbf{R}}^{\infty}(E)$. Show that the set A of points $x \in E$ such that $H(x)$ is bounded in **R** is both open and closed in E. If E is compact and connected and if for one point $x_0 \in E$, $H(x_0)$ is bounded in **R**, then H is relatively compact in $\mathscr{C}_{\mathbf{R}}(E)$.

11. Let E be a metric space, H an equicontinuous subset of $\mathscr{C}_{\mathbf{R}}^{\infty}(E)$. For each $x \in E$, let $v(x) = \sup_{f \in H} f(x)$, $w(x) = \inf_{f \in H} f(x)$; show that if v (resp. w) is finite at one point x_0, it is finite and continuous in a neighborhood of x_0; if $v(x_0) = +\infty$ (resp. $w(x_0) = -\infty$) then $v(x) = +\infty$ (resp. $w(x) = -\infty$) in a neighborhood of x_0. Conclude that the set of points $x \in E$ for which $v(x)$ (resp. $w(x)$) is finite is both open and closed in E.

12. Let $I = [a, b]$ a compact interval in **R**. A function $f \in \mathscr{C}_{\mathbf{R}}(I)$ is said to be *lipschitzian* for the constant $k > 0$ if, for every pair (x, x') of points of I, $|f(x) - f(x')| \leqslant k\,|x' - x|$. Let K be the subset of $\mathscr{C}_{\mathbf{R}}(I)$ consisting of all functions f which are lipschitzian for k, and such that $f(a) = 0$. Show that the ε-entropy $H_\varepsilon(K)$ and the ε-capacity $C_\varepsilon(K)$ (Section **3.16**, Problem 4) are given by the formulas

$$H_\varepsilon(K) = C_{2\varepsilon}(K) = \left(\frac{k(b-a)}{\varepsilon} - 1\right) \log 2 \quad \text{if} \quad \frac{k(b-a)}{\varepsilon} \quad \text{is an integer}$$

$$H_\varepsilon(K) = C_{2\varepsilon}(K) = \left[\frac{k(b-a)}{\varepsilon}\right] \log 2 \quad \text{if} \quad \frac{k(b-a)}{\varepsilon} \quad \text{is not an integer}$$

($[t]$ is the largest integer $\leqslant t$). (One may assume $k = 1$ by a suitable linear transformation. Suppose $b - a = n\varepsilon$, where n is an integer. Consider the set M_{n-1} of the 2^{n-1} functions $g \in K$ which are equal to affine functions in each of the intervals

$$\left]a+h\frac{b-a}{n-1}, a+(h+1)\frac{b-a}{n-1}\right[\qquad (0 \leqslant h \leqslant n-2)$$

and have in each such interval a derivative equal to 1 or to -1; prove that the distance of any two distinct elements of M_{n-1} is $\geqslant 2/(n-1)$. Similarly, consider the subset M_n' of M_n consisting of the 2^{n-1} functions of M_n which are equal to $x-a$ in the interval $[a, a+(b-a)/n]$, and for each function $g \in M_n'$, consider the set of all functions $f \in K$ such that $g(x)-(2/n) \leqslant f(x) \leqslant g(x)$ for every $x \in I$. Use a similar construction when $(b-a)/\varepsilon$ is not an integer.)

6. REGULATED FUNCTIONS

Let I be an interval in **R**, of origin a and extremity b (a or b or both may be infinite), F a Banach space. We say that a mapping f of I into F is a *step-function* if there is an increasing finite sequence $(x_i)_{0 \leqslant i \leqslant n}$ of points of $\bar{I}$ (closure of I in $\overline{\mathbf{R}}$) such that $x_0 = a$, $x_n = b$, and that f is *constant* in each of the open intervals $]x_i, x_{i+1}[$ $(0 \leqslant i \leqslant n-1)$.

For any mapping f of I into F and any point $x \in I$ distinct from b, we say that f has a *limit on the right* if $\lim_{y \in I, y>x, y \to x} f(y)$ exists; we then write the limit $f(x+)$. Similarly we define for each point $x \in I$ distinct from a, the *limit on the left* of f at x, which we write $f(x-)$; we also say these limits are *one-sided limits* of f. A mapping f of I into F is called a *regulated function* if it has one-sided limits at every point of I. It is clear that any step-function is regulated.

(7.6.1) *In order that a mapping f of a compact interval* $I = [a, b]$ *into* F *be regulated, a necessary and sufficient condition is that f be the limit of a uniformly convergent sequence of step-functions.*

(a) *Necessity.* For every integer n, and every $x \in I$, there is an open interval $V(x) =]y(x), z(x)[$ containing x, such that $\|f(s)-f(t)\| \leqslant 1/n$ if either both s, t are in $]y(x), x[\cap I$ or both in $]x, z(x)[\cap I$. Cover I with a finite number of intervals $V(x_i)$, and let $(c_j)_{0 \leqslant j \leqslant m}$ be the strictly increasing sequence consisting of the points a, b, x_i, $y(x_i)$ and $z(x_i)$. As each c_j is in some $V(x_i)$, c_{j+1} is either in the same $V(x_i)$ or we have $c_{j+1} = z(x_i)$, for $j \leqslant m-1$; in other words if s, t are both the same interval $]c_j, c_{j+1}[$, then $\|f(s)-f(t)\| \leqslant 1/n$. Now define g_n as the step-function equal to f at the points c_j, and at the midpoint of each interval $]c_j, c_{j+1}[$, and constant in each of these intervals. It is clear that $\|f-g_n\| \leqslant 1/n$.

(b) *Sufficiency.* Suppose f is the uniform limit of a sequence (f_n) of step-functions. For each $\varepsilon > 0$ there is an n such that $\|f - f_n\| \leqslant \varepsilon/3$; now for each $x \in \mathrm{I}$, there is an interval $]c, d[$ containing x and such that $\|f_n(s) - f_n(t)\| \leqslant \varepsilon/3$ if both s and t are in $]c, x[$ or both in $]x, d[$; hence under the same assumption we have $\|f(s) - f(t)\| \leqslant \varepsilon$, and this proves the existence of one-sided limits of f at x, since F is complete (3.14.6).

Another way of formulating (7.6.1) is to say that the set of regulated functions is *closed* in $\mathscr{B}_{\mathrm{F}}(\mathrm{E})$, and that the set of step-functions is *dense* in the set of regulated functions.

(7.6.2) *Any continuous mapping of an interval* $\mathrm{I} \subset \mathbf{R}$ *into a Banach space is regulated; so is any monotone mapping of* I *into* $\mathbf{R}$.

This follows from the definition, taking into account (3.16.5) and (4.2.1).

PROBLEMS

1. Let f be a regulated mapping of an interval $\mathrm{I} \subset \mathbf{R}$ into a Banach space F. Show that for each compact subset H of I, $f(\mathrm{H})$ is relatively compact in F; give an example showing that $f(\mathrm{H})$ need not be closed in F.
2. The function $f(x) = x \sin(1/x)$ ($f(0) = 0$) is continuous, hence regulated in $\mathrm{I} = [0, 1]$, and the function $g(x) = \operatorname{sgn} x$ ($g(x) = 1$ if $x > 0$, $g(0) = 0$, $g(x) = -1$ if $x > 0$) is regulated in $\mathbf{R}$, but the composed function $g \circ f$ is not regulated in I.
3. Let $\mathrm{I} = [a, b]$ be a compact interval in $\mathbf{R}$. A *function of bounded variation* in I is a mapping f of I into a Banach space F, having the following property: there is a number $\mathrm{V} \geqslant 0$ such that, for *any* strictly increasing finite sequence $(t_i)_{0 \leqslant i \leqslant n}$ of points of I, the inequality $\sum_{i=0}^{n-1} \|f(t_{i+1}) - f(t_i)\| \leqslant \mathrm{V}$ holds.
   (a) Show that $f(\mathrm{I})$ is relatively compact in F (prove that $f(\mathrm{I})$ is precompact, by an indirect proof).
   (b) Show that f is a regulated function in I (use (a) and (3.16.4)).
   (c) The function g defined in $[0, 1]$ as equal to $x^2 \sin(1/x^2)$ for $x \neq 0$ and to 0 for $x = 0$ is not of bounded variation, although it has a derivative at each point of I.

CHAPTER VIII

DIFFERENTIAL CALCULUS

▲The subject matter of this chapter is nothing else but the elementary theorems of calculus, which however are presented in a way which will probably be new to most students. That presentation, which throughout adheres strictly to our general "geometric" outlook on analysis, aims at keeping as close as possible to the fundamental idea of calculus, namely the "local" approximation of functions by *linear* functions. In the classical teaching of calculus, this idea is immediately obscured by the accidental fact that, on a one-dimensional vector space, there is a one-to-one correspondence between linear forms and numbers, and therefore the derivative at a point is defined as a *number* instead of a *linear form*. This slavish subservience to the shibboleth of numerical interpretation at any cost becomes much worse when dealing with functions of several variables: one thus arrives, for instance, at the classical formula (8.9.2) giving the partial derivatives of a composite function, which has lost any trace of intuitive meaning, whereas the natural statement of the theorem is of course that the (total) derivative of a composite function is the composite of their derivatives (8.2.1), a very sensible formulation when one thinks in terms of linear approximations.

▲ This "intrinsic" formulation of calculus, due to its greater "abstraction," and in particular to the fact that again and again, one has to leave the initial spaces and to climb higher and higher to new "function spaces" (especially when dealing with the theory of higher derivatives), certainly requires some mental effort, contrasting with the comfortable routine of the classical formulas. But we believe that the result is well worth the labor, as it will prepare the student to the still more general idea of calculus on a differentiable manifold, which we shall develop in Chapters XVI to XX. Of course, he will observe that in these applications, all the vector spaces which intervene have finite dimension; if that gives him an additional feeling of security, he may of course add that assumption to all the theorems of this chapter. But he will inevitably realize that this does not make the proofs shorter or simpler by a single line; in other words, the hypothesis of finite dimension is entirely irrelevant to the material developed below; we have therefore thought it best to dispense with it altogether, although the applications of calculus which deal with the finite dimensional case still by far exceed the others in number and in importance.

▲ After the formal rules of calculus have been derived (Sections 8.1 to 8.4), the other sections of the chapter are various applications of what is probably the most useful theorem in analysis, the mean value theorem, proved in Section 8.5. The reader will observe that the formulation of that theorem, which is of course given for vector valued functions, differs in appearance from the classical mean value theorem (for real valued functions), which one usually writes as an *equality* $f(b) - f(a) = f'(c)(b - a)$. The trouble with that classical formulation is that: (1) there is nothing similar to it as soon as f has vector values or when there are a finite number of points where f' is not defined; (2) it completely conceals the fact that *nothing* is known on the number c, except that it lies between a and b, and for most purposes, all one need know is that $f'(c)$ is a number which lies between the g.l.b. and l.u.b. of f' in the interval $[a, b]$ (and *not* the fact that it actually is a value of f'). In other words, the real nature of the mean value theorem is exhibited by writing it as an *inequality*, and not as an equality.

▲ Finally, the reader will probably observe the conspicuous absence of a time-honored topic in calculus courses, the "Riemann integral." It may well be suspected that, had it not been for its prestigious name, this would have been dropped long ago, for (with due reverence to Riemann's genius) it is certainly quite clear to any working mathematician that nowadays such a "theory" has at best the importance of a mildly interesting exercise in the general theory of measure and integration (see Section 13.9, Problem 7). Only the stubborn conservatism of academic tradition could freeze it into a regular part of the curriculum, long after it had outlived its historical importance. Of course, it is perfectly feasible to limit the integration process to a category of functions which is large enough for all purposes of elementary analysis (at the level of this first volume), but close enough to the continuous functions to dispense with any consideration drawn from measure theory; this is what we have done by defining only the integral of regulated functions (sometimes called the "Cauchy integral"). When one needs a more powerful tool, there is no point in stopping halfway, and the general theory of ("Lebesgue") integration (Chapter XIII) is the only sensible answer.

1. DERIVATIVE OF A CONTINUOUS MAPPING

▲ Let E, F be Banach spaces (both real or both complex) and A an open subset of E. Let f, g be two continuous mappings of A into F; we say that f and g are *tangent* at a point $x_0 \in A$ if $\lim_{x \to x_0, x \neq x_0} \|f(x) - g(x)\|/\|x - x_0\| = 0$; this implies of course that $f(x_0) = g(x_0)$. We note that this definition only depends on the topologies of E and F; for if f, g are tangent for the given norms on E and F, they are still tangent for equivalent norms (Section 5.6). If f, g are tangent at x_0, and g, h tangent at x_0, then f, h are tangent at x_0, as follows from the inequality $\|f(x) - h(x)\| \leqslant \|f(x) - g(x)\| + \|g(x) - h(x)\|$.

▲ Among all functions tangent at x_0 to a function f, there is *at most one* mapping of the form $x \to f(x_0) + u(x - x_0)$ where u is *linear*. For if two such functions $x \to f(x_0) + u_1(x - x_0)$, $x \to f(x_0) + u_2(x - x_0)$ are tangent at x_0, this means, for the linear mapping $v = u_1 - u_2$, that $\lim_{y \to 0, y \neq 0} \|v(y)\|/\|y\| = 0$. But this implies $v = 0$, for if, given $\varepsilon > 0$, there is $r > 0$ such that $\|y\| \leqslant r$ implies $\|v(y)\| \leqslant \varepsilon \|y\|$, then this last inequality is still valid for *any* $x \neq 0$, by applying it to $y = rx/\|x\|$; as ε is arbitrary, we see that $v(x) = 0$ for any x.

▲ We say that a continuous mapping f of A into F is *differentiable* at the point $x_0 \in A$ if there is a linear mapping u of E into F such that $x \to f(x_0) + u(x - x_0)$ is tangent to f at x_0. We have just seen that this mapping is then *unique*; it is called the *derivative* (or *total derivative*) of f at the point x_0, and written $f'(x_0)$ or $Df(x_0)$.

•(8.1.1) *If the continuous mapping f of* A *into* F *is differentiable at the point x_0, the derivative $f'(x_0)$ is a continuous linear mapping of* E *into* F.

▲ Let $u = f'(x_0)$. Given $\varepsilon > 0$, there is r such that $0 < r < 1$ and that $\|t\| \leqslant r$ implies $\|f(x_0 + t) - f(x_0)\| \leqslant \varepsilon/2$ and $\|f(x_0 + t) - f(x_0) - u(t)\| \leqslant \varepsilon\|t\|/2$; hence $\|t\| \leqslant r$ implies $\|u(t)\| \leqslant \varepsilon$, which proves u is continuous by (5.5.1).

▲ The derivative (when it exists) of a continuous mapping f of A into F, at a point $x_0 \in A$, is thus *an element of the Banach space* $\mathscr{L}(E; F)$ (see Section 5.7) and *not* of F. In what follows, for $u \in \mathscr{L}(E; F)$ and $t \in E$, we will write $u \cdot t$ instead of $u(t)$; we recall (Section 5.7) that $\|u \cdot t\| \leqslant \|u\| \cdot \|t\|$ and that $\|u\| = \sup_{\|t\| \leqslant 1} \|u \cdot t\|$.

▲When E has finite dimension n and F has finite dimension m, $f'(x_0)$ can thus be identified to a *matrix* with m rows and n columns; this matrix will be determined in Section 8.10.

Examples

(8.1.2)▲ A *constant* function is differentiable at every point of A, and its derivative is the element 0 of $\mathscr{L}(E; F)$.

•(8.1.3)▲ *The derivative of a continuous linear mapping u of* E *into* F *exists at every point $x \in$ E and $Du(x) = u$.*

For by definition $u(x_0) + u(x - x_0) = u(x)$.

(8.1.4) *Let* E, F, G *be three Banach spaces, $(x, y) \to [x \cdot y]$ a continuous bilinear mapping of* E × F *into* G. *Then that mapping is differentiable at every point $(x, y) \in$ E × F and the derivative is the linear mapping $(s, t) \to [x \cdot t] + [s \cdot y]$.*

For we have

$$[(x + s) \cdot (y + t)] - [x \cdot y] - [x \cdot t] - [s \cdot y] = [s \cdot t]$$

and by assumption, there is a constant $c > 0$ such that $\|[s \cdot t]\| \leqslant c \cdot \|s\| \cdot \|t\|$ (5.5.1). For any $\varepsilon > 0$, the relation $\sup(\|s\|, \|t\|) = \|(s, t)\| \leqslant \varepsilon/c$ implies therefore

$$\|[(x + s) \cdot (y + t)] - [x \cdot y] - [x \cdot t] - [s \cdot y]\| \leqslant \varepsilon \|(s, t)\|$$

which proves our assertion.

That result is easily generalized to a continuous multilinear mapping.

(8.1.5) *Suppose* $F = F_1 \times F_2 \times \cdots \times F_m$ *is a product of Banach spaces, and $f = (f_1, \ldots, f_m)$ a continuous mapping of an open subset* A *of* E *into* F. *In order that f be differentiable at x_0, a necessary and sufficient condition is that each f_i be differentiable at x_0, and then $f'(x_0) = (f_1'(x_0), \ldots, f_m'(x_0))$ (when $\mathscr{L}(E; F)$ is identified with the product of the spaces $\mathscr{L}(E; F_i)$).*

Indeed, any linear mapping u of E into F can be written in a unique way $u = (u_1, \ldots, u_m)$, where u_i is a linear mapping of E into F_i, and we have by definition $\|u(x)\| = \sup(\|u_1(x)\|, \ldots, \|u_m(x)\|)$, whence it follows (by (5.7.1) and (2.3.7)) that $\|u\| = \sup(\|u_1\|, \ldots, \|u_m\|)$, which allows the identification of $\mathscr{L}(E; F)$ with the product $\prod_{i=1}^{m} \mathscr{L}(E; F_i)$. From the definition, it follows at once that u is the derivative of f at x_0 if and only if u_i is the derivative of f_i at x_0 for $1 \leqslant i \leqslant m$.

Remark. Let E, F be *complex* Banach spaces, and E_0, F_0 the underlying *real* Banach spaces. Then if a mapping f of an open subset A of E into F is differentiable at a point x_0, it is also differentiable with the same derivative, when considered as a mapping of A *into* F_0 (a linear mapping of E into F being also linear as a mapping of E_0 into F_0). But the converse is not true, as the example of the mapping $z \to \bar{z}$ (complex conjugate) of $\mathbf{C}$ into itself shows at once; as a mapping of $\mathbf{R}^2$ into itself, $u: z \to \bar{z}$ (which can be written $(x, y) \to (x, -y)$) is differentiable and has at each point a derivative equal to u, by (8.1.3); but u is not a *complex* linear mapping, hence the result. We return to that question in Chapter IX (9.10.1).

When the mapping f of A into F is differentiable at every point of A, we say that f is *differentiable in* A; the mapping $x \to f'(x) = Df(x)$ of A *into* $\mathscr{L}(E; F)$ will be written f' or Df and called the *derivative of f in* A.

2. FORMAL RULES OF DERIVATION

(8.2.1) *Let* E, F, G *be three Banach spaces,* A *an open neighborhood of* $x_0 \in E$, f *a continuous mapping of* A *into* F, $y_0 = f(x_0)$, B *an open neighborhood of* y_0 *in* F, g *a continuous mapping of* B *into* G. *Then if f is differentiable at* x_0 *and g differentiable at* y_0, *the mapping* $h = g \circ f$ (which is defined and continuous in a neighborhood of x_0) *is differentiable at* x_0, *and we have*

$$\boxed{h'(x_0) = g'(y_0) \circ f'(x_0).}$$

By assumption, given ε such that $0 < \varepsilon < 1$, there is an $r > 0$ such that, for $\|s\| \leqslant r$ and $\|t\| \leqslant r$, we can write

$$f(x_0 + s) = f(x_0) + f'(x_0) \cdot s + o_1(s)$$

$$g(y_0 + t) = g(y_0) + g'(y_0) \cdot t + o_2(t)$$

with $\|o_1(s)\| \leqslant \varepsilon \|s\|$ and $\|o_2(t)\| \leqslant \varepsilon \|t\|$. On the other hand, by (8.1.1) and (5.5.1), there are constants a, b such that, for any s and t,

$$\|f'(x_0) \cdot s\| \leqslant a \|s\| \qquad \text{and} \qquad \|g'(y_0) \cdot t\| \leqslant b \|t\|$$

hence

$$\|f'(x_0) \cdot s + o_1(s)\| \leqslant (a + 1)\,\|s\|$$

for $\|s\| \leqslant r$. Therefore, for $\|s\| \leqslant r/(a + 1)$, we have

$$\|o_2(f'(x_0) \cdot s + o_1(s))\| \leqslant (a + 1)\varepsilon\,\|s\|$$

and

$$\|g'(y_0) \cdot o_1(s)\| \leqslant b\varepsilon\,\|s\|$$

hence we can write

$$h(x_0 + s) = g(y_0 + f'(x_0) \cdot s + o_1(s)) = g(y_0) + g'(y_0) \cdot (f'(x_0) \cdot s) + o_3(s)$$

with

$$\|o_3(s)\| \leqslant (a + b + 1)\varepsilon\,\|s\|,$$

which proves the theorem.

(8.2.1) has of course innumerable applications, of which we mention only the following one:

(8.2.2) *Let f, g be two continuous mappings of the open subset* A *of* E *into* F. *If f and g are differentiable at x_0, so are $f + g$ and αf (α scalar), and we have $(f + g)'(x_0) = f'(x_0) + g'(x_0)$ and $(\alpha f)'(x_0) = \alpha f'(x_0)$.*

The mapping $f + g$ is composed of $(u, v) \to u + v$, mapping of $\mathrm{F} \times \mathrm{F}$ into F, and of $x \to (f(x), g(x))$, mapping of A into $\mathrm{F} \times \mathrm{F}$; both are differentiable by (8.1.3) and (8.1.5), and the result follows (for $f + g$) from (8.2.1). For αf the argument is still simpler, using the fact that the mapping $u \to \alpha u$ of F into itself is differentiable by (8.1.3). Of course, (8.2.2) could also be proved very simply by direct arguments.

Let E, F be two Banach spaces, A an open subset of E, B an open subset of F. If A and B are *homeomorphic*, and there exists a *differentiable homeomorphism* f of A onto B, it does *not* follow that, for each $x_0 \in \mathrm{A}$, $f'(x_0)$ is a linear homeomorphism of E onto F (consider e.g. the mapping $\xi \to \xi^3$ of **R** onto itself).

(8.2.3) *Let f be a homeomorphism of an open subset* A *of a Banach space* E *onto an open subset* B *of a Banach space* F, *g the inverse homeomorphism. Suppose f is differentiable at the point x_0, and $f'(x_0)$ is a linear homeomorphism of* E *onto* F*; then g is differentiable at $y_0 = f(x_0)$ and $g'(y_0)$ is the inverse mapping to $f'(x_0)$* (cf. (10.2.5)).

By assumption, the mapping $s \to f(x_0 + s) - f(x_0)$ is a homeomorphism of a neighborhood V of 0 in E onto a neighborhood W of 0 in F, and the inverse homeomorphism if $t \to g(y_0 + t) - g(y_0)$. By assumption, the linear mapping $f'(x_0)$ of E onto F has an inverse u which is continuous, hence **(5.5.1)** there is $c > 0$ such that $\|u(t)\| \leqslant c\|t\|$ for any $t \in \mathrm{F}$. Given any ε such that $0 < \varepsilon \leqslant 1/2c$, there is an $r > 0$ such that, if we write $f(x_0 + s) - f(x_0) = f'(x_0) \cdot s + o_1(s)$, the relation $\|s\| \leqslant r$ implies $\|o_1(s)\| \leqslant \varepsilon\|s\|$. Let r' now be a number such that the ball $\|t\| \leqslant r'$ is contained in W and that its image by the mapping $t \to g(y_0 + t) - g(y_0)$ is contained in the ball $\|s\| \leqslant r$. Let $z = g(y_0 + t) - g(y_0)$; by definition, for $\|t\| \leqslant r'$, this equation implies $t = f(x_0 + z) - f(x_0)$ and as $\|z\| \leqslant r$, we can write $t = f'(x_0) \cdot z + o_1(z)$, with $\|o_1(z)\| \leqslant \varepsilon\|z\|$. From that relation we deduce

$$u \cdot t = u \cdot (f'(x_0) \cdot z) + u \cdot o_1(z) = z + u \cdot o_1(z)$$

by definition of u, and moreover $\|u \cdot o_1(z)\| \leqslant c\|o_1(z)\| \leqslant c\varepsilon\|z\| \leqslant \frac{1}{2}\|z\|$, hence $\|u \cdot t\| \geqslant \|z\| - \frac{1}{2}\|z\| = \frac{1}{2}\|z\|$; therefore $\|z\| \leqslant 2\|u \cdot t\| \leqslant 2c\|t\|$, and finally $\|u \cdot o_1(z)\| \leqslant c\varepsilon\|z\| \leqslant 2c^2\varepsilon\|t\|$. We have therefore proved that the relation $\|t\| \leqslant r'$ implies $\|g(y_0 + t) - g(y_0) - u \cdot t\| \leqslant 2c^2\varepsilon\|t\|$, and as ε is arbitrary, this completes the proof.

The result **(8.2.3)** can also be written (under the same assumptions)

(8.2.3.1)
$$(f^{-1})'(f(x_0)) = (f'(x_0))^{-1}.$$

PROBLEMS

1. Let E be a real prehilbert space. Show that in E the mapping $x \to \|x\|$ of E into $\mathbf{R}$ is differentiable at every point $x \neq 0$ and that its derivative at such a point is the linear mapping $s \to (s \mid x)/\|x\|$.
2. (a) In the space (c_0) of Banach (Section **5.3**, Problem 5) show that the norm $x \to \|x\|$ is differentiable at a point $x = (\xi_n)$ if and only if there is an index n_0 such that $|\xi_{n_0}| > |\xi_n|$ for every $n \neq n_0$. Compute the derivative.
   (b) In the space l^1 of Banach (Section **5.7**, Problem 1), show that the norm $x \to \|x\|$ is not differentiable at any point (use **(8.1.1)** and Problem 1(c) of Section **5.7**).
3. Let f be a differentiable real valued function defined in an open subset A of a Banach space E.
   (a) Show that if at a point $x_0 \in \mathrm{A}$, f reaches a relative maximum (Section **3.9**, Problem 6), then $\mathrm{D}f(x_0) = 0$.
   (b) Suppose E is finite dimensional, A is relatively compact, f is defined and continuous in $\bar{\mathrm{A}}$, and equal to 0 in the boundary of A. Show that there exists a point $x_0 \in \mathrm{A}$ where $\mathrm{D}f(x_0) = 0$ ("Rolle's theorem"; use (a) and **(3.17.10)**).

3. DERIVATIVES IN SPACES OF CONTINUOUS LINEAR FUNCTIONS

(8.3.1) *Let* E, F, G *be three Banach spaces. Then the mapping* $(u, v) \to v \circ u$ (also written vu) of $\mathscr{L}(\mathrm{E}; \mathrm{F}) \times \mathscr{L}(\mathrm{F}; \mathrm{G})$ *into* $\mathscr{L}(\mathrm{E}; \mathrm{G})$ *is differentiable, and the derivative at the point* (u_0, v_0) *is the mapping* $(s, t) \to v_0 \circ s + t \circ u_0$.

If we observe that, by (5.7.5), the mapping $(u, v) \to v \circ u$ is bilinear and continuous, the result is a special case of (8.1.4).

(8.3.2) *Let* E, F *be two Banach spaces, such that there exists at least a linear homeomorphism of* E *onto* F. *Then the set* $\mathscr{H}$ *of these linear homeomorphisms is open in* $\mathscr{L}(\mathrm{E}; \mathrm{F})$; *the mapping* $u \to u^{-1}$ *of* $\mathscr{H}$ *onto the set* $\mathscr{H}^{-1}$ *of linear homeomorphisms of* F *onto* E *is continuous and differentiable, and the derivative of* $u \to u^{-1}$ *at the point* u_0 *is the linear mapping (of* $\mathscr{L}(\mathrm{E}; \mathrm{F})$ *into* $\mathscr{L}(\mathrm{F}; \mathrm{E})$) $s \to -u_0^{-1} \circ s \circ u_0^{-1}$.

1. We consider first the case F = E, and write 1_{E} for the identity mapping of E. Then:

(8.3.2.1) *If* $\|w\| < 1$ *in* $\mathscr{L}(\mathrm{E}; \mathrm{E})$, *the linear mapping* $1_{\mathrm{E}} + w$ *is a homeomorphism, its inverse* $(1_{\mathrm{E}} + w)^{-1}$ *is equal to the sum of the absolutely convergent series* $\sum_{n=0}^{\infty} (-1)^n w^n$, *and we have*

$$\|(1_{\mathrm{E}} + w)^{-1} - 1_{\mathrm{E}} + w\| \leqslant \|w\|^2/(1 - \|w\|). \tag{8.3.2.2}$$

We have $\sum_{n=0}^{\mathrm{N}} \|w\|^n = (1 - \|w\|^{\mathrm{N}+1})/(1 - \|w\|) \leqslant 1/(1 - \|w\|)$, hence, by (5.7.5), (5.3.1), (5.3.2) and (5.7.3), the series $\sum_{n=0}^{\infty} (-1)^n w^n$ is absolutely convergent in $\mathscr{L}(\mathrm{E}; \mathrm{E})$. Moreover, we have

$$\begin{aligned}(1_{\mathrm{E}} + w)&(1_{\mathrm{E}} - w + w^2 + \cdots + (-1)^{\mathrm{N}} w^{\mathrm{N}}) \\ &= (1_{\mathrm{E}} - w + w^2 + \cdots + (-1)^{\mathrm{N}} w^{\mathrm{N}})(1_{\mathrm{E}} + w) = 1_{\mathrm{E}} - (-1)^{\mathrm{N}+1} w^{\mathrm{N}+1}.\end{aligned}$$

and as $w^{\mathrm{N}+1}$ tends to 0 with $1/\mathrm{N}$, we have by definition and by (5.7.5), for the element $v = \sum_{n=0}^{\infty} (-1)^n w^n$ of $\mathscr{L}(\mathrm{E}; \mathrm{E})$, $(1_{\mathrm{E}} + w)v = v(1_{\mathrm{E}} + w) = 1_{\mathrm{E}}$, which proves the first two statements; the inequality (8.3.2.2) follows from the relation $(1_{\mathrm{E}} + w)^{-1} - 1_{\mathrm{E}} + w = w^2(1_{\mathrm{E}} - w + w^2 + \cdots)$, and from (5.7.5) and (5.3.2).

2. Consider now the general case; suppose $s \in \mathscr{L}(E; F)$ is such that $\|s\| \cdot \|u_0^{-1}\| < 1$; then the element $1_E + u_0^{-1}s$, which belongs to $\mathscr{L}(E; E)$, has an inverse, due to (5.7.5) and (8.3.2.1); as we can write $u_0 + s = u_0(1_E + u_0^{-1}s)$, the same is true for $u_0 + s$, the inverse being $(1_E + u_0^{-1}s)^{-1}u_0^{-1}$; hence we have

$$(u_0 + s)^{-1} - u_0^{-1} = ((1_E + u_0^{-1}s)^{-1} - 1_E)u_0^{-1}.$$

Applying (8.3.2.2) to $w = u_0^{-1}s$, we obtain, for $\|s\| < 1/\|u_0^{-1}\|$

$$\|(u_0 + s)^{-1} - u_0^{-1} + u_0^{-1}su_0^{-1}\| \leqslant \|u_0^{-1}\|^3 \cdot \|s\|^2/(1 - \|u_0^{-1}\| \cdot \|s\|).$$

Therefore, if we take $\|s\| \leqslant 1/2\|u_0^{-1}\|$, we have

$$\|(u_0 + s)^{-1} - u_0^{-1} + u_0^{-1}su_0^{-1}\| \leqslant c\|s\|^2$$

with $c = 2\|u_0^{-1}\|^3$, and this ends the proof.

4. DERIVATIVES OF FUNCTIONS OF ONE VARIABLE

When we specialize E to a *one-dimensional* vector space (identified to **R** or **C**), we know that $\mathscr{L}(E; F)$ is naturally identified to F itself, a vector $b \in F$ being identified to the linear mapping $\xi \to b\xi$ of E into F (5.7.6). If f is a differentiable mapping of an open set $A \subset E$ into F, its derivative $Df(\xi_0)$ at a point $\xi_0 \in A$ is thus identified to a *vector of* F, and the mapping Df to a mapping of A into F. If F itself is one-dimensional (identified to **R** or **C**), we obtain the classical case of the derivative (at a point) as a *number*. The general results obtained above boil down in that last case to the classical formulas of calculus; for instance, (8.3.2), when E and F are one-dimensional, is simply the formula giving the derivative of $1/\xi$ as equal to $-1/\xi^2$ for $\xi \neq 0$. We explicitly formulate the following consequence of (8.2.1):

(8.4.1) *Let* E, F *be two real* (resp. *complex*) *Banach spaces, f a differentiable mapping of an open subset* A *of* E *into* F, *g a differentiable mapping of an open subset* I *of* **R** (resp. **C**) *into* A; *then the derivative at $\xi \in I$ of the composed mapping $h = f \circ g$ of* I *into* F *is the vector of* F *equal to* $Df(g(\xi)) \cdot g'(\xi)$ (remember $g'(\xi)$ is in E, and $Df(g(\xi))$ in $\mathscr{L}(E; F)$).

Remarks. Suppose F is a *complex* Banach space, f a differentiable mapping of an open subset $A \subset \mathbf{C}$ into F; its derivative at $z \in A$ is thus identified with a vector of F. Let now g be a differentiable mapping of an open subset I of **R** into **C** (considered as the underlying two-dimensional real vector space);

then $f \circ g$ is a differentiable mapping of I into the underlying real Banach space F_0 of F, and (8.4.1) shows that its derivative at a point $\xi \in I$ is $g'(\xi)(Df(g(\xi)))$ (remember here $g'(\xi)$ is a complex number).

When $E = \mathbf{R}$ and F is a real Banach space, the notion of derivative can be greatly generalized: for any subset $J \subset \mathbf{R}$ and any point $\xi_0 \in J$ such that ξ_0 is a cluster point of $J - \{\xi_0\}$, we can define, for a mapping f of J into F, the *derivative of f at ξ_0 (with respect to* J) as the limit (when it exists)

$$\lim_{\xi \to \xi_0,\, \xi \in J - \{\xi_0\}} (f(\xi) - f(\xi_0))/(\xi - \xi_0).$$

When the limit exists, we say that f is *differentiable at ξ_0, with respect to* J. We shall only consider the case in which J is an *interval* of $\mathbf{R}$; then at the interior points of I, the derivative with respect to J coincides (when it exists) with the usual one; at the origin α (resp. extremity β) of J, when it belongs to J, the derivative of f with respect to J is also called the *derivative on the right* (resp. *on the left*) of f at the point α (resp. β) and written $f_d'(\alpha)$ or $D_+f(\alpha)$ (resp. $f_g'(\beta)$ or $D_-f(\beta)$). Theorem (8.4.1) is still valid when in the assumptions we suppose I is an interval and g has a derivative with respect to I at ξ; then if f is differentiable in A, $f \circ g$ has a derivative at ξ with respect to I given by the same formula ($g'(\xi)$ being replaced by the derivative of g with respect to I). The proof is that of (8.2.1) with the obvious modifications. We omit the most usual consequences of that theorem, such as the result corresponding to (8.2.2).

PROBLEMS

1. (a) Let f be a continuous mapping of an interval $I \subset \mathbf{R}$ into a Banach space E. In order that f be differentiable at an interior point x_0 of I, it is necessary and sufficient that $(f(x_0 + h) - f(x_0 - k))/(h + k)$ have a limit in E when the point (h, k) tends to $(0, 0)$ in the set of pairs such that $h > 0, k > 0$.
(b) The real function f equal to $x^2 \sin(1/x)$ for $x \neq 0$, to 0 for $x = 0$, is differentiable in $\mathbf{R}$, but $(f(x) - f(y))/(x - y)$ has no limit when (x, y) tends to $(0, 0)$ in the set of pairs such that $x > 0, y > 0, x \neq y$.
(c) In the interval $I = [0, 1]$, the sequence of continuous functions f_n is defined as follows: $f_0(t) = t$; for each $n \geqslant 1$, f_n has the form $\alpha t + \beta$ in each of the 3^n intervals

$$\frac{k}{3^n} \leqslant t \leqslant \frac{k+1}{3^n} \qquad \text{for} \quad 0 \leqslant k \leqslant 3^n - 1;$$

moreover

$$f_n\left(\frac{k}{3^{n-1}}\right) = f_{n-1}\left(\frac{k}{3^{n-1}}\right), \qquad f_n\left(\frac{k}{3^{n-1}} + \frac{1}{3^n}\right) = f_{n-1}\left(\frac{k}{3^{n-1}} + \frac{2}{3^n}\right),$$

$$f_n\left(\frac{k}{3^{n-1}} + \frac{2}{3^n}\right) = f_{n-1}\left(\frac{k}{3^{n-1}} + \frac{1}{3^n}\right).$$

Show that the sequence (f_n) converges uniformly in I towards a continuous function which has no derivative at *any* point of I (use (a)).

2. Let f be a continuous mapping of an open interval $I \subset \mathbf{R}$ into a Banach space E, which has at every point $t \in I$ both a derivative on the left $f_g'(t)$ and a derivative on the right $f_d'(t)$.

(a) Let U be a nonempty open subset of E, A the set of points $t \in I$ such that $f_d'(t) \in U$. For any $\alpha > 0$, let B_α be the subset of I consisting of points t such that there is at least a point $s \in I$ for which $t - \alpha \leqslant s < t$ and $(f(t) - f(s))/(t - s) \in U$; show that B_α is open and that $A \cap \complement B_\alpha$ is denumerable (use Problem 3 of Section **3.9**). Conclude from that result that the set of points $t \in A$ such that $f_g'(t) \notin \bar{U}$ is at most denumerable.

(b) Deduce from (a) that the set of points $t \in I$ such that $f_g'(t) \neq f_d'(t)$ is at most denumerable. (Observe first that $f(I)$ is a denumerable union of compact metric spaces, and by considering the closed vector subspace of E generated by $f(I)$, reduce the problem to the case in which the topology of E has a denumerable basis (U_n) of open sets; then remark that for every pair of distinct points a, b of E there is a pair of sets U_p, U_q such that $a \in U_p$, $b \in U_q$ and $U_p \cap U_q = \varnothing$.)

3. (a) Let f be defined in $\mathbf{R}^2$ by the conditions

$$f(x) = \frac{\xi_1 \xi_2^2}{\xi_1^2 + \xi_2^2} \quad \text{for} \quad x = (\xi_1, \xi_2) \neq (0, 0), \qquad f(0) = 0.$$

Show that for any $x \in \mathbf{R}^2$ and any $y \in \mathbf{R}^2$, the limit $\lim_{t \to 0,\, t \neq 0} (f(x + ty) - f(x))/t = g(x, y)$ exists but that $y \to g(0, y)$ is not linear (hence f is not differentiable at the point 0).

(b) Let f be defined in $\mathbf{R}^2$ by the conditions

$$f(x) = \frac{\xi_1^3 \xi_2}{\xi_1^4 + \xi_2^2} \quad \text{for} \quad x = (\xi_1, \xi_2) \neq (0, 0), \qquad f(0) = 0.$$

Show that the limit $g(x, y)$ exists for every x and y and $y \to g(x, y)$ is linear for every $x \in \mathbf{R}^2$, but that f is not differentiable at the point 0. (Consider the points (ξ_1, ξ_2) such that $\xi_2 = \xi_1^2$.)

4. (a) Let f be a continuous mapping of an open subset A of a Banach space E into a Banach space F. We say that at $x_0 \in A$ the function f is *quasi-differentiable* if there exists a linear mapping u of E into F, having the following property: for *any* continuous mapping g of $I = [0, 1]$ into A such that $g(0) = x_0$ and that the derivative $g'(0)$ of g at 0 (with respect to I) exists, then $t \to f(g(t))$ has at the point $t = 0$ a derivative (with respect to I) equal to $u(g'(0))$. The linear mapping u is then called a *quasi-derivative* of f at x_0. Show that if f is quasi-differentiable at x_0, its quasi-derivative is unique. Extend property (8.2.1) to quasi-differentiable mappings.

(b) Show that if f is quasi-differentiable at x_0, its quasi-derivative u is a *continuous* linear mapping of E into F. (Suppose, as one may, that $x_0 = 0$, $f(x_0) = 0$. Use contradiction: if u is not bounded in the ball $B(0; 1)$, there exists a sequence (a_n) of vectors in E such that $\|a_n\| = 1$, and a sequence (t_n) of numbers > 0, such that $\lim_{n \to \infty} t_n = 0$ and that $\|t_n^{-1} f(t_n a_n)\| = \alpha_n$ tends to $+\infty$; one can suppose that the sequences (t_n) and $(\sqrt{\alpha_n}\, t_n)$ are decreasing and tend to 0. Define a continuous mapping g of $[0, 1]$ into E such that $g(0) = 0$, that $g'(0)$ exists and is equal to 0, and that $g(\sqrt{\alpha_n}\, t_n) = t_n a_n$).)

5. (a) Let E, F be two Banach spaces, f a continuous mapping of an open subset A of E into F. Show that if is differentiable at $x_0 \in A$, it is quasi-differentiable at x_0 and its quasi-derivative is equal to its derivative.

(b) Suppose E has *finite* dimension. Show that if f is quasi-differentiable at $x_0 \in A$, f is differentiable at x_0. (Use contradiction: let u be the quasi-derivative of f at x_0, and suppose there is $\alpha > 0$ and a sequence (x_n) of points of A, tending to x_0, such that $\|f(x_n) - f(x_0) - u \cdot (x_n - x_0)\| \geqslant \alpha \|x_n - x_0\|$. Using the local compactness of E, show that one may suppose that the sequence $(\|x_n - x_0\|)$ is decreasing, and that the sequence of the vectors $z_n = (x_n - x_0)/\|x_n - x_0\|$ tends to a limit in E; then define a continuous mapping g of [0, 1] into E such that $g(0) = x_0$, that $g'(0)$ exists, but that $u(g'(0))$ is not the derivative of $t \to f(g(t))$ at $t = 0$.)

6. Let $I = [0, 1]$, and let E be the Banach space $\mathscr{C}_{\mathbf{R}}(I)$. In order that the mapping $x \to \|x\|$ of E into **R** be quasi-differentiable at a point x_0, it is necessary and sufficient that the function $t \to |x_0(t)|$ reaches its maximum in I at a single point $t_0 \in I$; the quasi-derivative of $x \to \|x\|$ at x_0 is then the linear mapping u such that $u(z) = z(t_0)$ if $x_0(t_0) > 0$, $u(z) = -z(t_0)$ if $x_0(t_0) < 0$ (compare Section **8.2**, Problem 3). (To prove the condition is necessary, suppose $|x_0|$ reaches its maximum at two distinct points t_0, t_1 at least; let y be a continuous mapping of I into itself, equal to 1 at t_0, to 0 at t_1; examine the behavior of $(\|x_0 + \lambda y\| - \|x_0\|)/\lambda$ as the real number $\lambda \neq 0$ tends to 0. To prove the condition is sufficient, let $\lambda \to z_\lambda$ be a continuous mapping of I into E, having a derivative $a \in E$ at $\lambda = 0$ and such that $z_0 = 0$; observe that if t_λ is the largest number in I (or the smallest number in I) where $t \to |x_0(t) + z_\lambda(t)|$ reaches its maximum, then t_λ tends to t_0 when λ tends to 0.) Deduce from that result that the mapping $x \to \|x\|$ of E into **R** is not differentiable at any point (compare to Section **8.2**, Problem 2).

7. Let f be a continuous mapping of an open subset A of a Banach space E into a Banach space F. Suppose f is *lipschitzian* in A: this means (**7.6**, Problem 12) that there exists a constant $k > 0$ such that $\|f(x_1) - f(x_2)\| \leqslant k\|x_1 - x_2\|$ for any pair of points of A. Let $x_0 \in A$, and suppose there is a linear mapping u of E into F such that, for any vector $a \neq 0$ in E, the limit of $(f(x_0 + at) - f(x_0))/t$ when $t \neq 0$ tends to 0 in **R**, exists and is equal to $u(a)$. Show that f is quasi-differentiable at x_0.

8. (a) Let a, b be two points in a Banach space E. Show that the mapping $t \to \|a + tb\|$ of **R** into itself has a derivative on the right and a derivative on the left for every $t \in \mathbf{R}$ (prove that if $0 < t < s$, then $(\|a + bt\| - \|a\|)/t \leqslant (\|a + bs\| - \|a\|)/s$ and use (**4.2.1**)).
(b) Let u be a continuous mapping of an interval $I \in \mathbf{R}$ into E. Show that if at a point $t_0 \in I$, u has a derivative on the right, then $t \to \|u(t)\|$ has at t_0 a derivative on the right and

$$(D_+ \|u\|)(t_0) \leqslant \|D_+ u(t_0)\|$$

(apply (a)).
(c) Let U be a continuous mapping of I into $\mathscr{L}(E; E)$. Show that if at a point $t_0 \in I$, U has a derivative on the right and $U(t_0)$ is a linear homeomorphism of E onto itself, then the mapping $t \to \|(U(t))^{-1}\| = f(t)$, which is defined in a neighborhood of t_0, has a derivative on the right at t_0, and that

$$|(D_+(f^{-1}))(t_0)| \leqslant \|D_+ U(t_0)\|.$$

5. THE MEAN VALUE THEOREM

(**8.5.1**) *Let $I = [\alpha, \beta]$ be a compact interval in* **R**, *f a continuous mapping of* I *into a Banach space* F, *φ a continuous mapping of* I *into* **R**. *We suppose that there is a denumerable subset* D *such that, for each $\xi \in I - D$, f and φ have both a derivative at ξ with respect to* I (**8.4**), *and that $\|f'(\xi)\| \leqslant \varphi'(\xi)$. Then $\|f(\beta) - f(\alpha)\| \leqslant \varphi(\beta) - \varphi(\alpha)$.*

Let $n \to \rho_n$ be a bijection of **N** onto D; for any $\varepsilon > 0$, we will prove that $\|f(\beta) - f(\alpha)\| \leqslant \varphi(\beta) - \varphi(\alpha) + \varepsilon(\beta - \alpha + 2)$; the left hand side being independent of ε, this will complete the proof. Define A as the subset of I consisting of the points ξ such that, for $\alpha \leqslant \zeta < \xi$,

$$\|f(\zeta) - f(\alpha)\| \leqslant \varphi(\zeta) - \varphi(\alpha) + \varepsilon(\zeta - \alpha) + \varepsilon \sum_{\rho_n < \zeta} 2^{-n}.$$

It is clear that $\alpha \in A$; if $\xi \in A$ and $\alpha < \eta < \xi$, then $\eta \in A$ also, by definition; this shows that if γ is the l.u.b. of A, then A must be either the interval $[\alpha, \gamma[$ or the interval $[\alpha, \gamma]$; but in fact, from the definition of A it follows at once that $A = [\alpha, \gamma]$. Moreover, from the continuity of f and φ it follows that

$$\|f(\gamma) - f(\alpha)\| \leqslant \varphi(\gamma) - \varphi(\alpha) + \varepsilon(\gamma - \alpha) + \varepsilon \sum_{\rho_n < \gamma} 2^{-n} \tag{8.5.1.1}$$

and therefore we need only prove that $\gamma = \beta$. Suppose $\gamma < \beta$; if $\gamma \notin D$, then from the definition of the derivative, it follows that there is an interval $[\gamma, \gamma + \lambda]$ contained in I such that, for $\gamma \leqslant \zeta < \gamma + \lambda$

$$\|f(\zeta) - f(\gamma) - f'(\gamma)(\zeta - \gamma)\| \leqslant (\varepsilon/2)(\zeta - \gamma)$$

and

$$|\varphi(\zeta) - \varphi(\gamma) - \varphi'(\gamma)(\zeta - \gamma)| \leqslant (\varepsilon/2)(\zeta - \gamma)$$

hence

$$\begin{aligned}\|f(\zeta) - f(\gamma)\| &\leqslant \|f'(\gamma)\|(\zeta - \gamma) + (\varepsilon/2)(\zeta - \gamma)\\ &\leqslant \varphi'(\gamma)(\zeta - \gamma) + (\varepsilon/2)(\zeta - \gamma) \leqslant \varphi(\zeta) - \varphi(\gamma) + \varepsilon(\zeta - \gamma)\end{aligned}$$

and from **(8.5.1.1)** we deduce

$$\begin{aligned}\|f(\zeta) - f(\alpha)\| &\leqslant \varphi(\zeta) - \varphi(\alpha) + \varepsilon(\zeta - \alpha) + \varepsilon \sum_{\rho_n < \gamma} 2^{-n}\\ &\leqslant \varphi(\zeta) - \varphi(\alpha) + \varepsilon(\zeta - \alpha) + \varepsilon \sum_{\rho_n < \zeta} 2^{-n}\end{aligned}$$

contrary to the definition of γ. If $\gamma \in D$, let $\gamma = \rho_m$; it follows from the continuity of f and φ that there is an interval $[\gamma, \gamma + \lambda]$ contained in I, such that for $\gamma \leqslant \zeta < \gamma + \lambda$,

$$\|f(\zeta) - f(\gamma)\| \leqslant (\varepsilon/2)2^{-m}, \qquad |\varphi(\zeta) - \varphi(\gamma)| \leqslant (\varepsilon/2)2^{-m}$$

hence, from **(8.5.1.1)** we deduce again

$$\begin{aligned}\|f(\zeta) - f(\alpha)\| &\leqslant \varphi(\zeta) - \varphi(\alpha) + \varepsilon(\gamma - \alpha) + \varepsilon \sum_{\rho_n < \zeta} 2^{-n}\\ &\leqslant \varphi(\zeta) - \varphi(\alpha) + \varepsilon(\zeta - \alpha) + \varepsilon \sum_{\rho_n < \zeta} 2^{-n}\end{aligned}$$

and we reach again a contradiction. Q.E.D.

The most important case is that in which $\varphi(\xi) = M(\xi - \alpha)$ with $M > 0$:

(8.5.2) *If there is a denumerable subset* D *of* I *such that, for each* $\xi \in \mathrm{I} - \mathrm{D}$, f *has at* ξ *a derivative with respect to* I *such that* $\|f'(\xi)\| \leqslant \mathrm{M}$, *then* $\|f(\beta) - f(\alpha)\| \leqslant \mathrm{M}(\beta - \alpha)$.

For real-valued functions, the same argument as in (8.5.1) proves the first part of:

(8.5.3) *Suppose* φ *is a continuous mapping of* I *into* **R** *such that, at every point* $\xi \in \mathrm{I} - \mathrm{D}$, φ *has a derivative with respect to* I, *and* $m \leqslant \varphi'(\xi) \leqslant \mathrm{M}$. *Then* $m(\beta - \alpha) \leqslant \varphi(\beta) - \varphi(\alpha) \leqslant \mathrm{M}(\beta - \alpha)$; *and in fact*

$$m(\beta - \alpha) < \varphi(\beta) - \varphi(\alpha) < \mathrm{M}(\beta - \alpha),$$

except when $\varphi(\xi) = \varphi(\alpha) + m(\xi - \alpha)$ *or* $\varphi(\xi) = \varphi(\alpha) + \mathrm{M}(\xi - \alpha)$ *for* $\xi \in \mathrm{I}$.

To prove the second part, observe that by the first part, the function $\varphi(\xi) - \varphi(\alpha) - m(\xi - \alpha)$ is *increasing* in I; if it is not identically 0, then $\varphi(\beta) - \varphi(\alpha) - m(\beta - \alpha) > 0$. Similar argument for the other inequality.

In a normed space E, we define the *segment* joining two points a, b as the set of points $a + \xi(b - a)$ with $0 \leqslant \xi \leqslant 1$.

(8.5.4) *Let* E, F *be two Banach spaces,* f *a continuous mapping into* F *of a neighborhood of a segment* S *joining two points* $x_0, x_0 + t$ *of* E. *If* f *is differentiable at every point of* S, *then*

$$\|f(x_0 + t) - f(x_0)\| \leqslant \|t\| \cdot \sup_{0 \leqslant \xi \leqslant 1} \|f'(x_0 + \xi t)\|.$$

Consider the mapping g of the interval $\mathrm{I} = [0, 1]$ into F defined by $g(\xi) = f(x_0 + \xi t)$; by (8.4.1), (8.2.2) and (8.1.3), g is differentiable at every point of I (with respect to I) and its derivative is $f'(x_0 + \xi t) \cdot t$; hence the result by (8.5.2) and (5.7.4).

PROBLEMS

1. (a) Let $\mathrm{I} =]a, b[$ be an open interval in **R**, and let f be a real function defined and continuous in I. Suppose there is an at most denumerable subset D of I such that, for each $t \in \mathrm{I} - \mathrm{D}$, f is *increasing to the right* at the point t, which means that there is an interval $[t, t + h]$ $(h > 0)$ such that $f(t) \leqslant f(t')$ for $t \leqslant t' \leqslant t + h$. Show that f is increasing in I (apply the same kind of argument as in (8.5.1)). Same conclusion when f is only continuous on the left at each $t \in \mathrm{I}$ (i.e. $f(t-) = f(t)$), but $\mathrm{D} = \varnothing$.

(b) For each number $t \in J = [0, 1[$, let $\sum_{n=0}^{\infty} a_n/2^n$ be the unique "dyadic" development of t such that each a_n is either 0 or 1, and there is no index m such that $a_n = 1$ for all $n \geqslant m$ (see Section **4.2**, Problem 2). Let $f(t) = \sum_{n=0}^{\infty} a_n/4^n$. Show that f is continuous on the right at every point $t \in J$ (i.e. $f(t+) = f(t)$), is not constant in any subinterval of J having more than one point, and that it has at every point $t \in J$ a derivative on the right, equal to 0.

2. Show that the conclusion of **(8.5.1)** is still true if it is only supposed that f and φ have both a derivative on the right at every point ξ of $I - D$ (β being excepted), and that $\|f'_d(\xi)\| \leqslant \varphi'_d(\xi)$.

3. Let f be a real continuous function defined in a compact interval $[\alpha, \beta]$, and having a derivative on the right at every point of $]\alpha, \beta[$. Let m and M be the g.l.b. and l.u.b. of f'_d in $]\alpha, \beta[$.
(a) Show that if f is not a mapping $t \to \lambda t + \mu$, the set of all numbers $(f(x) - f(y))/(x - y)$ when x and y are arbitrary numbers in $[\alpha, \beta]$ such that $x \neq y$, is identical to $]m, M[$. (By suitable substraction of a function of the form $t \to \lambda t + \mu$, reduce the problem to showing that if $f'_d(\gamma) f'_d(\delta) < 0$ with $\alpha < \gamma < \delta < \beta$, there are two distinct points in the interval $]\alpha, \beta[$, where f takes the same value.)
(b) Show that if in addition f has also a derivative on the left at every point of $]\alpha, \beta[$, then the g.l.b. (resp l.u.b.) of f'_d and f'_g in $]\alpha, \beta[$ are the same.
(c) Deduce from (b) that if f has a derivative at every point of $]\alpha, \beta[$, the image by f' of any interval contained in $]\alpha, \beta[$ is connected (see **(3.19.1)**).

4. In the interval $I = [-1, +1]$ of **R**, let f be the mapping of I into $\mathbf{R}^2$ defined as follows: $f(t) = (0, 0)$ if $-1 \leqslant t \leqslant 0$; $f(t) = (t^2 \sin(1/t), t^2 \cos(1/t))$ if $0 < t \leqslant 1$. Show that f has a derivative at every point of $]-1, +1[$, but that the image of that interval by f' is not connected.

5. Extend **(8.5.4)** when f is only supposed to be quasi-differentiable (Section **8.4**, Problem 4) at every point of S, and f' stands for the quasi-derivative.

6. Suppose F is a real Hilbert space. Deduce **(8.5.1)** from the same theorem for *real* functions g, by applying it to the real valued functions $\xi \to (f(\xi) \mid a)$, where $a \in F$. (This method can in fact be applied to any Banach space, and even to more general classes of topological vector spaces; see [6] in the Bibliography.)

7. Let $I = [a, b]$ be a compact interval in **R** not reduced to a single point, f a continuous mapping of I in a Banach space E. Suppose the derivative on the right f'_d exists at every point of $I - D$, where D is an at most denumerable subset of I containing b. Show that there exists a point $\xi \in I - D$ such that $\|f(b) - f(a)\| \leqslant \|f'_d(\xi)\|(b - a)$. (One may assume that $k = \|f(b) - f(a)\|/(b - a)$ is not 0. Use contradiction, assuming that $\|f'_d(t)\| < k$ for every $t \in I - D$; then there would be a point $x_0 \in I - D$ and an $h > 0$ such that $\|f(x_0 + h) - f(x_0)\| < kh$; obtain a contradiction by applying Problem 2 to each of the intervals $[a, x_0]$ and $[x_0 + h, b]$.)

8. A subset A of a real vector space E is called *convex* if, for any pair of points x, y in A, the closed segment of extremities x, y (set of all points $\lambda x + (1 - \lambda)y$ for $0 \leqslant \lambda \leqslant 1$) is contained in A. In order that A be convex, a necessary and sufficient condition is that the intersection of A and of a line, image of **R** by an affine mapping $\varphi : \xi \to a\xi + b$ (where $a \neq 0$ and b are vectors of E), be the image by φ of an interval in **R**.
A mapping f of the convex set $A \subset E$ into **R** is called *convex* if, in the vector space $E \times \mathbf{R}$, the set D_f of all pairs (x, ζ) such that $x \in A$ and $\zeta \geqslant f(x)$, is convex. It is equivalent to say that for any pair of points x, y of A and every number λ such that $0 \leqslant \lambda \leqslant 1$,

$$f(\lambda x + (1 - \lambda)y) \leqslant \lambda f(x) + (1 - \lambda) f(y).$$

In order that f be convex in A, a necessary and sufficient condition is that, for any affine mapping $\varphi : \xi \to a\xi + b$ of $\mathbf{R}$ into E (with $a \neq 0$) such that $\varphi(\mathbf{R}) \cap \mathrm{A} \neq \varnothing$, the mapping $f \circ \varphi$ be convex in the interval $\varphi^{-1}(\mathrm{A}) \subset \mathbf{R}$.
Let $\mathrm{I} \supset \mathbf{R}$ be an interval, f a real function defined in I. In order that f be convex in I it is necessary and sufficient that, for every $a \in \mathrm{I}$, the function $t \to (f(t) - f(a))/(t - a)$ be increasing in $\mathrm{I} \cap \complement\{a\}$. Conclude from that result that at every point a interior to I, f is continuous, and has both a derivative on the right and a derivative on the left; furthermore, if $a < b$ are two points interior to I, we have

$$f_d'(a) \leqslant \frac{f(b) - f(a)}{b - a} \leqslant f_g'(b).$$

Conversely, if I is an open interval, f is continuous in I, has at every point a derivative on the right, and f_d' is increasing in I, then f is convex in I (use contradiction, and problem 2).
If A is convex set in a real vector space E, a mapping f of A into R is called *strictly convex* if, for every pair of *distinct* points x, y in A and every number λ such that $0 < \lambda < 1$, one has

$$f(\lambda x + (1 - \lambda)y) < \lambda f(x) + (1 - \lambda) f(y).$$

If $\mathrm{A} = \mathrm{I}$ is an open interval in $\mathbf{R}$, in order that f be strictly convex in I, a necessary and sufficient condition is that f_d' be strictly increasing in I.

6. APPLICATIONS OF THE MEAN VALUE THEOREM

(8.6.1) *Let* A *be an open connected subset of a Banach space* E, f *a continuous mapping of* A *into a Banach space* F; *if* f *has a derivative equal to* 0 *at every point of* A, *then* f *is a constant.*

Let x_0 be a point of A, and let B be the set of points $x \in \mathrm{A}$ such that $f(x) = f(x_0)$. B is closed with respect to A (3.15.1); on the other hand, if $x \in \mathrm{B}$ and if U is an open ball of center x contained in A, then U contains the segment joining x to any of its points y, hence by (8.5.4) $f(y) = f(x) = f(x_0)$. This shows that B is also open with respect to A, hence equal to A by assumption (Section 3.19).

Better results are available, using (8.5.2): for instance, if $\mathrm{E} = \mathbf{R}$ and A is an interval in $\mathbf{R}$, it is only necessary to assume that the derivative of f exists and is 0 *except at the points of a denumerable set.*

(8.6.2) *Let* E, F *be two Banach spaces,* f *a differentiable mapping into* F *of an open neighborhood* A *of a segment* S *joining two points* a, b. *Then, for each* $x_0 \in \mathrm{A}$, *we have*

$$\|f(b) - f(a) - f'(x_0) \cdot (b - a)\| \leqslant \|b - a\| \cdot \sup_{x \in \mathrm{S}} \|f'(x) - f'(x_0)\|.$$

Apply (8.5.4) to the mapping

$$x \to f(x) - f'(x_0) \cdot x$$

whose derivative is $t \to (f'(x) - f'(x_0)) \cdot t$ by (8.2.2) and (8.1.3).

(8.6.3) *Let* A *be an open connected subset in a Banach space* E, (f_n) *a sequence of differentiable mappings of* A *into a Banach space* F. *Suppose that*: (1) *there exists one point* $x_0 \in A$ *such that the sequence* $(f_n(x_0))$ *converges in* F; (2) *for every point* $a \in A$, *there is a ball* $B(a)$ *of center* a *contained in* A *and such that in* $B(a)$ *the sequence* (f_n') *converges uniformly. Then for each* $a \in A$, *the sequence* (f_n) *converges uniformly in* $B(a)$; *moreover, if, for each* $x \in A$, $f(x) = \lim_{n\to\infty} f_n(x)$ *and* $g(x) = \lim_{n\to\infty} f_n'(x)$, *then* $g(x) = f'(x)$ *for each* $x \in A$.

Let r be the radius of $B(a)$; then by (8.5.4), for any point $x \in B(a)$, we have

$$\|f_n(x) - f_m(x) - (f_n(a) - f_m(a))\| \leqslant \|x - a\| \cdot \sup_{z \in B(a)} \|f_n'(z) - f_m'(z)\|$$

$$\leqslant r \cdot \sup_{z \in B(a)} \|f_n'(z) - f_m'(z)\|. \tag{8.6.3.1}$$

As the sequence (f_n') is uniformly convergent in $B(a)$, and F is complete, this proves that if the sequence $(f_n(x))$ is convergent at *any* point of $B(a)$, it is also convergent at *every* point of $B(a)$, and in fact uniformly convergent in $B(a)$. This result first shows that the set U of the points x such that $(f_n(x))$ is a convergent sequence, is both open and closed in A; as it is not empty by assumption, and A is connected, U = A. We finally prove g is the derivative of f: given $\varepsilon > 0$, there is by assumption an integer n_0 such that for $n \geqslant n_0$, $m \geqslant n_0$, $\|f_n'(z) - f_m'(z)\| \leqslant \varepsilon/r$ for every $z \in B(a)$, and moreover $\|g(a) - f_n'(a)\| \leqslant \varepsilon$; letting m tend to $+\infty$ in (8.6.3.1), we see that, for $n \geqslant n_0$ and $x \in B(a)$, we have

$$\|f(x) - f(a) - (f_n(x) - f_n(a))\| \leqslant \varepsilon\|x - a\|.$$

On the other hand, for any $n \geqslant n_0$, there is $r' \leqslant r$ such that, for $\|x - a\| \leqslant r'$, we have $\|f_n(x) - f_n(a) - f_n'(a) \cdot (x - a)\| \leqslant \varepsilon\|x - a\|$; using (5.7.4), we finally see that for $\|x - a\| \leqslant r'$, we have

$$\|f(x) - f(a) - g(a) \cdot (x - a)\| \leqslant 3\varepsilon\|x - a\|$$

which proves that $f'(a)$ exists and is equal to $g(a)$. Q.E.D.

Again, we can state better results when $E = \mathbf{R}$ and A is an interval in $\mathbf{R}$:

(8.6.4) *Let* (g_n) *be a sequence of mappings of an interval* $I \subset \mathbf{R}$ *into* F, *and suppose that, for each* n, $g_n(\xi)$ *is the derivative of a continuous function* f_n *except for the points* ξ *of a denumerable subset* $D_n \subset I$. *Suppose in addition that*: (1) *there exists a point* $\xi_0 \in I$ *such that the sequence* $(f_n(\xi_0))$ *converges in* F; (2) *for every point* $\zeta \in I$, *there is a neighborhood* $B(\zeta)$ *with respect to* I *such that in* $B(\zeta)$ *the sequence* (g_n) *converges uniformly. Then for each* $\zeta \in A$, *the sequence* (f_n) *converges uniformly in* $B(\zeta)$; *and if we put* $f_n(\xi) = \lim_{n\to\infty} f_n(\xi)$ *and* $g(\xi) = \lim_{n\to\infty} g_n(\xi)$, *then at every point of* A *not in* $\bigcup_n D_n$, $f'(\xi) = g(\xi)$.

The proof repeats that of (8.6.3), using (8.5.2) instead of (8.5.4).

(8.6.3) yields in particular:

(8.6.5) *Let* A *be an open connected subset in a Banach space,* (u_n) *a sequence of differentiable mappings of* A *into a Banach space* F. *If for every* $a \in A$, *there is a ball* $B(a)$ *of center* a *contained in* A *and such that the series* (u_n') *is uniformly convergent in* $B(a)$, *and if there exists a point* $x_0 \in A$ *such that the series* $(u_n(x_0))$ *is convergent, then for each* $a \in A$, *the series* (u_n) *is uniformly convergent in* $B(a)$, *and its sum* $s(x)$ *has a derivative equal to* $\sum_{n=0}^{\infty} u_n'(x)$ *at every* $x \in A$.

PROBLEMS

1. Let f, g be two real valued differentiable functions defined in an open interval $I \subset \mathbf{R}$. It is supposed that $f(t) > 0, g(t) > 0, f'(t) > 0$ and $g'(t) > 0$ in I. Show that if the function f'/g' is strictly increasing in I, either f/g is strictly increasing in I, or there exists $c \in I$ such that f/g is strictly decreasing for $t \leqslant c$ and strictly increasing for $t \geqslant c$. (Prove that if $f'(s)/g'(s) < f(s)/g(s)$, then for any $t < s$, $f'(t)/g'(t) < f(t)/g(t)$.) Apply to the function

$$\frac{\dfrac{\tan t}{t} - \dfrac{\tan a}{a}}{t \tan t - a \tan a}$$

in the interval $]a, \pi/2[$.

2. (a) Let I be an open interval in $\mathbf{R}$, $x_0 \in \mathbf{R}$ one of its extremities, f a continuous mapping of I into a Banach space E. Suppose there is a denumerable subset D of I such that at each point of $I - D$, f has a derivative on the right. In order that $f_d'(t)$ have a limit when t tends to x_0 in $I - D$, a necessary and sufficient condition is that $(f(t) - f(s))/(t - s)$ have a limit when the pair (s, t) tends to (x_0, x_0) in the set defined by $s \in I, t \in I, s \neq t$. Both limits are then the same; if c is their common value, show that $f(t)$ has a limit in E when t tends to x_0 in I, and that if f is extended by continuity to $I \cup \{x_0\}$ (3.15.5), $(f(t) - f(x_0))/(t - x_0)$ tends to c when t tends to x_0 in I. (Use the mean value theorem and Cauchy's criterion.)

(b) Show that at every point $t \in \mathrm{I} - \mathrm{D}$ where f_d' is continuous on the left, f has a derivative on the left. If at $t \in \mathrm{I} - \mathrm{D}$, f_d' is continuous, f has a derivative at the point t. (Use (a).)

3. Let f be a differentiable mapping of an open subset A of E into F (E, F Banach spaces).
(a) In order that f' be continuous at x_0, a necessary and sufficient condition is that, for any $\varepsilon > 0$, there exist $\delta > 0$ such that the relations $\|s\| \leqslant \delta$, $\|t\| \leqslant \delta$ imply $\|f(x_0 + s) - f(x_0 + t) - f'(x_0) \cdot (s - t)\| \leqslant \varepsilon \|s - t\|$.
(b) In order that f' be uniformly continuous in A, a necessary condition is that, for any $\varepsilon > 0$, there exist $\delta > 0$ such that the relations $\|s\| \leqslant \delta$, $x \in \mathrm{A}$, $x + \xi s \in \mathrm{A}$ for $0 \leqslant \xi \leqslant 1$ imply $\|f(x + s) - f(x) - f'(x) \cdot s\| \leqslant \varepsilon \|s\|$. The condition is sufficient when A is *convex* (Section **8.5**, Problem 8).

4. Let f be a continuous mapping of a compact interval $\mathrm{I} \subset \mathbf{R}$ into $\mathbf{R}$, having a continuous derivative in I. Let S be the set of points $t \in \mathrm{I}$ such that $f'(t) = 0$. Show that for any $\varepsilon > 0$, there exist a sequence (r_n) of numbers >0 such that $\sum_{n=0}^{\infty} r_n \leqslant \varepsilon$ and that the set $f(\mathrm{S})$ is contained in a denumerable union of intervals J_n, such that $\delta(\mathrm{J}_n) \leqslant r_n$. (For any $\alpha > 0$, consider the open subset U_α of I consisting of the points t where $|f'(t)| < \alpha$; use (**3.19.6**) and the mean value theorem.)

5. Let f be a continuous mapping of an interval $\mathrm{I} \subset \mathbf{R}$ into $\mathbf{C}$, such that $f(t) \neq 0$ in I and and that $f_d'(t)$ exists in the complement of a denumerable subset D of I. In order that $|f|$ be an increasing function in I, show that a necessary and sufficient condition is that $\mathscr{R}(f_d'(t)/f(t)) \geqslant 0$ in $\mathrm{I} - \mathrm{D}$.

6. Let E, F be two Banach spaces, A an open subset of E, B a closed subset of the subspace A, whose interior is empty and such that any segment in E which is not contained in B has an at most denumerable intersection with B. Let f be a continuously differentiable mapping of $\mathrm{A} - \mathrm{B}$ into F, and suppose that at each point $b \in \mathrm{B}$, the limit of $f'(x)$ with respect to $\mathrm{A} - \mathrm{B}$ exists. Show that f can be extended by continuity to a continuously differentiable mapping $\bar{f}$ of A into F (same method as in Problem 2(a)).

7. PRIMITIVES AND INTEGRALS

Let f be a mapping of an interval $\mathrm{I} \subset \mathbf{R}$ into a Banach space F. We say that a continuous mapping g of I into F is a *primitive* of f in I if there exists a denumerable set $\mathrm{D} \subset \mathrm{I}$ such that, for any $\xi \in \mathrm{I} - \mathrm{D}$, g is differentiable at ξ and $g'(\xi) = f(\xi)$.

(**8.7.1**) *If g_1, g_2 are two primitives of f in* I, *then $g_1 - g_2$ is constant in* I.

This follows at once from the remark following (**8.6.1**).

Any interval I in $\mathbf{R}$ (not reduced to a point) is the union of an increasing sequence of compact intervals J_n; to check that a function f defined in I has a primitive, it is only necessary to do so for the restriction of f to each of the J_n: for if ξ_0 is an interior point of J_1, and if, for each n, g_n is the primitive in J_n of the restriction of f to J_n, such that $g_n(\xi_0) = 0$ (which is uniquely determined by (8.7.1)), then the restriction of g_{n+1} to J_n is a primitive of f in J_n vanishing at ξ_0, hence equal to g_n. We can therefore define the mapping g of I into F as equal to g_n in each of the J_n, and it is obvious that g is a primitive of f in I.

(8.7.2) *Let* I *be an interval of* **R**; *any regulated mapping of* I *into* F (Section 7.6) (*and in particular any continuous mapping into* F, *or — when* F = **R** — *any monotone function*) *has a primitive in* I.

From the preceding remarks, it follows that we can assume I is compact. Then, from (8.6.4) and (7.6.1) it follows that we need only prove the theorem for *step-functions*. Suppose f is a step-function, $(\lambda_i)_{0 \leqslant i \leqslant n}$ an increasing sequence of points in $I = [\alpha, \beta]$ such that $\lambda_0 = \alpha$, $\lambda_n = \beta$ and $f(\xi)$ is equal to a constant c_i in $]\lambda_i, \lambda_{i+1}[$ $(0 \leqslant i \leqslant n-1)$. Then if we define g such that in each interval $[\lambda_i, \lambda_{i+1}]$ $(0 \leqslant i \leqslant n-1)$, we have $g(\xi) = c_i(\xi - \lambda_i) + \sum_{k=0}^{i-1} c_k(\lambda_{k+1} - \lambda_k)$, it is readily verified that g is a primitive of f.

A primitive of a step-function is also called a *piecewise linear* function. For a continuous function, we have furthermore:

(8.7.3) *If g is a primitive of a continuous mapping f of* I *into* F, *then g has at every point $\xi \in$ I a derivative with respect to* I *equal to $f(\xi)$.*

For it follows from (8.5.2) that for every interval $[\xi, \xi + \lambda] \subset I$

$$\|g(\xi + \zeta) - g(\xi) - f(\xi)\zeta\| \leqslant \zeta \sup_{0 \leqslant \eta \leqslant \lambda} \|f(\xi + \eta) - f(\xi)\|$$

for $0 \leqslant \zeta \leqslant \lambda$, and $\sup_{0 \leqslant \eta \leqslant \lambda} \|f(\xi + \eta) - f(\xi)\|$ is arbitrarily small with λ, by assumption.

If g is any primitive of a regulated function f, the difference $g(\beta) - g(\alpha)$, for any two points of I, is independent of the particular primitive g which is considered, owing to (8.7.1); it is written $\int_\alpha^\beta f(\xi)\, d\xi$, and called the *integral of f between α and β*. Any formal rule of derivation can be translated into that notation and yields a corresponding formula of "integral calculus"; we only write explicitly the three most important ones; for convenience, if g is a primitive of a regulated function f, we write g' instead of f, although

g does not have in general a derivative everywhere, and when the derivative exists it may fail to be equal to f (at the points of a denumerable set):

(8.7.4) ("Change of variables") *Let φ be a real-valued primitive of a regulated function defined in an interval* I*; let f be any regulated function defined in an interval* $J \supset \varphi(I)$*; then, if either f is continuous or φ is monotone, for any two points α, β of* I, *we have*

$$\int_\alpha^\beta f(\varphi(\xi))\varphi'(\xi)\,d\xi = \int_{\varphi(\alpha)}^{\varphi(\beta)} f(\zeta)\,d\zeta.$$

The only point to check is that $f(\varphi(\xi))\varphi'(\xi)$ is a regulated function, which follows at once from the assumptions and from the definition of a regulated function (Section 7.6); then, if g is a primitive of f, both sides of the formula are equal to $g(\varphi(\beta)) - g(\varphi(\alpha))$, due to (8.4.1).

(8.7.5) ("Integration by parts") *Let f, g be primitives of regulated functions defined in an interval* I, *and taking their values in two Banach spaces* E, F *respectively; and let $(x, y) \to [x \cdot y]$ be a continuous bilinear mapping of* $E \times F$ *into a Banach space* G*; then, for any points α, β of* I

$$\int_\alpha^\beta [f(\xi)\cdot g'(\xi)]\,d\xi = [f(\beta)\cdot g(\beta)] - [f(\alpha)\cdot g(\alpha)] - \int_\alpha^\beta [f'(\xi)\cdot g(\xi)]\,d\xi.$$

Again, the only point to check is that $[f\cdot g']$ and $[f'\cdot g]$ are regulated functions, and then the formula follows from (8.1.4) and (8.4.1).

8.7.6) *Let f be a regulated mapping of* I *into a Banach space* F, *and let u be any continuous linear mapping of* F *into a Banach space* G. *Then*

$$\int_\alpha^\beta u(f(\xi))\,d\xi = u\left(\int_\alpha^\beta f(\xi)\,d\xi\right).$$

This follows from (8.4.1) and (8.1.3).

The translation in terms of integrals of the mean value theorem reads:

(8.7.7) *For any regulated function f in a compact interval,*

$$\left\|\int_\alpha^\beta f(\xi)\,d\xi\right\| \leqslant \int_\alpha^\beta \|f(\xi)\|\,d\xi \leqslant (\beta-\alpha)\sup_{\xi\in I}\|f(\xi)\|.$$

Here again, to apply (8.5.1) we have only to verify that $\xi \to \|f(\xi)\|$ is regulated.

Finally, we express for integrals results corresponding to (8.6.4) and (8.6.5):

(8.7.8) *If a sequence* (g_n) *of regulated functions, defined in a compact interval* $\mathrm{I} = [\alpha, \beta]$, *converges uniformly in* I *to* g, *then the sequence* $\left(\int_\alpha^\beta g_n(\xi)\, d\xi\right)$ *converges to* $\int_\alpha^\beta g(\xi)\, d\xi$. (Remember g is regulated by (7.6.1).)

(8.7.9) *If a series* (u_n) *of regulated functions, defined in a compact interval* $\mathrm{I} = [\alpha, \beta]$, *is normally convergent* (Section 7.1) *in* I, *then, if* $u = \sum_{n=0}^{\infty} u_n$, *the series of general term* $\int_\alpha^\beta u_n(\xi)\, d\xi$ *is absolutely convergent, and* $\int_\alpha^\beta u(\xi)\, d\xi = \sum_{n=0}^{\infty} \int_\alpha^\beta u_n(\xi)\, d\xi$.

The absolute convergence follows at once from the assumption and the mean value theorem (8.7.7).

(8.7.10) *Remark.* Due to (8.6.4) and the proof of (7.6.1), for any regulated function f defined in $[\alpha, \beta]$, and for any $\varepsilon > 0$, there is an increasing sequence

$$\alpha = x_0 \leqslant t_0 \leqslant x_1 \leqslant t_1 \leqslant \cdots \leqslant x_k \leqslant t_k \leqslant x_{k+1} \leqslant \cdots \leqslant x_n = \beta$$

such that

$$\left\| \int_\alpha^\beta f(x)\, dx - \sum_{k=0}^{n-1} f(t_k)(x_{k+1} - x_k) \right\| \leqslant \varepsilon.$$

If f is continuous, one may (due to (3.16.5)) take all numbers $x_{k+1} - x_k$ equal to $(\beta - \alpha)/n$, and $t_k = x_k$ (see Problem 1).

PROBLEMS

1. Let f be a regulated function defined in a compact interval $\mathrm{I} \subset \mathbf{R}$. Show that for any $\varepsilon > 0$, there is a number $\delta > 0$ such that for any increasing sequence $x_0 \leqslant t_0 \leqslant x_1 \leqslant \cdots \leqslant x_k \leqslant t_k \leqslant x_{k+1} \leqslant \cdots \leqslant x_n$ of points of I for which $x_{k+1} - x_k \leqslant \delta$, we have

$$\left\| \int_{x_0}^{x_n} f(t)\, dt - \sum_{k=0}^{n-1} f(t_k)(x_{k+1} - x_k) \right\| \leqslant \varepsilon$$

("Riemann sums"; consider first the case in which f is a step-function).

2. (a) Let f be a regulated function defined in a compact interval $I = [a, b]$. Show that for any $\varepsilon > 0$, there exists a continuous function g defined in I and such that $\int_a^b \|f(t) - g(t)\| \, dt \leqslant \varepsilon$.

(b) Suppose f takes its values in E; let h be a regulated function defined in I and taking its values in F, and let $(x, y) \to [x \cdot y]$ be a continuous bilinear mapping of $E \times F$ into G (E, F, G Banach spaces). Show that

$$\lim_{s \to 0,\, s > 0} \int_a^b [f(t) \cdot h(t+s)] \, dt = \int_a^b [f(t) \cdot h(t)] \, dt.$$

(c) Show that

$$\lim_{n \to \infty} \int_a^b f(t) \sin nt \, dt = \lim_{n \to \infty} \int_a^b f(t) \cos nt \, dt = 0, \qquad \lim_{n \to \infty} \int_a^b f(t) |\sin nt| \, dt = \frac{2}{\pi} \int_a^b f(t) \, dt.$$

(d) Let u be a primitive of f, and suppose $u(I)$ is contained in a ball $B \subset E$. Show that if g is a *monotone* function in I, then there exists a number $c \in B$ such that

$$\int_a^b f(t) g(t) \, dt = (u(b) - c) g(b) + (c - u(a)) g(a).$$

In particular, if f is a real regulated function, there exists $s \in I$ such that

$$\int_a^b f(t) g(t) \, dt = g(a) \int_a^s f(t) \, dt + g(b) \int_s^b f(t) \, dt$$

("the second mean value theorem").

(For all these properties, use the same method as in Problem 1.)

3. Let f be a regulated function defined in a compact interval $I = [a, b]$. For any integer $n > 0$ and any integer k such that $0 \leqslant k \leqslant n$, let $x_k = a + k((b-a)/n)$; let

$$r(n) = \frac{b-a}{n} \sum_{k=1}^{n} f(x_k) - \int_a^b f(t) \, dt.$$

(a) Suppose f has a continuous derivative in I. Show that

$$\lim_{n \to \infty} n r(n) = \frac{b-a}{2} (f(b) - f(a)).$$

(Write $r(n) = \sum_{k=0}^{n-1} \int_{x_k}^{x_{k+1}} (f(x_{k+1}) - f(t)) \, dt$; use the mean value theorem and Problem 1.)

(b) Suppose f is an increasing real function in I; show that

$$0 \leqslant r(n) \leqslant \frac{b-a}{n} (f(b) - f(a)).$$

(c) Give an example of an increasing continuous function f in I such that $nr(n)$ does not tend to $((b-a)/2)(f(b) - f(a))$ when n tends to $+\infty$. (Take for f the limit of a sequence (f_n) of increasing continuous piecewise linear functions, satisfying the conditions

$$(b-a) \sum_{k=1}^{2^n} f_n\left(a + k\frac{b-a}{2^n}\right) - 2^n \int_a^b f_n(t) \, dt \geqslant \tfrac{3}{4} (b-a)(f_n(b) - f_n(a))$$

and

$$f_{n+1}\left(a + k\frac{b-a}{2^n}\right) = f_n\left(a + k\frac{b-a}{2^n}\right) \quad \text{for} \quad 0 \leqslant k \leqslant 2^n.)$$

4. Show that, when n tends to $+\infty$, the polynomial

$$f_n(x) = \int_0^x (1-t^2)^n\,dt \Big/ \int_0^1 (1-t^2)^n\,dt$$

converges uniformly to -1 in any interval $[-1, -\varepsilon]$ and converges uniformly to $+1$ in any interval $[\varepsilon, +1]$ ($\varepsilon > 0$ arbitrary; use the inequality $\int_0^1 (1-t^2)^n\,dt \geqslant \int_0^1 (1-t)^n\,dt$).

Let $g_n(x) = \int_0^x f_n(t)\,dt$; show that the polynomial g_n converges uniformly to the function $|x|$ in $[-1, +1]$, obtaining thus a new proof of **(7.3.1.3)**).

5. Let f be a continuous mapping of an interval $[x_0, +\infty[$ into a Banach space E, such that for each $\lambda > 0$, $\lim_{x \to +\infty} (f(x+\lambda) - f(x)) = 0$.

(a) Show that $f(x+\lambda) - f(x)$ converges *uniformly* to 0 when x tends to $+\infty$ and λ remains in a *compact* interval $\mathrm{K} = [a, b] \subset [0, +\infty[$ (i.e., for every $\varepsilon > 0$ there exists $\mathrm{A} > 0$ such that $x \geqslant \mathrm{A}$ implies $\|f(x+\lambda) - f(x)\| \leqslant \varepsilon$ for every $\lambda \in \mathrm{K}$). (Use contradiction: suppose there is a sequence (x_n) such that $\lim_{n\to\infty} x_n = +\infty$, and a sequence (λ_n) of points of K such that $\|f(x_n + \lambda_n) - f(x_n)\| > \alpha > 0$, for every n. Observe that there is a neighborhood J_n of λ_n in K such that $\|f(x_n + \lambda) - f(x_n)\| > \alpha$ for *any* $\lambda \in \mathrm{J}_n$. Define by induction a *decreasing* sequence of closed intervals $\mathrm{I}_k \subset \mathrm{K}$, and a subsequence (x_{n_k}) of (x_n) such that $\|f(x_{n_k} + \mu) - f(x_{n_k})\| \geqslant \alpha/3$ for every $\mu \in \mathrm{I}_k$; to define I_{k+1} when I_k is known, observe that if δ_k is the length of I_k, and q an integer such that $q\delta_k > b - a$, then $\|f(x + \delta_k) - f(x)\| \leqslant \alpha/3q$ as soon as x is large enough.)

(b) Deduce from (a) that $\lim_{x\to+\infty} \left(\int_x^{x+1} f(t)\,dt - f(x) \right) = 0$, and conclude that $\lim_{x\to\infty} f(x)/x = 0$.

6. (a) Show that there exists a differentiable real function f (resp. g) defined in **R** and such that $f'(t) = \sin(1/t)$ (resp. $g'(t) = \cos(1/t)$) for $t \neq 0$ and $f'(0) = 0$ (resp. $g'(0) = 0$). (Consider the derivatives of the functions $t^2 \cos(1/t)$ and $t^2 \sin(1/t)$.) The functions f' and g' are not regulated.

(b) Let $\mathrm{P}(t, u, v)$ be a polynomial in u and v with coefficients which are continuous real functions of t in an open interval $\mathrm{I} \subset \mathbf{R}$ containing 0. Show that there exists a differentiable function f defined in I, such that $f'(t) = \mathrm{P}(t, \sin(1/t), \cos(1/t))$ for $t \neq 0$ (express monomials in $\sin(1/t)$ and $\cos(1/t)$ as linear combinations of terms of the form $\sin(k/t)$ or $\cos(k/t)$, and use (a)). What is the value of $f'(0)$? Show that one may have $f'(0) \neq \mathrm{P}(0, 0, 0)$.

(c) Show that there exists a differentiable function f defined in $[-1, +1]$ and such that $f'(t) = \sin(1/\sin(1/t))$ at every point t other than 0 and the points $1/n\pi$ (n positive or negative integer). (In the neighborhood of $t = 1/n\pi$, write $t = (n\pi + \arcsin u)^{-1}$ and use (b) to prove the existence of $f'(1/n\pi)$; furthermore, show that there is a constant $a > 0$, independent of n, such that

$$\left| \int_{2/(2n+1)\pi}^{2/(2n-1)\pi} \sin(1/\sin(1/t))\,dt \right| \leqslant a/n^3$$

for every integer $n > 0$; consider then the function

$$g(t) = \lim_{\varepsilon \to 0} \int_\varepsilon^t \sin(1/\sin(1/s))\,ds$$

for $t > 0$, and define f similarly for $t < 0$.)

7. Let $I = [0, 1[$ and let E be the vector space of regulated complex functions defined in I, bounded and continuous on the right (i.e. $f(t+) = f(t)$ for $t \in I$).

(a) Show that on E, $(f \mid g) = \int_{-1}^{+1} f(t)\overline{g(t)}\, dt$ is a nondegenerate positive hermitian form (see (8.5.3)). Prove that the prehilbert space E thus defined is not complete (use the fact that the function equal to $\sin(1/t)$ for $t > 0$, to 0 for $t = 0$, is not in E).

(b) Define the sequence (f_n) of elements of E in the following way:

(1) f_0 is the constant 1;

(2) for each integer $n > 0$, let m be the largest integer such that $2^m \leqslant n$, and let $n = 2^m + k$; f_n is taken as equal to $2^{m/2}$ for $\frac{2k}{2^{m+1}} \leqslant t < \frac{2k+1}{2^{m+1}}$, to $-2^{m/2}$ for $\frac{2k+1}{2^{m+1}} \leqslant t < \frac{2k+2}{2^{m+1}}$, and to 0 for all other values of t in I.

Prove that in the prehilbert space E, (f_n) is an orthonormal system (the "Haar orthonormal system").

(c) For each $n \geqslant 0$, let V_n be the supspace of E generated by the f_k of indices $k \leqslant n$. Show that there is a decomposition of I into $n + 1$ intervals of type $[\alpha, \beta[$ without common points, such that, in each of these intervals, every function belonging to V_n is constant; conversely, every function having that property belongs to V_n (consider the dimension of the vector subspace of E generated by these functions).

(d) Let g be an arbitrary function of E, h its orthogonal projection (Section 6.3) on V_n; show that in each of the intervals $[\alpha, \beta[$ in which all the functions of V_n are constant,

$$h(t) = \frac{1}{\beta - \alpha} \int_{\alpha}^{\beta} g(u)\, du.$$

(e) Show, by using (d), that for any function $g \in E$ which is *continuous* in I, the series of general term $(g \mid f_n) f_n(t)$ is uniformly convergent in I and that its sum is equal to $g(t)$. Conclude from that result that (f_n) is a total orthonormal system in E.

8. Let f be a regulated real valued function in a compact interval $I = [a, b]$; let $\int_a^b |f(t)|\, dt = c$. Show that for any $\varepsilon > 0$, there is a real valued continuous function g in I, such that $|g(t)| \leqslant 1$ in I, and that $\int_a^b f(t)g(t)\, dt \geqslant c - \varepsilon$. (Reduce the problem to the case in which f is a step function.)

8. APPLICATION: THE NUMBER e

For any number $a > 0$, the function $x \to a^x$ is continuous in $\mathbf{R}$ (Section 4.3), hence the function $g(x) = \int_0^x a^t\, dt$ is defined and differentiable in $\mathbf{R}$, with $g'(x) = a^x$ everywhere. Now we have $g(x+1) = \int_0^{x+1} a^t\, dt = \int_0^x a^t\, dt + \int_x^{x+1} a^t\, dt$. But by (8.7.4), $\int_x^{x+1} a^t\, dt = \int_0^1 a^{x+u}\, du = a^x \int_0^1 a^u\, du$; as $a^x \geqslant \inf(a, 1)$ for $0 \leqslant x \leqslant 1$, $c = \int_0^1 a^u\, du$ is > 0 by (8.5.3), hence we can write

$$a^x = c^{-1}(g(x+1) - g(x))$$

and therefore a^x is *differentiable* in $\mathbf{R}$, and $D(a^x) = \varphi(a) \cdot a^x$, where $\varphi(a) \neq 0$ if $a \neq 1$. Suppose $a \neq 1$, and let b be any number > 0; we can write

$$b^x = a^{x \log_a b}$$

and therefore, by (8.4.1)

$$\varphi(b) \cdot b^x = \log_a b \cdot \varphi(a) \cdot b^x,$$

in other words

$$\varphi(b) = \varphi(a) \log_a b.$$

There is therefore one and only one number $e > 0$ such that $\varphi(e) = 1$, namely $e = a^{1/\varphi(a)}$; as $D(e^x) = e^x > 0$, e^x is strictly increasing (by (8.5.3)), and hence $e = e^1 > e^0 = 1$. The function e^x is also written $\exp(x)$ or $\exp x$. The function $\log_e x$ is written $\log x$ and it follows from (8.2.3) and (4.2.2) that $D(\log x) = 1/x$ for $x > 0$. Furthermore $D(a^x) = \log a \cdot a^x$.

PROBLEM

Study the variation of the functions

$$\left(1 + \frac{1}{x}\right)^{x+p}, \quad \left(1 + \frac{1}{x}\right)^{x-p}, \quad \left(1 + \frac{p}{x}\right)\left(1 + \frac{1}{x}\right)^x, \quad \left(1 + \frac{p}{x}\right)^{x+1}$$

for $x > 0$, p being a fixed arbitrary positive number; find their limits when x tends to $+\infty$.

9. PARTIAL DERIVATIVES

Let f be a differentiable mapping of an open subset A of a Banach space E into a Banach space F; Df is then a mapping of A into $\mathscr{L}(E; F)$. We say that f is *continuously differentiable* in A if Df is continuous in A.

Suppose now $E = E_1 \times E_2$. For each point $(a_1, a_2) \in A$ we can consider the partial mappings $x_1 \to f(x_1, a_2)$ and $x_2 \to f(a_1, x_2)$ of open subsets of E_1 and E_2 respectively into F. We say that at (a_1, a_2), f is *differentiable with respect to the first* (resp. *second*) *variable* if the partial mapping $x_1 \to f(x_1, a_2)$ (resp. $x_2 \to f(a_1, x_2)$) is differentiable at a_1 (resp. a_2); the derivative of that mapping, which is an element of $\mathscr{L}(E_1; F)$ (resp. $\mathscr{L}(E_2; F)$) is called the *partial derivative* of f at (a_1, a_2) with respect to the first (resp. second) variable, and written $D_1 f(a_1, a_2)$ (resp. $D_2 f(a_1, a_2)$).

(8.9.1) *Let f be a continuous mapping of an open subset* A *of* $E_1 \times E_2$ *into* F. *In order that f be continuously differentiable in* A, *a necessary and sufficient condition is that f be differentiable at each point with respect to the first and the second variable, and that the mappings $(x_1, x_2) \to D_1 f(x_1, x_2)$ and $(x_1, x_2) \to D_2 f(x_1, x_2)$ (of* A *into $\mathscr{L}(E_1; F)$ and $\mathscr{L}(E_2; F)$ respectively) be continuous in* A. *Then, at each point (x_1, x_2) of* A, *the derivative of f is given by*

$$Df(x_1, x_2) \cdot (t_1, t_2) = D_1 f(x_1, x_2) \cdot t_1 + D_2 f(x_1, x_2) \cdot t_2 . \tag{8.9.1.1}$$

(a) *Necessity* The mapping $x_1 \to f(x_1, a_2)$ is obtained by composing f and the mapping $x_1 \to (x_1, a_2)$ of E_1 into $E_1 \times E_2$, the derivative of this second mapping being $t_1 \to (t_1, 0)$ by (8.1.2), (8.1.3), and (8.1.5). Then by (8.2.1), $x_1 \to f(x_1, a_2)$ has at (a_1, a_2) a derivative equal to $t_1 \to Df(a_1, a_2) \cdot (t_1, 0)$. If we call i_1 (resp. i_2) the natural injection $t_1 \to (t_1, 0)$ (resp. $t_2 \to (0, t_2)$), which is a constant element of $\mathscr{L}(E_1; E_1 \times E_2)$ (resp. $\mathscr{L}(E_2; E_1 \times E_2)$), we therefore see that $D_1 f(a_1, a_2) = Df(a_1, a_2) \circ i_1$, and similarly $D_2 f(a_1, a_2) = Df(a_1, a_2) \circ i_2$ (all this is valid if f is simply supposed to be *differentiable* in A). As the mapping $(v, u) \to v \circ u$ of $\mathscr{L}(E_1 \times E_2; F) \times \mathscr{L}(E_1; E_1 \times E_2)$ into $\mathscr{L}(E_1; F)$ is continuous ((5.7.5) and (5.5.1)), the continuity of $D_1 f$ and $D_2 f$ follows from that of Df; finally, as $(t_1, t_2) = i_1(t_1) + i_2(t_2)$, we have (8.9.1.1).

(b) *Sufficiency* Write

$$\begin{aligned} &f(a_1 + t_1, a_2 + t_2) - f(a_1, a_2) \\ &\quad = (f(a_1 + t_1, a_2 + t_2) - f(a_1 + t_1, a_2)) + (f(a_1 + t_1, a_2) - f(a_1, a_2)). \end{aligned}$$

Given $\varepsilon > 0$, there is, by assumption, an $r > 0$ such that, for $\|t_1\| \leqslant r$

$$\|f(a_1 + t_1, a_2) - f(a_1, a_2) - D_1 f(a_1, a_2) \cdot t_1\| \leqslant \varepsilon \|t_1\|.$$

On the other hand, we have in a ball B of center (a_1, a_2) contained in A, by (8.6.2)

$$\begin{aligned} &\|f(a_1 + t_1, a_2 + t_2) - f(a_1 + t_1, a_2) - D_2 f(a_1 + t_1, a_2) \cdot t_2\| \\ &\quad \leqslant \|t_2\| \cdot \sup_{\|z\| \leqslant \|t_2\|} \|D_2 f(a_1 + t_1, a_2 + z) - D_2 f(a_1 + t_1, a_2)\|. \end{aligned}$$

The continuity of the mapping $D_2 f$ therefore implies that there is $r' > 0$ such that for $\|t_2\| \leqslant r'$ and $\|t_1\| \leqslant r'$, we have

$$\|f(a_1 + t_1, a_2 + t_2) - f(a_1 + t_1, a_2) - D_2 f(a_1 + t_1, a_2) \cdot t_2\| \leqslant \varepsilon \|t_2\|$$

and on the other hand

$$\|D_2 f(a_1 + t_1, a_2) - D_2 f(a_1, a_2)\| \leqslant \varepsilon$$

hence, by (5.7.4)

$$\|D_2 f(a_1 + t_1, a_2) \cdot t_2 - D_2 f(a_1, a_2) \cdot t_2\| \leqslant \varepsilon \|t_2\|.$$

Finally, for $\sup(\|t_1\|, \|t_2\|) \leqslant \inf(r, r')$ we have

$$\|f(a_1 + t_1, a_2 + t_2) - f(a_1, a_2) - D_1 f(a_1, a_2) \cdot t_1 - D_2 f(a_1, a_2) \cdot t_2\| \leqslant 4\varepsilon \sup(\|t_1\|, \|t_2\|)$$

which proves (8.9.1.1); the continuity of Df follows from the fact that (8.9.1.1) can be written $Df = D_1 f \circ \mathrm{pr}_1 + D_2 f \circ \mathrm{pr}_2$ and from (5.7.5).

Theorem (8.9.1) can be immediately generalized to a product of n Banach spaces by induction on n; if we combine that result with (8.2.1), we obtain

(8.9.2) *Let f be a continuously differentiable mapping of an open subset* A *of* $E = \prod_{i=1}^{n} E_i$ *into* F, *and, for each i, let g_i be a continuously differentiable mapping of an open subset* B *of a Banach space* G *into* E_i, *such that* $(g_1(z), \ldots, g_n(z)) \in A$ *for each* $z \in B$. *Then the composed mapping* $h = f \circ (g_1, \ldots, g_n)$ *is continuously differentiable in* B, *and we have*

$$Dh(z) = \sum_{k=1}^{n} (D_k f(g_1(z), \ldots, g_n(z))) \circ Dg_k(z).$$

PROBLEMS

1. Let E, F be two Banach spaces, f a continuous mapping of an open subset A of E into F. Suppose that for each $x \in A$, there is an element $u(x) \in \mathscr{L}(E; F)$ such that, for every vector $y \in E$, the limit of $(f(x + ty) - f(x))/t$ when $t \neq 0$ tends to 0 in **R**, exists and is equal to $u(x) \cdot y$. Suppose in addition that $x \to u(x)$ is a continuous mapping of A into $\mathscr{L}(E; F)$. Show that f is then continuously differentiable in A and that $u(x) = Df(x)$ for every $x \in A$. (Apply the mean value theorem to the function $t \to f(x + ty)$ for $t \in [0, 1]$.)
2. Let E be the space (c_0) of Banach (Section **5.3**, Problem 5); let F be the complex Banach space $(c_0) + i(c_0)$, consisting of all sequences $z = (\zeta_n)_{n \geqslant 0}$ of complex numbers such that $\lim_{n \to \infty} \zeta_n = 0$, with the norm $\|z\| = \sup_n |\zeta_n|$. We denote by F_0 the real Banach space underlying F (Section **5.1**). Let $I \subset \mathbf{R}$ be an open interval containing 0, and for each integer $n \geqslant 0$, let f_n be a continuous mapping of I into **C** such that the condition $\lim_{n \to \infty} t_n = 0$ implies $\lim_{n \to \infty} f_n(t_n) = 0$; this defines a mapping $f: (\xi_n) \to (f_n(\xi_n))$ of E into F_0.

   (a) Suppose f is continuous in a neighborhood of 0. In order that f be quasi-differentiable at the point 0 (Section **8.4**, Problem 4), it is necessary and sufficient that for each n the derivative $f_n'(0)$ exist and that there exist two numbers $A > 0$ and $\delta > 0$ such that the relation $|t| \leqslant \delta$ implies $|f_n(t) - f_n(0)| \leqslant A|t|$ for every n; this implies that $\sup_n |f_n'(0)| < +\infty$.

   (b) In order that f be differentiable at 0, it is necessary and sufficient that for every $\varepsilon > 0$, there is a $\delta > 0$ such that the relation $|t| \leqslant \delta$ implies $|f_n(t) - f_n(0) - f_n'(0)t| \leqslant \varepsilon |t|$ for *every n*.

(c) In order that the derivative f' exist in a neighborhood of 0 in E and be continuous at 0, a necessary and sufficient condition is that there exist a neighborhood $J \subset I$ of 0 such that: (1) each f_n' exists in J; (2) $\sup_n |f_n'(0)| < +\infty$; (3) the sequence (f_n') is equicontinuous at the point 0 (Section 7.5). (See Section 8.6, Problem 3.)

(d) Let $f_n(t) = e^{nit}/n$ for every $n \geqslant 1, f_0(t) = 1$. Show that f is quasi-differentiable at every point $x \in E$; if $u(x)$ is the quasi-derivative of f at the point x, show that the mapping $(x, y) \to u(x) \cdot y$ of $E \times E$ into F_0 is continuous, but that f is not differentiable at any point of E.

3. Let f be a continuous mapping of an open set A of a Banach space E into a Banach space F. Suppose that for any $x \in A$ and any $y \in E$, $\lim_{t \to 0, t \neq 0} (f(x + ty) - f(x))/t = g(x, y)$ exists in E. If, for $y_i \in E$, $1 \leqslant i \leqslant n$, and $x_0 \in A$, each of the mappings $x \to g(x, y_i)$ is continuous at x_0, show that $g(x_0, y_1 + y_2 + \cdots + y_n) = \sum_{i=1}^{n} g(x_0, y_i)$ (apply the mean value theorem).

4. Let E_1, E_2, F be three Banach spaces, f a continuous mapping of an open subset A of $E_1 \times E_2$ into F. In order that f be differentiable at $(a_1, a_2) \in A$, it is necessary and sufficient that: (1) $D_1 f(a_1, a_2)$ and $D_2 f(a_1, a_2)$ exist; (2) for any $\varepsilon > 0$, there exists $\delta > 0$ such that the relations $\|t_1\| \leqslant \delta$, $\|t_2\| \leqslant \delta$ imply

$$\|f(a_1 + t_1, a_2 + t_2) - f(a_1 + t_1, a_2) - f(a_1, a_2 + t_2) + f(a_1, a_2)\| \leqslant \varepsilon(\|t_1\| + \|t_2\|).$$

Show that the second condition is satisfied if $D_1 f(a_1, a_2)$ exists and there is a neighborhood V of (a_1, a_2) in $E_1 \times E_2$ such that $D_2 f$ exists in V and the mapping $(x_1, x_2) \to D_2 f(x_1, x_2)$ of V into $\mathscr{L}(E_2; F)$ is continuous.

5. Let f be the real function defined in $\mathbf{R}^2$ by $f(x, y) = (xy/r)\sin(1/r)$ for $(x, y) \neq (0, 0)$, with $r = (x^2 + y^2)^{1/2}$, and $f(0, 0) = 0$. Show that $D_1 f$ and $D_2 f$ exist at every point $(x, y) \in \mathbf{R}^2$, and that the four mappings $x \to D_1 f(x, b)$, $y \to D_1 f(a, y)$, $x \to D_2 f(x, b)$, $y \to D_2 f(a, y)$ are continuous in $\mathbf{R}$ for any $(a, b) \in \mathbf{R}^2$, but that f is not differentiable at $(0, 0)$.

6. Let I be an interval in $\mathbf{R}$, f a mapping of I^p into a real Banach space E, such that, for any $(a_1, \ldots, a_p) \in I^p$, each of the mappings $x_j \to f(a_1, \ldots, a_{j-1}, x_j, a_{j+1}, \ldots, a_p)$ $(1 \leqslant j \leqslant p)$ is continuous and differentiable in I, and furthermore, the p functions $D_j f$ $(1 \leqslant j \leqslant p)$ are bounded in I^p. Show that f is continuous in I^p (use the mean-value theorem).

10. JACOBIANS

We now specialize the general result (8.9.1) to the most important cases.

1. $E = \mathbf{R}^n$ (resp. $E = \mathbf{C}^n$). If f is a differentiable mapping of an open subset A of E into F, the partial derivative $D_k f(\alpha_1, \ldots, \alpha_n)$ is identified to a vector of F (Section 8.4), and the derivative of f is the mapping

$$(\zeta_1, \ldots, \zeta_n) \to \sum_{k=1}^{n} D_k f(\alpha_1, \ldots, \alpha_n)\zeta_k.$$

If Df is continuous, so is each of the $D_k f$. Conversely, if each of the mappings $D_k f$ exists and is continuous in A, then f is continuously differentiable in A.

2. $E = \mathbf{R}^n$ and $F = \mathbf{R}^m$ (resp. $E = \mathbf{C}^n$ and $F = \mathbf{C}^m$). Then we can write

$f = (\varphi_1, \ldots, \varphi_m)$, where the φ_i are *scalar* functions defined in E, and by (8.1.5) f is continuously differentiable if and only if each of the φ_i is continuously differentiable; again, by case 1, φ_i is continuously differentiable if and only if each of the partial derivatives $D_j \varphi_i$ (which is now a scalar function) exists and is continuous. Furthermore, the (total) derivative of f is the linear mapping

$$(\zeta_1, \ldots, \zeta_n) \to (\eta_1, \ldots, \eta_m)$$

with

$$\eta_i = \sum_{j=1}^{n} (D_j \varphi_i(\alpha_1, \ldots, \alpha_n))\zeta_j;$$

in other words, f', which is a linear mapping of $\mathbf{R}^n$ into $\mathbf{R}^m$ (resp. of $\mathbf{C}^n$ into $\mathbf{C}^m$), corresponds to the matrix $(D_j \varphi_i(\alpha_1, \ldots, \alpha_n))$, which is called the *jacobian matrix* of f (or of $\varphi_1, \ldots, \varphi_m$) at $(\alpha_1, \ldots, \alpha_n)$. When $m = n$, the determinant of the jacobian (square) matrix of f is called the *jacobian* of f (or of $\varphi_1, \ldots, \varphi_n$). Theorem (8.9.2) specializes to

(8.10.1) *Let φ_j $(1 \leqslant j \leqslant m)$ be m scalar functions, continuously differentiable in an open subset* A *of* $\mathbf{R}^n$ (resp. $\mathbf{C}^n$)*; let ψ_i $(1 \leqslant i \leqslant p)$ be p scalar functions, continuously differentiable in an open subset* B *of* $\mathbf{R}^m$ (resp. $\mathbf{C}^m$) *containing the image of* A *by* $(\varphi_1, \ldots, \varphi_m)$*; then if $\theta_i(x) = \psi_i(\varphi_1(x), \ldots, \varphi_m(x))$ for $x \in$ A and $1 \leqslant i \leqslant p$, we have the relation*

$$(D_k \theta_i) = (D_j \psi_i)(D_k \varphi_j)$$

between the jacobian matrices; in particular, when $m = n = p$, we have the relation

$$\det(D_k \theta_i) = \det(D_j \psi_i) \det(D_k \varphi_j)$$

between the jacobians.

We mention here the usual notations $f'_{\xi_i}(\xi_1, \ldots, \xi_n)$, $\dfrac{\partial}{\partial \xi_i} f(\xi_1, \ldots, \xi_n)$, for $D_i f(\xi_1, \ldots, \xi_n)$, which unfortunately lead to hopeless confusion when substitutions are made (what does $f'_y(y, x)$ or $f'_x(x, x)$ mean?); the jacobian $\det(D_j \varphi_i(\xi_1, \ldots, \xi_n))$ is also written $D(\varphi_1, \ldots, \varphi_n)/D(\xi_1, \ldots, \xi_n)$ or $\partial(\varphi_1, \ldots, \varphi_n)/\partial(\xi_1, \ldots, \xi_n)$.

11. DERIVATIVE OF AN INTEGRAL DEPENDING ON A PARAMETER

(8.11.1) *Let* $\mathrm{I} = [\alpha, \beta] \subset \mathbf{R}$ *be a compact interval,* E, F *real Banach spaces, f a continuous mapping of* I × A *into* F (A *open subset of* E). *Then* $g(z) = \int_\alpha^\beta f(\xi, z)\, d\xi$ *is continuous in* A.

Given $\varepsilon > 0$ and $z_0 \in A$, for any $\xi \in I$, there is a neighborhood $V(\xi)$ of ξ in I and a number $r(\xi) > 0$ such that for $\eta \in V(\xi)$ and $\|z - z_0\| \leqslant r(\xi)$, $\|f(\eta, z) - f(\xi, z_0)\| \leqslant \varepsilon$. Cover I with a finite number of neighborhoods $V(\xi_i)$, and let $r = \inf(r(\xi_i))$. Then $\|f(\xi, z) - f(\xi, z_0)\| \leqslant \varepsilon$ for $\|z - z_0\| \leqslant r$ and *any* $\xi \in I$; hence, by (8.7.7)

$$\|g(z) - g(z_0)\| \leqslant \varepsilon(\beta - \alpha)$$

for $\|z - z_0\| \leqslant r$. Q.E.D.

(8.11.2) (Leibniz's rule) *With the same assumptions as in* (8.11.1), *suppose in addition that the partial derivative* $D_2 f$ *with respect to the second variable exists and is continuous in* $I \times A$. *Then* g *is continuously differentiable in* A, *and*

$$Dg(z) = \int_\alpha^\beta D_2 f(\xi, z)\, d\xi$$

(observe that both sides of that formula are in $\mathscr{L}(E; F)$).

The same argument as in (8.11.1) applied to $D_2 f$, shows that given $\varepsilon > 0$ and $z_0 \in A$, there exists $r > 0$ such that $\|D_2 f(\xi, z) - D_2 f(\xi, z_0)\| \leqslant \varepsilon$ for $\|z - z_0\| \leqslant r$ and *any* $\xi \in I$; hence, by (8.6.2)

$$\|f(\xi, z_0 + t) - f(\xi, z_0) - D_2 f(\xi, z_0) \cdot t\| \leqslant \varepsilon \|t\|$$

for *any* $\xi \in I$ and any t such that $\|t\| \leqslant r$. By (8.7.7) we therefore have

$$\left\| g(z_0 + t) - g(z_0) - \int_\alpha^\beta (D_2 f(\xi, z_0) \cdot t)\, d\xi \right\| \leqslant \varepsilon(\beta - \alpha)\|t\|.$$

But by (8.7.6) and (5.7.4) we have $\int_\alpha^\beta (D_2 f(\xi, z_0) \cdot t)\, d\xi = \left(\int_\alpha^\beta D_2 f(\xi, z_0)\, d\xi\right) \cdot t$ for any t, and this ends the proof.

PROBLEMS

1. Let $J \subset \mathbf{R}$ be an open interval, E, F two Banach spaces, A an open subset of E, f a continuous mapping of $J \times A$ into F such that $D_2 f$ exists and is continuous in $J \times A$, α and β two continuously differentiable mappings of A into J. Let

$$g(z) = \int_{\alpha(z)}^{\beta(z)} f(\xi, z)\, d\xi.$$

Show that g is continuously differentiable in A, and that $g'(z)$ is the linear mapping

$$t \to \left(\int_{\alpha(z)}^{\beta(z)} D_2 f(\xi, z)\, d\xi\right) \cdot t + (\beta'(z) \cdot t) f(\beta(z), z) - (\alpha'(z) \cdot t) f(\alpha(z), z)$$

(apply **(8.9.1)** and **(8.11.2)**).

2. Let f, g be two real valued regulated functions in a compact interval $[a, b]$, such that f is decreasing in $[a, b]$ and $0 \leqslant g(t) \leqslant 1$. Show that

$$\int_{b-\lambda}^{b} f(t)\, dt \leqslant \int_a^b f(t)g(t)\, dt \leqslant \int_a^{a+\lambda} f(t)\, dt$$

where $\lambda = \int_a^b g(t)\, dt$. When is there equality? (Consider the integrals $\int_a^y f(t)g(t)\, dt$ and $\int_a^{a+h(y)} f(t)\, dt$, where $h(y) = \int_a^y g(t)\, dt$, as functions of y, and similarly for the other inequality.)

3. Let the assumptions be the same as in Problem 1, except that α and β are merely supposed to be continuous, but not necessarily differentiable, but in addition it is supposed that $f(\alpha(z), z) = 0$ and $f(\beta(z), z) = 0$ for any $z \in A$. Show that $g(z)$ is continuously differentiable in A, and that $g'(z) = \int_{\alpha(z)}^{\beta(z)} D_2 f(\xi, z)\, d\xi$. (Use Bolzano's theorem **(3.19.8)** to prove that if ξ belongs to the interval of extremities $\beta(z_0)$ and $\beta(z)$, there is $z' \in A$ such that $\|z' - z_0\| \leqslant \|z - z_0\|$ and $\xi = \beta(z')$; if M is the l.u.b. of $\|D_2 f\|$ in a neighborhood of $(\beta(z_0), z_0)$, use the mean value theorem to show that $\|f(\xi, z)\| \leqslant M\|z - z_0\|$.

4. Let $I = [a, b]$, $A = [c, d]$ be two compact intervals in $\mathbf{R}$, f a mapping of $I \times A$ into a Banach space E, such that: (1) for every $y \in A$, the function $x \to f(x, y)$ is regulated in I and for every $x \in I$, the function $y \to f(x, y)$ is regulated in A; (2) f is bounded in $I \times A$; (3) if D is the subset of $I \times A$ consisting of the points (x, y) where f is not continuous, then, for every $x_0 \in I$ (resp. every $y_0 \in A$), the set of points y (resp. x) such that $(x_0, y) \in D$ (resp. $(x, y_0) \in D$) is finite.

(a) Show that the function $g(y) = \int_a^b f(t, y)\, dt$ is continuous in A. (If $\varepsilon > 0$ and $y_0 \in A$ are given, show that there is a neighborhood V of y_0 in A and a finite number of intervals $J_k \subset I$ $(1 \leqslant k \leqslant n)$ such that the sum of the lengths of the J_k is $\leqslant \varepsilon$ and that, if $W = I - \bigcup_{k=1}^{n} J_k$, f is continuous in $W \times V$; to prove that result, use the Borel–Lebesgue theorem **(3.17.6)**.)

(b) Deduce from (a) that

$$\int_c^d dy \int_a^b f(x, y)\, dx = \int_a^b dx \int_c^d f(x, y)\, dy.$$

(Consider the two functions $z \to \int_c^z dy \int_a^b f(x, y)\, dx$ and $z \to \int_a^b dx \int_c^z f(x, y)\, dy$ for $z \in A$.) (Cf. Section **13.21**).

(c) Deduce from (b) that if $a = c$, $b = d$, then

$$\int_a^b dy \int_y^b f(t, y)\, dt = \int_a^b dx \int_a^x f(x, u)\, du$$

(consider the function equal to $f(x, y)$ for $y \leqslant x$, to 0 for $y > x$).

5. (a) Let f be a strictly increasing continuous function in an interval $[0, a]$, such that $f(0)=0$; let g be the inverse mapping, which is continuous and strictly increasing in the interval $[0, f(a)]$. Show that $\int_0^a f(t)\,dt = \int_0^{f(a)} (a - g(u))\,du$ (apply Problem 4 to the function equal to 1 for $0 \leqslant x \leqslant a, 0 \leqslant y \leqslant f(x)$, to 0 for $0 \leqslant x \leqslant a, f(x) < y \leqslant f(a)$).
(b) Show that if $0 \leqslant x \leqslant a$ and $0 \leqslant y \leqslant f(a)$, the following inequality holds

$$xy \leqslant \int_0^x f(t)\,dt + \int_0^y g(u)\,du;$$

the two sides are equal if and only if $y = f(x)$.

(c) Deduce from (b) the inequalities

$$xy \leqslant x \cdot \log x + e^{y-1} \qquad \text{for} \quad x > 0, \quad y \in \mathbf{R};$$

$$xy \leqslant ax^p + by^q \qquad \text{for} \quad x \geqslant 0, \quad y \geqslant 0, \quad p > 1, \quad q > 1, \quad \frac{1}{p} + \frac{1}{q} = 1,$$

$$a > 0, \quad b > 0 \quad \text{and} \quad (pa)^q (qb)^p \geqslant 1.$$

12. HIGHER DERIVATIVES

Suppose f is a continuously differentiable mapping of an open subset A of a Banach space E into a Banach space F. Then $\mathrm{D}f$ is a continuous mapping of A into the Banach space $\mathscr{L}(\mathrm{E}; \mathrm{F})$. If that mapping is differentiable at a point $x_0 \in \mathrm{A}$ (resp. in A), we say that f is *twice differentiable* at x_0 (resp. in A), and the derivative of $\mathrm{D}f$ at x_0 is called the *second derivative* of f at x_0, and written $f''(x_0)$ or $\mathrm{D}^2 f(x_0)$. This is an element of $\mathscr{L}(\mathrm{E}; \mathscr{L}(\mathrm{E}; \mathrm{F}))$; but we have seen (5.7.8) that this last space is naturally identified with the space $\mathscr{L}(\mathrm{E}, \mathrm{E}; \mathrm{F})$ (written $\mathscr{L}_2(\mathrm{E}; \mathrm{F})$) of continuous bilinear mappings of $\mathrm{E} \times \mathrm{E}$ into F: we recall that this is done by identifying $u \in \mathscr{L}(\mathrm{E}; \mathscr{L}(\mathrm{E}; \mathrm{F}))$ to the bilinear mapping $(s, t) \to (u \cdot s) \cdot t$; this last element will also be written $u \cdot (s, t)$.

(8.12.1) *Suppose f is twice differentiable at x_0; then, for any fixed $t \in \mathrm{E}$, the derivative of the mapping $x \to \mathrm{D}f(x) \cdot t$ of* A *into* F*, at the point x_0, is $s \to \mathrm{D}^2 f(x_0) \cdot (s, t)$.*

If we observe that $x \to \mathrm{D}f(x) \cdot t$ is composed of the linear mapping $u \to u \cdot t$ of $\mathscr{L}(\mathrm{E}; \mathrm{F})$ into F and of the mapping $x \to \mathrm{D}f(x)$ of E into $\mathscr{L}(\mathrm{E}; \mathrm{F})$ the result follows from (8.2.1) and (8.1.3).

(8.12.2) *If f is twice differentiable at x_0, then the bilinear mapping $(s, t) \to D^2 f(x_0) \cdot (s, t)$ is symmetric, in other words*

$$D^2 f(x_0) \cdot (s, t) = D^2 f(x_0) \cdot (t, s).$$

Consider the function of the real variable ξ in the interval $[0, 1]$:

$$g(\xi) = f(x_0 + \xi s + t) - f(x_0 + \xi s)$$

where s, t are such that $\|s\| \leqslant \frac{1}{2}r$, $\|t\| \leqslant \frac{1}{2}r$, the ball of center x_0 and radius r being contained in A. From (8.6.2) we get

$$\|g(1) - g(0) - g'(0)\| \leqslant \sup_{0 \leqslant \xi \leqslant 1} \|g'(\xi) - g'(0)\|.$$

Now by (8.4.1)

$$\begin{aligned} g'(\xi) &= (f'(x_0 + \xi s + t) - f'(x_0 + \xi s)) \cdot s \\ &= ((f'(x_0 + \xi s + t) - f'(x_0)) - (f'(x_0 + \xi s) - f'(x_0))) \cdot s. \end{aligned}$$

By assumption, given $\varepsilon > 0$, there is $r' \leqslant r$ such that for $\|s\| \leqslant \frac{1}{2}r'$, $\|t\| \leqslant \frac{1}{2}r'$, we have

$$\|f'(x_0 + \xi s + t) - f'(x_0) - f''(x_0) \cdot (\xi s + t)\| \leqslant \varepsilon(\|s\| + \|t\|)$$

and

$$\|f'(x_0 + \xi s) - f'(x_0) - f''(x_0) \cdot (\xi s)\| \leqslant \varepsilon \|s\|$$

hence

$$\|g'(\xi) - (f''(x_0) \cdot t) \cdot s\| \leqslant 2\varepsilon \|s\| \cdot (\|s\| + \|t\|)$$

and therefore

$$\|g(1) - g(0) - (f''(x_0) \cdot t) \cdot s\| \leqslant 6\varepsilon \|s\| (\|s\| + \|t\|).$$

But $g(1) - g(0) = f(x_0 + s + t) - f(x_0 + t) - f(x_0 + s) + f(x_0)$ is symmetric in s and t, hence, by exchanging s and t, we get

$$\|(f''(x_0) \cdot t) \cdot s - (f''(x_0) \cdot s) \cdot t\| \leqslant 6\varepsilon(\|s\| + \|t\|)^2.$$

Now this inequality holds for $\|s\| \leqslant \frac{1}{2}r'$, $\|t\| \leqslant \frac{1}{2}r'$; but if we replace s and t by λs and λt, both sides are defined and multiplied by $|\lambda|^2$, hence the result is true for *all* s and t in E, in particular for $\|s\| = \|t\| = 1$, which proves (by (5.7.7)) that

$$\|f''(x_0) \cdot (t, s) - f''(x_0) \cdot (s, t)\| \leqslant 24\varepsilon \|s\| \cdot \|t\|$$

for all s and t; as ε is arbitrary, this ends the proof.

In particular,

(8.12.3) *Let* A *be an open set in* $\mathbf{R}^n$ (resp. $\mathbf{C}^n$); *if a mapping* f *of* A *into a Banach space* F *is twice differentiable at* x_0, *then the partial derivatives* $D_i f$ *are differentiable at* x_0, *and*

$$D_i D_j f(x_0) = D_j D_i f(x_0)$$

for $1 \leqslant i \leqslant n$, $1 \leqslant j \leqslant n$.

We have only to use (8.12.1) for special values of t, and to observe that for $s = (\xi_i)$, $t = (\eta_i)$, the value of $D^2 f(x_0) \cdot (s, t) = (D^2 f(x_0) \cdot s) \cdot t$ is $\sum_{i,j} (D_i D_j f(x_0)) \xi_i \eta_j$ (see Section 8.10).

By induction on p, we now define a p *times differentiable* mapping f of an open subset $A \subset E$ into F as a $(p-1)$-times differentiable mapping whose $(p-1)$th derivative $D^{p-1}f$ is differentiable in A, and we call the derivative $D(D^{p-1}f)$ the pth *derivative* of f, which is written $D^p f$ or $f^{(p)}$. The element $D^p f(x_0)$ is identified to an element of the space $\mathscr{L}_p(E; F)$ of the p-linear continuous mappings of E into F, and we write it

$$(t_1, t_2, \ldots, t_p) \to D^p f(x_0) \cdot (t_1, \ldots, t_p).$$

As in (8.12.1) we see that the mapping

$$t_1 \to D^p f(x_0) \cdot (t_1, t_2, \ldots, t_p)$$

is the derivative, at x_0, of the mapping

$$x \to D^{p-1} f(x) \cdot (t_2, \ldots, t_p).$$

(8.12.2) generalizes to

(8.12.4) *If* f *is* p *times differentiable in* A, *then the multilinear mapping* $D^p f(x)$ *is symmetric for each* $x \in A$.

This is proved by induction on p. Let $t_3, \ldots, t_p$ be fixed, and consider the mapping $x \to g(x) = D^{p-2} f(x) \cdot (t_3, \ldots, t_p)$; from the preceding remark it follows that the second derivative of g at x is

$$(t_1, t_2) \to D^p f(x) \cdot (t_1, t_2, t_3, \ldots, t_p)$$

hence by (8.12.2)

(8.12.4.1) $$D^p f(x) \cdot (t_2, t_1, t_3, \ldots, t_p) = D^p f(x) \cdot (t_1, t_2, t_3, \ldots, t_p).$$

On the other hand, for any permutation σ of the set of indices $\{2, 3, \ldots, p\}$, the inductive hypothesis yields

$$D^{p-1}f(x) \cdot (t_{\sigma(2)}, t_{\sigma(3)}, \ldots, t_{\sigma(p)}) = D^{p-1}f(x) \cdot (t_2, t_3, \ldots, t_p)$$

and taking the first derivative of both sides (where the t_i are fixed), we obtain

(8.12.4.2) $$D^p f(x) \cdot (t_1, t_{\sigma(2)}, \ldots, t_{\sigma(p)}) = D^p f(x) \cdot (t_1, t_2, \ldots, t_p).$$

Combining (8.12.4.1) and (8.12.4.2) we first see that $D^p f(x) \cdot (t_1, t_2, \ldots, t_p)$ does not change when the index 1 is exchanged with any other index, and also when any two of the indices $\geqslant 2$ are exchanged; but these transpositions generate any permutation of the indices $1, 2, \ldots, p$. Q.E.D.

(8.12.5) *If f is m times differentiable and $D^m f$ is n times differentiable in* A, *then f is $m + n$ times differentiable in* A, *and* $D^{m+n}f = D^n(D^m f)$.

This is the definition when $n = 1$, and is proved immediately by induction on n, applying the definition.

(8.12.6) *Suppose $f = (f_1, \ldots, f_m)$ is a continuous mapping of an open subset* A *of* E *into a product* $F_1 \times \cdots \times F_m$ *of Banach spaces. In order that f be p times differentiable in* A, *it is necessary and sufficient that each f_i be p times differentiable in* A, *and then* $D^p f = (D^p f_1, \ldots, D^p f_m)$.

This follows from (8.1.5) by induction on p.

(8.12.7) *Let* A *be an open set in* $\mathbf{R}^n$ (resp. $\mathbf{C}^n$); *if a mapping f of* A *into a Banach space* F *is p times differentiable, then, for $t_i = (\xi_{ij})$ $(1 \leqslant i \leqslant p, 1 \leqslant j \leqslant n)$ we have*

$$D^p f(x) \cdot (t_1, \ldots, t_p) = \sum_{(j_1, j_2, \ldots, j_p)} D_{j_1} D_{j_2} \cdots D_{j_p} f(x) \xi_{1, j_1} \xi_{2, j_2} \cdots \xi_{p, j_p}$$

the sum being extended to all n^p distinct sequences $(j_k)_{1 \leqslant k \leqslant p}$ of integers from $[1, n]$.

This is immediately proved by induction on p, using Section 8.10. The n^p elements $D_{j_1} D_{j_2} \cdots D_{j_p} f(x)$ are called the *partial derivatives of order p* of f at x; any two which differ only by a permutation of the indices are equal by (8.12.4). We say that f is *p times continuously differentiable in* A if $D^p f$ exists and is continuous in A.

(8.12.8) *Let* A *be an open subset of* $\mathbf{R}^n$ (resp. $\mathbf{C}^n$), f *a continuous mapping of* A *into a Banach space* F; *if the* n^p *partial derivatives of* f *exist and are continuous in* A, *then* f *is* p *times continuously differentiable in* A.

For $p = 1$, this is (8.9.1) (extended to a product of n spaces); in general, we only have to use induction on p and the formula (8.12.7).

We say that f is *indefinitely differentiable* in A if it is p times differentiable in A for any p; all the derivatives $D^p f$ are then indefinitely differentiable in A.

Example

(8.12.9) *Any continuous bilinear mapping is indefinitely differentiable, and all its derivatives of order* $\geqslant 3$ *are* 0.

From (8.1.4) it follows that the derivative of a bilinear continuous mapping at (x, y) is $(s, t) \to [x \cdot t] + [s \cdot y]$; write $g(x, y) \in \mathscr{L}(E \times F; G)$ that linear mapping; by assumption and (5.5.1), there exists $c > 0$ such that $\|[x \cdot y]\| \leqslant c\|x\| \cdot \|y\|$ in $E \times F$; by definition of the norm in $\mathscr{L}(E \times F; G)$ (5.7.1), we have

$$\|g(x, y)\| \leqslant c(\|x\| + \|y\|) \leqslant 2c \sup(\|x\|, \|y\|)$$

hence g is a continuous linear mapping of $E \times F$ into $\mathscr{L}(E \times F; G)$, and therefore $(x, y) \to [x \cdot y]$ is twice differentiable and its second derivative at (x, y) is (by (8.1.3) and (8.12.1))

$$((s_1, t_1), (s_2, t_2)) \to [s_1 \cdot t_2] + [s_2 \cdot t_1].$$

This is a mapping independent of (x, y), hence the result.

(8.12.10) *Let* E, F, G *be three Banach spaces,* A *an open subset of* E, B *an open subset of* F; *if* f *is a* p *times continuously differentiable mapping of* A *into* B, g *a* p *times continuously differentiable mapping of* B *into* G, *then* $h = g \circ f$ *is a* p *times continuously differentiable mapping of* A *into* G.

For $p = 1$, the result follows from (8.2.1) and from the fact that $(u, v) \to v \circ u$ is a bilinear continuous mapping of $\mathscr{L}(E; F) \times \mathscr{L}(F; G)$ into $\mathscr{L}(E; G)$ by (5.7.5). Use now induction on p; as $h'(x) = g'(f(x)) \circ f'(x)$, and f and g' are $p - 1$ times continuously differentiable, the induction hypothesis shows that $g' \circ f$ is $p - 1$ times continuously differentiable; from (8.12.6) and (8.12.9), it then follows that h' is $p - 1$ times continuously differentiable, hence h is p times continuously differentiable by (8.12.5).

Example

(8.12.11) Suppose there is a linear homeomorphism of a Banach space E into a Banach space F, and let $\mathscr{H} \subset \mathscr{L}(E; F)$ be the open set of these homeomorphisms in $\mathscr{L}(E; F)$ (8.3.2). Then the mapping $u \to u^{-1}$ of $\mathscr{H}$ onto $\mathscr{H}^{-1}$ is *indefinitely differentiable.*

We prove by induction on p that $u \to u^{-1}$ is p times differentiable, the property being true for $p = 1$ by (8.3.2). Given v and w in $\mathscr{L}(F; E) = M$, let $f(v, w)$ be the linear mapping $t \to -v \circ t \circ w$ of $L = \mathscr{L}(E; F)$ into M; it is clear that f is *bilinear* (and maps $M \times M$ into $\mathscr{L}(L; M)$) and (5.7.5) proves that $\|f(v, w)\| \leqslant \|v\| \cdot \|w\|$, hence f is continuous, and therefore indefinitely differentiable by (8.12.9). Now the first derivative of $u \to u^{-1}$ is, by (8.3.2), the mapping $u \to f(u^{-1}, u^{-1})$; by (8.12.6) and (8.12.10) it follows that if $u \to u^{-1}$ is p times differentiable, so is $u \to f(u^{-1}, u^{-1})$, and therefore, by (8.12.5), $u \to u^{-1}$ is $p + 1$ times differentiable.

Remark. When f is a mapping of an *interval* $J \subset \mathbf{R}$ into a real Banach space F, we have defined earlier (Section 8.4) the notion of derivative of f at $\xi_0 \in J$ with respect to J. By induction on p, we define the pth *derivative of f at ξ_0, with respect to* J, as the derivative at ξ_0 (with respect to J) of the $(p - 1)$th derivative of f (which is therefore supposed to exist in a neighborhood of ξ_0 in J); it is an element of F, written again $D^pf(\xi_0)$ or $f^{(p)}(\xi_0)$; if ξ_0 is interior to J, the pth derivative, as defined for general mappings, coincides with the multilinear mapping $(\zeta_1, \ldots, \zeta_p) \to f^{(p)}(\xi_0)\zeta_1\zeta_2 \cdots \zeta_p$ of $\mathbf{R}^p$ into F.

PROBLEMS

1. Let f be an n times differentiable mapping of an interval $I \subset \mathbf{R}$ into a Banach space E. Show that for any $x \in I$ such that $\frac{1}{x} \in I$

$$\frac{1}{x^{n+1}} f^{(n)}\left(\frac{1}{x}\right) = (-1)^n D^n\left[x^{n-1} f\left(\frac{1}{x}\right)\right]$$

(use induction on n).

2. (a) Let ρ be the function defined on $\mathbf{R}$ by the conditions:

$$\rho(t) = \exp\left(-\frac{1}{(1+t)^2} - \frac{1}{(1-t)^2}\right) \quad \text{for} \quad -1 < t < 1$$

$$\rho(t) = 0 \quad \text{for} \quad t \leqslant -1 \quad \text{or} \quad t \geqslant 1.$$

Show that the function ρ is indefinitely differentiable in $\mathbf{R}$. (Use the relation $\lim_{x \to +\infty} x^n e^{-x} = 0$ for any $n > 0$.)

(b) In this problem, we agree to extend any regulated function f defined in a compact interval $[a, b]$ of $\mathbf{R}$, to the whole of $\mathbf{R}$, by giving it the value 0 for $t < a$ and for $t > b$; we then write $\int_{-\infty}^{+\infty} f(t)\,dt$ for the integral $\int_a^b f(t)\,dt$, which is also equal to $\int_c^d f(t)\,dt$ for $c \leqslant a$ and $d \geqslant b$.

For any such function f, let

$$f_n(t) = nc \int_{-\infty}^{+\infty} f(s)\rho(n(t-s))\,ds = nc \int_{-\infty}^{+\infty} f(t-s)\rho(ns)\,ds$$

where $1/c = \int_{-1}^{+1} \rho(t)\,dt$ ("regularization" of f by ρ; we write $\rho_n(t) = nc\rho(nt)$ and $f_n = f * \rho_n$). Show that f_n is indefinitely differentiable and vanishes in the complement of a compact interval (use (8.11.2); if f is real and increasing (resp. strictly increasing, resp. convex) in $[a, b]$, then f_n is increasing (resp. strictly increasing, resp. convex) in $[a + 1/n, b - 1/n]$. If f (extended to $\mathbf{R}$) is p times continuously differentiable, then

$$\begin{aligned} \mathrm{D}^p f_n(t) &= nc \int_{-\infty}^{+\infty} (\mathrm{D}^p f(s))\rho(n(t-s))\,ds \\ &= nc \int_{-\infty}^{+\infty} (\mathrm{D}^p f(t-s))\rho(ns)\,ds. \end{aligned}$$

(c) Show that for any n, $\int_{-\infty}^{+\infty} f_n(t)\,dt = \int_{-\infty}^{+\infty} f(t)\,dt$.

(d) If f (extended to $\mathbf{R}$) is continuous (resp. p times continuously differentiable), then the sequence (f_n) (resp. $\mathrm{D}^p f_n$) converges *uniformly* in $\mathbf{R}$ to f (resp. $\mathrm{D}^p f$).

(e) To what limit does $f_n(t_0)$ ($t_0 \in \mathbf{R}$) tend when f is only supposed to be regulated in $[a, b]$ (first consider the case in which f is a step-function, then use (7.6.1)).

(f) Show that for any regulated function f in $[a, b]$,

$$\lim_{n \to \infty} \int_a^b |f(t) - f_n(t)|\,dt = 0.$$

3. Let f be an n times differentiable real function defined in $]-1, 1[$ and such that $|f(t)| \leqslant 1$ in that interval.

(a) Let $m_k(\mathrm{J})$ be the smallest value of $|f^{(k)}(t)|$ in an interval J contained in $]-1, 1[$. Show that, if J is decomposed into three consecutive intervals $\mathrm{J}_1, \mathrm{J}_2, \mathrm{J}_3$, and if J_2 has length μ, then, for $k \leqslant n$,

$$m_k(\mathrm{J}) \leqslant \frac{1}{\mu}(m_{k-1}(\mathrm{J}_1) + m_{k-1}(\mathrm{J}_3))$$

(use the mean value theorem). Deduce from that inequality that if J has length λ,

$$m_k(\mathrm{J}) \leqslant \frac{2^{k(k+1)/2} k^k}{\lambda^k}$$

(use induction on k).

(b) Deduce from (a) that there exists a number α_n depending only on n, such that if $|f'(0)| \geqslant \alpha_n$, $f^{(n)}(t) = 0$ has at least $n - 1$ distinct roots in $]-1, 1[$. (Show by induction on k that there is a strictly increasing sequence $x_{k,1} < x_{k,2} < \cdots < x_{k,k}$ of points of $]-1, 1[$ such that $f^{(k)}(x_{k,i}) f^{(k)}(x_{k,i+1}) < 0$ for $1 \leqslant i \leqslant k-1$; use Rolle's theorem.)

4. Let E, F be two Banach spaces, A an open subset of E, f an n times differentiable mapping of A into F. Let $x_0 \in \mathrm{A}$, $h_i \in \mathrm{E}$ $(1 \leqslant i \leqslant n)$ be such that $x_0 + \sum_{i=1}^{n} \xi_i h_i \in \mathrm{A}$ for $0 \leqslant \xi_i \leqslant 1$, $1 \leqslant i \leqslant n$. We define by induction on k $(1 \leqslant k \leqslant n)$

$$\Delta^1 f(x_0; h_1) = f(x_0 + h_1) - f(x_0)$$

$$\Delta^k f(x_0; h_1, \ldots, h_k) = \Delta^{k-1} g_k(x_0; h_1, \ldots, h_{k-1})$$

with

$$g_k(x) = f(x + h_k) - f(x).$$

(a) Show that

$$\|\Delta^n f(x_0; h_1, \ldots, h_n)\| \leqslant \|h_1\| \cdot \|h_2\| \cdots \|h_n\| \sup_{z \in \mathrm{P}} \|\mathrm{D}^n f(z)\|$$

where P is the set of points $x_0 + \sum_{i=1}^{n} \xi_i h_i$, $0 \leqslant \xi_i \leqslant 1$. (Use induction on n.)
(b) Deduce from (a) that

$$\|\Delta^n f(x_0; h_1, \ldots, h_n) - \mathrm{D}^n f(x_0) \cdot (h_1, \ldots, h_n)\|$$
$$\leqslant \|h_1\| \cdot \|h_2\| \cdots \|h_n\| \sup_{z \in \mathrm{P}} \|\mathrm{D}^n f(z) - \mathrm{D}^n f(x_0)\|.$$

5. Let f be a continuously differentiable mapping of an open subset A of $\mathbf{R}^2$ into a Banach space E. Suppose that in a neighborhood V of $(a, b) \in \mathrm{A}$, the derivative $\mathrm{D}_2(\mathrm{D}_1 f)$ exists and is continuous.
(a) Let $(x, y) \in \mathrm{V}$; show that for every $\varepsilon > 0$, there exists $\delta > 0$ such that the relations $|h| \leqslant \delta$, $|k| \leqslant \delta$ imply

$$\|\Delta^2 f(x, y; h, k) - \mathrm{D}_2 \mathrm{D}_1 f(x, y) hk\| \leqslant \varepsilon |hk|$$

(apply the mean value theorem of the function

$$g(t) = f(x + t, y + k) - f(x + t, y) - \mathrm{D}_2 \mathrm{D}_1 f(x, y) tk$$

and use **(8.6.2)**).
(b) Prove that $\mathrm{D}_1(\mathrm{D}_2 f)$ exists in V and is equal to $\mathrm{D}_2(\mathrm{D}_1 f)$ (use (a)).
(c) Give an example of a function f satisfying the previous assumptions and for which $\mathrm{D}_1(\mathrm{D}_1 f)$ and $\mathrm{D}_2(\mathrm{D}_2 f)$ do not exist anywhere (see Section **8.4**, Problem 1).

6. Let f the real function defined in $\mathbf{R}^2$ by the conditions $f(0, 0) = 0$, $f(x, y) = xy(x^2 - y^2)/(x^2 + y^2)$ for $(x, y) \neq (0, 0)$. Show that all four derivatives $\mathrm{D}_1(\mathrm{D}_1 f)$, $\mathrm{D}_1(\mathrm{D}_2 f)$, $\mathrm{D}_2(\mathrm{D}_1 f)$, $\mathrm{D}_2(\mathrm{D}_2 f)$ exist everywhere in $\mathbf{R}^2$ but that $\mathrm{D}_1(\mathrm{D}_2 f) \neq \mathrm{D}_2(\mathrm{D}_1 f)$ at the point $(0, 0)$.

7. The notations are the same as in Problem 2 of Section **8.9**. Let $g_n(t) = t/(1 + n|t|)$, and $f_n(t) = \int_0^t g_n(u)\, du$ for every $t \in \mathbf{R}$. Show that the function $f : (\xi_n) \to (f_n(\xi_n))$ is continuously differentiable in E, and that for each $y = (\eta_n) \in \mathrm{E}$, the mapping $x \to f'(x) \cdot y$ is differentiable at $x = 0$, but that f' is not differentiable at that point (compare **(8.12.1)**).

8. Let E, F be two Banach spaces, A an open subset of E, $\mathscr{D}_{\mathrm{F}}^{(p)}(\mathrm{A})$ the vector space of p times continuously differentiable mappings of A into F, such that f and all its derivatives $D^k f$ ($1 \leqslant k \leqslant p$) be bounded in A. For any $f \in \mathscr{D}_F^{(p)}(A)$, let

$$\|f\|_p = \sup_{x \in A} (\|f(x)\| + \|Df(x)\| + \cdots + \|D^p f(x)\|);$$

show that $\|f\|_p$ is a norm on $\mathscr{D}_F^{(p)}(A)$ for which that space becomes a Banach space (use **(8.6.3)**). The mapping $f \to Df$ is a continuous linear mapping of $\mathscr{D}_F^{(p)}(A)$ into $\mathscr{D}^{(p-1)}(A)$ (resp. in $\mathscr{C}^\infty_{\mathscr{L}(E; F)}(A)$ for $p = 1$).

9. Let E, F, G be three Banach spaces, L, M, N the Banach spaces $\mathscr{D}_F^{(p)}(E)$, $\mathscr{D}_G^{(p)}(F)$, $\mathscr{D}_G^{(p)}(E)$, respectively. For $f \in L$, $g \in M$, let $\Phi(f, g) = g \circ f \in N$.

(a) Let $(f_0, g_0) \in L \times M$. Show that if $D^p g_0$ is uniformly continuous in F, the mapping Φ is continuous at (f_0, g_0) (use induction on p). If E, F, G are finite dimensional, Φ is continuous in $L \times M$ (use **(3.16.5)**).

(b) Let $N_k = \mathscr{D}_G^{(p-k)}(E)$ for $1 \leqslant k \leqslant p$ with $\mathscr{D}_G^{(0)}(E) = \mathscr{C}_G^{(\infty)}(E)$. Show that, as a mapping of $L \times M$ into N_1, Φ is continuous at every point; in order that Φ (as a mapping of $L \times M$ into N_1) be differentiable at (f_0, g_0), it is sufficient that $D^p g_0$ be uniformly continuous, and the derivative $D\Phi$ is the linear mapping

$$(u, v) \to ((Dg_0) \circ f_0) \cdot u + v \circ f_0 .$$

(c) Let U_f be the linear mapping $g \to g \circ f$ of M into N; show that U_f is continuous. We may also consider U_f as an element of $\mathscr{L}(M; N_k)$ for any $k \leqslant p$. Show that the mapping $f \to U_f$ of L into $\mathscr{L}(M; N_1)$ is continuous, and that the mapping $f \to U_f$ of L into $\mathscr{L}(M; N_2)$ is differentiable, the element $DU_f \in \mathscr{L}(L; \mathscr{L}(M; N_2))$ being the bilinear mapping $(u, v) \to ((Dv) \circ f) \cdot u$.

(d) Deduce from (b) and (c) that as a mapping of $L \times M$ into N_k, Φ is $k - 1$ times differentiable.

10. Let f be a real valued twice differentiable function defined in an open subset A of a Banach space E.

(a) Suppose that at a point $x_0 \in E$ there is a constant $c > 0$ such that $Df(x_0) = 0$ and $D^2 f(x_0) \cdot (t, t) \leqslant -c\|t\|^2$ for every $t \in E$. Show that f reaches a strict relative maximum (Section **3.9**, Problem 6) at the point x_0. If E is finite dimensional, the preceding condition can be replaced by the condition $D^2 f(x_0) \cdot (t, t) < 0$ for any $t \neq 0$ in E (use the compactness of the sphere $\|t\| = 1$ in E).

(b) Suppose A is an open ball, f is majorized in A, and there exists a real number a such that the set F of points $x \in A$ for which $f(x) \geqslant a$ is a non empty closed set in E (hence a complete subspace), and finally $D^2 f(x) \cdot (t, t) \leqslant -c\|t\|^2$ for every $x \in A$ and every $t \in E$. Show that under these conditions, f reaches its maximum in A at a single point. (Let $m = \sup f(x)$, which is a finite number; for every $\varepsilon > 0$ such that $a \leqslant m - \varepsilon < m$, let $F_\varepsilon \subset F$ be the set of $x \in A$ for which $f(x) \geqslant m - \varepsilon$. Prove that the diameter of F_ε tends to 0 with ε. To do this, first prove the following lemma: if h is a twice continuously differentiable real function in $[0, 1]$ and $h''(t) \leqslant b$ in $[0, 1]$, then $h(0) - 2h(\frac{1}{2}) + h(1) \leqslant b/4$. Apply the lemma to the function $t \to f(x + t\xi)$ for x and $x + \xi$ in A).

11. (a) Let f be a real valued function defined in an open interval $I \subset \mathbf{R}$, and differentiable in I; let $[a, b] \subset I$, and suppose f'' exists in the open interval $]a, b[$, but f' is not necessarily supposed to be continuous at a and b (cf. Section **8.7**, Problem 6). Show that there exists $c \in]a, b[$ such that $f'(b) - f'(a) = (b - a)f''(c)$ (use Problem 3 of Section **8.5**).

(b) What is the corresponding property for functions defined in I and with values in a Hilbert space (see Section **8.5**, Problem 6)?

13. DIFFERENTIAL OPERATORS

Let A be an open set in $\mathbf{R}^n$ (resp. $\mathbf{C}^n$), F a real (resp. complex) Banach space; we denote by $\mathscr{E}_{\mathrm{F}}^{(p)}(\mathrm{A})$ the set of all p times continuously differentiable mappings of A into F. It is clear by (8.12.10) that $\mathscr{E}_{\mathrm{F}}^{(p)}(\mathrm{A})$ is a real (resp. complex) vector space; and, more generally, (8.12.10) shows that $\mathscr{E}_{\mathbf{R}}^{(p)}(\mathrm{A})$ (resp. $\mathscr{E}_{\mathbf{C}}^{(p)}(\mathrm{A})$) is a *ring*, and $\mathscr{E}_{\mathrm{F}}^{(p)}(\mathrm{A})$ a *module* over that ring. For any system $(\alpha_1, \ldots, \alpha_n) = \boldsymbol{\alpha}$ of integers $\geqslant 0$ with $|\boldsymbol{\alpha}| = \sum_{i=1}^{n} \alpha_i \leqslant p$, let $\mathrm{M}_{\boldsymbol{\alpha}} = \mathrm{X}_1^{\alpha_1} \mathrm{X}_2^{\alpha_2} \cdots \mathrm{X}_n^{\alpha_n}$ and define $\mathrm{D}^{\boldsymbol{\alpha}}$ or $\mathrm{D}_{\mathrm{M}_{\boldsymbol{\alpha}}}$ as the mapping $\mathrm{D}_1^{\alpha_1} \mathrm{D}_2^{\alpha_2} \cdots \mathrm{D}_n^{\alpha_n}$ of $\mathscr{E}_{\mathrm{F}}^{(p)}(\mathrm{A})$ into $\mathscr{E}_{\mathrm{F}}^{(p-|\boldsymbol{\alpha}|)}(\mathrm{A})$. A *linear differential operator* is a linear combination $\mathrm{D} = \sum_{i=1}^{n} a_{\boldsymbol{\alpha}} \mathrm{D}^{\boldsymbol{\alpha}}$ where $|\boldsymbol{\alpha}| \leqslant p$ and the $a_{\boldsymbol{\alpha}}$ are continuous scalar functions defined in A; if $a_{\boldsymbol{\alpha}} = 0$ for $|\boldsymbol{\alpha}| > k$ and each $a_{\boldsymbol{\alpha}}$ is $(p-k)$ times continuously differentiable, D maps $\mathscr{E}_{\mathrm{F}}^{(p)}(\mathrm{A})$ linearly into $\mathscr{E}_{\mathrm{F}}^{(p-k)}(\mathrm{A})$.

(8.13.1) *If the operator* $\sum_{\boldsymbol{\alpha}} a_{\boldsymbol{\alpha}} \mathrm{D}^{\boldsymbol{\alpha}}$ *is identically* 0, *then each of the functions* $a_{\boldsymbol{\alpha}}$ *is identically* 0 *in* A.

Write $\mathrm{D}f = 0$ for $f(x) = c \cdot \exp(\lambda_1 \xi_1 + \cdots + \lambda_n \xi_n)$, where $c \neq 0$ is in F and the λ_i are arbitrary constants; we obtain (by Section 8.8 and (8.4.1))

$$c \cdot \left(\sum_{\boldsymbol{\alpha}} a_{\boldsymbol{\alpha}}(x) \mathrm{M}_{\boldsymbol{\alpha}}(\lambda_1, \ldots, \lambda_n) \right) \exp(\lambda_1 \xi_1 + \cdots + \lambda_n \xi_n) = 0$$

identically in A, which is equivalent to $\sum_{\boldsymbol{\alpha}} a_{\boldsymbol{\alpha}}(x) \mathrm{M}_{\boldsymbol{\alpha}}(\lambda_1, \ldots, \lambda_n) = 0$; for any particular $x \in \mathrm{A}$, this implies $a_{\boldsymbol{\alpha}}(x) = 0$ for each $\boldsymbol{\alpha}$, since the λ_i are arbitrary.

The coefficients $a_{\boldsymbol{\alpha}}$ of a linear differential operator are thus uniquely determined; the highest value of $|\boldsymbol{\alpha}|$ such that $a_{\boldsymbol{\alpha}} \neq 0$ is called the *order* of D.

To each *polynomial* $\mathrm{P} = \sum_{\boldsymbol{\alpha}} b_{\boldsymbol{\alpha}} \mathrm{M}_{\boldsymbol{\alpha}}$ of degree $\leqslant p$ with *constant* coefficients we can thus associate a linear operator $\mathrm{D}_{\mathrm{P}} = \sum_{\boldsymbol{\alpha}} b_{\boldsymbol{\alpha}} \mathrm{D}^{\boldsymbol{\alpha}}$ of order $\leqslant p$; it is clear that $\mathrm{D}_{\mathrm{P}_1 + \mathrm{P}_2} = \mathrm{D}_{\mathrm{P}_1} + \mathrm{D}_{\mathrm{P}_2}$, and it follows from (8.12.3) that if $\mathrm{P}_1 \mathrm{P}_2$ had a total degree $\leqslant p$, then $\mathrm{D}_{\mathrm{P}_1 \mathrm{P}_2} = \mathrm{D}_{\mathrm{P}_1} \mathrm{D}_{\mathrm{P}_2}$. In particular, from (8.12.7) if follows that for fixed ξ_{ij}, the operator $f \to \mathrm{D}f$, where

$$\mathrm{D}f(x) = \mathrm{D}^p f(x) \cdot (t_1, \ldots, t_p)$$

can be written

$$\prod_{i=1}^{p} (\xi_{i1} \mathrm{D}_1 + \cdots + \xi_{in} \mathrm{D}_n).$$

(8.13.2) (Leibniz's formula) *Let* $P(X_1, \ldots, X_n)$ *be a polynomial of degree* $\leqslant p$, *and suppose*

$$P(X_1 + Y_1, \ldots, X_n + Y_n) = \sum_k \gamma_k M'_k(X_1, \ldots, X_n) M''_k(Y_1, \ldots, Y_n),$$

the M'_k *and* M''_k *being monomials. Let* $(x, y) \to [x \cdot y]$ *be a bilinear continuous mapping of* $E \times F$ *into* G. *Then, for any mapping* $f \in \mathscr{E}_E^{(p)}(A)$ *and any mapping* $g \in \mathscr{E}_F^{(p)}(A)$, $[f \cdot g]$ *belongs to* $\mathscr{E}_G^{(p)}(A)$ *and we have*

$$D_P[f \cdot g] = \sum_k \gamma_k [D_{M'_k} f \cdot D_{M''_k} g].$$

It is enough to prove the formula when P is a monomial M; using induction on the total degree of P, we can suppose $P = X_i M$, hence $D_P = D_i D_M$. We have by assumption

$$D_M[f \cdot g] = \sum_k \gamma_k [D_{M'_k} f \cdot D_{M''_k} g]$$

hence by (8.1.4)

$$D_P[f \cdot g] = \sum_k \gamma_k ([D_i D_{M'_k} f \cdot D_{M''_k} g] + [D_{M'_k} f \cdot D_i D_{M''_k} g])$$

which we can write

$$\sum_h \gamma'_h [D_{N'_h} f \cdot D_{N''_h} g]$$

the summation being extended over all pairs of monomials

$$(N'_h(X_1, \ldots, X_n), N''_h(Y_1, \ldots, Y_n))$$

such that either $N'_h = X_i M'_k$ and $N''_h = M''_k$ for an index k, or $N'_h = M'_k$ and $N''_h = Y_i M''_k$ for an index k; there is exactly one such index k for each suitable index h, and we have $\gamma'_h = \gamma_k$. The result is then obvious.

PROBLEMS

1. Let A be an open subset of $\mathbf{R}^n$, E, F, G three Banach spaces, $(x, y) \to [x \cdot y]$ a continuous bilinear mapping of $E \times F$ into G. Show that the mapping $(f, g) \to [f \cdot g]$ of $\mathscr{D}_E^{(p)}(A) \times \mathscr{D}_F^{(p)}(A)$ into $\mathscr{D}_G^{(p)}(A)$ (Section 8.12, Problem 8) is continuous.
2. Let I be any compact interval in $\mathbf{R}$, J an open neighborhood of I. Show that there exists an indefinitely differentiable mapping f of $\mathbf{R}$ into [0, 1], which is equal to 1 in I and to 0 in the complement of J (consider the functions $g * \rho_n$ (Section 8.12, Problem 2) where g is equal to 1 in a compact interval K such that $I \subset K \subset J$, and to 0 in $\mathbf{R} - K$). If u is an indefinitely differentiable mapping of $\mathbf{R}$ into a Banach space E, show that there exists an indefinitely differentiable mapping v of $\mathbf{R}$ into E such that $v(t) = u(t)$ in I, $v(t) = 0$ in $\mathbf{R} - J$.

14. TAYLOR'S FORMULA

(8.14.1) *Let* I *be an open interval in* **R**, *f*, *g two functions of* $\mathscr{E}_{\mathrm{E}}^{(p)}(\mathrm{I})$ *and* $\mathscr{E}_{\mathrm{F}}^{(p)}(\mathrm{I})$ *respectively*, $(x, y) \to [x \cdot y]$ *a continuous bilinear mapping of* E × F *into* G. *Then*

$$[f \cdot \mathrm{D}^p g] - (-1)^p [\mathrm{D}^p f \cdot g]$$
$$= \mathrm{D}([f \cdot \mathrm{D}^{p-1} g] - [\mathrm{D}f \cdot \mathrm{D}^{p-2} g] + \cdots + (-1)^{p-1}[\mathrm{D}^{p-1} f \cdot g]).$$

This is immediately verified by application of (8.1.4).

(8.14.2) *Let* I *be an open interval in* **R**, *f a function of* $\mathscr{E}_{\mathrm{E}}^{(p)}(\mathrm{I})$; *then, for any pair of points* α, ξ *in* I

$$f(\xi) = f(\alpha) + \frac{\xi - \alpha}{1!} f'(\alpha) + \frac{(\xi - \alpha)^2}{2!} f''(\alpha) + \cdots + \frac{(\xi - \alpha)^{p-1}}{(p-1)!} f^{(p-1)}(\alpha)$$
$$+ \int_\alpha^\xi \frac{(\xi - \zeta)^{p-1}}{(p-1)!} f^{(p)}(\zeta)\, d\zeta.$$

Apply (8.14.1) to the bilinear mapping $(\lambda, x) \to \lambda x$ and to the function $g(\zeta) = (\xi - \zeta)^{p-1}/(p-1)!$, and integrate both sides between α and ξ.

(8.14.3) *Let* E, F *be two Banach spaces*, A *an open subset of* E, *f a p-times continuously differentiable mapping of* A *into* F. *Then, if the segment joining* x *and* $x + t$ *is in* A, *we have*

$$f(x + t) = f(x) + \frac{1}{1!} f'(x) \cdot t + \frac{1}{2!} f''(x) \cdot t^{(2)} + \cdots + \frac{1}{(p-1)!} f^{(p-1)}(x) \cdot t^{(p-1)}$$
$$+ \left(\int_0^1 \frac{(1 - \zeta)^{p-1}}{(p-1)!} f^{(p)}(x + \zeta t)\, d\zeta \right) \cdot t^{(p)}$$

where $t^{(k)}$ *stands for* $(t, t, \ldots, t)$ (k *times*). *In particular, for every* $\varepsilon > 0$, *there is* $r > 0$ *such that for* $\|t\| \leqslant r$

$$\left\| f(x + t) - f(x) - \frac{1}{1!} f'(x) \cdot t - \frac{1}{2!} f''(x) \cdot t^{(2)} - \cdots - \frac{1}{p!} f^{(p)}(x) \cdot t^{(p)} \right\|$$
$$\leqslant \varepsilon \|t\|^p.$$

To obtain the first formula, apply (8.14.2) to the function $g(\xi) = f(x + \xi t)$ in the interval [0, 1]; by (8.12.10), g is p times continuously differentiable, and it is immediately seen by induction on k that $g^{(k)}(\xi) = f^{(k)}(x + \xi t) \cdot t^{(k)}$, using (8.4.1) and (8.1.3). To get the second formula, observe that by continuity of $f^{(p)}$, r can be chosen such that $\|f^{(p)}(x + \zeta t) - f^{(p)}(x)\| \leqslant p!\,\varepsilon$ for $0 \leqslant \zeta \leqslant 1$ and $\|t\| \leqslant r$. Then the mean value theorem (8.7.7) yields

$$\left\| \int_0^1 \frac{(1-\zeta)^{p-1}}{(p-1)!} f^{(p)}(x + \zeta t)\, d\zeta - \frac{1}{p!} f^{(p)}(x) \right\| \leqslant \varepsilon$$

and the conclusion follows from (5.5.7).

PROBLEMS

1. The nth *Legendre polynomial* is defined by

$$P_n(t) = \frac{1}{2^n n!} D^n((t^2 - 1)^n).$$

(a) Show that up to a positive factor, P_n is the nth term in the sequence obtained by orthonormalization in the prehilbert space $\mathscr{C}_C(I)$, with $I = [-1, +1]$, from the sequence (t^n) (Section 6.6). (To prove that the scalar product of $P_n(t)$ and of the t^m with $m < n$ is 0, use (8.14.1)).

(b) Show that $P_n(1) = 1$, $P_n(-1) = (-1)^n$ (use (8.13.2)).

(c) Show that between three consecutive Legendre polynomials there is the following recursive relation

$$nP_n(t) - (2n-1)tP_{n-1}(t) + (n-1)P_{n-2}(t) = 0.$$

(Observe that if c_n is chosen such that $P_n(t) - c_n t P_{n-1}(t)$ has degree $\leqslant n-1$, it is orthogonal to the t^k with $k \leqslant n-3$, hence must be a linear combination of P_{n-2} and P_{n-1}; use also (b).)

(d) Show that all the roots of P_n are real and simple and in $]-1, 1[$ (if P_n changed sign at $k \leqslant n-1$ points only in $]-1, 1[$, there would be a polynomial $g(t) = (t - t_1) \cdots (t - t_k)$ such that $P_n(t)g(t) \geqslant 0$ for $-1 \leqslant t \leqslant 1$; show that this leads to a contradiction with the fact that $P_n(t)$ is orthogonal to t^h for $h < n$).

(e) Show that P_n satisfies the differential equation

$$(1 - t^2)P_n''(t) - 2tP_n'(t) + n(n+1)P_n(t) = 0$$

(show that $D((1 - t^2)P_n'(t))$ is orthogonal to t^k for $k < n$).

2. (a) Let f be a real k times continuously differentiable function defined in an interval $I \subset \mathbf{R}$ of length a, and suppose that in I, $|f^{(k)}(t)| \geqslant c > 0$. Show, by induction on p, that for $0 < p \leqslant k$, there exists an interval $I_p \subset I$ of length $a/4^p$ such that in I_p the inequality $|f^{(k-p)}(t)| \geqslant ca^p/4^p$ holds.

(b) Let f be a real k times continuously differentiable function defined in an interval $I \subset \mathbf{R}$ of length a, and, for $0 \leqslant p \leqslant k$, let $M_p = \sup_{t \in I} |f^{(p)}(t)|$. Show that

$$M_{k-1} \leqslant \frac{8^{k-1}}{a^{k-1}} M_0 + \frac{a}{2} M_k$$

(use (a)).

(c) The assumptions being those of (b), suppose that in addition $k=2$ and $I=[-a/2, a/2]$. Show that for every $t \in I$,

$$|f'(t)| \leqslant \frac{2}{a} M_0 + \frac{4t^2+a^2}{4a} M_2$$

(use Taylor's formula to express $f(a/2)-f(t)$ and $f(-a/2)-f(t)$). Deduce from that inequality that, if $a \geqslant 2(M_0/M_2)^{1/2}$, then $M_1 \leqslant 2(M_0 M_2)^{1/2}$. Show that in this inequality the number 2 cannot be replaced by a smaller one. (If f' is only supposed to have a derivative on the right f''_d, both sides of the inequality may become equal when f' is piecewise linear; use then Problem 2(d) of Section **8.12**.)

(d) Let f be a real twice continuously differentiable function defined in **R**, and such that $M_0 = \sup_{t \in \mathbf{R}} |f(t)|$ and $M_2 = \sup_{t \in \mathbf{R}} |f''(t)|$ are finite. Show that $M_1 = \sup_{t \in \mathbf{R}} |f'(t)|$ is then finite and $M_1 \leqslant (2M_0 M_2)^{1/2}$ (use (c)). In that inequality, the number $\sqrt{2}$ cannot be replaced by a smaller one (same method as in (c)).

(e) Show that if f is a real k times continuously differentiable function defined in **R**, and if $M_0 = \sup_{t \in \mathbf{R}} |f(t)|$ and $M_k = \sup_{t \in \mathbf{R}} |f^{(k)}(t)|$ are finite, then, for $1 \leqslant p \leqslant k-1$, the numbers $M_p = \sup_{t \in \mathbf{R}} |f^{(p)}(t)|$ are all finite, and one has

$$M_p \leqslant 2^{p(k-p)} M_0^{1-(p/k)} M_k^{p/k}.$$

(First show that M_{k-1} is finite by using (b), then use induction on $k \geqslant 2$ and (d).)

3. Let E, F be two Banach spaces, A an open ball in E (or the whole space E). Show that in the space $\mathscr{D}_F^{(p)}(A)$, the norm

$$\sup_{x \in A}(\|f(x)\| + \|D^p f(x)\|)$$

is equivalent (Section **5.6**) to the norm $\|f\|_p$ defined in Problem 8 of Section **8.12** (use the result of problem 2(c)).

4. Let E be a Banach space, (c_n) an *arbitrary* sequence of elements of E.

(a) Let f be an indefinitely differentiable mapping of **R** into $[0, 1]$, equal to 1 in $[-\frac{1}{2}, \frac{1}{2}]$, and to 0 in the complement of $[-1, 1]$ (Section **8.13**, Problem 2). Consider the series

$$u(x) = \sum_{n=0}^{\infty} f(x/t_n) \frac{x^n}{n!} c_n.$$

Show that, for a suitable choice of the sequence of numbers $t_n > 0$, that series converges for every $x \in \mathbf{R}$, and for every integer $m \geqslant 1$, the series of mth derivatives

$$D^m\left(f(x/t_n)\frac{x^n}{n!}\right) c_n$$

is uniformly convergent in **R** (one can take $t_n = \frac{1}{2}$ if $\|c_n\| \leqslant 1$, $t_n = 1/2\|c_n\|$ if $\|c_n\| > 1$; use Leibniz's formula to majorize the terms of the series). Deduce that u is indefinitely differentiable in **R** and that, for every $m \geqslant 0$, one has $D^m u(0) = c_m$ ("E. Borel's theorem").

(b) Prove in the same way that, given an arbitrary family $(c_{\boldsymbol{\alpha}})$ of elements of E, where $\boldsymbol{\alpha} = (\alpha_1, \ldots, \alpha_p)$ ranges through all systems of p integers $\alpha_i \geqslant 0$, there exists an indefinitely differentiable mapping f of $\mathbf{R}^p$ into E such that $D^{\boldsymbol{\alpha}} f(0) = c_{\boldsymbol{\alpha}}$ for every $\boldsymbol{\alpha}$.

(c) Deduce from (a) that if g is an indefinitely differentiable mapping of a closed interval $I \subset \mathbf{R}$ into E, and J an open interval containing I, there exists an indefinitely differentiable mapping f of $\mathbf{R}$ into E which coincides with g in I and with 0 in $\mathbf{R} - J$.

5. Let f be a mapping of an interval $I \subset \mathbf{R}$ into a Banach space E, and suppose f is n times differentiable at a point $\alpha \in I$. Show that

$$\lim_{\xi \to \alpha,\ \xi \neq \alpha,\ \xi \in I} \left(f(\xi) - f(\alpha) - f'(\alpha)\frac{\xi - \alpha}{1!} - \cdots - f^{(n)}(\alpha)\frac{(\xi - \alpha)^n}{n!} \right) \Big/ (\xi - \alpha)^n = 0$$

(use induction on n and (**8.5.1**) with $\varphi(\xi) = (\xi - \alpha)^{n-1}$).

6. Let $I \subset \mathbf{R}$ be an interval containing 0, f an $n - 1$ times differentiable mapping of I into a Banach space E. Write

$$f(t) = f(0) + f'(0)\frac{t}{1!} + \cdots + f^{(n-1)}(0)\frac{t^{n-1}}{(n-1)!} + f_n(t)t^n$$

which defines f_n in $I - \{0\}$.

(a) Show that if f is $n + p$ times differentiable at $t = 0$, f_n can be continuously extended to I and becomes a function which is $n + p - 1$ times differentiable at all points $t \neq 0$ in a neighborhood V of 0 in I, and p times differentiable at $t = 0$; furthermore $f_n^k(0) = \dfrac{k!}{(n+k)!} f^{(n+k)}(0)$ for $0 \leqslant k \leqslant p$, and $\lim_{t \to 0,\ t \neq 0,\ t \in V} f_n^{(p+k)}(t)t^k = 0$ for $1 \leqslant k \leqslant n - 1$. (Express the derivatives of f_n with the help of the Taylor developments (Problem 5) of the derivatives of f, and use Problem 2 of Section **8.6**.)

(b) Conversely, let g be an $n + p - 1$ times differentiable mapping of $I - \{0\}$ into E, such that $\lim_{t \to 0,\ t \neq 0,\ t \in I} g^{(p+k)}(t)t^k$ exists for $0 \leqslant k \leqslant n - 1$. Show that the function g can be extended to a $p - 1$ times differentiable mapping of I into E, and that the function $g(t)t^n$ is $n + p - 1$ times differentiable in I; if furthermore $g^{(p)}(0)$ exists, then $g(t)t^n$ is $n + p$ times differentiable at 0.

(c) Suppose $I =]-1, 1[$, and suppose f is *even* in I, i.e. $f(-t) = f(t)$. Show, using (a) and (b), that if f is $2n$ times differentiable in I, there exists an n times differentiable mapping h of I into E such that $f(t) = h(t^2)$.

7. (a) Let f be an indefinitely differentiable mapping of $\mathbf{R}^n$ into a Banach space E. Show that

$$f(x_1, \ldots, x_n) = f(0, \ldots, 0) + x_1 f_1(x_1, \ldots, x_n) + x_2 f_2(x_2, \ldots, x_n) + \cdots + x_n f_n(x_n)$$

where f_k is indefinitely differentiable in $\mathbf{R}^{n-k+1}$ $(1 \leqslant k \leqslant n)$. Write $f(x_1, \ldots, x_n) = (f(x_1, \ldots, x_n) - f(0, x_2, \ldots, x_n)) + f(0, x_2, \ldots, x_n)$ and apply (**8.14.2**) to the first summand, considered as a function of x_1; with a suitable value of p (depending on k), this will prove that $(f(x_1, \ldots, x_n) - f(0, x_2, \ldots, x_n))/x_1$ is k times differentiable at $(0, \ldots, 0)$; finally, use induction on n.)

(b) Deduce from (a) that for any $p > 0$,

$$f(x) = \sum_{|\alpha| \leq p} x_1^{\alpha_1} \ldots x_n^{\alpha_n} f_\alpha(x)$$

where all the f_α are indefinitely differentiable and $f_0(x) = f(0, \ldots, 0)$.

(c) Let f be an indefinitely differentiable mapping from $\mathbf{R}^n$ into $\mathbf{R}$; suppose that $f(0) = 0$, $D_i f(0) = 0$ for $1 \leqslant i \leqslant n$, and that the quadratic form

$$(\xi_1, \ldots, \xi_n) \to \sum_{i,j} D_i D_j f(0)\xi_i \xi_j$$

is nondegenerate. Show that, by using a linear transformation in $\mathbf{R}^n$ one can assume that $D_i D_j f(0) = 0$ for $i \neq j$ and $a_i = D_i^2 f(0) \neq 0$ for $1 \leqslant i \leqslant n$. Prove that there exists a neighborhood U of 0 and n indefinitely differentiable functions g_i defined in U, such that in U

$$f(x) = \sum_{i=1}^{n} a_i (x_i g_i(x))^2$$

and $g_i(0) = 1$ for $1 \leqslant i \leqslant n$. (Use again (a) applied to each of the functions f_i defined in (a), and then apply the usual method of reduction of a quadratic form to a form having a diagonal matrix.)

8. (a) Let S be a metric space, A, B two nonempty subsets of S, M a vector subspace of the space $\mathscr{C}_{\mathbf{R}}(S)$ of real continuous functions in S, N a vector subspace of M, $u \to L(u)$ a linear mapping of M into the space $\mathbf{R}^A$ of all mappings of A into $\mathbf{R}$. We suppose that: (1) there exists a function $u_0 \in N$ such that $L(u_0)$ is the constant 1 on A; (2) if $u \in N$ and there is a $t \in B$ such that $u(t) = 0$, then there is $x \in A$ such that $(L(u))(x) = 0$.
Let $v \in M$ such that $L(v) = 0$; show that for any function $u \in M$ such that $u - v \in N$, and any $t \in B$, there exists $\theta \in A$ (depending on t) such that $u(t) = v(t) + u_0(t)(L(u))(\theta)$ (Observe that $u_0(t) \neq 0$, and therefore there is a constant c (depending on t) such that $u(t) - v(t) - cu_0(t) = 0$).
(b) Suppose S is compact, A is connected and dense in S, and all functions $u \in N$ vanish on $S - B$. Suppose that $L(u)$ is continuous in A for every $u \in M$, and that if a function $u \in N$ is such that $(L(u))(t) > 0$ for any $t \in A$, then u has no strict maximum on B. Show that in such a case condition (2) of (a) is also verified.

9. (a) Let f be an n times differentiable real function defined in an interval I; let $x_1 < x_2 < \cdots < x_p$ be points of I, n_i $(1 \leqslant i \leqslant p)$ integers >0 such that $n_1 + n_2 + \cdots + n_p = n$. Suppose that at each of the points x_i, $f^{(k)}(x_i) = 0$ for $0 \leqslant k \leqslant n_i - 1$. Show that there is a point ξ in the interval $]x_1, x_p[$ such that $f^{(n-1)}(\xi) = 0$ (apply Rolle's theorem iteratively).
(b) Let g be an n times differentiable real function defined in I, and let P be the real polynomial of degree $n - 1$ such that $g^{(k)}(x_i) = P^{(k)}(x_i)$ for $0 \leqslant k \leqslant n_i - 1$, $1 \leqslant i \leqslant p$. Show that for any $x \in I$, there exists ξ in the interior of the smallest interval containing x and the x_i $(1 \leqslant i \leqslant p)$, such that

$$g(x) = P(x) + \frac{(x - x_1)^{n_1}(x - x_2)^{n_2} \cdots (x - x_p)^{n_p}}{n!} g^{(n)}(\xi).$$

(Use Problem 8(a), or give a direct proof, using (a) in both cases.)

10. Let g be a real *odd* function, defined and 5 times differentiable in a symmetric neighborhood I of 0 in $\mathbf{R}$. Show that, for each $x \in I$

$$g(x) = \frac{x}{3}(g'(x) + 2g'(0)) - \frac{x^5}{180} g^{(5)}(\xi)$$

where ξ is a number belonging to the open interval of extremities 0 and x.
Deduce from that result that, if f is a real function, defined and 5 times differentiable in $[a, b]$, then

$$f(b) - f(a) = \frac{b - a}{6}\left[f'(a) + f'(b) + 4f'\left(\frac{a + b}{2}\right)\right] - \frac{(b - a)^5}{2880} f^{(5)}(\xi)$$

with $a < \xi < b$ ("Simpson's formula").

11. Let $I = [a, b]$ be a compact interval, and let M_0 be the vector space of real continuous functions defined in I and such that, for any $t \in]a, b[$, the limit

$$(L(f))(t) = \lim_{h \to 0,\, h \neq 0} (f(t+h) + f(t-h) - 2f(t))/h^2$$

exists in **R**. All real functions which are twice differentiable in I belong to M_0.
(a) Let M be the vector subspace of M_0 consisting of functions f for which $L(f)$ is continuous in $]a, b[$. Show that any function of $f \in M$ is twice differentiable in $]a, b[$ and that $L(f) = f''$. (Use Problem 8(a) and 8(b), taking $S = I$, $A = B =]a, b[$, and for N the subspace of M consisting of functions f for which $f(a) = f(b) = 0$.)
(b) Show that the function $f(t) = t \cos(1/t)$ belongs to M_0, although it is not differentiable at $t = 0$.

12. What are the properties of functions with values in a Hilbert space which correspond to the properties of real functions discussed in Problems 9(b), 10, and 11? (Cf. Section 8.5, Problem 6.)

13. Let f be an indefinitely differentiable mapping of a compact interval $I = [a, b] \subset \mathbf{R}$ (with $a \geqslant 0$) into a Banach space.
(a) Show that, for any two integers p, q such that $0 < p < q$,

$$\sum_{n=p}^{q-1} \|f^n(a)\| \frac{a^n}{n!} \leqslant \sum_{n=p}^{q-1} \|f^{(n)}(b)\| \frac{b^n}{n!} + \int_a^b \|f^{(q)}(x)\| \frac{x^{q-1}}{(q-1)!}\, dx$$

(For $p \leqslant n < q$, express $f^{(n)}(a)$ using Taylor's formula at the point b.)
(b) Under the same conditions, show that

$$\int_a^b \|f^{(p)}(x)\| \frac{x^{p-1}}{(p-1)!}\, dx \leqslant \int_a^b \|f^{(q)}(x)\| \frac{x^{q-1}}{(q-1)!}\, dx + \sum_{n=p}^{q-1} \|f^{(n)}(b)\| \frac{f^n}{n!}$$

(apply Taylor's formula to $f^{(p)}$ and use Problem 4(c) of Section 8.11).
(c) Suppose f is indefinitely differentiable in the interval $[a, +\infty[$ where $a \geqslant 0$, and that for every integer $n \geqslant 0$, there is a finite number M_n such that $\|f^{(n)}(x)\| x^n/n! \leqslant M_n$ for every $x \geqslant a$. Show that for $b > a$ and $n < q$,

$$f^{(n)}(b) = -\int_b^{+\infty} f^{(q)}(x) \frac{(b-x)^{q-n-1}}{(q-n-1)!}\, dx$$

and for $a \leqslant x \leqslant b$

$$f^{(q)}(x) = \sum_{m=q}^{\infty} f^{(m)}(b) \frac{(x-b)^{m-q}}{(m-q)!}$$

where the series and the integral are convergent (use Taylor's formula). Conclude that one has

$$\sum_{n=p}^{q-1} \|f^{(n)}(b)\| \frac{b^n}{n!} \leqslant \int_b^{+\infty} \|f^{(q)}(x)\| \frac{x^{q-1}}{(q-1)!}\, dx$$

and

$$\int_a^b \|f^{(p)}(x)\| \frac{x^{p-1}}{(p-1)!}\, dx \leqslant \sum_{n=p}^{\infty} \|f^{(n)}(b)\| \frac{b^n}{n!}$$

(d) Show that, under the assumptions of (c), the function

$$S_p(x) = \sum_{n=p}^{\infty} \|f^{(n)}(x)\| \frac{x^n}{n!}$$

(whose values are finite and $\geqslant 0$, or $+\infty$) is increasing in $[a, +\infty[$.

(e) Suppose f is indefinitely differentiable in $[a, +\infty[$ and that

$$\lim_{x \to +\infty} f^{(n)}(x) = 0 \qquad \text{for every} \quad n \geqslant 0.$$

Prove that the sequence of numbers (finite and $\geqslant 0$ or equal to $+\infty$)

$$J_n = \int_a^{+\infty} \|f^{(n)}(x)\| \frac{x^{n-1}}{(n-1)!}\, dx \qquad (n \geqslant 1)$$

is increasing. (When these numbers are all finite, write

$$f^{(n)}(x) = -\int_x^{+\infty} f^{(n+1)}(t)\, dt$$

and use Problem 4(c) of Section **8.11**.)

(f) Suppose f is indefinitely differentiable in $[a, +\infty[$ and that the integrals

$$J_n = \int_a^{+\infty} \|f^{(n)}(x)\| \frac{x^{n-1}}{(n-1)!}\, dx \qquad \text{and} \qquad J_{n+1} = \int_a^{+\infty} \|f^{(n+1)}(x)\| \frac{x^n}{n!}\, dx$$

are finite. Show that, for $x \geqslant a$,

$$\|f^{(n)}(x)\| \frac{x^n}{n!} \leqslant \|f^{(n)}(a)\| \frac{a^n}{n!} + J_n + J_{n+1}.$$

14. Let f be an indefinitely differentiable mapping of the interval $[a, +\infty[$, where $a \geqslant 0$, into a Banach space.

(a) Show that, for every $p > 0$,

$$(*) \qquad \sup_{x \geqslant a} \sum_{n=p}^{\infty} \|f^{(n)}(x)\| \frac{x^n}{n!} = \sup_{n \geqslant p} \int_a^{+\infty} \|f^{(n)}(x)\| \frac{x^{n-1}}{(n-1)!}\, dx$$

where both sides may be equal to $+\infty$. Show that if both sides are finite, they are also equal to both limits

$$(**) \qquad \lim_{x \to +\infty} \sum_{n=p}^{\infty} \|f^{(n)}(x)\| \frac{x^n}{n!} \qquad \text{and} \qquad \lim_{n \to \infty} \int_a^{+\infty} \|f^{(n)}(x)\| \frac{x^{n-1}}{(n-1)!}\, dx$$

(Use Problem 13).

(b) If f satisfies the assumptions of Problem 13(c), then the limits $(**)$ always exist and are equal to both sides of $(*)$.

CHAPTER IX

ANALYTIC FUNCTIONS

In this chapter, we have tried to emphasize the most general facts pertaining to the theory of analytic functions, and in particular to state as many results as possible for analytic functions of any number of variables; until Section 9.13, the theorems which concern only functions of one variable are inserted in a context in which they appear as technical intermediates to the general statements; it is only in Sections 9.14 to 9.17, and in many problems in this chapter and the next one, that we really deal with properties special to the one variable case. Furthermore, we have discussed simultaneously the case of analytic functions of real variables and of analytic functions of complex variables as long as it can be done (i.e. until Section 9.5). Finally, we have kept throughout our general principle of dealing from the start with vector valued functions; as usual, this does not require any change in the proofs, and the reader will see in Chapter XI how useful the consideration of such functions can be.

Of course, one can only expect to find here the most elementary part of the very extensive theory of analytic functions. The definition is given by the local existence of power series representing the function, and it is by the technique of power series that the differential properties of analytic functions are obtained (9.3.5) (the usual definition of analytic functions by the existence of continuous derivatives only applies, of course, to functions of complex variables, and therefore that characterization is postponed until Section 9.10). The fundamental results about power series are Abel's lemma (9.1.2)—from which is derived the vital possibility of substituting power series into power series (9.2.2)—and the principle of isolated zeros (9.1.5), whose most important consequence is the principle of analytic continuation (9.4.2), which expresses the "solidarity" between the values of an analytic function at different points of the domain where it is defined.

From that point on, we have to assume that the variables are *complex*;

with the exception of the principle of maximum (9.5.9), all additional properties of analytic functions of complex variables derive from a single new idea, that of " complex integration," and from its fundamental features, Cauchy's theorem (9.6.3), Cauchy's formula (9.9.1), and its generalization, the theorem of residues (9.16.1). The form of Cauchy's theorem which we give here is not the best possible, for it expresses the integral along a circuit as an invariant of the *homotopy class* of that circuit, whereas in fact it is an invariant of its *homology class*. In most applications, however, this has no inconvenience whatsoever, and in contrast to the fact that the proof of the weak form of Cauchy's theorem needs almost no topological preparation, the proof of the complete theorem would have required some developments of algebraic topology, which we feel are above the level of the present volume. The interested reader will find the complete Cauchy theorem, together with all the necessary prerequisites, in Ahlfors [1], Cartan [8], and Springer [17]; we shall come back to that question in Chapter XXIV. Instead of using more results from algebraic topology in order to obtain such refinements, we have thought it might interest some readers to see how, by the very simple device introduced by S. Eilenberg, it is possible to obtain quite deep information on the topology of the real plane (including the Jordan curve theorem), using merely the most elementary facts about complex integration; this is the purpose of the Appendix (which, by the way, is not used anywhere in the later chapters and may therefore be bypassed without any inconvenience).

As we have announced in Chapter I, the reader will find no mention in this chapter of the so-called "multiple-valued" or "multiform" functions. It is of course a great nuisance that one cannot define in the field **C** a genuine continuous function $\sqrt{z}$ which would satisfy the relation $(\sqrt{z})^2 = z$; but the solution to this difficulty is certainly not to be sought in a deliberate perversion of the general concept of mapping, by which one suddenly decrees that there is after all such a "function," with, however, the uncommon feature that for each $z \neq 0$ it has *two* distinct "values." The penalty for this indecent and silly behavior is immediate: it is impossible to perform even the simplest algebraic operations with any reasonable confidence; for instance, the relation $2\sqrt{z} = \sqrt{z} + \sqrt{z}$ is certainly *not true*, for if we follow the "definition" of $\sqrt{z}$, we are compelled to attribute for $z \neq 0$, *two* distinct values to the left-hand side, and *three* distinct values to the right-hand side! Fortunately, there *is* a solution to the difficulty, which has nothing to do with such nonsense; it was discovered more than 100 years ago by Riemann, and consists in restoring the uniqueness of the value of $\sqrt{z}$ by "doubling," so to speak, the domain of the variable z, so that the two values of $\sqrt{z}$ correspond to *two* different points instead of a single z; a stroke of genius if ever there was one, and which is at the origin of the great theory of *Riemann surfaces*, and of their modern generalizations, the *complex manifolds* which we shall define in Chapter XVI. The student who wishes to get acquainted with these beautiful and active theories should read H. Weyl's classic [19] and the modern presentation by Springer [17] of Riemann surfaces, and H. Cartan's seminar [7] and the recent book of A. Weil [18] on complex manifolds.

1. POWER SERIES

In what follows K will denote either the real field **R** or the complex field **C**; its elements will be called *scalars*. In the vector space K^p over K, an *open* (resp. *closed*) *polydisk* is a product of p open (resp. closed) balls; in other words it is a set P defined by conditions of the form $|z_i - a_i| < r_i$ (resp. $|z_i - a_i| \leqslant r_i$), $1 \leqslant i \leqslant p$, on the point $z = (z_1, \dots, z_p)$, with $r_i > 0$ for every index; $a = (a_1, \dots, a_p)$ is the *center* or P, $r_1, \dots, r_p$ its *radii* (a ball is thus a polydisk having all its radii equal).

(9.1.1) *Let* P, Q *be two open polydisks in* K^p *such that* $P \cap Q \neq \varnothing$; *for any two points* x, y *in* $P \cap Q$, *the segment* (Section 8.5) *joining* x *and* y *is contained in* $P \cap Q$; *in particular* $P \cap Q$ *is connected.*

Indeed, if $|x_i - a_i| < r_i$, $|y_i - a_i| < r_i$, then $|tx_i + (1-t)y_i - a_i| \leqslant t|x_i - a_i| + (1-t)|y_i - a_i| < r_i$ for $0 \leqslant t \leqslant 1$; the last statement follows from the fact that a segment is connected (by (3.19.1) and (3.19.7)) and from (3.19.3).

We introduce the following notation: for any element $\nu = (n_1, \dots, n_p)$ in $\mathbf{N}^p$ (n_i integers $\geqslant 0$) and any vector $z = (z_1, \dots, z_p) \in K^p$, we write $z^\nu = z_1^{n_1} z_2^{n_2} \dots z_p^{n_p}$ and $|\nu| = n_1 + n_2 + \cdots + n_p$. If E is a Banach space (over K), $(c_\nu)_{\nu \in \mathbf{N}^p}$ a family of elements of E having $\mathbf{N}^p$ as set of indices, we say that the family $(c_\nu z^\nu)_{\nu \in \mathbf{N}^p}$ of elements of E is a *power series in p variables* z_i $(1 \leqslant i \leqslant p)$, *with coefficients* c_ν.

(9.1.2) *Let* $b = (b_1, \dots, b_p) \in K^p$ *be such that* $b_i \neq 0$ *for* $1 \leqslant i \leqslant p$, *and that the family* $(c_\nu b^\nu)$ *be bounded in* E. *Then for any system of radii* (r_i) *such that* $0 < r_i < |b_i|$ *for* $1 \leqslant i \leqslant p$, *the power series* $(c_\nu z^\nu)$ *is normally summable* (7.1) *in the closed polydisk of center* 0 *and radii* r_i ("Abel's lemma").

For if $\|c_\nu b^\nu\| \leqslant A$ for any $\nu \in \mathbf{N}^p$, it follows from the definition of the norm in K^p that if $|z_i| \leqslant r_i < |b_i|$ $(1 \leqslant i \leqslant p)$, we have $\|c_\nu z^\nu\| \leqslant Aq^\nu$, with $q = (q_1, \ldots, q_p)$, $q_i = r_i/|b_i| < 1$. It follows from **(5.5.3)** that the family $(q^\nu)_{\nu \in \mathbf{N}^p}$ of positive numbers is absolutely summable, hence the result by **(5.3.1)**.

(9.1.3) *Under the assumptions of* **(9.1.2)**, *the sum of the power series* $(c_\nu z^\nu)$ *is continuous in the open polydisk of center* 0 *and radii* $|b_i|$.

As every point of that polydisk is interior to a closed polydisk of radii $r_i < |b_i|$, the result follows from **(7.2.1)**.

Let q be any integer such that $1 \leqslant q \leqslant p$; for any $\nu = (n_1, \ldots, n_p)$, write $\nu' = (n_1, \ldots, n_q)$, $\nu'' = (n_{q+1}, \ldots, n_p)$; consider K^p as identified to the product $K^q \times K^{p-q}$, and for $z = (z_1 \ldots, z_p) \in K^p$, write $z' = (z_1, \ldots, z_q)$, $z'' = (z_{q+1}, \ldots, z_p)$. With these notations:

(9.1.4) *Suppose the power series* $(c_\nu z^\nu)$ *is absolutely summable in the polydisk* P *of radii* r_i *and center* 0 *in* K^p. *Then, for any* $\nu'' \in \mathbf{N}^{p-q}$ *the series* $(c_{(\nu', \nu'')} z'^{\nu'})$ *is absolutely summable in the polydisk* P′, *projection of* P *on* K^q; *let* $g_{\nu''}(z')$ *be its sum. Then, for any* $z' \in$ P′, *the power series* $(g_{\nu''}(z') z''^{\nu''})$ *is absolutely summable in the polydisk* P″, *projection of* P *on* K^{p-q}, *and its sum is equal to the sum of the series* $(c_\nu z^\nu)$.

As $z^\nu = z'^{\nu'} z''^{\nu''}$, the fact that each of the series $(c_{(\nu', \nu'')} z'^{\nu'} z''^{\nu''})$ (ν'' fixed) is absolutely summable, and that $\sum_{\nu''} g_{\nu''}(z') z''^{\nu''} = \sum_\nu c_\nu z^\nu$, follows from **(5.3.5)** and from the associativity theorem **(5.3.6)** for absolutely summable families. If we take $z'' \in$ P″ such that $z_i \neq 0$ for $q + 1 \leqslant i \leqslant p$, the absolute summability of $(c_{(\nu', \nu'')} z'^{\nu'})$ follows.

(9.1.5) ("Principle of isolated zeros") *Suppose* $(c_n z^n)$ *is a power series in one variable which converges in an open ball* P *of radius* r, *and let* $f(z) = \sum_{n=0}^{\infty} c_n z^n$. *Then, unless all the* c_n *are* 0, *there is* $r' < r$ *such that for* $0 < |z| < r'$, $f(z) \neq 0$.

Suppose h is the smallest integer such that $c_h \neq 0$; then we can write $f(z) = z^h (c_h + c_{h+1} z + \cdots + c_{h+m} z^m + \cdots)$ and the series $(c_{h+m} z^m)$ converges in P; if $g(z) = c_h + c_{h+1} z + \cdots + c_{h+m} z^m + \ldots$, g is continuous in P by **(9.1.3)** and as $g(0) = c_h \neq 0$, there is $r' > 0$ such that $g(z) \neq 0$ for $|z| < r'$; hence the result.

(9.1.6) *Suppose two power series* $(a_\nu z^\nu)$ *and* $(b_\nu z^\nu)$ *are absolutely summable and have the same sum in a polydisk* P; *then* $a_\nu = b_\nu$ *for every* $\nu \in \mathbf{N}^p$.

Use induction on p; for $p = 1$, the result follows at once from (9.1.5). Taking the difference of the two power series, we can assume $b_\nu = 0$ for every ν; applying (9.1.4) with $q = p - 1$, we have $\sum_{n=0}^{\infty} g_n(z')z_p^n = 0$, hence $g_n(z') = 0$ for every n and every z' in the projection P′ of P on $\mathbf{K}^{p-1}$; the induction hypothesis applied to each g_n yields then $a_\nu = 0$ for every ν.

PROBLEMS

1. Let $(c_\nu z^\nu)$ be a power series in p variables z_i $(1 \leqslant i \leqslant p)$; let $a = (a_1, \ldots, a_p) \in \mathbf{K}^p$. In order that a real number $r > 0$ be such that, for any $t \in \mathbf{K}$ such that $|t| < r$, the series $(c_\nu(ta_1)^{n_1} \cdots (ta_p)^{n_p})$ be absolutely summable, it is necessary and sufficient that

$$\log r + \frac{1}{|\nu|}\log\|c_\nu\| + \sum_{i=1}^{p} n_i \log|a_i| \leqslant 0$$

for all but a finite number of indices $\nu = (n_1, \ldots, n_p)$ (apply (9.1.2).)

In particular, for $p = 1$, there is a largest number $\mathrm{R} \geqslant 0$ (the "convergence radius," which may be $+\infty$) such that the series $(c_n z^n)$ is convergent for $|z| < \mathrm{R}$, and that number is given by $1/\mathrm{R} = \lim_{n\to\infty}(\sup_{k\geqslant 0}(\|c_{n+k}\|^{1/(n+k)}))$, which is also written $\lim_{n\to\infty} \cdot \sup \|c_n\|^{1/n}$ (cf. Section 12·7). When in particular $\lim_{n\to\infty}\|c_n\|^{1/n}$ exists, it is equal to $1/\mathrm{R}$.

2. Give examples of power series in one complex variable, having a radius of convergence $\mathrm{R} = 1$ (Problem 1) and such that:
   (1) the series is normally convergent for $|z| = \mathrm{R}$;
   (2) the series is convergent for some z such that $|z| = \mathrm{R}$, but not for other points of that circle;
   (3) the series is not convergent at any point of $|z| = \mathrm{R}$.
3. Give an example of a power series in two variables, which is absolutely summable at two points (a_1, a_2), (b_1, b_2), but not at the point $\left(\dfrac{a_1 + b_1}{2}, \dfrac{a_2 + b_2}{2}\right)$. (Replace z by $z_1 z_2$ in a power series in one variable.)
4. Let $(c_n z^n)$, $(d_n z^n)$ be two power series in one variable with scalar coefficients; if their radii of convergence (Problem 1) are R and R′, and neither R nor R′ is 0, then the radius of convergence R″ of the power series $(c_n d_n z^n)$ is at least RR′ (taken equal to $+\infty$ if R or R′ is $+\infty$). Give an example in which $\mathrm{R}'' > \mathrm{RR}'$.

2. SUBSTITUTION OF POWER SERIES IN A POWER SERIES

Let Q be a polydisk of center 0 in $\mathbf{K}^q$, and suppose the p power series in q variables $(b_\mu^{(k)} u^\mu)$ with *scalar* coefficients are absolutely summable in Q (with $\mu = (m_1, \ldots, m_q)$, $u = (u_1, \ldots, u_q)$, $u^\mu = u_1^{m_1} \ldots u_q^{m_q}$). We write

$g_k(u) = \sum_\mu b_\mu^{(q)} u^\mu$, $G_k(u) = \sum_\mu |b_\mu^{(q)}| u^\mu$. On the other hand, let $(a_\nu z^\nu)$ be a power series in p variables with coefficients in E, which is absolutely summable in a polydisk P of K^p, of center 0 and radii r_k $(1 \leqslant k \leqslant p)$. If, in a monomial $z^\nu = z_1^{n_1} \ldots z_p^{n_p}$, we replace "formally" each z_k by the power series $g_k(u)$, we are led to take the formal "product" of $n_1 + n_2 + \cdots + n_p$ series, i.e. to pick a term in each of the $n_1 + \cdots + n_p$ factors, to take their product and then to "sum" all terms thus obtained. We are thus led to consider, for each $\nu = (n_1, n_2, \ldots, n_p)$ the set A_ν of all finite families $(\mu_{kj}) = \rho$ where $\mu_{kj} \in \mathbf{N}^q$, k ranges from 1 to p, and for each k, j ranges from 1 to n_k; to such a ρ we associate the element

$$t_\rho(u) = a_\nu \prod_{k=1}^{p} \prod_{j=1}^{n_k} b_{\mu_{kj}}^{(k)} u^{\mu_{kj}}.$$

With these notations:

(9.2.1) *Suppose $s_1, \ldots, s_q$ are q numbers >0 satisfying the conditions $G_k(s_1, \ldots, s_q) < r_k$ for $1 \leqslant k \leqslant p$. Then, for each u in the open polydisk $S \subset K^q$ of center 0 and radii s_i $(1 \leqslant i \leqslant q)$, the family $(t_\rho(u))$ (where ρ ranges through the denumerable set of indices $A = \bigcup_{\nu \in \mathbf{N}^p} A_\nu$) is absolutely summable, and if $f(z) = \sum_\nu a_\nu z^\nu$, its sum is equal to $f(g_1(u), g_2(u), \ldots, g_p(u))$.*

In other words, under the conditions $G_k(s_1, \ldots, s_q) < r_k$ $(1 \leqslant k \leqslant p)$, "substitution" of the series $g_k(u)$ for z_k $(1 \leqslant k \leqslant p)$ in the series f yields an absolutely summable family, even *before* all the terms $t_\rho(u)$ having the same degrees in $u_1, \ldots, u_q$ have been gathered together.

To prove (9.2.1), we need only prove that the family $(t_\rho(u))$ is absolutely summable; that its sum is $f(g_1(u), \ldots, g_p(u))$ follows by application of the associativity theorem (5.3.6) to the subsets A_ν of A, and by using (5.5.3), which shows that $\sum_{\rho \in A_\nu} t_\rho(u)$ is equal to $a_\nu (g_1(u))^{n_1} \ldots (g_p(u))^{n_p}$. To prove the family $(t_\rho(u))$ $(\rho \in A)$ is absolutely summable, we apply (5.3.4). For any finite subset B of A, we have, by (5.3.5) and (5.5.3)

$$\sum_{\rho \in B \cap A_\nu} \|t_\rho(u)\| \leqslant \|a_\nu\| \cdot (G_1(s_1, \ldots, s_q))^{n_1} \ldots (G_p(s_1, \ldots, s_q))^{n_p}$$

and by assumption, the right-hand side of that inequality is the element of index ν of an absolutely summable family; hence the result.

Write $t_\rho(u) = c_\rho u^\lambda$, with $\lambda = (\lambda_1, \ldots, \lambda_q)$, $\lambda_i = \sum_{k=1}^{p} \sum_{j=1}^{n_k} m_{kji}$ (if we have $\mu_{kj} = (m_{kj1}, \ldots, m_{kjq})$). From (9.2.1) and (5.3.5) it follows (taking all the u_i

to be $\neq 0$, $u \in S$), that for each λ, the family of the c_ρ, where ρ ranges over all elements of A which correspond to the *same* λ, is absolutely summable in E; if d_λ is its sum, we see, by the associativity theorem (5.3.6), that

(9.2.1.1) $$f(g_1(u), \ldots, g_p(u)) = \sum_\lambda d_\lambda u^\lambda$$

the series on the right-hand side being absolutely summable in the polydisk S. By definition, that power series is *the power series obtained by substituting* $g_k(u)$ *to* z_k, *for* $1 \leqslant k \leqslant p$, *in the power series* $(a_\nu z^\nu)$.

(9.2.2) *If the point* $(g_1(0), \ldots, g_p(0))$ *of* K^p *belongs to* P, *then there exists in* K^q *an open polydisk* S *such that, for* $u \in S$, *the series* $g_k(u)$ *may be substituted to* z_k $(1 \leqslant k \leqslant p)$ *in the power series* $(a_\nu z^\nu)$.

Observe that by definition, $G_k(0) = |g_k(0)|$ for $1 \leqslant k \leqslant p$. As G_k is continuous at 0 by (9.1.3), the existence of numbers $s_i > 0$ $(1 \leqslant i \leqslant q)$ such that $G_k(s_1, \ldots, s_q) < r_k$ for $1 \leqslant k \leqslant p$ follows at once from the assumption.

3. ANALYTIC FUNCTIONS

Let D be an open subset of K^p. We say that a mapping f of D into a Banach space E over K is *analytic* if, for every point $a \in D$, there is an open polydisk $P \subset D$ of center a, such that in P, $f(z)$ is equal to the sum of an absolutely summable power series in the p variables $z_k - a_k$ $(1 \leqslant k \leqslant p)$ (that series being necessarily *unique* by (9.1.6)). Suppose $K = \mathbf{C}$, let b be a point of D, and let B be the inverse image of D by the mapping $x \to b + x$ of $\mathbf{R}^p$ into $\mathbf{C}^p$. Then it follows at once from the definitions that $x \to f(b + x)$ is analytic in the open subset B of $\mathbf{R}^p$.

(9.3.1) *Let* $(a_\nu z^\nu)$ *be an absolutely summable power series in an open polydisk* $P \subset K^p$. *Then* $f(z) = \sum_\nu a_\nu z^\nu$ *is analytic in* P; *more precisely, if* r_i $(1 \leqslant i \leqslant p)$ *are the radii of* P, *for any point* $b = (b_i) \in P$, $f(z)$ *is equal to the sum of an absolutely summable power series in the* $z_k - b_k$ *in the open polydisk of center* b *and of radii* $r_i - |b_i|$ $(1 \leqslant i \leqslant p)$.

This follows at once from (9.2.1) applied to the case $q = p$, $g_k(u) = b_k + u_k$; we have then $G_k(u) = |b_k| + u_k$, and the conditions $G_k(s_1, \ldots, s_p) < r_k$ $(1 \leqslant k \leqslant p)$ boil down to $s_k < r_k - |b_k|$ $(1 \leqslant k \leqslant p)$.

An *entire function* of p variables is a mapping f of K^p into E which is equal to the sum of a power series which is absolutely summable *in the whole space* K^p (cf. (9.9.6)). For each $b \in K^p$, $f(z)$ is then equal to the sum of a power series in the $z_k - b_k$, which is absolutely summable in the whole space K^p, by (9.3.1).

(9.3.2) *Let A be an open subset of K^p, B an open subset of K^q, g_k $(1 \leqslant k \leqslant p)$ p scalar functions defined and analytic in B, and suppose the image of B by $(g_1, \ldots, g_p)$ is contained in A. Then, for any analytic mapping f of A into E, $f(g_1, \ldots, g_p)$ is analytic in B.*

This follows at once from the definition and from (9.2.2). In particular, if f is analytic in $A \subset K^p$, then, for any system $(a_{q+1}, \ldots, a_p)$ of $p-q$ scalars, $(z_1, \ldots, z_q) \to f(z_1, \ldots, z_q, a_{q+1}, \ldots, a_p)$ is analytic in the open set $A(a_{q+1}, \ldots, a_p)$ (3.20.12) in K^q.

(9.3.3) *In order that a mapping $f = (f_1, \ldots, f_q)$ of $A \subset K^p$ into K^q be analytic in A, it is necessary and sufficient that each of the scalar functions f_i $(1 \leqslant i \leqslant q)$ be analytic in A.*

Obvious from the definition.

(9.3.4) *Let $z_k = x_k + iy_k$ for $1 \leqslant k \leqslant p$, x_k and y_k being real. If f is analytic in $A \subset \mathbf{C}^p$, then $(x_1, y_1, \ldots, x_p, y_p) \to f(x_1 + iy_1, \ldots, x_p + iy_p)$ is analytic in A, considered as an open set in $\mathbf{R}^{2p}$.*

Indeed, that function is analytic in the open subset $B \subset \mathbf{C}^{2p}$, inverse image of A by the mapping $(u_1, v_1, \ldots, u_p, v_p) \to (u_1 + iv_1, \ldots, u_p + iv_p)$ of $\mathbf{C}^{2p}$ into $\mathbf{C}^p$, by (9.3.2). Hence it is analytic in $A = B \cap \mathbf{R}^{2p}$, when A is considered as a subset of $\mathbf{R}^{2p}$.

(9.3.5) *Let $(c_{n_1 n_2 \ldots n_p} z_1^{n_1} \ldots z_p^{n_p})$ be a power series which is absolutely summable in an open polydisk P of center 0, and let $f(z)$ be its sum. Then the power series $(n_k c_{n_1 n_2 \ldots n_p} z_1^{n_1} \ldots z_k^{n_k - 1} \ldots z_p^{n_p})$ is absolutely summable in P and its sum is the partial derivative $D_k f$ $(= \partial f / \partial z_k)$.*

For any $z \in \mathrm{P}$, we can in the series substitute z_i to itself for $i \neq k$ and $z_k + u_k$ to z_k, and we thus obtain a power series in $p+1$ variables $z_1, \ldots, z_p, u_k$, which, by (9.2.1), is absolutely summable for $|z_i| < r_i (i \neq k)$ and $|z_k| + |u_k| < r_k$ (if $r_1, \ldots, r_p$ are the radii of P). By (9.1.4) we can therefore write $f(z_1, \ldots, z_k + u_k, \ldots, z_p) = f(z) + u_k f_1(z) + \cdots + u_k^n f_n(z) + \cdots$, where each f_n is a power series absolutely summable in P, and the right-hand side, for each $z \in \mathrm{P}$, is a power series in u_k which is absolutely summable in some open ball B of center 0 (depending on z). Moreover it follows from the binomial theorem that

$$f_1(z) = \sum_{\nu} n_k c_{n_1 \ldots n_p} z_1^{n_1} \ldots z_k^{n_k - 1} \ldots z_p^{n_p}$$

and as $(f(z_1, \ldots, z_k + u_k, \ldots, z_p) - f(z))/u_k = f_1(z) + \cdots + u_k^{n-1} f_n(z) + \cdots$ is an absolutely summable power series (in u_k) in B (for fixed z) by (9.1.4), we deduce from (9.1.3) that $f_1(z) = \mathrm{D}_k f(z)$ for any $z \in \mathrm{P}$. From that result and from (9.13) we deduce the values of the c_p in terms of the derivatives of f, namely

$$\nu!\, c_\nu = \mathrm{D}^\nu f(0) \tag{9.3.5.1}$$

where $\mathrm{D}^\nu = \mathrm{D}_1^{n_1} \ldots \mathrm{D}_p^{n_p}$ and $\nu! = n_1!\, n_2! \ldots n_p!$; this is immediate by induction on $|\nu| = n_1 + \cdots + n_p$.

(9.3.6) *An analytic function in an open set* $\mathrm{A} \subset \mathrm{K}^p$ *is indefinitely differentiable and all its derivatives are analytic in* A.

This is an obvious consequence of (9.3.5) and (8.12.8).

For $p = 1$, we have a "converse" to (9.3.5):

(9.3.7) *Let* $(c_n z^n)$ *be a power series convergent in the ball* P: $|z| < r$ *in* K, *and let* $f(z) = \sum_{n=0}^{\infty} c_n z^n$ *in* P. *Then the power series* $((1/(n+1))c_n z^{n+1})$ *is convergent in* P *and its sum is a primitive of* f.

Due to (9.3.5) we have only to check the convergence of the series $\left(\dfrac{1}{n+1} c_n z^{n+1}\right)$, which follows at once from the inequality

$$\left\| \frac{1}{n+1} c_n z^{n+1} \right\| \leqslant \|c_n\| \cdot |z|^{n+1},$$

and from (9.1.2).

PROBLEMS

1. Let $(a_n z^n)$, $(b_n z^n)$ be two power series in one variable, the b_n being real and >0; suppose $\lim_{n\to\infty} a_n/b_n = s$.

(a) Suppose the series $(b_n z^n)$ is convergent for $|z|<1$, but not for $z=1$ (which means that if $c_k = \sum_{n=0}^{k} b_n$, $\lim_{k\to\infty} c_k = +\infty$). Show that the series $(a_n z^n)$ is absolutely convergent for $|z|<1$, and that, if $I = [0, 1[$,

$$\lim_{z\to 1,\, z\in I} \left(\sum_{n=0}^{\infty} a_n z^n\right) \Big/ \left(\sum_{n=0}^{\infty} b_n z^n\right) = s.$$

(Observe that, for any given k, $\lim_{z\to 1,\, z\in I}\left(\sum_{n\geqslant k} b_n z^n\right) = +\infty$).

(b) Suppose the series $(b_n z^n)$ is convergent for every z. Show that the series $(a_n z^n)$ is absolutely convergent for every z, and that if J is the interval $[0, +\infty[$ in $\mathbf{R}$, then

$$\lim_{z\to +\infty,\, z\in J} \left(\sum_{n=0}^{\infty} a_n z^n\right) \Big/ \left(\sum_{n=0}^{\infty} b_n z^n\right) = s.$$

(Same method.)

(c) Show that if the series (a_n) is convergent and $\sum_{n=0}^{\infty} a_n = s$, then the series $(a_n z^n)$ is absolutely convergent for $|z|<1$, and that $\lim_{z\to 1,\, z\in I} \sum_{n=0}^{\infty} a_n z^n = s$. (Apply (a) with $b_n = 1$ for every n; this is "Abel's theorem".)

(d) The power series $((-1)^n z^n)$ has a radius of convergence 1, and its sum $1/(1+z)$ tends to a limit when z tends to 1 in I, but the series $((-1)^n)$ is not convergent (see Problem 2).

2. Let $(a_n z^n)$ be a power series in one variable having a radius of convergence equal to 1; let $f(z)$ be its sum, and suppose that $f(1-)$ exists. If *in addition* $\lim_{n\to\infty} na_n = 0$, show that the series (a_n) is convergent and has a sum equal to $f(1-)$. ("Tauber's theorem": observe that if $|na_n| \leqslant \varepsilon$ for $n \geqslant k$, then, for any $N > k$, and $0 \leqslant x < 1$

$$\left\| \sum_{n=k}^{N} a_n(1-x^n) \right\| \leqslant \varepsilon N(1-x)$$

and

$$\left\| \sum_{n\geqslant N} a_n x^n \right\| \leqslant \varepsilon/N(1-x).)$$

3. Let $(a_n z^n)$ be a power series in one variable having a radius of convergence $r>0$, and let (b_n) be a sequence of scalars $\neq 0$ such that $q = \lim_{n\to\infty}(b_n/b_{n+1})$ exists and $|q| < r$. Show that, if

$$c_n = a_0 b_n + a_1 b_{n-1} + \cdots + a_n b_0$$

$\lim_{n\to\infty}(c_n/b_n)$ exists and is equal to $f(q)$.

4. Let $(p_n z^n)$, $(q_n z^n)$ be two power series with complex coefficients, and radius of convergence $\neq 0$, and let $f(z) = \sum_n p_n z^n$, $g(z) = \sum_n q_n z^n$ in a neighborhood U of 0 where both series are absolutely convergent. Suppose $q_0 = g(0) \neq 0$; then there is a power series $\sum_n c_n z^n$ which is absolutely convergent in a neighborhood $V \subset U$ of 0 and has a sum equal to $f(z)/g(z)$ in V (remark that the series (z^n) is convergent for $|z| < 1$, and use (9.2.2)). If all the q_n are >0, the sequence (q_{n+1}/q_n) is increasing, the p_n are real and such that the sequence (p_n/q_n) is decreasing (resp. decreasing), show that $c_n \geqslant 0$ (resp. $c_n \leqslant 0$) for every $n \geqslant 1$. (Write the difference

$$\frac{p_n}{q_n} - \frac{p_{n-1}}{q_{n-1}}$$

as an expression in the q_k and c_k, and use induction on n.) Deduce from that result that all the derivatives of $x/\log(1-x)$ are <0 for $0 < x < 1$.

5. Let g_k $(1 \leqslant k \leqslant p)$ be p scalar entire functions defined in K^q. If f is an entire function defined in K^p, then $f(g_1, \ldots, g_p)$ is an entire function in K^q.

6. Let P be the disk $|z| \leqslant r$ in **C**. Show that

$$\iint_P z^n \, dx \, dy = 0 \qquad \text{for any integer } n \geqslant 1.$$

(Use the fact that Lebesgue measure on $\mathbf{R}^2$ is invariant by rotation (cf. (14.3.9)).) Deduce from that relation that for every function f which is analytic in an open set $A \subset \mathbf{C}$ containing P, one has

$$\iint_P f(z) \, dx \, dy = \pi r^2 f(0).$$

Show similarly that

$$\iint_P z^n \bar{z}^m \, dx \, dy = 0 \qquad \text{if} \quad m \neq n$$

$$\iint_P |z|^{2n} \, dx \, dy = \frac{\pi r^{2n+2}}{n+1}.$$

4. THE PRINCIPLE OF ANALYTIC CONTINUATION

(9.4.1) *In K^p, let P, Q be two open polydisks of centers a, b, such that $P \cap Q \neq \varnothing$. Let $(c_{n_1 \ldots n_p}(x_1 - a_1)^{n_1} \ldots (x_p - a_p)^{n_p})$ be a power series in the $x_i - a_i$, absolutely summable in P, and let $f(x)$ be its sum. Let $(d_{n_1 \ldots n_p}(x_1 - b_1)^{n_1} \ldots (x_p - b_p)^{n_p})$ be a power series in the $x_i - b_i$, absolutely summable in Q, and let $g(x)$ be its sum. If there is a nonempty open subset U of $P \cap Q$ such that $f(x) = g(x)$ for any $x \in U$, then $f(x) = g(x)$ for any $x \in P \cap Q$.*

Let $u \in U$, and let v be any point of $P \cap Q$; then the *segment* joining u and v is contained in $P \cap Q$ by (9.1.1). Let $h(t) = f(u + t(v - u)) - g(u + t(v - u))$ with *t real*; by (9.3.2), this is an analytic function of t in an open interval I containing [0, 1]. Let A be the closed subset of the interval [0, 1] consisting of the t such that $h(s) = 0$ for $0 \leqslant s \leqslant t$; by assumption there is an open neighborhood of 0 in [0, 1] which is contained in A, hence the l.u.b. ρ of A is certainly >0; we will prove that $\rho = 1$, which will establish (9.4.1). Note first that $h(t) = 0$ for $0 \leqslant t < \rho$, hence by continuity $h(\rho) = 0$; as h is analytic at the point ρ, there is a power series in $t - \rho$, which converges for $|t - \rho| < \alpha$, with $\alpha > 0$ and whose sum is equal to $h(t)$ for $|t - \rho| < \alpha$. But for $0 \leqslant t \leqslant \rho$, $h(t) = 0$ by assumption; from the principle of isolated zeros (9.1.5) it follows that $h(t) = 0$ for $|t - \rho| < \alpha$, which would contradict the definition of ρ if we had $\rho < 1$.

(9.4.2) ("Principle of analytic continuation") *Let* $A \subset K^p$ *be an open* connected *set,* f *and* g *two analytic functions in* A *with values in* E. *If there is a nonempty open subset* U *of* A *such that* $f(x) = g(x)$ *in* U, *then* $f(x) = g(x)$ *for every* $x \in A$.

Let B be the *interior* of the set of points $x \in A$ such that $f(x) = g(x)$. It is clear that B is open and nonempty by assumption; we prove that B is also *closed* in A, hence equal to A since A is connected (see (3.19)). Let $a \in A$ be a cluster point of B; as f, g are analytic, there is an open polydisk P of center a, contained in A, such that in P, $f(x)$ and $g(x)$ are equal to the sums of two power series in the $x_i - a_i$, absolutely summable in P. But by definition, $P \cap B$ contains an open polydisk U in which $f(x) = g(x)$. By (9.4.1) applied to $P = Q$, we conclude that $f(x) = g(x)$ in P, in other words $P \subset B$, and in particular $a \in B$. Q.E.D.

For $p = 1$, we can improve (9.4.2) as follows:

(9.4.3) *Let* $A \subset K$ *be an open* connected *subset of* K, f *and* g *two analytic functions in* A *with values in* E. *Suppose there is a compact subset* H *of* A *such that the set* M *of points* $x \in H$ *for which* $f(x) = g(x)$ *be infinite. Then* $f(x) = g(x)$ *for every* $x \in A$.

Let (z_n) be an infinite sequence of distinct points of M; as H is compact, there is a cluster value $b \in H$ for the sequence (z_n), hence any ball P of center b, contained in A, contains an infinity of points of M. But we can suppose f and g are equal to convergent power series in $z - b$ in a ball $P \subset A$ of center b; the principle of isolated zeros (9.1.6) then shows that $f(x) = g(x)$ in P, and we can then apply (9.4.2).

For $K = \mathbf{C}$ we can also improve (9.4.2) in the following way:

(9.4.4) *Let* $A \subset \mathbf{C}^p$ *be an open* connected *set, f and g two analytic functions in* A *with values in a complex Banach space* E. *Let* U *be an open subset of* A, *b a point of* U, *and suppose that* $f(x) = g(x)$ *in the set* $U \cap (b + \mathbf{R}^p)$; *then* $f(x) = g(x)$ *for every* $x \in A$.

We can suppose, by a translation, that $b = 0$; let $h = f - g$, and let P be a polydisk *in* $\mathbf{C}^p$, of center 0, contained in U and such that in P, $h(z)$ is equal to the sum of an absolutely summable power series $(c_\nu z^\nu)$. Now $P \cap \mathbf{R}^p$ is a polydisk *in* $\mathbf{R}^p$, and $h(x) = 0$ in $P \cap \mathbf{R}^p$; this shows by (9.1.6) that $c_\nu = 0$ for every ν, hence $h(z) = 0$ in P and (9.4.2) can be applied.

In an open connected set $A \subset K^p$, we say that a subset $M \subset A$ is a *set of uniqueness* if any two functions, defined and analytic in A, coincide in A as soon as they coincide in M. (9.4.2), (9.4.3), and (9.4.4) show that a non-empty *open* subset U of A, or the intersection $U \cap (b + \mathbf{R}^p)$ (if not empty), or, for $p = 1$, a compact infinite subset of A, are sets of uniqueness. We shall see another example in Section 9.9 for $K = \mathbf{C}$.

The preceding result shows that if an open connected subset $A \subset \mathbf{C}^p$ is such that $A \cap \mathbf{R}^p \neq \varnothing$, any analytic function f in A is completely determined by its values in $A \cap \mathbf{R}^p$. The restriction of f to $A \cap \mathbf{R}^p$ is an analytic function, but in general an analytic function *in* $A \cap \mathbf{R}^p$ cannot be extended to an analytic function *in* A; we have however the weaker result:

(9.4.5) *Let* E *be a complex Banach space,* A *an open subset of* $\mathbf{R}^p$, *f an analytic mapping of* A *into* E. *Then there is an open set* $B \subset \mathbf{C}^p$ *such that* $B \cap \mathbf{R}^p = A$, *and an analytic mapping g of* B *into* E *which extends f.*

Indeed, for each $a = (a_1, \ldots, a_p) \in A$, there is an open polydisk P_a *in* $\mathbf{R}^p$ defined by $|x_i - a_i| < r_i$ $(1 \leqslant i \leqslant p)$ contained in A and such that, in P_a, $f(x)$ is equal to the sum of an absolutely summable power series $(c_{n_1 \ldots n_p}(x_1 - a_1)^{n_1} \ldots (x_p - a_p)^{n_p})$. Let Q_a be the open polydisk *in* $\mathbf{C}^p$, of center a and radii r_i; then, by (9.1.2), the power series $(c_{n_1 \ldots n_p}(z_1 - a_1)^{n_1} \ldots (z_p - a_p)^{n_p})$ is absolutely summable in Q_a; let $g_a(z)$ be its sum. If a, b are two points of A such that $Q_a \cap Q_b \neq \varnothing$, then $P_a \cap P_b = (Q_a \cap Q_b) \cap \mathbf{R}^p$ is not empty, and we have $g_a(x) = g_b(x) = f(x)$ in $P_a \cap P_b$. Moreover $Q_a \cap Q_b$ is connected by (9.1.1); it follows from (9.4.4) that $g_a(z) = g_b(z)$ in $Q_a \cap Q_b$. We can now take $B = \bigcup_{a \in A} Q_a$, and define g as equal to g_a in each Q_a; the analyticity of g follows from (9.3.1).

The proof of (9.4.5) shows that when f is an *entire* function defined in $\mathbf{R}^p$, it can be extended to an *entire* function defined in $\mathbf{C}^p$, and that function is unique by (9.4.4).

PROBLEMS

1. (a) Let $P(u_1, \ldots, u_{r+1})$ be a polynomial with coefficients in K, $\alpha_1, \ldots, \alpha_r$ elements of K such that $|\alpha_i| < 1$ for $1 \leqslant i \leqslant r$. Suppose there exists a ball B in K of center 0 and a scalar function f analytic in B and such that $f(z) = P(z, f(\alpha_1 z), \ldots, f(\alpha_r z))$ for every $z \in B$. Show that f can be extended to a function g analytic in the whole set K and satisfying the same functional equation in K (use (9.4.2)).
(b) Suppose $K = \mathbf{C}$, and suppose there is a real number β and a scalar function f analytic for $\mathscr{R}(z) > \beta$, and satisfying in that subset the equation $f(z) = P(z, f(z + a_1), \ldots, f(z + a_r))$, where the a_i are complex numbers with $\mathscr{R}(a_i) > 0$. Show that f can be extended to a function g analytic in $\mathbf{C}$ and satisfying the same functional equation.
(c) Generalize the preceding results to functions of any number of variables.
2. Let D be a connected open set in $\mathbf{C}^p$, D′ the image of D by the mapping

$$(z_1, \ldots, z_p) \to (\bar{z}_1, \ldots, \bar{z}_p).$$

Let f be a complex function analytic in D, and suppose $D \cap \mathbf{R}^p$ is not empty, $D \cap D'$ is connected and f takes real values in $D \cap \mathbf{R}^p$. Show that f can be extended to a function g analytic in $D \cup D'$. (Consider in D′ the function $(z_1, \ldots, z_p) \to f(\bar{z}_1, \ldots, \bar{z}_p)$, and use (9.4.4).)

5. EXAMPLES OF ANALYTIC FUNCTIONS; THE EXPONENTIAL FUNCTION; THE NUMBER π

(9.5.1) *Let* $P(z)$, $Q(z)$ *be two polynomials in* K^p, *such that* Q *is not identically* 0; *then* $P(z)/Q(z)$ *is analytic in the* (*open*) *set of the points z such that* $Q(z) \neq 0$ (i.e., the set of points where the function is defined).

It is obvious that any polynomial is an entire function. By (9.3.2) all we have to do is to show that $1/z$ is analytic for $z \neq 0$; but if $z_0 \neq 0$, we can write

$$\frac{1}{z} = \frac{1}{z_0\left(1 + \dfrac{z - z_0}{z_0}\right)}$$

$$= \frac{1}{z_0} - \frac{z - z_0}{z_0^2} + \frac{(z - z_0)^2}{z_0^3} + \cdots + (-1)^n \frac{(z - z_0)^n}{z_0^{n+1}} + \cdots$$

where the power series is absolutely summable for $|z - z_0| < |z_0|$. Q.E.D.

Consider now the function e^x of the *real* variable x; we prove it is an *entire* function. From the Taylor formula (8.14.3) we derive, for any n (using Section 8.8)

$$e^x = 1 + \frac{x}{1!} + \frac{x^2}{2!} + \cdots + \frac{x^n}{n!} + \int_0^x \frac{(x - t)^n}{n!} e^t \, dt.$$

As e^x is increasing by (8.5.3), we have $|e^t| \leqslant e^{|x|}$ for $|t| \leqslant |x|$, hence

$$\left| \int_0^x \frac{(x-t)^n}{n!} e^t \, dt \right| \leqslant \frac{|x|^{n+1} e^{|x|}}{(n-1)!}.$$

But if n_0 is an integer $> |x|$, we have

$$\left| \frac{x^n}{n!} \right| \leqslant \left| \frac{x}{n_0} \right|^{n-n_0} \frac{|x|^{n_0}}{n_0!} \qquad \text{for} \quad n > n_0,$$

hence, for any $x \in \mathbf{R}$

$$e^x = 1 + \frac{x}{1!} + \frac{x^2}{2!} + \cdots + \frac{x^n}{n!} + \cdots$$

and by (9.1.2) the series is normally convergent in any compact interval. Using the remark which follows (9.4.5), we can *define* in $\mathbf{C}$ an entire function e^z (also written $\exp z$) as equal to the sum of the power series $(z^n/n!)$. We have

(9.5.2) $$e^{z+z'} = e^z e^{z'}$$

for both sides are entire functions in $\mathbf{C}^2$ which coincide in $\mathbf{R}^2$, and we apply (9.4.4).

For *real* x, e^{-ix} is the complex conjugate of e^{ix}, since $(-ix)^n$ is the complex conjugate of $(ix)^n$; from (9.5.2) it follows that $|e^{ix}| = 1$. We *define* $\cos x = \mathscr{R}(e^{ix})$, $\sin x = \mathscr{I}(e^{ix})$ for real x; they are entire functions of the real variable x by (9.3.3), and the relation $|e^{ix}| = 1$ is equivalent to $\cos^2 x + \sin^2 x = 1$, and implies $|\cos x| \leqslant 1$ and $|\sin x| \leqslant 1$ for any real x. Moreover, we have

(9.5.3) $$\mathrm{D}(e^z) = e^z$$

since both sides are entire functions (by (9.3.5) in $\mathbf{C}$, which coincide in $\mathbf{R}$. In particular (see *Remark* following (8.4.1)), $\mathrm{D}(e^{ix}) = ie^{ix}$ for real x, hence

(9.5.4) $$\mathrm{D}(\cos x) = -\sin x, \qquad \mathrm{D}(\sin x) = \cos x.$$

The definitions of $\cos x$ and $\sin x$ for real x can also be written $\cos x = \frac{1}{2}(e^{ix} + e^{-ix})$, $\sin x = (e^{ix} - e^{-ix})/2i$; these formulas may be used to define $\cos z$ and $\sin z$ for *complex* z, replacing x by z in the right-hand sides. With these definitions, formulas (9.5.4) are still valid for complex values of x.

(9.5.5) *There is a number $\pi > 0$ such that the solutions of the equation $e^z = 1$ are the numbers $2n\pi i$ (n positive or negative integer).*

If $z = x + iy$, we have $|e^z| = e^x|e^{iy}| = e^x$, hence $e^z = 1$ implies $x = 0$, $z = iy$. We first prove:

(9.5.5.1) *The set of points $x \geqslant 0$ such that* $\cos x = 0$ *is not empty.*

One has

$$1 - \cos 2 = \sum_{k=0}^{\infty} \frac{2^{4k+2}}{(4k+2)!}\left(1 - \frac{4}{(4k+3)(4k+4)}\right)$$

and obviously the convergent series on the right hand side has all its terms $\geqslant 0$; therefore

$$1 - \cos 2 \geqslant \left(1 - \frac{1}{3}\right)\frac{2^2}{2!} = \frac{4}{3} > 1$$

in other words, $\cos 2 < 0$; therefore (3.19.8) the continuous function $\cos x$ takes the value 0 in the interval $]0, 2[$.

As $\cos x$ is continuous, the set D of the roots of $\cos x = 0$ such that $x \geqslant 0$ is closed (3.15.1) and does not contain 0, hence has a smallest element which we denote by $\pi/2$. Then we have $\sin^2 \pi/2 = 1$, and as $\sin x$ is increasing for $0 \leqslant x \leqslant \pi/2$, $\sin \pi/2 = 1$, $e^{i\pi/2} = i$. This already shows that $e^{2\pi i} = 1$, hence $e^{2n\pi i} = 1$ for every integer n, and by (9.5.2)

(9.5.6)
$$e^{z + 2n\pi i} = e^z.$$

To end the proof of (9.5.5) we have only to show that the equation $e^{ix} = 1$ has no root in the interval $]0, 2\pi[$. But from (9.5.2) we deduce $\cos(x + \pi/2) = -\sin x$, hence $\cos x \leqslant 0$ for $\pi/2 \leqslant x \leqslant \pi$, and as $\cos(x + \pi) = -\cos x$, we see that $\cos x < 1$ for $0 < x < 2\pi$, and this ends the proof.

(9.5.7) *The mapping $x \to e^{ix}$ is a continuous bijection of any interval $[a, a + 2\pi]$ on the "unit circle"* $\mathbf{U}$: $|z| = 1$ *in* $\mathbf{C}$, *and a homeomorphism of $]a, a + 2\pi[$ on the complement of e^{ia} in* $\mathbf{U}$.

The mapping is obviously continuous, and it is injective by (9.5.2) and (9.5.5). To prove it is surjective in $[a, a + 2\pi[$, we can obviously suppose $a = 0$, for if $\zeta \in \mathbf{U}$, ζe^{-ia} is also in $\mathbf{U}$. Let $\zeta = \alpha + i\beta$, $\alpha^2 + \beta^2 = 1$; as $|\alpha| \leqslant 1$ and, in the interval $[0, \pi]$, $\cos x$ is continuous and $\cos 0 = 1$, $\cos \pi = -1$, there is $y \in [0, \pi]$ such that $\cos y = \alpha$ by Bolzano's theorem (3.19.8). Then $\sin y = \pm \beta$; if $\sin y = \beta$, we are through; if not we have $\cos(2\pi - y) = \cos y = \alpha$ and $\sin(2\pi - y) = -\sin y = \beta$. Let V be the complement of e^{ia} in $\mathbf{U}$, and $\zeta_0 = e^{ib} \in \mathrm{V}$ with $a < b < a + 2\pi$; if the inverse mapping of the restriction of $x \to e^{ix}$ to $]a, a + 2\pi[$ was not continuous at ζ_0, there would be in $]a, a + 2\pi[$ a sequence (x_n) whose elements would belong to the complement of a neighborhood of b, and such that $\lim_{n\to\infty} e^{ix_n} = \zeta_0$; but then a subsequence (x_{n_k}) would tend to a limit $c \neq b$ in the compact set $[a, a + 2\pi]$ by (3.16.1), and as $e^{ic} \neq e^{ib}$ we arrive at a contradiction. (For another proof, see (10.3.1).)

(9.5.8) *The unit circle* **U** *is connected.*

This follows from (9.5.7), (3.19.1) and (3.19.7).

(9.5.9) ("Principle of maximum") *Let* $(c_\nu z^\nu)$ *be a power series with complex coefficients, absolutely summable in an open polydisk* $\mathrm{P} \subset \mathbf{C}^p$ *of center* 0 *and let* $f(z)$ *be its sum. Suppose that there is an open ball* $\mathrm{B} \subset \mathrm{P}$ *of center* 0 *such that* $|f(z)| \leqslant |f(0)|$ *for every* $z \in \mathrm{B}$. *Then* $c_\nu = 0$ *for every index* $\nu \neq (0, \ldots, 0)$, *in other words, f is a constant.*

We first prove that the theorem is true for any p if it is true for $p = 1$. Indeed, for any $z = (z_1, \ldots, z_p) \in \mathrm{P}$, consider the function of one complex variable $g(t) = f(tz_1, \ldots, tz_p)$ which is analytic for $|t| < 1 + \varepsilon$ with ε small enough. As $|g(t)| \leqslant |g(0)|$ for small values of t, we have $g(t) = g(0)$ by assumption, and in particular $f(z_1 \ldots, z_p) = g(1) = f(0)$. For $p = 1$, we can suppose $c_0 \neq 0$, otherwise the result is obvious by (9.1.6). Suppose there are indices $n > 0$ such that $c_n \neq 0$, and let m be the smallest of them. We can write

$$f(z) = c_0(1 + b_m z^m + z^m h(z))$$

where $b_m \neq 0$, h is analytic in P and $h(0) = 0$. Let $r > 0$ be such that $|z| \leqslant r$ is contained in B and $|h(z)| \leqslant \frac{1}{2}|b_m|$ for $|z| \leqslant r$ (9.1.3). Write $b_m = |b_m|\zeta$ with $|\zeta| = 1$; by (9.5.7) there is a real t such that $e^{mit} = \zeta^{-1}$; for $z = re^{it}$, we therefore have

$$|1 + b_m z^m + z^m h(z)| = |1 + |b_m| r^m + z^m h(z)| \geqslant 1 + \tfrac{1}{2}|b_m| r^m$$

which contradicts the assumption $|f(z)| \leqslant |c_0|$ in B.

The result (9.5.9) does not hold if $\mathbf{C}^p$ is replaced by $\mathbf{R}^p$, as the example of the power series $1/(1 + z^2) = \sum_{n=0}^{\infty} (-1)^n z^{2n}$ (for $|z| < 1$) shows.

(9.5.10) *Let f be a complex valued analytic function defined in an open subset $\mathrm{A} \subset \mathbf{C}^p$, and which is not constant in any connected component of* A. *For any compact subset $\mathrm{H} \subset \mathrm{A}$, the points $z \in \mathrm{H}$ where $|f(z)| = \sup_{x \in \mathrm{H}} |f(x)|$ (which exist by* (3.17.10)) *are frontier points of* H.

Follows at once from (9.5.9) and the principle of analytic continuation (9.4.1).

PROBLEMS

1. Show that if $\mathscr{R}(z) \leqslant 0$, then, for any integer $n > 0$

$$\left| e^z - \left(1 + \frac{z}{1!} + \frac{z^2}{2!} + \cdots + \frac{z^n}{n!}\right) \right| \leqslant \left| \frac{z^{n+1}}{(n+1)!} \right|$$

(use Taylor's formula (8.14.2) applied to $t \to e^{zt}$).

2. Prove that, for real x

$$\left| \cos x - \left(1 - \frac{x^2}{2!} + \frac{x^4}{4!} - \cdots + (-1)^n \frac{x^{2n}}{(2n)!}\right) \right| \leqslant \frac{|x|^{2n+2}}{(2n+2)!}$$

and the difference has the sign of $(-1)^{n+1}$; similarly

$$\left| \sin x - \left(x - \frac{x^3}{3!} + \frac{x^5}{5!} - \cdots + (-1)^{n-1} \frac{x^{2n-1}}{(2n-1)!}\right) \right| \leqslant \frac{|x|^{2n+1}}{(2n+1)!}$$

and the difference has the sign of $(-1)^n x$. (Use induction on n.)

3. (a) Let U be a relatively compact open subset of $\mathbf{C}^p$, f a complex valued analytic function in U, which is not constant in any connected component of U. Suppose there is a number $\mathrm{M} > 0$ such that for every frontier point x of U, and any $\varepsilon > 0$, there is a neighborhood V of x such that $|f(z)| \leqslant \mathrm{M} + \varepsilon$ for any $z \in \mathrm{U} \cap \mathrm{V}$. Show that $|f(z)| \leqslant \mathrm{M}$ for any $z \in \mathrm{U}$, and equality cannot be reached at any point of U (use (9.5.10) and the compactness of the frontier of U).
(b) In **C**, let U be the open set defined by the conditions

$$\mathscr{R}(z) > 0, \quad -\pi/2 < \mathscr{I}(z) < \pi/2.$$

Show that the entire function $\exp(\exp(z))$ is bounded on the frontier of U, but not in U.

4. (a) Let E be the Banach space $\mathbf{C}^2$, with the norm $\|(z_1, z_2)\| = \sup(|z_1|, |z_2|)$. The function $z \to f(z) = (1, 0) + (0, 1)z$ is an analytic mapping of **C** into $\mathbf{C}^2$, such that $\|f(z)\|$ is constant for $|z| < 1$.
(b) Extend the result of (9.5.10) to functions defined in an open set $\mathrm{A} \subset \mathbf{C}^p$, and taking their values in a complex Hilbert space. (If $\|f(z)\|$ reaches a maximum at $z_0 \in \mathrm{A}$, consider the complex-valued function $z \to (f(z) | f(z_0))$; compare with (a).)

5. Let U be an open set in $\mathbf{C}^p$, P a closed polydisk contained in U, of center $a = (a_1, \ldots, a_p)$ and radii r_k $(1 \leqslant k \leqslant p)$. Let f be a complex valued analytic function in U, and suppose that on the set $\mathrm{S} = \{(z_i) \mid |z_i - a_i| = r_i \text{ for } 1 \leqslant i \leqslant p\}$ (i.e., the product of the circles $|z_i - a_i| = r_i$), $|f(z)| \leqslant \mathrm{M}$. Show that for any $z \in \mathrm{P}$, $|f(z)| \leqslant \mathrm{M}$. (Use induction on p, considering the function $(z_2, \ldots, z_p) \to f(b_1, z_2, \ldots, z_p)$ for $|b_1 - a_1| = r_1$.)

6. Let $P(x, y)$ be a polynomial in two complex variables, with complex coefficients, of maximal degree m in x, n in y. Suppose that for *real* x, y such that $-1 \leqslant x \leqslant 1$, $-1 \leqslant y \leqslant 1$, $|P(x, y)| \leqslant M$. Show that for real x, y such that $|x| \geqslant 1$, $|y| \geqslant 1$, $|P(x, y)| \leqslant M(|x| + \sqrt{x^2 - 1})^m(|y| + \sqrt{y^2 - 1})^n$. (Apply Problem 5 to the function $s^m t^n P\left(\frac{1}{2}\left(s + \frac{1}{s}\right), \frac{1}{2}\left(t + \frac{1}{t}\right)\right)$ for $|s| < 1$, $|t| < 1$.) Extend to polynomials in any number of variables.

7. (a) Let $f(z)$ be a complex analytic function of one complex variable in the disk B: $|z| < 1$; suppose $|f(z)| < M$ in B and $f(0) = 0$. Show that $|f(z)| \leqslant M|z|$ in B (consider the function $f(z)/z$, which is analytic in B) ("Schwarz's lemma"). When is equality possible?

(b) Consider on $\mathbf{C}^p$ the norm $\|z\| = (|z_1|^2 + \cdots + |z_p|^2)^{1/2}$, for $z = (z_1, \ldots, z_p)$ (called the "hermitian norm"). Let B be the ball $\|z\| < 1$ for that norm, and let f be a complex valued analytic function in B, such that $f(0) = 0$ and $|f(z)| \leqslant M$ in B. Show that $|f(z)| \leqslant M\|z\|$ in B (consider the function $t \to f(z_1 t, \ldots, z_p t)$ of one complex variable and use a)).

8. (a) In the complex field, let $\mathbf{R}_-$ (the "negative real half-line") be the subset defined by $\mathscr{I}(z) = 0$, $\mathscr{R}(z) \leqslant 0$; let F be the complement of $\mathbf{R}_-$ in $\mathbf{C}$. On the other hand, let S be the set defined by $-\pi < \mathscr{I}(z) < \pi$. Show that the mapping $z \to e^z$ is a *homeomorphism* of S onto F (use (9.5.7)); the inverse mapping is written $z \to \log z$, and called the "principal determination of the logarithm of z"; one has $\log z = \log|z| + \text{am}(z)$ where $\text{am}(z)$ is the unique number θ such that $-\pi < \theta < \pi$ and $z = |z|e^{i\theta}$ (the "amplitude" of z). If z, z' and zz' are all in F, show that the difference $\log(zz') - \log z - \log z'$ is equal to $0, 2\pi i$ or $-2\pi i$.

(b) In the ball B: $|z| < 1$, the power series $((-1)^n z^n/n)_{n \geqslant 1}$ is absolutely convergent; if $f(z)$ is its sum, show that $f(z) = \log(1 + z)$. (Observe that if $z \in B$, $1 + z \in F$; show that $f'(z) = 1/(1 + z)$, and deduce from that result that $f(z) = \log(1 + z)$ for z real and $-1 < z < 1$; finally, consider the analytic function $e^{f(z)}$ and use (9.9.4).) Conclude that $\log z$ is analytic in F.

(c) For any complex number t and any integer $n > 0$, let

$$\binom{t}{n} = t(t-1)\cdots(t-n+1)/n! = \sum_{k=0}^{n} c_{kn} t^k,$$

where the c_{kn} are rational numbers $\left(\text{we put } \binom{t}{0} = 1\right)$. Show that the power series $(c_{kn} z^n t^k)$ is absolutely summable in $\mathring{B} \times \mathbf{C}$ (observe that for any number $r > 0$,

$$\left(1 + \frac{r}{1}\right)\left(1 + \frac{r}{2}\right) \cdots \left(1 + \frac{r}{n}\right) \leqslant \exp\left(r\left(1 + \frac{1}{2} + \cdots + \frac{1}{n}\right)\right) \leqslant a \cdot n^r$$

where a is a constant). Prove that the sum of that series is $\exp(t \log(1 + z))$. (Consider first the case in which z and t are real, and apply Taylor's formula (8.14.2) to the function $z \to (1 + z)^t$. Then use (9.4.4).) The function $\exp(t \log(1 + z))$ is also written $(1 + z)^t$; show that for real values of t, $|(1 + z)^t| = |1 + z|^t$.

(d) If $t > 0$, show that $z \to (1 + z)^t$ can be extended by continuity to the closed disk $|z| \leqslant 1$. (Use a majoration of $\left|\binom{t}{n}\right|$ similar to the one obtained in (c), observing that for $s > 0$, $1 - s < e^{-s}$.)

9. (a) Let f_{jk} $(1 \leqslant j \leqslant m,\ 1 \leqslant k \leqslant n)$ be scalar analytic functions defined in an open connected subset A of $\mathbf{C}^p$; let α_{jk} be real numbers $\geqslant 0$. Show that the continuous function $u(z) = \sum_{k=1}^{n} |f_{1k}(z)|^{\alpha_{1k}} |f_{2k}(z)|^{\alpha_{2k}} |f_{mk}(z)|^{\alpha_{mk}}$ cannot reach a relative maximum at a point of A, unless each of the products $|f_{1k}(z)|^{\alpha_{1k}} \cdots |f_{mk}(z)|^{\alpha_{mk}}$ $(1 \leqslant k \leqslant n)$ is constant in A. (Observe that if $f(z)$ is analytic in A and $f(z_0) \neq 0$, then, for every real number λ, there is a function $g_\lambda(z)$ which is analytic in a neighborhood of z_0 and such that $|g_\lambda(z)| = |f(z)|^\lambda$ in that neighborhood; use Problem 8(c) to that effect.) Extend the result to the case in which the α_{jk} are arbitrary real numbers, provided none of the f_{jk} vanishes in A.

(b) Generalize to $u(z)$ the result of Problem 3(a).

10. Let $f(z)$ be a complex function of one complex variable, analytic in the open set A defined by $R_1 < |z| < R_2$ (where $0 \leqslant R_1 < R_2$). For any r such that $R_1 < r < R_2$, let $M(r) = \sup_{|z|=r} |f(z)|$. Show that if $R_1 < r_1 < r_2 < r_3 < R_2$, then

$$\log M(r_2) \leqslant \frac{\log r_2 - \log r_1}{\log r_3 - \log r_1} \log M(r_3) + \frac{\log r_3 - \log r_2}{\log r_3 - \log r_1} \log M(r_1)$$

("Hadamard's three circles theorem".) (Apply Problem 9 to $|z|^\alpha \cdot |f(z)|$, where the real number α is conveniently chosen, and the function $|z|^\alpha \cdot f(z)$ is considered in the set $r_1 < |z| < r_3$.) When can equality occur?

11. We put on $\mathbf{C}^p$ and $\mathbf{C}^q$ the hermitian norms (Problem 7). Let f be an analytic mapping of the ball B: $\|z\| < 1$ in $\mathbf{C}^p$, into $\mathbf{C}^q$; we have $f = (f_1, \ldots, f_q)$, where the f_k are complex valued analytic functions in B. Suppose that $f(0) = 0$; show that if $\|f(z)\| \leqslant M$ for $z \in B$, then $\|f(z)\| \leqslant M \cdot \|z\|$ for $z \in B$ (for each $z \in B$, consider the functions $t \to f_k(tz)/t$ and apply Problems 9 and 3). When is there equality?

12. We put on $\mathbf{C}^p$ the hermitian norm (Problem 7). Let F, G be two analytic mappings of B: $\|z\| < 1$ into $\mathbf{C}^p$, which are homeomorphisms of B onto open sets $U = F(B)$ and $V = G(B)$, respectively, and such that the inverse mappings are analytic in F(B) and G(B), respectively (this last condition actually follows from the others; see Section **10.3**, Problem 2). For any r such that $0 < r < 1$, let B be the ball $\|z\| < r$, and let $U_r = F(B_r)$, $V_r = G(B_r)$, which are open subsets of U and V respectively. Show that if an analytic mapping u of U into V is such that $u(F(0)) = G(0)$, then $u(U_r) \subset V_r$, for every r such that $0 < r < 1$ (use Problem 11).

13. Let f be a complex valued analytic function of one complex variable in the ball B: $|z| < R$; for any r such that $0 \leqslant r < R$, let $A(r) = \sup_{|z| \leqslant r} \mathscr{R}(f(z))$.

(a) Show that $r \to A(r)$ is strictly increasing unless f is constant (consider $\exp(f(z))$).

(b) Show that, when $A(R-) < +\infty$,

$$A(r) \leqslant \frac{R - r}{R + r} A(0) + \frac{2r}{R + r} A(R-)$$

(Apply Problem 12, with $F(z) = Rz$, and $G(z)$ of the type $(az + b)/(cz + d)$, where the constants a, b, c, d are chosen such that G(B) is the half-plane defined by $\mathscr{R}(z) < A(R-)$.)

14. (a) Let A be a relatively compact open subset of $\mathbf{C}^p$, E a closed subset of the frontier of A. Suppose there exists a complex valued function g, which is analytic in a neighborhood of $\bar{A}$, equal to 0 in E and is not identically 0 in any connected component of A. Let f be a complex valued analytic function in A, *bounded* in A, and suppose there is a number M such that, for every frontier point $x \notin E$ of A, and every $\varepsilon > 0$, there is a neighborhood V of x in $\mathbf{C}^p$ such that $|f(z)| \leqslant M + \varepsilon$ for $z \in A \cap V$. Show that $|f(z)| \leqslant M$ for every $z \in A$. (One can suppose that $|g(z)| \leqslant 1$ for $z \in A$. Consider the function $|f(z)| \cdot |g(z)|^\alpha$, where $\alpha > 0$ is arbitrary, and apply the result of Problem 9(b) to that function.)

(b) Show that the result of (a) does not hold if the assumption that f is bounded in A is deleted (consider the function $\exp(\exp((1-z)/z))$ and use Problem 3(b)).

15. Let $\omega(x)$ be a real function defined in $[0, +\infty[$, such that

$$\omega(x) > 0 \text{ and } \lim_{x \to +\infty} \omega(x) = +\infty.$$

Show that if a complex-valued function f is analytic in a neighborhood of the closed half-plane A: $\mathscr{R}(z) \geqslant 0$, then there is at least one point $\zeta \in A$ such that $|f(\zeta)| < \exp(\omega(|\zeta|)|\zeta|)$. (Use contradiction: if the conclusion was not true, prove that the function $|e^z| \cdot |f(z)|^{-\varepsilon}$ would be $\leqslant 1$ in A, for every value of $\varepsilon > 0$, by applying Problem 9(a).)

16. Let A be an open relatively compact subset of $\mathbf{C}^p$, f a complex-valued function, analytic in A. Suppose there exists a number $M > 0$ and a complex-valued function g, analytic in A, such that $g(z) \neq 0$ for any $z \in A$, and having the following property: for every point x of the frontier of A, and every $\varepsilon > 0$, there is a neighborhood V of x such that $|f(z)| \leqslant M|g(z)|^\varepsilon$ for $z \in A \cap V$. Show that $|f(z)| \leqslant M$ in A ("Phragmén-Lindelöf's principle"; use Problem 9(b)).

17. Let U be the open set defined in Problem 3(b), and suppose f is a complex valued analytic function in a neighborhood A of $\overline{U}$, having the following properties: (1) $|f(z)| \leqslant 1$ on the frontier of U; (2) there exists a constant a such that $0 < a < 1$ and $|f(z)| \leqslant \exp(\exp(a\mathscr{R}(z)))$ for $z \in U$. Prove that $|f(z)| \leqslant 1$ in U. (Remark that

$$z \to \frac{1}{z+1}$$

transforms U into a relatively compact set, and use Phragmén–Lindelöf's principle (Problem 16) with $g(z)$ of the form $\exp(\exp(bz))$.)

6. INTEGRATION ALONG A ROAD

A *path* in $\mathbf{C}$ is a continuous mapping γ of a compact interval $I = [a, b] \supset \mathbf{R}$, not reduced to a point, into $\mathbf{C}$; if $\gamma(I) \subset A \subset \mathbf{C}$, we say that γ is *a path in* A; $\gamma(a)$ (resp. $\gamma(b)$) is called the *origin* (resp. the *extremity*) of the path, both points are also called the *extremities* of γ; if $\gamma(a) = \gamma(b)$, γ is called a *loop*; if γ is constant in I, we also say that the path γ is *reduced to a point*. The mapping γ^0 of I into $\mathbf{C}$ such that $\gamma(t) = \gamma(a+b-t)$ is a path which is said to be *opposite* to γ. Let $I_1 = [b, c]$ be a compact interval in $\mathbf{R}$ whose origin is the extremity of I, and let $I_2 = I \cup I_1 = [a, c]$; if γ_1 is a path defined in I_1, and such that $\gamma_1(b) = \gamma(b)$, and if we define γ_2 to be equal to γ in I, to γ_1 in I_1, γ_2 is a path which we denote $\gamma \vee \gamma_1$, and which we call the *juxtaposition* of γ and γ_1.

We will say that a path γ, defined in $I = [a, b] \subset \mathbf{R}$, is a *road*, if γ is a *primitive of a regulated function* (8.7.2); if in addition $\gamma(a) = \gamma(b)$ we will say that γ is a *circuit*. It is clear that the opposite of a road is a road, and so is the juxtaposition of two roads. Let γ, γ_1 be two roads, defined in the intervals I, I_1 respectively. We say that γ and γ_1 are *equivalent* if there is a bijection φ of I onto I_1, such that φ and φ^{-1} are primitives of regulated functions, and that $\gamma = \gamma_1 \circ \varphi$ (hence $\gamma_1 = \gamma \circ \varphi^{-1}$); it is immediate (by (8.4.1)) that this is indeed an equivalence relation between roads.

If the road γ is defined in $I = [a, b]$, there is a road γ_1 equivalent to γ and defined in any other interval $J = [c, d]$, for there is a linear bijection $t \to \varphi(t) = \alpha t + \beta$ of J onto I, and $\gamma_1 = \gamma \circ \varphi$ has the required properties.

Let γ be a road, defined in $I = [a, b]$, and let f be a continuous mapping of the compact set $\gamma(I)$ into a complex Banach space E; the function $t \to f(\gamma(t))$ is then continuous in I, hence $t \to f(\gamma(t))\gamma'(t)$ is a regulated function; the integral $\int_a^b f(\gamma(t))\gamma'(t)\,dt$ is called the *integral of f along the road γ* and written $\int_\gamma f(z)\,dz$; from (8.7.4) it follows at once that if γ_1 is a road *equivalent* to γ, then $\int_{\gamma_1} f(z)\,dz = \int_\gamma f(z)\,dz$. Moreover, from the definition, it follows immediately that

(9.6.1) $$\int_{\gamma^0} f(z)\,dz = -\int_\gamma f(z)\,dz$$

(9.6.2) $$\int_{\gamma_1 \vee \gamma_2} f(z)\,dz = \int_{\gamma_1} f(z)\,dz + \int_{\gamma_2} f(z)\,dz$$

when the juxtaposition $\gamma_1 \vee \gamma_2$ is defined.

Let γ be a *circuit*, defined in $I = [a, b]$; for any $c \in I$, consider the mapping γ_1 of $J = [c, c + b - a]$ defined as follows: $\gamma_1(t) = \gamma(t)$ if $c \leqslant t \leqslant b$, $\gamma_1(t) = \gamma(t - b + a)$ if $b \leqslant t \leqslant c + b - a$. It is immediately verified that γ_1 is a circuit such that $\gamma_1(J) = \gamma(I)$, and that $\int_{\gamma_1} f(z)\,dz = \int_\gamma f(z)\,dz$ for any continuous mapping of $\gamma(I)$ into E. In other words, the integral of f along a circuit *does not depend on the origin* of the circuit.

Let γ_0, γ_1 be two paths defined in the same interval I, and let A be an open set in $\mathbf{C}$ such that $\gamma_0(I) \subset A$ and $\gamma_1(I) \subset A$. A *homotopy of γ_0 into γ_1 in* A is a continuous mapping φ of $I \times [\alpha, \beta]$ ($\alpha < \beta$ in $\mathbf{R}$) *into* A such that $\varphi(t, \alpha) = \gamma_0(t)$ and $\varphi(t, \beta) = \gamma_1(t)$ in I; γ_1 is said to be *homotopic to γ_0 in* A if there is a homotopy of γ_0 into γ_1 in A. It is clear that for any $\xi \in [\alpha, \beta]$, $t \to \varphi(t, \xi)$ is a path in A. When both γ_0 and γ_1 are *loops*, we say that φ is a *loop homotopy* of γ_0 into γ_1 in A if $t \to \varphi(t, \xi)$ is a *loop* for any $\xi \in [\alpha, \beta]$; when we say that two loops γ_0, γ_1 are homotopic in A, we mean that there is a *loop homotopy* (and not merely a homotopy) of γ_0 into γ_1 in A.

If φ is a homotopy of γ_0 into γ_1 in A, defined in $I \times [\alpha, \beta]$, then the mapping $(t, \xi) \to \varphi(t, \alpha + \beta - \xi)$ is a homotopy of γ_1 into γ_0 in A; on the other hand, if ψ is a homotopy of γ_1 into γ_2 in A, defined in $I \times [\alpha', \beta']$, then we can define a homotopy θ of γ_0 into γ_2 in A in the following way; we take $\theta = \varphi$ in $I \times [\alpha, \beta]$; putting $\beta'' = \beta' + \beta - \alpha'$, we take $\theta(t, \xi) = \psi(t, \xi + \alpha' - \beta)$ in $I \times [\beta, \beta'']$; this is meaningful, for both definitions give $\theta(t, \beta) = \gamma_1(t)$ by assumption, and it is immediate to verify that θ is continuous in $I \times [\alpha, \beta'']$, takes its values in A, and is such that $\theta(t, \alpha) = \gamma_0(t)$, $\theta(t, \beta'') = \gamma_2(t)$. This shows that the relation "γ_1 is homotopic to γ_0 in A" between paths in A, is an *equivalence relation*; it is also an equivalence relation between loops in A, for the preceding definitions yield loop homotopies when φ and ψ are loop homotopies.

(9.6.3) (Cauchy's theorem) *Let $A \subset \mathbf{C}$ be an open set, f an analytic mapping of* A *into a complex Banach space* E. *If Γ_1, Γ_2 are two circuits in* A *which are homotopic in* A, *then* $\int_{\Gamma_1} f(z)\,dz = \int_{\Gamma_2} f(z)\,dz$.

Suppose Γ_1, Γ_2 are defined in $I = [a, b]$, and let φ be a homotopy of Γ_1 into Γ_2 in A, defined in $I \times [\alpha, \beta]$ (N.B. It is *not* supposed that for $\xi \neq \alpha, \beta$, the loop $t \to \varphi(t, \xi)$ is a circuit). As φ is continuous, $L = \varphi(I \times [\alpha, \beta])$ is a *compact* set contained in A; by definition and the Borel–Lebesgue axiom, there exist a finite number of points a_k $(1 \leqslant k \leqslant m)$ in L and for each k an open ball $P_k \subset A$ of center a_k such that: (1) the P_k form a covering of L; (2) in each P_k, $f(z)$ is equal to the sum of a power series in $z - a_k$, convergent in P_k. There exists a number $\rho > 0$ such that for *every* $x \in L$, the open ball of center x and radius ρ is contained in at least one of the P_k **(3.16.6)**. It follows from **(9.3.1)** that for *every* $x \in L$, $f(z)$ is equal in the ball $B(x; \rho)$ to a convergent power series in $z - x$.

As φ is uniformly continuous in $I \times [\alpha, \beta]$ **(3.16.5)**, there is $\varepsilon > 0$ such that $|t - t'| \leqslant \varepsilon$, $|\xi - \xi'| \leqslant \varepsilon$ imply $|\varphi(t, \xi) - \varphi(t', \xi')| \leqslant \rho/4$. Let $(t_i)_{0 \leqslant i \leqslant r}$ be an increasing sequence in I such that $t_0 = a$, $t_r = b$, $t_{i+1} - t_i \leqslant \varepsilon$, for $0 \leqslant i \leqslant r - 1$, $(\xi_j)_{0 \leqslant j \leqslant s}$ an increasing sequence in $[\alpha, \beta]$ such that $\xi_0 = \alpha$, $\xi = \beta$, $\xi_{j+1} - \xi_j \leqslant \varepsilon$ for $0 \leqslant j \leqslant s - 1$. Define γ_j as follows

$$\gamma_j(t) = \varphi(t_i, \xi_j) + \frac{t - t_i}{t_{i+1} - t_i}(\varphi(t_{i+1}, \xi_j) - \varphi(t_i, \xi_j))$$

for $t_i \leqslant t \leqslant t_{i+1}$, $0 \leqslant i \leqslant r - 1$, $1 \leqslant j \leqslant s - 1$; in addition, let $\gamma_0 = \Gamma_1$, $\gamma_s = \Gamma_2$. Then γ_j is a *circuit* in A for $0 \leqslant j \leqslant s$; all we have to do is to prove that $\int_{\gamma_j} f(z)\,dz = \int_{\gamma_{j+1}} f(z)\,dz$ for $0 \leqslant j \leqslant s - 1$. Note now that from the choice of the t_i and ξ_j, *all* the points $\gamma_j(t)$ and $\gamma_{j+1}(t)$, where $t_i \leqslant t \leqslant t_{i+1}$, belong to the open ball Q_{ij} of center $\varphi(t_i, \xi_j)$ and radius ρ. By (9.3.7) and (9.3.1) there is a function g_{ij} analytic in Q_{ij} and such that $g'_{ij}(z) = f(z)$ in Q_{ij}. As $Q_{i-1,j} \cap Q_{ij}$ is not empty and is connected by (9.1.1), the difference $g_{i-1,j} - g_{ij}$ is *constant* in $Q_{i-1,j} \cap Q_{ij}$ by (8.6.1). Now, by definition

$$\int_{\gamma_j} f(z)\,dz = \sum_{i=0}^{r-1} \int_{t_i}^{t_{i+1}} f(\gamma_j(t))\gamma'_j(t)\,dt = \sum_{i=0}^{r-1} \int_{t_i}^{t_{i+1}} g'_{ij}(\gamma_j(t))\gamma'_j(t)\,dt$$
$$= \sum_{i=0}^{r-1} (g_{ij}(\gamma_j(t_{i+1})) - g_{ij}(\gamma_j(t_i))).$$

Therefore we are reduced to proving the relation

$$\sum_{i=0}^{r-1} (g_{ij}(\gamma_j(t_{i+1})) - g_{ij}(\gamma_j(t_i))) = \sum_{i=0}^{r-1} (g_{ij}(\gamma_{j+1}(t_{i+1})) - g_{ij}(\gamma_{j+1}(t_i)))$$

which can also be written

$$\sum_{i=0}^{r-1} (g_{ij}(\gamma_j(t_{i+1})) - g_{ij}(\gamma_{j+1}(t_{i+1})) - g_{ij}(\gamma_j(t_i)) + g_{ij}(\gamma_{j+1}(t_i))) = 0.$$

But $\gamma_j(t_i)$ and $\gamma_{j+1}(t_i)$ both belong to $Q_{i-1,j} \cap Q_{ij}$ for $1 \leqslant i \leqslant r$, hence, by what we have seen above

$$g_{ij}(\gamma_j(t_i)) - g_{ij}(\gamma_{j+1}(t_i)) = g_{i-1,j}(\gamma_j(t_i)) - g_{i-1,j}(\gamma_{j+1}(t_i))$$

hence the left-hand side of (9.6.3.1) is reduced to

$$g_{r-1,j}(\gamma_j(t_r)) - g_{r-1,j}(\gamma_{j+1}(t_r)) - g_{0j}(\gamma_j(t_0)) + g_{0j}(\gamma_{j+1}(t_0)).$$

But as γ_j and γ_{j+1} are circuits, we have $\gamma_j(t_0) = \gamma_j(t_r)$ and $\gamma_{j+1}(t_0) = \gamma_{j+1}(t_r)$; moreover, these two points belong to $Q_{0j} \cap Q_{r-1,j}$, which is connected; the difference $g_{r-1,j} - g_{0j}$ is thus constant in that set by (8.6.1), and this ends the proof.

(9.6.4) *Let γ_1, γ_2 be two roads in an open set $A \subset \mathbf{C}$, having same origin u and same extremity v, and such that there is a homotopy φ of γ_1 into γ_2 in A which leaves u and v fixed* (i.e., $\varphi(a, \xi) = u$ and $\varphi(b, \xi) = v$ for every $\xi \in [\alpha, \beta]$ if φ is defined in $[a, b] \times [\alpha, \beta]$). *Then, for every analytic function f in A, $\int_{\gamma_1} f(z)\,dz = \int_{\gamma_2} f(z)\,dz$.*

Let γ_1^0 be the road opposite to γ_1, and let $\gamma_3(t) = \gamma_1^0(t - b + a)$ for $b \leqslant t \leqslant 2b - a$; γ_3 is a road equivalent to γ_1^0. By definition, $\gamma_1 \vee \gamma_3$ and $\gamma_2 \vee \gamma_3$ are circuits. Moreover these circuits are homotopic in A, for if we define $\psi(t, \xi)$ as equal to $\varphi(t, \xi)$ for $a \leqslant t \leqslant b$, to $\gamma_3(t)$ for $b \leqslant t \leqslant 2b - a$, ψ is a loop homotopy in A. Applying (9.6.3), we get $\int_{\gamma_1} f(z)\,dz + \int_{\gamma_3} f(z)\,dz = \int_{\gamma_2} f(z)\,dz + \int_{\gamma_3} f(z)\,dz$. Q.E.D.

7. PRIMITIVE OF AN ANALYTIC FUNCTION IN A SIMPLY CONNECTED DOMAIN

A *simply connected domain* $A \subset \mathbf{C}$ is an open connected set such that any loop in A is homotopic in A to a loop *reduced to a point*; it is clear that any open subset of $\mathbf{C}$ homeomorphic to A is a simply connected domain.

Example

(9.7.1) A *star-shaped domain* $A \subset \mathbf{C}$ with respect to a point $a \in A$ is an open set such that for any $z \in A$, the *segment* joining a and z is *contained in* A. Such a set is clearly connected ((3.19.1) and (3.19.3)); if γ is any loop in A, write $\varphi(t, \xi) = a + (1 - \xi)(\gamma(t) - a)$ for $0 \leqslant \xi \leqslant 1$; φ is a loop homotopy of γ into the loop reduced to a. An open ball is a star-shaped domain with respect to any of its points.

(9.7.2) *If $A \subset \mathbf{C}$ is an open connected set, for any two points u, v of A there is a road of origin u and extremity v.*

We need only prove that the subset $B \subset A$ of all extremities of roads in A having origin u is both closed and open in A (Section 3.19). If $x \in A \cap \bar{B}$, there is a ball S of center x contained in A, and by assumption S contains the extremity v of a road γ of origin u; the segment of extremities v, x is contained in S, and if γ is defined in $[a, b]$, the road γ_1 equal to γ in $[a, b]$, to $\gamma_1(t) = v + (t - b)(x - v)$ in $[b, b + 1]$ is in A and has origin u, extremity x; hence $x \in B$. On the other hand, if $y \in B$, there is a ball S of center y contained in A; for any $v \in S$, the segment of extremities y, v is contained in S and we define in the same manner a road of origin u, extremity v, which is in A, hence $S \subset B$. Q.E.D.

(9.7.3) *If $A \subset \mathbf{C}$ is a simply connected domain, any function f analytic in A has a primitive which is analytic in A.*

Let a, z be two points of A, γ_1, γ_2 two roads in A of origin a and extremity z; then $\int_{\gamma_1} f(x)\,dx = \int_{\gamma_2} f(x)\,dx$. Indeed, we may suppose, by replacing γ_2 by an equivalent road, that γ_1 is defined in $[b, c]$ and γ_2 in $[c, d]$; then $\gamma = \gamma_1 \vee \gamma_2^0$ is a circuit in A, which is therefore homotopic to a point in A, hence $\int_\gamma f(x)\,dx = 0$ by Cauchy's theorem, and this proves our assertion. We can therefore define $g(z)$ as the value of $\int_\gamma f(x)\,dx$ for *any* road γ in A of origin a and extremity z, and by (9.7.2), g is defined in A. Now for any $z_0 \in \mathrm{A}$, there is an open ball $\mathrm{B} \subset \mathrm{A}$ of center z_0 in which $f(z)$ is equal to a convergent power series in $z - z_0$; by (9.3.7) there is therefore a primitive h of f in B which is analytic, and such that $h(z_0) = g(z_0)$; hence we have for $z \in \mathrm{B}$

$$h(z) - h(z_0) = \int_0^1 f(z_0 + t(z - z_0))(z - z_0)\,dt.$$

But the right-hand side is by definition $\int_\sigma f(x)\,dx$, where σ is the road $t \to z_0 + t(z - z_0)$ defined in $[0, 1]$; as that road is in $\mathrm{B} \subset \mathrm{A}$, we have $g(z) - g(z_0) = \int_\sigma f(x)\,dx$ by definition of g, and therefore $g(z) = h(z)$ in B. Q.E.D.

8. INDEX OF A POINT WITH RESPECT TO A CIRCUIT

(9.8.1) *Any path γ defined in an interval $\mathrm{I} = [a, b]$ and such that $\gamma(\mathrm{I})$ is contained in the unit circle $\mathbf{U} = \{z \in \mathbf{C} \mid |z| = 1\}$, has the form $t \to e^{i\psi(t)}$, where ψ is a continuous mapping of* I *into* **R**; *if γ is a road, ψ is a primitive of a regulated function.*

As γ is uniformly continuous in I, there is an increasing sequence of points t_k $(0 \leqslant k \leqslant p)$ in I such that $t_0 = a$, $t_p = b$, and that the oscillation (Section 3.14) of γ in each of the intervals $\mathrm{I}_k = [t_k, t_{k+1}]$ $(0 \leqslant k \leqslant p-1)$ be $\leqslant 1$. This implies that $\gamma(\mathrm{I}_k) \neq \mathbf{U}$; if $\theta_k \in \mathbf{R}$ is such that $e^{i\theta_k} \notin \gamma(\mathrm{I}_k)$ (9.5.7), then $x \to e^{i(x+\theta_k)}$ is a homeomorphism of the interval $]0, 2\pi[$ on the complement of $e^{i\theta_k}$ in $\mathbf{U}$ (9.5.7). If φ_k is the inverse homeomorphism, we can therefore write, for $t \in \mathrm{I}_k$, $\gamma(t) = e^{i\psi_k(t)}$, where $\psi_k(t) = \varphi_k(\gamma(t)) + \theta_k$ is continuous in I_k. By (9.5.5), we have $\psi_{k+1}(t_{k+1}) = \psi_k(t_{k+1}) + 2n_k\pi$ with n_k an integer $(0 \leqslant k \leqslant p-2)$. Define now ψ in I in the following way: $\psi(t) = \psi_0(t)$ for $t \in \mathrm{I}_0$; by induction on k, we put $\psi(t) = \psi_k(t) + \psi(t_k) - \psi_k(t_k)$ for $t_k < t \leqslant t_{k+1}$. By induction on k, it is immediately seen that $\psi(t_k) - \psi_k(t_k)$ is an integral multiple of 2π for $0 \leqslant k \leqslant p-1$; therefore $\gamma(t) = e^{i\psi(t)}$ for $t \in \mathrm{I}$, and ψ is obviously continuous in I. Moreover, if $\gamma(t) = \alpha(t) + i\beta(t)$, we have $\alpha(t) = \cos\psi(t)$, $\beta(t) = \sin\psi(t)$, and one of the numbers $\cos\psi(t)$, $\sin\psi(t)$ is not 0; from (9.5.4), and (8.2.3) applied to one of the functions $\cos x$, $\sin x$ at a point where it has a derivative $\neq 0$, we deduce that if γ has a derivative at a point t, so has ψ, and $i\psi'(t) = \gamma'(t)/\gamma(t)$, which ends our proof.

(9.8.2) *For any point* $a \in \mathbf{C}$, *and any circuit* γ *contained in* $\mathbf{C} - \{a\}$, $\int_\gamma dz/(z-a)$ *has the form* $2n\pi i$, *where* n *is a positive or negative integer.*

By a translation, we can suppose $a = 0$. Suppose γ is defined in $\mathrm{I} = [b, c]$; the function $\varphi(t, \xi) = \xi \dfrac{\gamma(t)}{|\gamma(t)|} + (1 - \xi)\gamma(t)$ is continuous in $\mathrm{I} \times [0, 1]$ and is a loop homotopy (in $\mathbf{C}^* = \mathbf{C} - \{0\}$) of the circuit γ into the circuit $\gamma_1(t) = \gamma(t)/|\gamma(t)|$, which is such that $\gamma_1(\mathrm{I}) \subset \mathrm{U}$. As $1/z$ is analytic in $\mathbf{C}^*$, Cauchy's theorem (9.6.3) shows that $\int_\gamma dz/z = \int_{\gamma_1} dz/z$. But by (9.8.1), $\gamma_1(t) = e^{i\psi(t)}$ where ψ is a primitive of a regulated function, hence $\int_{\gamma_1} dz/z = i\int_b^c \psi'(t)\, dt = i(\psi(c) - \psi(b))$ by definition; as $\gamma_1(b) = \gamma_1(c)$ by assumption, the conclusion results from (9.5.5).

Remark. A simpler proof of (9.8.2), which does not use (9.8.1), can be given as follows (Ahlfors): let $h(t) = \displaystyle\int_b^t \frac{\gamma'(s)\, ds}{\gamma(s) - a}$; it has a derivative equal to $h'(t) = \dfrac{\gamma'(t)}{\gamma(t) - a}$ except at the points of an at most denumerable subset of I; hence, if $g(t) = e^{-h(t)}(\gamma(t) - a)$, we see that $g'(t) = 0$ except in an at most denumerable subset of I. We conclude (8.6.1) that g is constant, hence $e^{h(t)} = \dfrac{\gamma(t) - a}{\gamma(b) - a}$. But we have $\gamma(c) = \gamma(b)$, and therefore $e^{h(c)} = 1$, which implies $h(c) = 2n\pi i$ for an integer n by (9.5.5).

We say that the number n is *the index of* a *with respect to* γ (or the *index of* γ *with respect to* a) and we write $n = j(a; \gamma)$. From Cauchy's theorem it follows that if γ_1, γ_2 are circuits in $\mathbf{C} - \{a\}$ which are homotopic in that set, they have the same index with respect to a.

(9.8.3) *The index* $j(x; \gamma)$ *is constant in each connected component of the complement* A *of the compact set* $\gamma(\mathrm{I})$.

Indeed, we remark that $x \to j(x; \gamma)$ is *continuous* in the open set A, for by definition, the index of $x + h$ with respect to γ (if $x + h \notin \gamma(\mathrm{I})$) is equal to that of x with respect to the circuit $\gamma_1 \colon t \to \gamma(t) - h$. But if B is a ball of center x and radius r, contained in A, $\varphi(t, \xi) = \gamma(t) - \xi h$ (defined in $\mathrm{I} \times [0, 1]$) is a loop homotopy, in $\mathbf{C} - \{x\}$, of γ into γ_1, as long as $|h| < r$, and therefore $j(x + h; \gamma) = j(x; \gamma)$ by Cauchy's theorem. As the set $\mathbf{Z}$ of integers is a discrete space, the conclusion follows from (3.19.7).

Example

(9.8.4) Let ε_n be the circuit $t \to e^{nit}$ defined in $I = [0, 2\pi]$, n being a positive or negative integer; we have $\varepsilon_n(I) = \mathbf{U}$; ε_n is called "the unit circle taken n times". We observe that the open set $\mathbf{C} - \mathbf{U}$ has *two* connected components, namely the ball B: $|z| < 1$ and the exterior E of B defined by $|z| > 1$. Indeed, B is connected as a star-shaped domain (9.7.1); and by Section 4.4 and (9.5.7) E is the image of $]1, +\infty[\times [0, 2\pi]$ by the continuous mapping $(x, t) \to xe^{it}$, hence the result by (3.19.1), (3.20.16), and (3.19.7) (a similar argument also proves the connectedness of B and of $B - \{0\}$); finally in $\mathbf{C} - \mathbf{U}$, B and E are open and closed since B is open in $\mathbf{C}$ and $B = (\mathbf{C} - \mathbf{U}) \cap \overline{B}$, and we have $B \cap E = \varnothing$. From the definition and (9.5.3) it follows that $j(0; \varepsilon_n) = n$, hence $j(z; \varepsilon_n) = n$ *for any point* z *of* B. Let us show that $j(z; \varepsilon_n) = 0$ *for any point of* E; more generally:

(9.8.5) *If a circuit* γ *is contained in a closed ball* D: $|z - a| \leqslant r$, *then* $j(z; \gamma) = 0$ *for any point* z *exterior to* D.

Indeed, suppose γ is defined in an interval $I = [b, c]$, and that $|\gamma'(t)| \leqslant M$ in that interval. By definition,

$$2\pi i j(z; \gamma) = \int_\gamma \frac{dx}{x - z} = \int_b^c \frac{\gamma'(t)\,dt}{\gamma(t) - z} \qquad \text{for} \quad |z - a| > r.$$

But as $|\gamma(t) - a| \leqslant r$, we have $|\gamma(t) - z| \geqslant |z - a| - r$ for any $t \in I$, and therefore, by the mean value theorem,

$$2\pi\, |j(z; \gamma)| \leqslant \frac{M(c - b)}{|z - a| - r};$$

when $|z - a|$ is large enough the right-hand side is $< 2\pi$, and as $j(z; \gamma)$ is an integer, this implies $j(z; \gamma) = 0$. But the exterior of D is connected, as seen above, hence the conclusion by (9.8.3).

(9.8.6) *For any circuit* γ *in* $\mathbf{C}$, *defined in* I, *the set of points* $x \in \mathbf{C} - \gamma(I)$ *such that* $j(x; \gamma) \neq 0$ *is relatively compact in* $\mathbf{C}$.

For by (9.8.5), that set is contained in any closed ball containing $\gamma(I)$.

(9.8.7) *Let* $A \subset \mathbf{C}$ *be a simply connected domain,* γ *a circuit in* A. *For any point* x *of* $\mathbf{C} - A$, $j(x; \gamma) = 0$.

By assumption, there is in A a loop homotopy φ, defined in $I \times J$, of γ into a circuit reduced to a point. As $x \notin \varphi(I \times J)$, Cauchy's theorem shows that $\int_\gamma dz/(z-x) = 0$.

9. THE CAUCHY FORMULA

(9.9.1) *Let* $A \subset \mathbf{C}$ *be a simply connected domain* (Section 9.7), *f an analytic mapping of* A *into a complex Banach space* E. *For any circuit* γ *in* A, *defined in* I *and any* $x \in A - \gamma(I)$, *we have* (Cauchy's formula)

$$j(x;\gamma)f(x) = \frac{1}{2\pi i}\int_\gamma \frac{f(z)\,dz}{z-x}.$$

Consider the function $g(z)$ defined in A, equal to $(f(z) - f(x))/(z-x)$ for $z \neq x$, to $f'(x)$ at the point x; g is analytic in A, for it is obviously analytic in $A - \{x\}$ by (9.3.2) and (9.5.1); on the other hand, there is a ball $B \subset A$ of center x such that for $z \in B$, $f(z) = f(x) + (z-x)f'(x) + \cdots + (z-x)^n f^{(n)}(x)/n! + \cdots$ the series being convergent in B; this proves that for any $z \in B$, $g(z)$ is equal to the sum of the convergent series

$$f'(x) + \tfrac{1}{2}(z-x)f''(x) + \cdots + (z-x)^{n-1}f^{(n)}(x)/n! + \cdots,$$

hence analytic at x. From Cauchy's theorem (9.6.3) we have $\int_\gamma g(z)\,dz = 0$, and writing

$$g(z) = \frac{f(z)}{z-x} - f(x)\frac{1}{z-x}$$

yields (9.9.1) by definition of the index.

Conversely:

(9.9.2) *Let* γ *be a road in* $\mathbf{C}$, *defined in an interval* $I = [b, c]$ *and let g be a continuous mapping of* $\gamma(I)$ *into a complex Banach space* E. *Then*

$$f(z) = \int_\gamma \frac{g(x)\,dx}{x-z}$$

is defined and analytic in the complement of $\gamma(I)$; *more precisely, for any point* $a \in \mathbf{C} - \gamma(I)$, *if we write*

$$c_k = \int_\gamma \frac{g(x)\,dx}{(x-a)^{k+1}},$$

the power series $(c_n(z-a)^n)$ *is convergent in any open ball* B *of center a contained in* $\mathbf{C} - \gamma(I)$, *and its sum is equal to* $f(z)$ *in* B.

Indeed, suppose $|z - a| \leqslant q \cdot d(a, \gamma(I))$ with $0 < q < 1$; then, for any $x \in \gamma(I)$, we have

$$\frac{1}{x - z} = \frac{1}{(x - a)\left(1 - \dfrac{z - a}{x - a}\right)} = \sum_{n=0}^{\infty} \frac{(z - a)}{(x - a)^{n+1}},$$

with

$$\left| \frac{(z - a)^n}{(x - a)^{n+1}} \right| \leqslant \frac{1}{\delta} q^n,$$

if $\delta = d(a, \gamma(I))$. If $\|g(x)\| \leqslant M$ in $\gamma(I)$ and $|\gamma'(t)| \leqslant m$ in I, we have, for any $t \in I$,

$$\left\| \frac{\gamma'(t)g(\gamma(t))(z - a)^n}{(\gamma(t) - a)^{n+1}} \right\| \leqslant \frac{Mm}{\delta} q^n,$$

hence the series of general term

$$\frac{\gamma'(t)g(\gamma(t))(z - a)^n}{(\gamma(t) - a)^{n+1}}$$

is normally convergent in I. It follows from (8.7.9) that the series $(c_n(z - a)^n)$ is convergent in the ball $|z - a| \leqslant q \cdot \delta$ and has sum $f(z)$ in that ball.

(9.9.3) *Under the assumptions of* (9.9.1), *we have, for every* $x \in A - \gamma(I)$, *and every integer* $k > 0$,

$$j(x; \gamma) f^{(k)}(x) = \frac{k!}{2\pi i} \int_\gamma \frac{f(z)\, dz}{(z - x)^{k+1}}.$$

This follows at once from Cauchy's formula, the uniqueness of the coefficients of a power series with given sum (9.1.6), the relations (9.3.5) between these coefficients and derivatives, and finally (9.9.2).

(9.9.4) *Let* $A \subset \mathbf{C}^p$ *be an open set, f a continuous mapping of* A *into a complex Banach space* E, *such that for* $1 \leqslant k \leqslant p$, *and an arbitrary point* $(a_k) \in \mathbf{C}^p$, *the mapping* $z_k \to f(a_1, \ldots, a_{k-1}, z_k, a_{k+1}, \ldots, a_p)$ *is analytic in the open set* $A(a_1, \ldots, a_{k-1}, a_{k+1}, \ldots, a_p) \subset \mathbf{C}$ *if that set is not empty* (notation of (3.20.12)). *Then f is analytic in* A. *More precisely, let* $a = (a_k)$ *be a point of* A, P *a closed polydisk of center a and radii* r_k $(1 \leqslant k \leqslant p)$ *contained in* A; *for each k, let* γ_k *be the circuit* $t \to a_k + r_k e^{it}$ *in* $\mathbf{C}$ $(0 \leqslant t \leqslant 2\pi)$, *and let*

$$c_{n_1 n_2 \cdots n_p} = \frac{1}{(2\pi i)^p} \int_{\gamma_1} dx_1 \int_{\gamma_2} dx_2 \cdots \int_{\gamma_p} \frac{f(x_1, \ldots, x_p)\, dx_p}{(x_1 - a_1)^{n_1+1} \cdots (x_p - a_p)^{n_p+1}}$$

Then the power series $(c_\nu(z-a)^\nu)$ *is absolutely summable in* $\mathring{\mathrm{P}}$ *and its sum is equal to* $f(z)$.

Using Cauchy's formula, and the fact that $j(0;\varepsilon_1)=1$ (see (9.8.4)), we have, by induction on $p-k$ and the assumption,

(9.9.4.1) $f(x_1, \ldots, x_k, z_{k+1}, \ldots, z_p)$

$$= \frac{1}{(2\pi i)^{p-k}} \int_{\gamma_{k+1}} dx_{k+1} \int_{\gamma_{k+2}} dx_{k+2} \cdots \int_{\gamma_p} \frac{f(x_1, \ldots, x_p)\, dx_p}{(x_{k+1}-z_{k+1}) \cdots (x_p - z_p)}$$

for $|x_j - a_j| = r_j$ $(1 \leqslant j \leqslant k)$ and $|z_j - a_j| < r_j$ $(k+1 \leqslant j \leqslant p)$. On the other hand, for $|z_k - a_k| < r_k$ $(1 \leqslant k \leqslant p)$, we can write, for $|x_k - a_k| = r_k$

$$\frac{1}{(x_1 - z_1)\cdots(x_p - z_p)} = \sum \frac{(z_1 - a_1)^{n_1} \cdots (z_p - a_p)^{n_p}}{(x_1 - a_1)^{n_1+1} \cdots (x_p - a_p)^{n_p+1}}$$

the power series on the right hand side being normally summable in the set F defined by $|x_k - a_k| = r_k$ $(1 \leqslant k \leqslant p)$, by (5.5.3). By induction on $p-k$, if we write

$g_{n_{k+1} \cdots n_p}(x_1, \ldots, x_k)$

$$= \frac{1}{(2\pi i)^{p-k}} \int_{\gamma_{k+1}} dx_{k+1} \cdots \int_{\gamma_p} \frac{f(x_1, \ldots, x_p)\, dx_p}{(x_{k+1} - a_{k+1})^{n_{k+1}+1} \cdots (x_p - a_p)^{n_p+1}}$$

we have by the mean value theorem

(9.9.4.2) $$\|g_{n_{k+1} \cdots n_p}(x_1, \ldots, x_k)\| \leqslant \frac{\mathrm{M}}{r_{k+1}^{n_{k+1}} \cdots r_p^{n_p}}$$

if $\|f(x_1, \ldots, x_p)\| \leqslant \mathrm{M}$ on F. It follows that the power series $(g_{n_{k+1} \cdots n_p}(x_1, \ldots, x_k)(z_{k+1} - a_{k+1})^{n_{k+1}} \cdots (z_p - a_p)^{n_p})$ in the $z_j - a_j$ is absolutely summable in $\mathring{\mathrm{P}}$; using induction on $p-k$, and applying (5.3.5) and (8.7.9), we see that the sum of that series is $f(x_1, \ldots, x_k, z_{k+1}, \ldots, z_p)$. The conclusion follows by taking $k=0$. Moreover (9.9.4.2), for $k=0$, proves that, with the same assumptions and notations as in (9.9.4)

(9.9.5) $$\|c_{n_1 n_2 \cdots n_p}\| \leqslant \mathrm{M}/r_1^{n_1} \cdots r_p^{n_p}$$

if $\|f(x)\| \leqslant \mathrm{M}$ *on the product of the circles* $|x_k - a_k| = r_k$ $(1 \leqslant k \leqslant p)$ *(Cauchy's inequalities).*

If in (9.9.4) we take $\mathrm{A} = \mathbf{C}^p$, we see that

(9.9.6) *An analytic mapping of* $\mathbf{C}^p$ *into a complex Banach space is an entire function.*

Observe that this last result is not true for analytic functions of *real* variables ($1/(1+x^2)$ is a counterexample). Also, a continuous function $f(x, y)$ of two *real* variables may be analytic in each of the variables without being analytic in $\mathbf{R}^2$; an example is given by $f(x, y) = xy^2/(x^2+y^2)$ for $(x, y) \neq (0, 0), f(0, 0) = 0$.

Remark. It follows from (9.9.4) that the set F, product of the circles $|x_k - a_k| = r_k$ $(1 \leqslant k \leqslant p)$ is a *set of uniqueness* in A (when A is connected); for the power series $(c_\nu(z-a)^\nu)$ is entirely determined by the values of f on F, hence if two analytic functions in A coincide in F, they coincide in P, and the result follows from (9.4.2).

PROBLEMS

1. Let A be a relatively compact open connected set in $\mathbf{C}$. Let φ be a continuous mapping of $[a, b] \times [0, 1]$ into $\bar{A}$ such that $t \to \varphi(t, \xi) = \gamma_\xi(t)$ is a circuit contained in A for $0 < \xi \leqslant 1$, and $t \to \gamma_0(t) = \varphi(t, 0)$ is a circuit contained in $\bar{A}$ (which may contain frontier points of A). Suppose in addition that for every $\varepsilon > 0$, there exists $\delta > 0$ such that the relation $|\lambda - \mu| \leqslant \delta$ implies $|\gamma_\lambda'(t) - \gamma_\mu'(t)| \leqslant \varepsilon$ for $t \in [a, b] - D$, where D is a denumerable subset.

   Let now f be a continuous mapping of $\bar{A}$ into a complex Banach space E, such that its restriction to A is analytic. Show that Cauchy's theorem $\int_{\gamma_0} f(z)\,dz = \int_{\gamma_1} f(z)\,dz$ still holds (use (8.7.8)).
2. Let A be an open subset of $\mathbf{C}$, f a continuous mapping of A into a complex Banach space E, such that f is analytic in $A \cap D_+$ and $A \cap D_-$, where D_+ (resp D_-) is defined by $\mathscr{I}(z) > 0$ (resp $\mathscr{I}(z) < 0$). Show that f is analytic in A. (Suppose the disk $|z| \leqslant r$ is contained in A. Let γ_+ (resp. γ_-) be the circuit defined in $[-1, +1]$ by $\gamma_+(t) = (2t+1)r$ for $-1 \leqslant t \leqslant 0$, $\gamma_+(t) = re^{\pi it}$ for $0 \leqslant t \leqslant 1$ (resp. $\gamma_-(t) = re^{\pi it}$ for $-1 \leqslant t \leqslant 0$, $\gamma_-(t) = (1-2t)r$ for $0 \leqslant t \leqslant 1$.) Show that if $|z| < r$ and $\mathscr{I}(z) > 0$, then

$$f(z) = \frac{1}{2\pi i}\int_{\gamma_+} \frac{f(x)\,dx}{x-z}, \qquad 0 = \frac{1}{2\pi i}\int_{\gamma_-} \frac{f(x)\,dx}{x-z}$$

   using Problem 1; hence if γ is the circuit $t \to re^{\pi it}$ in $[-1, +1]$,

$$f(z) = \frac{1}{2\pi i}\int_{\gamma} \frac{f(x)\,dx}{x-z}.$$

   Then use (9.9.2).)
3. Show that the conclusion of (9.9.4) still holds when f is merely assumed to be bounded in each bounded polydisk contained in A, but not necessarily continuous. (Use Problem 6 of Section 8.9; actually, a deep theorem of Hartogs shows that even this weakened assumption is not necessary; in other words, a function which is analytic separately with respect to each of the p complex variables z_i is analytic in A.)

4. Let $f(z) = \sum_{n=0}^{\infty} a_n z^n$ be an analytic complex-valued function in the circle $|z| < \mathrm{R}$. Show that, for $0 \leqslant r < \mathrm{R}$

$$\mathrm{M}_2^2(r; f) = \frac{1}{2\pi} \int_0^{2\pi} |f(re^{it})|^2 \, dt = \sum_{n=0}^{\infty} |a_n|^2 r^{2n}.$$

Deduce from that result another proof of Cauchy's inequalities.

5. Let $f(z) = \sum_{n=0}^{\infty} a_n z^n$ be an analytic function in $|z| < \mathrm{R}$, and let

$$\mathrm{M}_1(r; f) = \sum_{n=0}^{\infty} \|a_n\| r^n.$$

Let also $\mathrm{M}(r; f) = \sup_{|z|=r} \|f(z)\|$.

(a) Show that for $0 \leqslant r < r + \delta < \mathrm{R}$

$$\mathrm{M}(r; f) \leqslant \mathrm{M}_1(r; f) \leqslant \frac{r+\delta}{\delta} \mathrm{M}(r+\delta; f)$$

(use Cauchy's inequalities).

(b) If in addition, f is complex valued, show that (with the notations of Problem 4)

$$\frac{(\delta(2r+\delta))^{1/2}}{r+\delta} \mathrm{M}_1(r; f) \leqslant \mathrm{M}_2(r+\delta; f) \leqslant \mathrm{M}(r+\delta; f).$$

(Use the Cauchy–Schwarz inequality (6.2.1).)

(c) Under the same assumption, show that

$$\lim_{n\to\infty} (\mathrm{M}_1(r; f^n))^{1/n} = \lim_{n\to\infty} (\mathrm{M}_2(r; f^n))^{1/n} = \mathrm{M}(r; f)$$

(use the inequalities proved in (a) and (b), the fact that $\mathrm{M}(r; f^n) = (\mathrm{M}(r; f))^n$, and the continuity of $r \to \mathrm{M}(r; f)$).

6. Suppose the power series in one complex variable $(c_n z^n)$, with complex coefficients, is convergent for $|z| < \mathrm{R}$, and let $f(z) = \sum_n c_n z^n$. For any r such that $0 < r < \mathrm{R}$, let $\mathrm{A}(r) = \sup_{|z|=r} \mathscr{R}(f(z))$. Show that, for every $n \geqslant 0$

$$|c_n| r^n + 2\mathscr{R}(f(0)) \leqslant \sup(4\mathrm{A}(r), 0).$$

(Prove that

$$|c_n| r^n = \frac{1}{\pi} \left| \int_0^{2\pi} (\mathscr{R}(f(re^{i\theta})))e^{-ni\theta} \, d\theta \right|$$

for $n > 0$.)

7. (a) Let A be an open subset of K^p, and f an indefinitely differentiable mapping of A into a Banach space E. In order that f be analytic in A, it is necessary and sufficient that for every compact subset L of A, there exist an integer $r \geqslant 0$ and a number $a > 0$ such that, for any index $\boldsymbol{\alpha} = (\alpha_1, \ldots, \alpha_p)$, $\sup_{x \in \mathrm{L}} \|\mathrm{D}^{\boldsymbol{\alpha}} f(x)\| \leqslant a(|\boldsymbol{\alpha}| + r)!$. (To prove that the condition is necessary when $\mathbf{K} = \mathbf{C}$, apply Cauchy's inequalities to balls of fixed radius contained in A and having their centers in L; when $\mathbf{K} = \mathbf{R}$, use (9.4.5); to prove that the condition is sufficient, use Taylor's formula (8.14.3) and prove that the last term of that formula tends to 0 uniformly in any closed ball contained in A and of center x.)

(b) Give an example of an indefinitely differentiable function in **R** which is not analytic (cf. Section 8.12, Problem 2).
(c) Suppose f is real valued and indefinitely differentiable in an open interval $\mathrm{I} \subset \mathbf{R}$; in addition, suppose that there is an integer $p \geqslant 0$ such that $f^{(n)}$ does not vanish at more than p points of I, for any $n > 0$. Show that f is analytic in I. (Use (a), and Problem 3(b) of Section 8.12).

10. CHARACTERIZATION OF ANALYTIC FUNCTIONS OF COMPLEX VARIABLES

(9.10.1) *A continuously differentiable mapping f of an open subset* A *of* $\mathbf{C}^p$ *into a complex Banach space is analytic.*

Applying (9.9.4), we are immediately reduced to the case $p = 1$. To prove f is analytic at a point $a \in \mathrm{A}$, we may, by translation and homothetic mapping, suppose that $a = 0$ and that A contains the unit ball B: $|z| \leqslant 1$. For any $z \in \mathring{\mathrm{B}}$, and any λ such that $0 \leqslant \lambda \leqslant 1$, note that $|(1-\lambda)z + \lambda e^{it}| \leqslant 1 - \lambda + \lambda = 1$, and consider the integral

$$g(\lambda) = \int_0^{2\pi} \frac{f(z + \lambda(e^{it} - z)) - f(z)}{e^{it} - z} e^{it}\, dt. \tag{9.10.1.1}$$

By (8.11.1) and Leibniz's rule (8.11.2), g is continuous in $[0, 1]$ and has at each point of $]0, 1[$ a derivative equal to

$$g'(\lambda) = \int_0^{2\pi} f'(z + \lambda(e^{it} - z))e^{it}\, dt$$

(see *Remarks* after (8.4.1)). But $i\lambda f'(z + \lambda(e^{it} - z))e^{it}$ is the derivative of $t \to f(z + \lambda(e^{it} - z))$, hence, for $\lambda \neq 0$, $g'(\lambda) = 0$, and therefore (remark following (8.6.1)), g is *constant* in $[0, 1]$. But as $g(0) = 0$, $g(\lambda) = 0$ for $0 \leqslant \lambda \leqslant 1$. In particular, it follows, for $\lambda = 1$, that

$$f(z) = \frac{1}{2\pi i} \int_{\varepsilon_1} \frac{f(x)\, dx}{x - z}$$

for any $z \in \mathring{\mathrm{B}}$ (by (9.8.4)), and the conclusion follows from (9.9.2).

(9.10.2) *Let f be a continuously differentiable mapping of an open set* $\mathrm{A} \subset \mathbf{R}^{2p}$ *into a complex Banach space. In order that the function g defined in* A (considered as a subset of $\mathbf{C}^p$), *by* $f(x_1, x_2, \ldots, x_p, y_1, \ldots, y_p) = g(x_1 + iy_1, \ldots, x_p + iy_p)$ *be analytic in* A, *necessary and sufficient conditions are that*

$$\frac{\partial f}{\partial x_k} + i \frac{\partial f}{\partial y_k} = 0$$

in A *for* $1 \leqslant k \leqslant p$ (Cauchy's conditions).

We are again at once reduced to the case $p = 1$ by (8.9.1). Let (x, y) be a point of A, and put $a = \frac{\partial f}{\partial x}(x, y)$, $b = \frac{\partial f}{\partial y}(x, y)$; expressing that the limits $\lim_{h \to 0} (g(x + iy + h) - g(x + iy))/h$ and $\lim_{h \to 0} (g(x + iy + ih) - g(x + iy))/ih$ (h real and $\neq 0$) are the same, we obtain $a + ib = 0$. Conversely, if that condition is satisfied, for any $\varepsilon > 0$, there is $r > 0$ such that if $(h^2 + k^2)^{1/2} \leqslant r$, $\|g(x + iy + h + ik) - g(x + iy) - a(h + ik)\| \leqslant \varepsilon(h^2 + k^2)^{1/2}$ by (8.9.1.1) and this proves that $z \to g(z)$ has a derivative equal to a at the point $z = x + iy$. The result then follows from (9.10.1).

PROBLEMS

1. Show that a *differentiable* mapping of f an open subset A of $\mathbf{C}^p$ into a complex Banach space is analytic in A ("Goursat's theorem"; f' is not supposed to be continuous). (Given any λ in $]0, 1[$, prove (with the notations of (9.10.1)) that $g'(\lambda)$ exists and is equal to 0. First show that, given $\varepsilon > 0$, there are points $t_0 = 0 < t_1 < \cdots < t_m = 2\pi$, a number $\rho > 0$, and in each interval $[t_k, t_{k+1}]$ a point θ_k such that, if $\zeta_k = z + \lambda(e^{i\theta_k} - z)$, $\zeta_k + x = z + (\lambda + h)(e^{it} - z)$, then $|f(\zeta_k + x) - f(\zeta_k) - f'(\zeta_k)x| \leqslant \varepsilon|x|$ whenever $|h| \leqslant \rho$ and $t_k \leqslant t \leqslant t_{k+1}$ (prove this by contradiction, using a compactness argument and the existence of f' at each point). Compare then each integral

$$\int_{t_k}^{t_{k+1}} \frac{f(z + (\lambda + h)(e^{it} - z)) - f(z + \lambda(e^{it} - z))}{e^{it} - z} e^{it}\, dt$$

to the expression

$$\frac{h}{i\lambda}(f(z + \lambda(e^{it_{k+1}} - z)) - f(z + \lambda(e^{it_k} - z)))$$

for $|h| \leqslant \rho$.)
2. Let A be an open simply connected subset of $\mathbf{C}$; if f is a continuous mapping of into a complex Banach space E such that $\int_\gamma f(z)\, dz = 0$ for any circuit γ in A, show that f is analytic in A. ("Morera's theorem"; show that f has a primitive in A.)
3. Let A be an open subset of $\mathbf{C}^p$, γ a road defined in $\mathrm{I} = [a, b]$, f a continuous mapping of $\gamma(\mathrm{I}) \times \mathrm{A}$ into a complex Banach space E. Suppose that for each $x \in \gamma(\mathrm{I})$, the function $(z_1, \ldots, z_p) \to f(x, z_1, \ldots, z_p)$ is analytic in A, and that each of the functions $\frac{\partial f}{\partial z_k}(x, z_1, \ldots, z_p)$ is continuous in $\gamma(\mathrm{I}) \times \mathrm{A}$ $(1 \leqslant k \leqslant p)$. Show that under these conditions, the functions $g(z_1, \ldots, z_p) = \int_\gamma f(x, z_1, \ldots, z_p)\, dx$ is analytic in A. (Use (9.10.2). As $\gamma'(t)$ is merely a regulated function and may fail to be continuous, Leibniz's rule (8.11.2) is not directly applicable, but the proof of (8.11.2) subsists with minor modifications.)
4. Let A be an open connected subset of $\mathbf{R}^p$ $(p \geqslant 2)$, f an analytic mapping of A into a *complex* Banach space E. Suppose that there is an open polydisk $\mathrm{P} \subset \mathrm{A}$, of center $b = (b_k)_{1 \leqslant k \leqslant p}$ and radii r_k $(1 \leqslant k \leqslant p)$ such that for every point (c_k) of P, there is a

number $\rho < \inf(r_1, r_2)$ such that the function $x_1 + ix_2 \to f(x_1, x_2, c_3, \ldots, c_p)$ is analytic in the open subset $|x_1 + ix_2 - (c_1 + ic_2)| < \rho$ of $\mathbf{C}$ (identified to $\mathbf{R}^2$). Show that the same property holds for every point $(c_k) \in A$ (use (9.10.2) and (9.4.2)).

5. Let S be the "shell" in $\mathbf{R}^p$ ($p \geqslant 3$) defined by

$$(R - \varepsilon)^2 < x_1^2 + x_2^2 + \cdots + x_p^2 < (R + \varepsilon)^2 \qquad (0 < \varepsilon < R).$$

Suppose f is an analytic mapping of S into a *complex* Banach space E, and suppose that for any $u = (x_3, \ldots, x_p)$, the mapping $x_1 + ix_2 \to f(x_1, x_2, u)$ is analytic in a neighborhood (in $\mathbf{C}$) of every point of the cross section $S(u)$ (if $S(u)$ is not empty).
(a) For any $u = (x_3, \ldots, x_p)$ such that $\|u\|^2 = x_3^2 + \cdots + x_p^2 < R^2$, let $\gamma(u)$ be the road in $\mathbf{C}$ defined by $t \to (R^2 - \|u\|^2)^{1/2} e^{it}$ for $-\pi \leqslant t \leqslant \pi$. Let

$$g(z, u) = \frac{1}{2\pi i} \int_{\gamma(u)} \frac{f(y, u)\, dy}{y - z}$$

where $y = x_1 + ix_2$, and $f(y, u) = f(x_1, x_2, u)$; g is defined for $|z|^2 + \|u\|^2 < R^2$, and $z \to g(z, u)$ is analytic for $|z| < (R^2 - \|u\|^2)^{1/2}$. On the other hand, for any $v = (x_3', \ldots, x_p')$ such that $\|v\| < R$, let

$$h_v(z, u) = \frac{1}{2\pi i} \int_{\gamma(v)} \frac{f(y, u)\, dy}{y - z}.$$

Show that $h_v(z, u) = g(z, u)$ for $\|v\| < \|u\| < \|v\| + \varepsilon$ and $|z| < (R^2 - \|v\|^2)^{1/2}$ (apply Cauchy's theorem (9.6.3)). On the other hand, show that $g(z, u) = f(z, u)$ for $R - \varepsilon < \|u\| < R$ and $|z| < (R^2 - \|u\|^2)^{1/2}$. Conclude that f can be extended to a function $\tilde{f}$ which is analytic in the *whole ball* B: $x_1^2 + \cdots + x_p^2 < (R + \varepsilon)^2$ (apply (9.4.2) and Problem 3). Is the theorem still true for $p = 2$?
(b) When $E = \mathbf{C}$, show that $\tilde{f}(B) \subset f(S)$. (Apply the result of (a) to the function $1/(f - c)$, where $c \notin f(S)$.) In particular, if f is bounded in S, $\tilde{f}$ is bounded in B. Extend that last property to the case in which E is a complex Hilbert space (method of Problem 6 of Section 8.5).

11. LIOUVILLE'S THEOREM

(9.11.1) (Liouville's theorem) *Let f be an entire function in $\mathbf{C}^p$, with values in a complex Banach space* E. *Suppose there exists two numbers $a > 0$, $N > 0$ such that $\|f(z)\| \leqslant a(1 + (\sup |z_j|)^N)$ in $\mathbf{C}^p$. Then $f(z)$ is the sum of a finite number of "monomials" $c_{n_1 n_2 \cdots n_p} z_1^{n_1} \ldots z_p^{n_p}$ with $c_{n_1 \cdots n_p} \in E$ and*

$$n_1 + n_2 + \cdots + n_p \leqslant N.$$

Let $f(z) = \sum_\nu c_\nu z^\nu$ in $\mathbf{C}^p$, the power series being everywhere absolutely convergent. The Cauchy inequalities (9.9.5) applied to the polydisk $|z_j| \leqslant R$ $(1 \leqslant j \leqslant p)$ yields, for any $\nu = (n_1, \ldots, n_p)$

$$\|c_{n_1 \cdots n_p}\| \leqslant a \cdot (1 + R)^N R^{-(n_1 + \cdots + n_p)}.$$

Letting R tend to $+\infty$, we see that $c_{n_1 \cdots n_p} = 0$, unless $n_1 + \cdots + n_p \leqslant N$.

(9.11.2) (The "fundamental theorem of algebra"). *Any polynomial* $f(z) = a_0 z^n + a_1 z^{n-1} + \cdots + a_n$ $(a_0 \neq 0, n \geqslant 1)$ *with complex coefficients has at least one root in* **C**.

Otherwise, $1/f$ would be analytic in **C** (9.3.2), hence an entire function (9.9.6). Let r be a real number such that $r^k \geqslant (n+1)|a_k/a_0|$ for $1 \leqslant k \leqslant n$; then, for $|z| \geqslant r$

$$|f(z)| = |a_0 z^n| \cdot \left|1 + \frac{a_1}{a_0 z} + \cdots + \frac{a_n}{a_0 z^n}\right|$$

$$\geqslant |a_0 z^n| \left(1 - \frac{n}{n+1}\right) \geqslant |a_0| r^n/(n+1).$$

In other words, $1/f$ is bounded for $|z| \geqslant r$. On the other hand, $1/f$ being continuous in the compact set $|z| \leqslant r$, is also bounded in that set (3.17.10), hence $1/f$ is bounded in **C**. Liouville's theorem then implies $1/f$ is a constant, hence also f, contrary to assumption since $|f(z)| \geqslant |a_0| \cdot |z|^n/(n+1)$ for $|z| \geqslant r$.

PROBLEMS

1. If $p \geqslant 2$, show that a function which is analytic in the complement of a compact subset of $\mathbf{C}^p$ is an entire function; hence if in addition it is bounded in the complement of a compact subset of $\mathbf{C}^p$, it is a constant (use (9.11.1) and Problems 4 and 5 of Section 9.10). Is the result true for $p = 1$?
2. Let f be a complex valued entire function in $\mathbf{C}^p$. Show that the conclusion of (9.11.1) is still valid if it is supposed that

$$\mathscr{R}(f(z)) \leqslant a \cdot (\sup_j(1, |z_j|)^m)$$

for any z in the exterior of a polydisk of $\mathbf{C}^p$ (use Problem 6 of Section 9.9).
3. Let $f(z) = \sum_{n=0}^{\infty} a_n z^n$ be a nonconstant entire function. For any $r > 0$, let $\mu(r) = \sup_n \|a_n\| r^n$, $\mathrm{M}(r) = \sup_{|z|=r} \|f(z)\|$, so that $\mu(r) \leqslant \mathrm{M}(r)$; by Liouville's theorem, $\lim_{r \to \infty} \mu(r) = +\infty$. Suppose there are two constants $a > 0$, $\alpha > 0$ such that $\mu(r) \leqslant a \cdot \exp(r^\alpha)$; show that there are positive constants b, c such that $\mathrm{M}(r) \leqslant b r^\alpha \mu(r) + c$. (Observe that $\|a_n\| \leqslant a(e\alpha/n)^{n/\alpha}$.)

12. CONVERGENT SEQUENCES OF ANALYTIC FUNCTIONS

(9.12.1) *Let* (f_n) *be a sequence of analytic mappings of an open set* $\mathrm{A} \subset \mathbf{C}^p$ *into a complex Banach space* E. *Suppose that for each* $z \in \mathrm{A}$, *the sequence* $(f_n(z))$ *tends to a limit* $g(z)$, *and that the convergence is uniform in every compact subset of* A. *Then g is analytic in* A, *and for each* $\nu = (n_1, \ldots, n_p) \in \mathbf{N}^p$, *the sequence* $(\mathrm{D}^\nu f_n(z))$ *converges to* $\mathrm{D}^\nu g(z)$ *for each* $z \in \mathrm{A}$, *the convergence being uniform in every compact subset of* A.

As g is continuous in A (7.2.1), to prove g is analytic in A, we need only prove that each mapping $z_k \to g(a_1, \ldots, z_k, \ldots, a_p)$ is analytic in $\mathrm{A}(a_1, \ldots, a_{k-1}, a_{k+1}, \ldots, a_p)$, by (9.9.4); in other words we are reduced to the case $p = 1$. For each $a \in \mathrm{A} \subset \mathbf{C}$, let B be a closed ball of center a and radius r contained in A, and let γ be the circuit $t \to a + re^{it}$ $(0 \leqslant t \leqslant 2\pi)$; then, for each $z \in \mathring{\mathrm{B}}$ and each n, we have by Cauchy's formula

$$f_n(z) = \frac{1}{2\pi i} \int_\gamma \frac{f_n(x)}{x - z}\, dx.$$

But by assumption the sequence $(f_n(x))$ converges uniformly to $g(x)$ for $|x - a| = r$, and as $|z - x| \geqslant r - |z|$, the sequence $(f_n(x)/(x - z))$ (z fixed) also converges uniformly to $g(x)/(x - z)$ for $|x - a| = r$; hence, by (8.7.8)

$$g(z) = \frac{1}{2\pi i} \int_\gamma \frac{g(x)\, dx}{x - z},$$

which proves g is analytic in $\mathring{\mathrm{B}}$ by (9.9.2). Moreover, as

$$f_n'(z) = \frac{1}{2\pi i} \int_\gamma \frac{f_n(x)\, dx}{(x - z)^2}$$

by (9.9.3), the same argument (and (9.9.3) applied to g) shows that $f'(z)$ tends to $g'(z)$ for every $z \in \mathring{\mathrm{B}}$; furthermore, we have by the mean-value theorem

$$\|g'(a) - f_n'(a)\| \leqslant \frac{1}{r} \sup_{|x-a|=r} \|g(x) - f_n(x)\|. \tag{9.12.1.1}$$

Returning to the general case (p arbitrary), let us now show that the sequence $(\mathrm{D}_k f_n(z))$ converges uniformly to $\mathrm{D}_k g(z)$ in any compact set $\mathrm{M} \subset \mathrm{A}$. There is a number $r > 0$ and a compact neighborhood V of M contained in A, and containing all points of A having a distance $\leqslant r$ to M (3.18.2). For any $\varepsilon > 0$, let n_0 be such that $\|g(z) - f_n(z)\| \leqslant \varepsilon$ for every $n \geqslant n_0$ and every $z \in \mathrm{V}$. Then, applying (9.12.1.1) to the sequence of functions $z_k \to f_n(a_1, \ldots, a_{k-1}, z_k, a_{k+1}, \ldots, a_p)$, we obtain, for every point $z \in \mathrm{M}$, $\|\mathrm{D}_k g(z) - \mathrm{D}_k f_n(z)\| \leqslant \varepsilon/r$ as soon as $n \geqslant n_0$. This ends the proof of the theorem when $n_1 + \cdots + n_p = 1$; the general case is then proved by induction on $n_1 + \cdots + n_p$.

Observe again here that the theorem does not hold for analytic functions of *real* variables, since a sequence of polynomials can have as a limit an *arbitrary* (e.g. nondifferentiable) continuous function in a compact set, by the Weierstrass approximation theorem (7.4.1).

PROBLEMS

1. (a) Let $(a_k)_{1 \leqslant k \leqslant p}$ be a finite sequence of complex numbers, such that $\sum_{k=1}^{p} |a_k| = \alpha < 1$. Show that

$$\left| \prod_{k=1}^{p} (1 + a_k) - 1 - \sum_{k=1}^{p} a_k \right| \leqslant \frac{\alpha^2}{1 - \alpha}.$$

(b) The entire functions

$$E(z, 0) = 1 - z, \qquad E(z, p) = (1 - z) \exp\left(z + \frac{z^2}{2} + \cdots + \frac{z^p}{p} \right)$$

are called *primary factors*; show that, for $|z| \leqslant 1/2$

$$|E(z, p) - 1| \leqslant 4|z|^{p+1}.$$

(Observe that for $|z| \leqslant \frac{1}{2}$

$$\left| \log(1 - z) + z + \frac{z^2}{2} + \cdots + \frac{z^p}{p} \right| \leqslant 2|z|^{p+1}/(p + 1)$$

and that for $|z| \leqslant 1$, $|e^z - 1| \leqslant 2|z|$.)

(c) Let (a_n) be an infinite sequence of complex numbers $\neq 0$, such that the sequence $(|a_n|)$ is increasing and $\lim_{n \to \infty} |a_n| = +\infty$. Show that for any $z \in \mathbf{C}$, the series of general term $(z/a_n)^n$ is absolutely convergent.

(d) Deduce from (a), (b), and (c) that the sequence of entire functions

$$p_n(z) = \prod_{k=1}^{n} E\left(\frac{z}{a_k}, k - 1 \right)$$

is uniformly convergent in every compact subset of $\mathbf{C}$ (apply Cauchy's criterion, and evaluate the difference $1 - (p_m(z)/p_n(z))$ for $m > n$ by using (a) and (b); then apply (c)). The limit $f(z)$ of the sequence $(p_n(z))$ is thus an entire function, which is written

$$f(z) = \prod_{n=1}^{\infty} E\left(\frac{z}{a_n}, n - 1 \right);$$

show that the only points where $f(z) = 0$ are the points a_n (use the preceding estimate).

(e) Suppose that there is an integer $p > 0$ such that the series of general term $|a_n|^{-p}$ is convergent. Show similarly that the sequence of entire functions

$$q_n(z) = \prod_{k=1}^{n} E\left(\frac{z}{a_n}, p - 1 \right)$$

is uniformly convergent in every compact subset of $\mathbf{C}$; its limit is again written

$$g(z) = \prod_{n=1}^{\infty} \mathrm{E}\left(\frac{z}{a_n}, p-1\right).$$

Prove that there is a constant $c > 0$ such that

$$|g(z)| \leqslant \exp(c\,|z|^p).$$

(For any given z, consider separately the product of the factors for which $|a_n| \geqslant 2\,|z|$, and of the other factors; use (b) to majorize the first product; on the other hand, prove that there is a constant b such that $|\mathrm{E}(z, p-1)| \leqslant \exp(b\,|z|^{p-1})$ for any $z \in \mathbf{C}$.)

2. Show that the sequence of entire functions

$$f_n(z) = z(z+1)\cdots(z+n)/n^z\, n! \tag{1}$$

(where $n^z = \exp(z \log n)$ by definition) is uniformly convergent in every compact subset of $\mathbf{C}$ to the entire function

$$\frac{1}{\Gamma(z)} = z e^{\gamma z} \prod_{n=1}^{\infty} \left(1 + \frac{z}{n}\right) e^{-z/n} \tag{2}$$

where $\gamma = \lim_{n\to\infty} \left(1 + \frac{1}{2} + \cdots + \frac{1}{n} - \log n\right)$ ("Euler's constant"). (Use the result of Problem 1(e), writing $\log n = \sum_{k=2}^{n} \log(k/(k-1))$ to compare (1) and (2), and using the mean value theorem to majorize $\left|\frac{1}{k} - \log\frac{k}{k-1}\right|$.)

Prove that $\Gamma(z)$ satisfies the functional equation

$$\Gamma(z+1) = z\Gamma(z)$$

when z is not an integer $-n \leqslant 0$, and that $\Gamma(n) = (n-1)!$ for n integer and >0.

3. An *endless road* in an open subset $\mathrm{A} \subset \mathbf{C}$ is a continuous mapping γ of $\mathbf{R}$ into A such that in every compact interval $\mathrm{I} \subset \mathbf{R}$, γ is the primitive of a regulated function. If f is a continuous mapping of $\gamma(\mathbf{R})$ into a complex Banach space E, f is said to be *improperly integrable* along γ if the improper integral $\int_{-\infty}^{\infty} f(\gamma(t))\gamma'(t)\,dt$ exists (i.e., if both limits $\lim_{b\to+\infty} \int_0^b f(\gamma(t))\gamma'(t)\,dt$ and $\lim_{a\to-\infty} \int_a^0 f(\gamma(t))\gamma'(t)\,dt$ exist in E); the value of that integral is then callled the *integral of f along* γ and written $\int_\gamma f(z)\,dz$.

Let B be an open subset of $\mathbf{C}^p$, g a continuous mapping of $\gamma(\mathbf{R}) \times \mathrm{B}$ into E; suppose that for each $x \in \gamma(\mathbf{R})$, the function $(z_1, \ldots, z_p) \to g(x, z_1, \ldots, z_p)$ is analytic in B and that each of the functions $\frac{\partial g}{\partial z_k}(x, z_1, \ldots, z_p)$ is continuous in $\gamma(\mathbf{R}) \times \mathrm{B}$. Finally suppose that for each $(z_1, \ldots, z_p) \in \mathrm{B}$, $x \to g(x, z_1, \ldots, z_p)$ is improperly integrable along γ, and that $\int_{-n}^{n} g(\gamma(t), z_1, \ldots, z_p)\gamma'(t)\,dt$ tends uniformly to $\int_\gamma g(x, z_1, \ldots, z_p)\,dx$ when $(z_1, \ldots, z_p)$ remains in a compact subset of B and n tends to $+\infty$. Under these conditions, show that the function $(z_1, \ldots, z_p) \to \int_\gamma g(x, z_1, \ldots, z_p)\,dx$ is analytic in B (compare to (13.8.6)).

4. Extend the result of Problem 2 of Section 9.9 to functions of p complex variables, D_+ (resp. D_-) being defined by $\mathscr{I}(z_p) > 0$ (resp. $\mathscr{I}(z_p) < 0$). (Observe that, by (9.12.1), for each z_p such that $\mathscr{I}(z_p) = 0$ and the intersection B of A with the set $\mathbf{C}^{p-1} \times \{z_p\}$ is not empty, the function $(z_1, \ldots, z_{p-1}) \to f(z_1, \ldots, z_{p-1}, z_p)$ is analytic in B.)

5. In the plane $\mathbf{C}$, let Q be the square of center 0, defined by $|\mathscr{R}(z)| < 1$, $|\mathscr{I}(z)| < 1$. Let Q_0, Q_1, Q_2, Q_3 be the images of Q by the mappings

$$z \to \frac{1+i}{2} + \frac{z}{2}, \quad z \to \frac{-1+i}{2} + \frac{z}{2}, \quad z \to \frac{-1-i}{2} + \frac{z}{2}, \quad z \to \frac{1-i}{2} + \frac{z}{2}.$$

Let $m_0 = 0$, and for any $h \geqslant 1$, let $m_h = 4 + 4^2 + \cdots + 4^h$; if $n = m_h + 4k + j$, with $h \geqslant 1$, $0 \leqslant k \leqslant 4^h - 1$, $0 \leqslant j \leqslant 3$, define inductively Q_n as follows: let $n_1 = m_{h-1} + k$, and let z_{n_1} be the center of Q_{n_1}; let $\varphi_{n_1}(z) = z_{n_1} + z/2^h$ and take $Q_n = \varphi_{n_1}(Q)$.
(a) Let B be the unit disk $|z| \leqslant 1$, U the unit circle $|z| = 1$. Show by induction on n the existence of three sequence of numbers (α_n), (c_n), (t_n) defined for $n \geqslant 4$, having the following properties:

(1) $0 < \alpha_n < 1$, $|t_n| = 1$, $c_n \in \mathbf{C}$;

(2) if $g_n(z) = c_n\left(1 - \left(1 - \frac{z}{t_n}\right)^{\alpha_n}\right)$ (definition in Section 9.5, Problem 8) for $z \in \mathrm{B}$, and $f_n(z) = z + \sum_{q=4}^{n} g_q(z)$, then $f_n(\mathrm{B}) \subset \overline{\mathrm{Q}}$ and $f_n(t_k) \in \mathrm{Q}_k$ for $k \leqslant n$;

(3) the series $\sum_n |c_n|$ is convergent.

(Observe that $g_n(t_n) = c_n$, but that, given any neighborhood V_n of t_n in B, it is possible to take α_n small enough so that $g_n(z)$ will be arbitrarily small in $\mathrm{B} - \mathrm{V}_n$. Choose t_n close to t_{n_1} (with the notations introduced above), the t_n being all distinct, and take V_n so that it contains no t_k with $k < n$.)
(b) Under the preceding conditions, the limit $f(z)$ of $(f_n(z))$ exists for any $z \in \mathrm{B}$, f is continuous in B, and analytic in $\mathring{\mathrm{B}}$, and $f(\mathrm{U}) = \mathrm{Q}$ ("Peano curve," cf. Section 4.2, Problem 5).

13. EQUICONTINUOUS SETS OF ANALYTIC FUNCTIONS

(9.13.1) *Let* A *be an open set in* $\mathbf{C}^p$, Φ *a set of analytic mappings of* A *into a complex Banach space* E. *Suppose for each compact subset* L *of* A, *there is a constant* $m_{\mathrm{L}} > 0$ *such that* $\|f(z)\| \leqslant m_{\mathrm{L}}$ *for all* $f \in \Phi$ *and every* $z \in \mathrm{L}$. *Then* Φ *is equicontinuous in* A (Section 7.5); *if in addition* E *is finite dimensional, then for every compact subset* L *of* A, *the set* Φ_{L} *of restrictions to* L *of the functions* $f \in \Phi$, *is relatively compact in the space* $\mathscr{C}_{\mathrm{E}}(\mathrm{L})$ (Section 7.2).

Let $a \in \mathrm{A}$; there is a closed ball $\mathrm{P} \subset \mathrm{A}$ of center a, radius r, and as P is compact, $\|f(z)\| \leqslant m_{\mathrm{P}}$ for all $z \in \mathrm{P}$ and all $f \in \Phi$. Let Q be the closed ball of center a and radius $r/2$; for any $z \in \mathrm{Q}$ and $f \in \Phi$ we can write

$$f(z) - f(a)$$
$$= \sum_{k=1}^{p} (f(z_1, \ldots, z_k, a_{k+1}, \ldots, a_p) - f(z_1, \ldots, z_{k-1}, a_k, a_{k+1}, \ldots, a_p)).$$

Now

$$f(z_1, \ldots, z_{k-1}, z_k, a_{k+1}, \ldots, a_p) - f(z_1, \ldots, z_{k-1}, a_k, a_{k+1}, \ldots, a_p)$$
$$= \int_0^1 \mathrm{D}_k f(z_1, \ldots, z_{k-1}, a_k + t(z_k - a_k), a_{k+1}, \ldots, a_p)(z_k - a_k)\, dt.$$

Write $g_k(u) = f(z_1, \ldots, z_{k-1}, u, a_{k+1}, \ldots, a_p)$; g_k is analytic in an open set of $\mathbf{C}$ containing the ball $|u - a_k| \leqslant r$, and $\|g_k(u)\| \leqslant m_{\mathrm{P}}$ in that ball. Applying **(9.9.3)** to g_k and to the circuit $t \to a_k + re^{it}$ defined in $[0, 2\pi]$, we obtain

$$\|g_k'(u)\| \leqslant 4m_{\mathrm{P}}/r$$

for $|u - a_k| \leqslant r/2$. Therefore, for any $z \in \mathrm{Q}$, and *any* $f \in \Phi$ we have

$$\|f(z) - f(a)\| \leqslant \frac{4pm_{\mathrm{P}}}{r} |z - a|$$

which shows Φ is equicontinuous at the point a. The last statement of **(9.13.1)** follows from the fact that any bounded set in a finite dimensional space is relatively compact (**(3.17.6)** and **(3.20.17)**), and from Ascoli's theorem **(7.5.7)**.

(9.13.2) *Let* A *be an open connected set in* $\mathbf{C}^p$, Φ *a set of analytic mappings of* A *into a complex Banach space* E. *Suppose for each compact subset* L *of* A, *the set* Φ_{L} *of restrictions to* L *of the functions* $f \in \Phi$ *is relatively compact in* $\mathscr{C}_{\mathrm{E}}(\mathrm{L})$. *If* M *is a set of uniqueness* (Section **9.4**) *in* A, *and if a sequence* (f_n) *of functions of* Φ *converges simply in* M, *then* (f_n) *converges uniformly* (*to an analytic function*) *in any compact subset of* A.

From **(3.16.4)** it follows that we need only prove that, for every compact set $\mathrm{L} \subset \mathrm{A}$, the sequence of the restrictions of the f_n to L has *only one cluster value* in $\mathscr{C}_{\mathrm{E}}(\mathrm{L})$. Suppose the contrary, and let (g_n), (h_n) be two subsequences of (f_n), each of which converges uniformly in L, the limits being distinct. As A is locally compact **(3.18.4)** and separable, there exists an increasing sequence (U_n) of open subsets of A, such that $\overline{\mathrm{U}}_n$ (closure in $\mathbf{C}^p$) be compact and contained in U_{n+1}, and $\mathrm{A} = \bigcup_n \mathrm{U}_n$ **(3.18.3)**. Define by induction on k a sequence $(g_{kn})_{n=1,2,\ldots}$, such that (g_{kn}) is a subsequence of $(g_{k-1,n})$, with $g_{on} = g_n$, and that (g_{kn}) converges uniformly in $\overline{\mathrm{U}}_k$, which is possible by the assumption on Φ. Then the "diagonal" subsequence (g_{nn}) converges uniformly in every U_n, hence, by **(9.12.1)** its limit g is analytic in A. In a similar way it is possible to extract from (h_n) a subsequence (h_{nn}) which converges in A to an analytic function h. Now by assumption $g(z) = h(z)$ for $z \in M$, and by definition, we must have $g = h$. But this contradicts the definition of the subsequences (g_n), (h_n). Q.E.D.

PROBLEM

Let A be an open set in **C**, and let E be the set of all complex functions f analytic in A and such that the integral $\iint_A |f(z)|^2\,dx\,dy$ is finite.

(a) Show that E is a complex vector space, that for any pair f, g of functions in E, the integral $\iint_A f(z)\overline{g(z)}\,dx\,dy$ is finite and that the mapping $(f, g) \to \iint_A f(z)\overline{g(z)}\,dx\,dy$ defines on E a structure of prehilbert space, whose norm is written $\|f\|$.

(b) Show that for any compact subset $L \subset A$, there exists a number a_L such that $|f(t)| \leqslant a_L \|f\|$ for every function $f \in E$ and every $t \in L$ (use Section 9.3, Problem 6). Conclude that E is a *Hilbert* space.

(c) Deduce from (b) and from Section 6.3, Problem 5, that there exists in E a *reproducing kernel*, which is called the *Bergman kernel* of A. Prove that if A is the unit disk $|z| < 1$, the Bergman kernel of A is

$$K_B(s, t) = \frac{1}{\pi(1 - s\bar{t})^2}$$

(use Section 9.3, Problem 6). Compute similarly the Bergman kernel of a ring $r < |z| < 1$.

(d) Generalize to an open subset A of $\mathbf{C}^n$.

14. THE LAURENT SERIES

(9.14.1) *Let* A *be an open subset of* **C**, r_0, r_1 *two numbers such that* $0 < r_0 < r_1$, *and suppose the "open ring"* S *defined by* $r_0 < |r| < r_1$ *is such that its closure* $\bar{S}$ *in* **C** (i.e. *the "closed ring"* $r_0 \leqslant |z| \leqslant r_1$) *is contained in* A. *For any analytic mapping f of* A *into a complex Banach space* E, *we have, for any* $x \in S$

$$f(x) = \frac{1}{2\pi i}\int_{\gamma_1} \frac{f(z)\,dz}{z - x} - \frac{1}{2\pi i}\int_{\gamma_0} \frac{f(z)\,dz}{z - x}$$

where γ_0 (resp. γ_1) *is the circuit* $t \to r_0 e^{it}$ (resp. $t \to r_1 e^{it}$) *with* $0 \leqslant t \leqslant 2\pi$.

As in the proof of (9.9.1), we first see that the function $g(z)$ equal to $f'(x)$ at the point x and to $(f(z) - f(x))/(z - x)$ for $z \neq x$, $z \in A$, is analytic in A. Now, $\varphi(t, \xi) = \xi r_0 e^{it} + (1 - \xi) r_1 e^{it}$ $(0 \leqslant t \leqslant 2\pi,\ 0 \leqslant \xi \leqslant 1)$ is a loop homotopy in A of γ_0 into γ_1; hence $\int_{\gamma_0} g(z)\,dz = \int_{\gamma_1} g(z)\,dz$ by Cauchy's theorem (9.6.3). But for $r_0 < |x| < r_1$, we have $j(x; \gamma_0) = 0$ and $j(x; \gamma_1) = 1$ ((9.8.4) and (9.8.5)), hence the result.

(9.14.2) *Under the same assumptions as in* (9.14.1), *there exists a power series* $g_1(z) = \sum_{n=0}^{\infty} c_n z^n$, *convergent for* $|z| < r_1$, *and a power series in* $1/z$ *and without constant term,* $g_2(z) = \sum_{n=1}^{\infty} d_n z^{-n}$, *convergent for* $|z| > r_0$, *such that* $f(z) = g_1(z) + g_2(z)$ *in* S ("Laurent series" of f). *Moreover the power series* g_1, g_2 *having these properties are unique, and, for every circuit* γ *in* $\bar{\mathrm{S}}$, *we have*

$$j(0; \gamma)c_n = \frac{1}{2\pi i}\int_\gamma \frac{f(x)\,dx}{x^{n+1}}, \qquad j(0; \gamma)d_n = \frac{1}{2\pi i}\int_\gamma x^{n-1}f(x)\,dx.$$

By (9.9.4) we have

$$\frac{1}{2\pi i}\int_{\gamma_1} \frac{f(x)\,dx}{x - z} = \sum_{n=0}^{\infty} c_n z^n \quad \text{for} \quad |z| < r_1 \quad \text{with} \quad c_n = \frac{1}{2\pi i}\int_{\gamma_1} \frac{f(x)\,dx}{x^{n+1}},$$

the series being convergent for $|z| < r_1$. On the other hand, for $|z| > r_0$, $|x| = r_0$, we have

$$\frac{1}{z - x} = \sum_{n=1}^{\infty} \frac{x^{n-1}}{z^n}$$

where the right-hand side is normally convergent for $|x| = r_0$ (z fixed); by (8.7.9), we get

$$\frac{1}{2\pi i}\int_{\gamma_0} \frac{f(x)\,dx}{x - z} = \sum_{n=1}^{\infty} d_n z^{-n} \qquad \text{with} \quad d_n = \frac{1}{2\pi i}\int_{\gamma_0} x^{n-1}f(x)\,dx,$$

the series being convergent for $|z| > r_0$. This proves the first part of (9.14.2). Suppose next we have in S

(9.14.2.1)
$$f(z) = \sum_{n=0}^{\infty} a_n z^n + \sum_{n=1}^{\infty} b_n z^{-n}$$

both series being convergent in S; let first γ be a circuit in S, defined in I; there are points t, t' in I such that $\gamma(t) = \inf_{s \in \mathrm{I}} \gamma(s) = r$ and $\gamma(t') = \sup_{s \in \mathrm{I}} \gamma(s) = r'$ (3.17.10), hence $r_0 < r \leqslant \gamma(s) \leqslant r' < r_1$ for any $s \in \mathrm{I}$. But, for $r \leqslant |z| \leqslant r'$, both series in (9.14.2.1) are normally convergent (9.1.2), hence by (8.7.9), for any positive or negative integer m

$$\int_\gamma z^{m-1}f(z)\,dz = \sum_{n=0}^{\infty} a_n \int_\gamma z^{n+m-1}\,dz + \sum_{n=1}^{\infty} b_n \int_\gamma z^{m-n-1}\,dz.$$

As $z^{k+1}/(k+1)$ is a primitive of z^k for $k \neq -1$, we have $\int_\sigma z^k\,dz = 0$ for any circuit σ; (9.14.2) then follows from the definition of the index.

If now γ is in $\bar{\mathrm{S}}$, we remark that there is an open ring S_1: $(1 - \varepsilon)r_0 < |z| < (1 + \varepsilon)r_1$ contained in A (3.17.11), and we are back to the preceding case.

15. ISOLATED SINGULAR POINTS; POLES; ZEROS; RESIDUES

(9.15.1) *Let A be an open subset of* $\mathbf{C}$, *a an isolated point of* $\mathbf{C} - \mathrm{A}$ (3.10.10), *r a number* >0 *such that all points of the ball* $|z-a| \leqslant r$ *except a belong to* A. *If f is an analytic mapping of* A *into a complex Banach space* E, *then for* $0 < |z-a| < r$, *we have*

$$f(z) = \sum_{n=0}^{\infty} c_n (z-a)^n + \sum_{n=1}^{\infty} d_n (z-a)^{-n}$$

where both series are convergent for $0 < |z-a| < r$, *and*

$$c_n = \frac{1}{2\pi i} \int_\gamma \frac{f(x)\,dx}{(x-a)^{n+1}}, \qquad d_n = \frac{1}{2\pi i} \int_\gamma (x-a)^{n-1} f(x)\,dx,$$

where γ *is the circuit* $t \to a + re^{it}$ $(0 \leqslant t \leqslant 2\pi)$.

This follows at once from (9.14.2) applied to the ring $\rho \leqslant |z-a| \leqslant r$, where ρ is arbitrarily small.

Observe that the series $u(x) = \sum_{n=1}^{\infty} d_n x^n$ is an *entire function* such that $u(0) = 0$; we say that the function $u(1/(z-a))$ is the *singular part* of f in the neighborhood of a (or at a). When $u = 0$, f coincides in the open set U: $0 < |z-a| < r$ with the function $g(z) = \sum_{n=0}^{\infty} c_n (z-a)^n$, which is analytic for $|z-a| < r$; conversely, if f is the restriction to U of an analytic function f_1 defined for $|z-a| < r$, then $f_1 = g$ by (9.9.4) and (9.15.1), hence $u = 0$. When $u \neq 0$, we say that a is an *isolated singular point* of f. If u is a polynomial of degree $n \geqslant 1$, we say a is a *pole of order n* of f; if not (i.e. if $d_m \neq 0$ for an infinite number of values of m) we say a is an *essential singular point* (or *essential singularity*) of f. In general, we define the *order* $\omega(a; f)$ or $\omega(a)$ of f at the point a as follows: $\omega(a) = -\infty$ if a is an essential singularity; $\omega(a) = -n$ if a is a pole of order $n \geqslant 1$; $\omega(a) = m$ if $f \neq 0$, $u = 0$ and in the power series $\sum_{n=0}^{\infty} c_n (z-a)^n$ equal to $f(z)$ for $0 < |z-a| < r$, m is the smallest integer for which $c_m \neq 0$; finally $\omega(a; 0) = +\infty$. When $\omega(a; f) = m > 0$, we also say a is a *zero of order m* of f. Observe that if both f, g are analytic in the open set $\mathrm{U}: 0 < |z-a| < r$, and take their values in the same space, then $\omega(a; f+g) \geqslant \min(\omega(a; f), \omega(a; g))$; if one of the functions f, g is complex valued, then $\omega(a; fg) = \omega(a; f) + \omega(a; g)$ when one of the numbers $\omega(a; f)$, $\omega(a; g)$ is finite. Any function f analytic in U and of finite order n (positive or negative) can be written in a unique way $(z-a)^n f_1$, where f_1 is analytic in U and of order 0 at the point a. Finally, if f is analytic in U and complex valued, and of finite order m, then it follows from the principle of isolated zeros and from (9.3.2) that there exists a number r' such that $0 < r' < r$ and that $1/f$ is analytic in the open set $0 < |z-a| < r'$; we have then $\omega(a; 1/f) = -\omega(a; f)$.

(9.15.2) *Let f be analytic in the open set* $\mathrm{U}: 0 < |z-a| < r$. *In order that $\omega(a; f) \geqslant n$ where n is a positive or negative integer, it is necessary and sufficient that there exist a neighborhood* V *of a in* **C** *such that $(z-a)^{-n} f(z)$ be bounded in* $\mathrm{V} \cap \mathrm{U}$.

The condition is obviously necessary, since a function having order $\geqslant 0$ at a is the restriction of a function analytic in a ball $|z-a| < r$. Conversely, by considering the function $(z-a)^{-n} f(z)$, we can suppose $n = 0$. Then it follows from (9.15.1) and the mean value theorem that if $\|f(z)\| \leqslant \mathrm{M}$ in U, we have, for any ρ such that $0 < \rho < r$, $\|d_m\| \leqslant \mathrm{M}\rho^m$ for any $m \geqslant 1$; as ρ is arbitrary, this implies $d_m = 0$ for each $m \geqslant 1$. Q.E.D.

The coefficient d_1 in (9.15.1) is called the *residue* of f at the point a.

PROBLEMS

1. Show that there are no isolated singular points for analytic functions of $p \geqslant 2$ complex variables (in other words, if A is an open subset of $\mathbf{C}^p$, $a \in \mathrm{A}$ and a mapping f of $\mathrm{A} - \{a\}$ into a complex Banach space E is analytic, it is the restriction of an analytic mapping of A into E; use Problem 5 in Section 9.10).
2. Let f be a complex valued analytic function of one complex variable having an essential singularity at a point $a \in \mathbf{C}$; show that for any complex number λ, it is impossible that the function $1/(f-\lambda)$ should be defined and bounded in an open set of the form $\mathrm{V} - \{a\}$, where V is an open neighborhood (use (9.15.2)). Conclude that for any neighborhood V of a such that f is analytic in $\mathrm{V} - \{a\}$, $f(\mathrm{V} - \{a\})$ is *dense* in **C** ("Weierstrass' theorem"; see Section 10.3, Problem 8).
3. An entire function which is not a polynomial is called a *transcendental* entire function. Let f be a complex valued entire transcendental function of one complex variable.
(a) Show that for any integer $n > 0$, the open subset D(n) of **C** consisting of the points $z \in \mathbf{C}$ such that $|f(z)| > n$ is not empty and cannot contain the exterior of any ball (apply Problem 2 to the function $f(1/z)$).
(b) Let K(n) be a connected component (3.19.5) of D(n). Show that K(n) is not bounded and that $|f(z)|$ is not bounded in K(n) (if $a \notin \mathrm{K}(n)$, consider the function $f(1/(z-a))$ and use Problem 14 of Section 9.5).
(c) Show that there is a continuous mapping γ of $[0, +\infty[$ into **C**, such that in every interval $[0, \alpha]$, γ is the primitive of a regulated function, and that $\lim_{t \to +\infty} |\gamma(t)| = +\infty$

and $\lim_{t \to +\infty} |f(\gamma(t))| = +\infty$. (Consider a sequence of open subsets $L_n \subset \mathbf{C}$ such that L_n is a connected component of $D(n)$, and $L_{n+1} \subset L_n$ for every n; the existence of such a sequence follows from (b). Use then (9.7.2).)

(d) Extend the preceding results to complex valued entire transcendental functions of an arbitrary number of complex variables. (If $f(z_1, \ldots, z_p) = \sum a_{n_1 \ldots n_p} z_1^{n_1} \ldots z_p^{n_p}$, there exists at least an index k such that there are infinitely many monomials with non zero coefficient $a_{n_1 \ldots n_p}$ and arbitrarily large n_k. On the other hand, prove that if (g_m) is a denumerable family of entire complex valued functions of p complex variables, none of which is identically 0, then there exist points $(c_1, \ldots, c_p)$ for which $g_m(c_1, \ldots, c_p) \neq 0$ for every m; to do this, use induction on p, and the fact that for a function $h(z)$ of one complex variable, analytic in $A \subset \mathbf{C}$ and not identically 0, the set of solutions z of $h(z) = 0$ is at most denumerable (see (9.1.5)).)

4. Let $\varphi(x)$ be an arbitrary increasing and positive real function defined in $[0, +\infty[$. Let (k_n) be a strictly increasing sequence of integers such that $k_1 = 1$, and $(n(n-1))^{k_n} > \varphi(n+1)$ for $n > 1$. Show that the power series

$$f(z) = 1 + \sum_{n=2}^{\infty} \left(\frac{z}{n-1}\right)^{k_n}$$

is convergent for all $z \in \mathbf{C}$, and that for every real $x \geqslant 2$, $f(x) \geqslant \varphi(x)$ (in other words, there are entire functions which tend to infinity "faster" than any given real function).

5. For any real numbers α, β such that $\beta > 0$, let $L_{\alpha,\beta}$ be the endless road (Section 9.12, Problem 3) defined as follows: for $t \leqslant -1$, $L_{\alpha,\beta}(t) = \alpha - i\beta - t - 1$; for $-1 \leqslant t \leqslant 1$, $L_{\alpha,\beta}(t) = \alpha + i\beta t$; for $t \geqslant 1$, $L_{\alpha,\beta}(t) = \alpha + i\beta + t - 1$. Let $G_{\alpha,\beta} = L_{\alpha,\beta}(\mathbf{R})$.

(a) Show that if $\pi/2 < \beta < 3\pi/2$, and if $x \notin G_{\alpha,\beta}$ the function $z \to (\exp(\exp z))/(z - x)$ is improperly integrable along $L_{\alpha,\beta}$. Furthermore, is β_1, β_2 are such that $|\mathscr{I}(x)| < \beta_1 < \beta_2$ of $|\mathscr{I}(x)| > \beta_2 > \beta_1$, or $\mathscr{R}(x) < \alpha$, the integrals along L_{α,β_1} and L_{α,β_2} are the same; similarly, if $\mathscr{R}(x) < \alpha_1 < \alpha_2$, or $\alpha_1 < \alpha_2 < \mathscr{R}(x)$, or $|\mathscr{I}(x)| > \beta$ the integrals along $L_{\alpha_1,\beta}$ and $L_{\alpha_2,\beta}$ are the same (use Cauchy's theorem).

(b) Deduce from (a) that if $L = L_{0,\pi}$,

$$E(x) = \frac{1}{2\pi i} \int_L \frac{\exp(\exp z)}{z - x} \, dz$$

can be extended to an entire function.

(c) Show that

$$\frac{1}{2i\pi} \int_L \exp(\exp z) \, dz = 1$$

(prove that the integral along $L_{\alpha,\beta}$ of $\exp(\exp z)$ is independent of α and β (provided $\pi/2 < \beta < 3\pi/2$)).

(d) Show that if x belongs to the open set A defined by $\mathscr{R}(x) < 0$ or $|\mathscr{I}(x)| > \pi$,

$$E(x) = -\frac{1}{x} + \frac{F(x)}{x^2}$$

where $F(x)$ is bounded in A (express $F(x)$ by an integral along $L_{0,\beta}$ with $\beta < \pi$, using (a) and (c)).

(e) Show that if x belongs to the open set B defined by $\mathscr{R}(x) > 0$ and $|\mathscr{I}(x)| < \pi$, then

$$E(x) = \exp(\exp x) - \frac{1}{x} + \frac{G(x)}{x^2}$$

where G(x) is bounded in B (prove first, using Cauchy's formula, that if $-1 < \mathscr{R}(x) < 0$ and $|\mathscr{I}(x)| < \pi$, then

$$\mathrm{E}(x) = \exp(\exp x) + \frac{1}{2\pi i}\int_{\mathrm{L}'} \frac{\exp(\exp z)}{z - x}\,dz$$

where $\mathrm{L}' = \mathrm{L}_{-1,\pi}$. Show next that that formula is still valid for $x \in \mathrm{B}$ using (9.4.2) and express G(x) by an integral along $\mathrm{L}_{-1,\beta}$ with $\beta > \pi$).

(f) Let $\mathrm{H}(x) = \mathrm{E}(x)e^{-\mathrm{E}(x)}$; show that H is an entire transcendental function such that $\lim_{r\to+\infty} \mathrm{H}(re^{i\theta}) = 0$ for every real θ (use (d) and (e); compare with the result of Problem 3).

6. Let f be a complex valued entire function of $p \geqslant 2$ complex variables. Show that if $f(a_1, \ldots, a_p) = b$, then for every $r > 0$, there exists $z = (z_1, \ldots, z_p)$ such that $\sum_k |z_k - a_k|^2 = r^2$ and $f(z_1, \ldots, z_p) = b$ (use Problem 5(b) of Section 9.10).

7. Let f be an analytic mapping of an open subset $\mathrm{A} \subset \mathbf{C}^p$ into a complex Banach space E. A frontier point z_0 of A is called a *regular* point for f if there is an open neighborhood V of z_0 and an analytic mapping of $\mathrm{A} \cup \mathrm{V}$ into E which coincides with f in A. A frontier point of A is said to be *singular* for f if it is not regular.

(a) Let $\mathrm{R} < +\infty$ be the radius of convergence (Section 9.1, Problem 1) of a power series $f(z) = \sum_n a_n z^n$ of one complex variable. There is at least one point z_0 such that $|z_0| = \mathrm{R}$ which is a singular point for f. (Otherwise one could cover the circle $|z| = \mathrm{R}$ with a finite number of open balls B_k whose centers b_k are on that circle, and such that in each open set $\mathrm{B}(0; \mathrm{R}) \cup \mathrm{B}_k$ there is an analytic function f_k coinciding with f in $\mathrm{B}(0; \mathrm{R})$. Show that for any two indices h, k for which $\mathrm{B}_h \cap \mathrm{B}_k \neq \varnothing$, f_h and f_k coincide in $\mathrm{B}_h \cap \mathrm{B}_k$, using (9.4.2), and conclude from (9.9.1) and (9.9.2) that the radius of convergence of $\sum_n a_n z^n$ would be $> \mathrm{R}$.)

(b) With the notations of (a), suppose $a_n \geqslant 0$ for every n. Show that the point $z = \mathrm{R}$ is singular for f. (One may suppose $\mathrm{R} = 1$. Let $e^{i\alpha}$ be a singular point for f; then for $0 < r < 1$, the radius of convergence of the power series $\sum_n f^{(n)}(re^{i\alpha})z^n/n!$ is exactly $1 - r$ (9.9.1). Observe that $|f^{(n)}(re^{i\alpha})| \leqslant f^{(n)}(r)$, and use (9.1.2).)

(c) With the notations of (a), suppose $\mathrm{R} = 1$. Let b, c be two real numbers such that $0 < b < 1$, $c = 1 - b$, and let p be an integer $\geqslant 1$. In order that the point $z = 1$ be a singular point for f, it is necessary and sufficient that the Taylor series $\sum_n g^{(n)}(0)u^n/n!$ for the function $g(u) = f(bu^p + cu^{p+1})$ have a radius of convergence equal to 1. (Observe that if $|u| \leqslant 1$, $|bu^p + cu^{p+1}| \leqslant 1$, and that the two sides of the last inequality can only be equal for $u = 1$. The proof for the necessity of the condition has to use (10.2.5), in order to show that there is in the neighborhood of $z = 1$ an analytic function $h(z)$ such that $z = g(h(z))$ in that neighborhood.)

(d) Suppose (with the notations of (a)) that $a_n = 0$ except for a subsequence (n_k) of integers such that $n_{k+1} > (1 + \theta)n_k$ for every k, where $\theta > 0$ is a fixed number. Show that *every* point z_0 on the circle $|z| = \mathrm{R}$ is a singular point for f ("Hadamard's gap theorem"; the circle $|z| = \mathrm{R}$ is called a *natural boundary* for f). (One may suppose $\mathrm{R} = 1$. Use criterion of (c), taking $p > 1/\theta$, and let $g(u) = \sum_{n=0}^{\infty} d_n u^n$ be the Taylor development of g at $u = 0$. By assumption, for given $\varepsilon > 0$ there is a subsequence (m_j) of integers such that $\|a_{m_j}\| \geqslant (1 - \varepsilon)^{m_j}$ (Section 9.1, Problem 1). On the other hand the function $\mathrm{F}(u) = \sum_j (bu^p + cu^{p+1})^{m_j} = \sum_n e_n u^n$ has $u = 1$ as a singular point, by (b), hence there is a subsequence (q_l) of integers such that $|e_{q_l}| \geqslant (1 - \varepsilon)^{q_l}$. Prove that $\|d_{q_l}\| \geqslant (1 - \varepsilon)^{2q_l}$).

16. THE THEOREM OF RESIDUES

We first recall that any subset $S \subset \mathbf{C}$ the points of which are all *isolated* is *at most denumerable*, for the subspace S of **C** is then discrete and separable (by (3.9.2), (3.20.16), and (3.10.9)), hence S is the only dense subset of S (3.10.10).

(9.16.1) *Let $A \subset \mathbf{C}$ be a simply connected domain, (a_n) a (finite or infinite) sequence of distinct isolated points of* A, S *the set of points of that sequence. Let f be an analytic mapping of* $A - S$ *into a complex Banach space* E, *and let γ be a circuit in* $A - S$. *Then we have*

$$\int_\gamma f(z)\,dz = 2\pi i \sum_n j(a_n\,;\gamma)\mathrm{R}(a_n)$$

where $\mathrm{R}(a_n)$ is the residue of f at the point a_n, and there are only a finite number of terms $\neq 0$ on the right-hand side ("theorem of residues").

We can obviously suppose each a_n is a *singular point* for f, for we can extend f by continuity to all nonsingular points a_n, which does not change both sides of the formula (since $\mathrm{R}(a_n) = 0$ if a_n is not singular). Under that assumption, for any *compact* set $L \subset A$, $L \cap S$ is *finite*, for $L \cap S$ is *closed* in L, as $A - S$ is open in **C** by definition; hence $L \cap S$, being compact and discrete, is finite (3.16.3). Let I be the interval in which γ is defined, and let P be the set of points $x \in \bar{A}$ such that $j(x; \gamma) \neq 0$. We know (9.8.6) that the closure $\bar{P}$ of P in **C** is compact, and $\bar{P}$ does not contain any frontier point of A, for such a point cannot be in $\gamma(I)$, nor have index $\neq 0$ with respect to γ, by (9.8.7); as the set of points x in $\mathbf{C} - \gamma(I)$ where the index $j(x; \gamma)$ takes a given value is open (9.8.3), any point in P which does not belong to $\gamma(I)$ is in P, hence $\bar{P} \subset A$. On the other hand, let $\varphi(t, \xi)$ be a loop homotopy in A of γ into a one-point circuit ($t \in I$, $\xi \in J$, where J is a compact interval). Then $M = \varphi(I \times J)$ is a compact subset of A. Let $H \subset \mathbf{N}$ be the finite set of the integers n such that $a_n \in M \cup \bar{P}$; for each $n \in H$, let $u_n(1/(z - a_n))$ be the singular part of f at the point a_n. Let B be the complement in A of the set of points a_n such that $n \notin H$; then B is *open*, for a compact neighborhood of a point of B, contained in A, has a finite intersection with S. By definition of the singular parts, there is a function g, analytic in B, and which is equal to $f(z) - \sum_{n \in H} u_n\left(\frac{1}{z - a_n}\right)$ at every point $z \neq a_n$ $(n \in H)$.

As $\mathrm{M} \subset \mathrm{B}$ by definition, γ is homotopic *in* B to a one-point circuit; hence, by Cauchy's theorem, $\int_\gamma g(z)\,dz = 0$, in other words

$$\int_\gamma f(z)\,dz = \sum_{n \in \mathrm{H}} \int_\gamma u_n\left(\frac{1}{z - a_n}\right) dz;$$

the result then follows from (9.14.2), applied to each of the functions $u_n\left(\frac{1}{z - a_n}\right)$ in an open "ring" of center a_n, containing $\gamma(\mathrm{I})$.

17. MEROMORPHIC FUNCTIONS

Let A be an open subset of **C**, S a subset of A, all points of which are *isolated.* A mapping f of $\mathrm{A} - \mathrm{S}$ into a complex Banach space E is said (by abuse of language) to be *meromorphic in* A if it is analytic in $\mathrm{A} - \mathrm{S}$ and has order $> -\infty$ at each point of S. By abuse of language, we will always identify f to its extension by continuity to all points of S which are not poles of f; the argument used in (9.16.1) then shows that we can always suppose that for any *compact* subset L of A, $\mathrm{L} \cap \mathrm{S}$ is *finite.* If f, g are two meromorphic functions in A, taking their values in the same space, and whose sets of poles in A are respectively S, S′, then $\mathrm{S} \cup \mathrm{S}'$ has all its points isolated, due to the preceding remark; $f+g$ is defined and analytic in $\mathrm{A} - (\mathrm{S} \cup \mathrm{S}')$, and has order $> -\infty$ at each point of $\mathrm{S} \cup \mathrm{S}'$, hence is meromorphic in A (note that some points of $\mathrm{S} \cup \mathrm{S}'$ may fail to be singular for $f+g$). Similarly if f and g are meromorphic in A, and g is complex valued, fg is meromorphic in A. If f is meromorphic in A, S is the set of its poles, T the set of its zeros, then all the points of $\mathrm{S} \cup \mathrm{T}$ are isolated; for if $a \in \mathrm{A}$ and $\omega(a) = h$, then $f(z) = (z-a)^h f_1(z)$ in a set $0 < |z - a| < r$, where f_1 is analytic in $|z - a| < r$ and $f_1(a) \neq 0$; the principle of isolated zeros (9.1.5) shows that there is a number r' such that $0 < r' < r$, and $f(z) \neq 0$ for $0 < |z - a| < r'$. This proves our assertion, and shows moreover that $\mathrm{L} \cap (\mathrm{S} \cup \mathrm{T})$ is finite for any compact subset L of A (same argument as in (9.16.1)). In particular, if f is complex valued, $1/f$ is meromorphic in A, S is the set of its zeros and T the set of its poles. Moreover, with the same notation as above, we have $f'(z) = h(z-a)^{h-1} f_1(z) + (z-a)^h f_1'(z)$ for $0 < |z - a| < r$, hence f'/f, which is analytic for $0 < |z-a| < r'$, has order 0 at the point a if $h = 0$, order -1 and residue h at the point a if $h \neq 0$.

(9.17.1) *Let* A *be a simply connected domain in* **C**, f *a complex valued meromorphic function in* A, S (resp. T) *the set of its poles* (resp. *zeros*), g *an analytic function in* A. *Then, for any circuit* γ *in* $\mathrm{A} - (\mathrm{S} \cup \mathrm{T})$, *we have*

$$\int_\gamma g(z)\frac{f'(z)}{f(z)}\,dz = 2\pi i \sum_{a \in S \cup T} j(a;\gamma)g(a)\omega(a;f)$$

a finite number of terms only being $\neq 0$ *on the right-hand side.*

This follows at once from the theorem of residues, for the residue of gf'/f at a point $a \in S \cup T$ is the product of $g(a)$ by the residue of f'/f at the point a.

(9.17.2) *With the assumptions of* (9.17.1) *let* $t \to \gamma(t)$ $(t \in I)$ *be a circuit in* $A - (S \cup T)$. *If* Γ *is the circuit* $t \to f(\gamma(t))$, *then*

$$j(0;\Gamma) = \sum_{a \in S \cup T} j(a;\gamma)\omega(a;f).$$

For it follows at once from (8.7.4) that

$$\int_\Gamma \frac{du}{u} = \int_\gamma \frac{f'(z)}{f(z)}\,dz,$$

hence the result is a particular case of (9.17.1) for $g = 1$.

(9.17.3) (Rouché's theorem) *Let* $A \subset \mathbf{C}$ *be a simply connected domain,* f, g *two analytic complex valued functions in* A. *Let* T *be the (at most denumerable) set of zeros of* f, T′ *the set of zeros of* $f + g$ *in* A, γ *a circuit in* $A - T$, *defined in an interval* I. *Then, if* $|g(z)| < |f(z)|$ *in* $\gamma(I)$, *the function* $f + g$ *has no zeros on* $\gamma(I)$, *and*

$$\sum_{a \in T} j(a;\gamma)\omega(a;f) = \sum_{b \in T'} j(b;\gamma)\omega(b;f+g).$$

The first point is obvious, since $f(z) + g(z) = 0$ implies $|f(z)| = |g(z)|$. The function $h = (f+g)/f$ is defined in $A - T$ and meromorphic in A; we have

$$\frac{(f+g)'}{f+g} = \frac{f'}{f} + \frac{h'}{h} \quad \text{in} \quad A - (T \cup T').$$

Using (9.17.2), all we have to prove is that the index of 0 with respect to the circuit $\Gamma : t \to h(\gamma(t))$ is 0. As g/f is continuous and finite in the compact set $\gamma(I)$, it follows from (3.17.10) and the assumption that $r = \sup_{z \in \gamma(I)} |g(z)/f(z)| < 1$. In other words, Γ is in the ball $|z - 1| < r$, and as 0 is exterior to the ball, the result follows from (9.8.5).

(9.17.4) (Continuity of the roots of an equation as a function of parameters) *Let* A *be an open set in* **C**, F *a metric space,* f *a continuous complex valued function in* $A \times F$, *such that for each* $\alpha \in F$, $z \to f(z, \alpha)$ *is analytic in* A. *Let* B *be an open subset of* A, *whose closure* $\bar{B}$ *in* **C** *is compact and contained in* A, *and let* $\alpha_0 \in F$ *be such that no zero of* $f(z, \alpha_0)$ *is on the frontier of* B. *Then there exists a neighborhood* W *of* α_0 *in* F *such that*: (1) *for any* $\alpha \in W$, $f(z, \alpha)$ *has no zeros on the frontier of* B; (2) *for any* $\alpha \in W$, *the sum of the orders of the zeros of* $f(z, \alpha)$ *belonging to* B *is independent of* α.

The number of distinct zeros of $f(z, \alpha_0)$ in B is finite; let $a_1, \dots, a_n$ be these points. For each frontier point x of B, there is a compact neighborhood U_x of x, contained in A, such that $f(z, \alpha_0)$ has no zero in U_x (9.1.5); if we cover the (compact) frontier of B by a finite number of sets U_{x_j}, the union U of $\bar{B}$ and the U_{x_j} is a compact neighborhood of $\bar{B}$, contained in A and such that $f(z, \alpha_0)$ has no zero in $U \cap (A - \bar{B})$. Let r be the minimum of the numbers $|a_i - a_j|$ $(i \neq j)$, and for each i $(1 \leqslant i \leqslant n)$, let D_i be an open ball $|z - a_i| < r_i$ of radius $r_i < r/2$, contained in B; then $D_i \cap D_j = \varnothing$ if $i \neq j$. Let $H = U - \left(\bigcup_i D_i\right)$; this is a compact set; let m be the minimum value of $|f(z, \alpha_0)|$ in H; we have $m > 0$ by (3.17.10). Now, for each $x \in \bar{B}$, there is a neighborhood V_x of x contained in A and a neighborhood W_x of α_0 in F, such that $|f(y, \alpha) - f(x, \alpha_0)| < m/2$ for $y \in V_x$ and $\alpha \in W_x$. As $\bar{B}$ is compact it can be covered by a finite number of sets V_{x_k} $(1 \leqslant k \leqslant p)$; let $W = \bigcap_k W_{x_k}$; this is a neighborhood of α_0 in F, and by definition, for *any* $\alpha \in W$ and *any* $y \in \bar{B}$, we have $|f(y, \alpha) - f(y, \alpha_0)| < m$. As a first consequence, it follows that $f(y, \alpha) \neq 0$ for $y \in H$ and $\alpha \in W$; on the other hand, as $|f(z, \alpha) - f(z, \alpha_0)| < |f(z, \alpha_0)|$ in H, Rouché's theorem, applied to each circuit $t \to a_i + r_i e^{it}$ $(0 \leqslant t \leqslant 2\pi)$ shows that the sum of the orders of the zeros of $f(z, \alpha)$ in D_i is independent of $\alpha \in W$, hence the theorem.

PROBLEMS

1. Let $A \subset \mathbf{C}$ be an open simply connected set, f a meromorphic complex valued function in A, such that each pole of f is simple and the residue of f at each of these poles is a positive or negative *integer*. Show that there is in A a meromorphic function g such that $f = g'/g$. (If z_0 is not a pole of f, show that for any point $z_1 \in A$ which is not a pole of f, and any road γ in A, defined in $I \subset \mathbf{R}$, of origin z_0 and extremity z_1, and such that $\gamma(I)$ does not contain any pole of f, the number $\exp\left(\int_\gamma f(x)\,dx\right)$ only depends on z_0 and z_1, and not on the road γ satisfying the preceding conditions (use the theorem of residues).)
2. Let f be an entire function of one complex variable, such that for real x, y, $\|f(x+iy)\| \leqslant e^{|y|}$. Show that, for any z distinct from integral multiples $n\pi$ of π,

$$\frac{d}{dz}\left(\frac{f(z)}{\sin z}\right) = -\sum_{-\infty}^{+\infty} \frac{(-1)^n f(n\pi)}{(z - n\pi)^2}$$

where the series on the right-hand side is normally convergent in any compact subset of $\mathbf{C}$ which does not contain any of the points $n\pi$ (n integer). (Consider the integral

$$\frac{1}{2\pi i}\int_{\gamma_n} \frac{f(x)}{\sin x}\frac{dx}{(x - z)^2}$$

where γ_n is the circuit $t \to (n + \frac{1}{2})\pi e^{it}$ for $-\pi \leqslant t \leqslant \pi$. Observe that for every $\varepsilon > 0$, there is a number $c(\varepsilon) > 0$ such that the relations $|z - n\pi| \geqslant \varepsilon$ for every integer $n \in \mathbf{Z}$ imply $|\sin z| \geqslant c(\varepsilon)e^{|\mathscr{I}(z)|}$; and use the theorem of residues.)

3. (a) Show that for $z \neq n\pi$ (n integer)

$$\cot z = \frac{1}{z} + \sum_{n=1}^{\infty} \frac{2z}{z^2 - n^2\pi^2}$$

where the right-hand side is normally convergent in any compact subset of $\mathbf{C}$ which does not contain any of the points $n\pi$. (Use Problem 2 and the relation $\lim_{z\to 0} (\cot z - 1/z) = 0$.)

(b) Deduce from (a) that

$$\sin z = z\prod_{n=1}^{\infty}\left(1 - \frac{z^2}{n^2\pi^2}\right)$$

where the product is defined as the limit of $\prod_{k=1}^{n}\left(1 - \frac{z^2}{k^2\pi^2}\right)$, the convergence being uniform in every compact subset of $\mathbf{C}$. (Consider the entire function $f(z) = \prod_{-\infty}^{+\infty}\left(1 - \frac{z}{n\pi}\right)e^{-z/n\pi}$ (Section 9.12, Problem 1), and use (a) to prove that the function $(\sin z)/zf(z)$ is a constant.)

(c) Deduce from (b) the identity

$$\frac{1}{\Gamma(z)\Gamma(1 - z)} = \frac{1}{\pi}\sin \pi z$$

(see Section 9.12, Problem 2).

4. Let f be a complex valued function analytic in an open neighborhood A of 0 in $\mathbf{C}^p$; for convenience we write w instead of z_p and z instead of $(z_1, \ldots, z_{p-1})$. Suppose that $f(0, 0) = 0$ and that the function $f(0, w)$, which is analytic in a neighborhood of $w = 0$ in $\mathbf{C}$, is not identically 0. Then there exist an integer $r > 0$, r functions $h_j(z)$ analytic in a neighborhood of 0 in $\mathbf{C}^{p-1}$, and a function $g(z, w)$ analytic in a neighborhood $\mathrm{B} \subset \mathrm{A}$ of 0 in $\mathbf{C}^p$ and $\neq 0$ in that neighborhood, such that

$$f(z, w) = (w^r + h_1(z)w^{r-1} + \cdots + h_r(z))g(z, w)$$

in a neighborhood of 0 in $\mathbf{C}^p$ (the "Weierstrass preparation theorem"). (If $f(0, w)$ has a zero of order r at $w = 0$, use (9.17.4) to prove that there is a number $\varepsilon > 0$ and a neighborhood V of 0 in $\mathbf{C}^{p-1}$ such that for any $z \in \mathrm{V}$, the function $w \to f(z, w)$ has exactly r zeros in the disc $|w| < \varepsilon$ and no zero on the circle $|w| = \varepsilon$. Let γ be the circuit $t \to \varepsilon e^{it}$ for $-\pi \leqslant t \leqslant \pi$; using the theorem of residues, show that there are functions $h_j(z)$ $(1 \leqslant j \leqslant r)$ analytic in V and such that the polynomial $F(z, w) = w^r + h_1(z)w^{r-1} + \cdots + h_r(z)$ satisfies the identity

$$\frac{F'_w(z, w)}{F(z, w)} = \frac{1}{2\pi i}\int_\gamma \frac{f'_u(z, u)}{f(z, u)} \frac{1}{w-u}\, du$$

for $z \in V$ *and* $|w| > \varepsilon$).

5. Let (f_n) be a sequence of complex valued analytic functions in a connected open subset A of **C**. Suppose that for each $z \in A$, the sequence $(f_n(z))$ tends to a limit $g(z)$, and the convergence is uniform in every compact subset of A. Suppose in addition that each mapping $z \to f_n(z)$ of A into **C** is *injective*. Show that either g is constant in A or g is injective (for any $z_0 \in A$, consider the sequence $(f_n(z) - f_n(z_0))$ and apply (9.17.4) and the principle of isolated zeros).

6. Let φ be a real valued twice differentiable function in the interval $[0, 1]$. Suppose $|\varphi(0)| < |\varphi(1)|$, and let x_0 be one of the zeros of $\varphi(0) - \varphi(1)\cos x = 0$ in $]-\pi, \pi[$. Show that the entire function

$$F(z) = \int_0^1 \varphi(t) \sin zt\, dt$$

has a denumerable set of zeros; furthermore it is possible to define a surjective mapping $n \to z_n$ of **Z** onto the set of zeros of $zF(z)$, such that each zero corresponds to a number of indices equal to its order, and that $\lim_{n \to \pm\infty} (z_{2n} - x_0 - 2n\pi) = \lim_{n \to \pm\infty} (z_{2n+1} + x_0 - 2n\pi) = 0$. (Integrating twice by parts, show that one can write $zF(z) = \varphi(0) - \varphi(1) \cos z + G(z)$, where $|G(z)| \leqslant ae^{|\mathscr{I}(z)|}/|z|$; minorize $|\varphi(0) - \varphi(1) \cos z|$ outside of circles having centers at the zeros of that function, in the same was as $|\sin z|$ was minorized in Problem 2; and use Rouché's theorem in a suitable way.) Treat similarly the cases in which $|\varphi(0)| > |\varphi(1)|$ or $|\varphi(0)| = |\varphi(1)|$.

APPENDIX TO CHAPTER IX

APPLICATION OF ANALYTIC FUNCTIONS TO PLANE TOPOLOGY

(Eilenberg's Method)

1. INDEX OF A POINT WITH RESPECT TO A LOOP

(Ap.1.1) *If* $t \to \gamma(t)$ $(a \leqslant t \leqslant b)$ *is a path in an open subset* A *of* **C**, *there is in* A *a homotopy* φ *of* γ *into a road* γ_1, *such that* φ *is defined in* $[a, b] \times [0, 1]$ *and* $\varphi(a, \xi) = \gamma(a)$ *and* $\varphi(b, \xi) = \gamma(b)$ *for every* $\xi \in [0, 1]$.

Let $\mathrm{I} = [a, b]$; as $\gamma(\mathrm{I})$ is compact, $d(\gamma(\mathrm{I}), \mathbf{C} - \mathrm{A}) = \rho$ is > 0 (3.17.11). As γ is uniformly continuous in I (3.16.5), there is a strictly increasing sequence $(t_k)_{0 \leqslant k \leqslant m}$ of points of I such that $t_0 = a$, $t_m = b$, and the oscillation (Section 3.14) of γ in each of the intervals $[t_k, t_{k+1}]$ $(0 \leqslant k \leqslant m - 1)$ is $< \rho$. Define γ_1 in I as follows: for $t_k \leqslant t \leqslant t_{k+1}$, $\gamma_1(t) = \gamma(t_k) + \dfrac{t - t_k}{t_{k+1} - t_k}(\gamma(t_{k+1}) - \gamma(t_k))$ $(0 \leqslant k \leqslant m - 1)$; it is clear that γ_1 is a road, with $\gamma_1(a) = \gamma(a)$, $\gamma_1(b) = \gamma(b)$, and $\gamma_1(\mathrm{I})$ is contained in A, since $\gamma_1([t_k, t_{k+1}])$ is contained in the open ball of center $\gamma(t_k)$ and radius ρ. Define then $\varphi(t, \xi) = \xi\gamma_1(t) + (1 - \xi)\gamma(t)$; it is readily verified that $\varphi(t, \xi)$ is in the open ball of center $\gamma(t_k)$ and radius ρ for $t_k \leqslant t \leqslant t_{k+1}$ and $0 \leqslant \xi \leqslant 1$ $(0 \leqslant k \leqslant m - 1)$; hence φ verifies the required conditions.

In particular, if γ is a *loop*, we see that φ is a *loop homotopy* in A of γ into a *circuit* γ_1.

Consider now any loop γ in **C**, defined in I, and any point $a \notin \gamma(\mathrm{I})$. As there are, by (Ap.1.1), circuits γ_1 which are homotopic to γ in $\mathbf{C} - \{a\}$, we can define the *index* $j(a; \gamma)$ as equal to $j(a; \gamma_1)$ for any circuit homotopic to γ in $\mathbf{C} - \{a\}$; by Cauchy's theorem (9.6.3), this is independent of the particular circuit γ_1 homotopic to γ in $\mathbf{C} - \{a\}$.

Using (Ap.1.1) it is readily verified that the index of a point with respect to a loop does not depend on the origin of the loop (Section 9.6), and that properties (9.8.3), (9.8.5), (9.8.6), and (9.8.7) still hold when "circuit" is replaced by "loop" in their formulation.

2. ESSENTIAL MAPPINGS IN THE UNIT CIRCLE

Let E be a metric space. We say that a continuous mapping f of E into the unit circle $\mathbf{U}$: $|z| = 1$ is *inessential* if there is a continuous mapping g of E into $\mathbf{R}$ such that $f(x) = e^{ig(x)}$ for every $x \in \mathrm{E}$. A continuous mapping f of E into $\mathbf{U}$ is called *essential* if it is not inessential.

(Ap.2.1) *If f_1, f_2 are inessential mappings of* E *into* $\mathbf{U}$, $f_1 f_2$ *and* $1/f_1 = \bar{f}_1$ *are inessential; if f_1 is essential and f_2 inessential, then $f_1 f_2$ and f_1/f_2 are essential.*

(Ap.2.2) *If f is an inessential mapping of* E *into* $\mathbf{U}$, *and g a continuous mapping of a metric space* F *into* E, *then $f \circ g$ is inessential.*

These properties are obvious consequences of the definition.

(Ap.2.3) *Any continuous mapping f of a metric space* E *into* $\mathbf{U}$ *such that* $f(\mathrm{E}) \neq \mathbf{U}$ *is inessential.*

Let $\zeta_0 \in \mathbf{U} - f(\mathrm{E})$. There is $\alpha \in \mathbf{R}$ such that $\zeta_0 = e^{i\alpha}$, and the restriction of $t \to e^{it}$ to the open interval $]\alpha, \alpha + 2\pi[$ is a homeomorphism of that interval onto $\mathbf{U} - \{\zeta_0\}$ (9.5.7); if ψ is the inverse homeomorphism, we have $f(x) = e^{i\psi(f(x))}$ for every $x \in \mathrm{E}$. Q.E.D.

(Ap.2.4) *If f_1, f_2 are two continuous mappings of a metric space* E *into* $\mathbf{U}$, *such that $f_1(x) \neq -f_2(x)$ for any $x \in \mathrm{E}$, and if f_1 is essential* (resp. *inessential*), *so is f_2.*

For $f = f_1/f_2$ is a continuous mapping of E into $\mathbf{U}$ which does not take the value -1, hence is inessential by (Ap.2.3).

(Ap.2.5) *Let* E *be a compact metric space,* $I = [0, 1]$, f *a continuous mapping of* $E \times I$ *into* **U**. *If the mapping* $x \to f(x, 0)$ *is essential* (resp. *inessential*), *so is the mapping* $x \to f(x, 1)$.

As f is uniformly continuous in $E \times I$ (3.16.5), there is an integer $n \geqslant 1$ such that the relation $|s - t| \leqslant 1/n$ implies $|f(x, s) - f(x, t)| \leqslant 1$ for any $x \in E$. Let $f_k(x) = f(x, k/n)$ for $0 \leqslant k \leqslant n$; we therefore have $|f_k(x) - f_{k+1}(x)| \leqslant 1$ for any $x \in E$ and $0 \leqslant k \leqslant n - 1$, and as $|f_k(x)| = |f_{k+1}(x)| = 1$ for $x \in E$, we have $f_k(x) \neq -f_{k+1}(x)$ for $x \in E$. Hence the result by (Ap.2.4).

(Ap.2.6) *Any continuous mapping* f *of a closed ball (in* $\mathbf{R}^n$*) into* **U** *is inessential.*

Let E be the ball $d(x, a) \leqslant r$, and define $g(x, t) = f(a + t(x - a))$; then g is continuous in $E \times [0, 1]$, $g(x, 1) = f(x)$ and $g(x, 0) = f(a)$; as $x \to g(x, 0)$ is inessential (Ap.2.3), so is f by (Ap.2.5).

(Ap.2.7) *Let* A, B *be two closed subsets of a metric space* E, *such that* $E = A \cup B$, *and that* $A \cap B$ *be connected. Let* f *be a continuous mapping of* E *into* **U**; *if the restrictions of* f *to* A *and* B *are inessential,* f *is inessential.*

There are, by assumption, continuous mappings g, h of A and B into **R** such that $f(x) = e^{ig(x)}$ in A, $f(x) = e^{ih(x)}$ in B. For $x \in A \cap B$, we have therefore $e^{ig(x)} = e^{ih(x)}$, hence (9.5.5) $(g(x) - h(x))/2\pi$ is an integer; but as $g - h$ is continuous in the *connected* set $A \cap B$, this implies $g - h$ is a *constant* $2n\pi$ in $A \cap B$ by (3.19.7). Let then $u(x) = g(x)$ in A, $u(x) = h(x) + 2n\pi$ in B; it is clear that $f(x) = e^{iu(x)}$ in E, and as g and $h + 2n\pi$ coincide in $A \cap B$, u is continuous in E. Q.E.D.

(Ap.2.8) *In order that a continuous mapping* f *of* **U** *into itself be essential, a necessary and sufficient condition is that* $j(0; \gamma) \neq 0$ *for the loop* $\gamma\colon t \to f(e^{it})$ $(0 \leqslant t \leqslant 2\pi)$.

By (9.8.1) we can write $f(e^{it}) = e^{i\psi(t)}$, where ψ is continuous in $[0, 2\pi]$, and $\psi(2\pi) - \psi(0) = 2n\pi$ by (9.5.5), n being the index $j(0; \gamma)$. Let $\omega(t, \xi) = \psi(t) + \xi(nt + \psi(0) - \psi(t))$; if, for $\zeta = e^{it}$ $(0 < t < 2\pi)$ and for $0 \leqslant \xi \leqslant 1$, we write $g(\zeta, \xi) = e^{i\omega(t, \xi)}$, g is *continuous* in $(\mathbf{U} - \{1\}) \times [0, 1]$ by (9.5.7), and as $e^{i\omega(2\pi, \xi)} = e^{i\omega(0, \xi)} = f(1)$ for any ξ, g is extended by continuity to $\mathbf{U} \times [0, 1]$. By (Ap.2.5), we are thus reduced to proving the theorem for the mapping $f: \zeta \to \zeta^n$. It is clear that for $n = 0$, f is inessential. Suppose $n \neq 0$, and let us prove by contradiction that f cannot be inessential. Otherwise, there would exist a nonconstant continuous mapping h of $\mathbf{U}$ into $\mathbf{R}$ such that $\zeta^n = e^{ih(\zeta)}$ in $\mathbf{U}$. As $h(\mathbf{U})$ is a compact (3.17.9) and connected ((9.5.8) and (3.19.7)) subset of $\mathbf{R}$, $h(\mathbf{U})$ is a compact interval $[a, b]$ with $a < b$ (3.19.1). Let $\zeta_0 \in \mathbf{U}$ such that $h(\zeta_0) = a$. We therefore have $\zeta_0^n = e^{ia}$; there is a neighborhood V of ζ_0 in $\mathbf{U}$ such that the oscillation (Section 3.14) of h in V be $< \pi$; on the other hand, (9.5.7) applied to the interval $]a - \pi/n, a + \pi/n[$, proves that there exists a point $\zeta \in \mathrm{V}$ such that $\zeta^n = e^{i(a-\varepsilon)}$, where $\varepsilon > 0$ is sufficiently small. By (9.5.5), $h(\zeta) - (a - \varepsilon)$ is a multiple of 2π, and the choice of V implies that this multiple can only be 0 as soon as $\varepsilon < \pi$; but this contradicts the definition of a.

(Ap.2.9) *The identity mapping $\zeta \to \zeta$ of* $\mathbf{U}$ *onto itself is essential.*

3. CUTS OF THE PLANE

In a metric space E, we say a subset A of E *separates* two points x, y of $\mathrm{E} - \mathrm{A}$ if the connected components (Section 3.19) of x and y in $\mathrm{E} - \mathrm{A}$ are distinct. We say that A *cuts* E (or is a *cut* of E) if $\mathrm{E} - \mathrm{A}$ is not connected.

For any two points a, b of $\mathbf{C}$ such that $a \neq b$, let $s_{a,b}(z)$ be the function $z \to (z - a)/(z - b)$, defined in $\mathbf{C} - \{b\}$; it is readily verified that $s_{a,b}$ is a homeomorphism of $\mathbf{C} - \{b\}$ onto $\mathbf{C} - \{1\}$.

(Ap.3.1) (Eilenberg's criterion) *Let* H *be a compact subset of* $\mathbf{C}$*; in order that* H *separate two distinct points a, b of* $\mathbf{C} - \mathrm{H}$, *a necessary and sufficient condition is that the mapping $z \to s_{a,b}(z)/|s_{a,b}(z)|$ of* H *into* $\mathbf{U}$ *be essential.*

(a) *Sufficiency.* Suppose a and b are in the same connected component A of $\mathbf{C} - \mathrm{H}$. As $\mathbf{C} - \mathrm{H}$ is open in $\mathbf{C}$ and $\mathbf{C}$ is locally connected ((3.19.1) and (3.20.16)), A is open in $\mathbf{C}$ (3.19.5). By (9.7.2) there is a path $t \to \gamma(t)$ in A, defined in $\mathrm{I} = [0, 1]$, such that $\gamma(0) = a$, $\gamma(1) = b$. As $\gamma(t) \notin \mathrm{H}$ for any value of t, the mapping $(z, t) \to f(z, t) = s_{a,\gamma(t)}(z)/|s_{a,\gamma(t)}(z)|$ is continuous in $\mathrm{H} \times \mathrm{I}$, and $f(z, 0) = 1$, $f(z, 1) = s_{a,b}(z)/|s_{a,b}(z)|$; the result follows from (Ap.2.5).

(b) *Necessity.* Let A be the connected component of $\mathbf{C} - \mathrm{H}$ which contains a; A is open in $\mathbf{C}$ and all its frontier points are in H (they cannot be in another connected component of $\mathbf{C} - \mathrm{H}$, otherwise A would have common points with that open component (Section 3.8)); therefore $\mathrm{A} \cup \mathrm{H}$ is closed in $\mathbf{C}$, and as $b \notin \mathrm{A} \cup \mathrm{H}$, we have $d(b, \mathrm{A} \cup \mathrm{H}) > 0$. Let A′, H′ be the images of A, H under the homeomorphism $z \to s_{a,b}(z)$ of $\mathbf{C} - \{b\}$ onto $\mathbf{C} - \{1\}$; H′ is compact and A′ is a connected open subset of $\mathbf{C} - \mathrm{H}'$, which is *bounded* and *contains* 0. Moreover, the frontier points of A′ in $\mathbf{C}$ are points of H′ and (possibly) 1; hence $\bar{\mathrm{A}}'$ is compact and so is $\bar{\mathrm{A}}' \cup \mathrm{H}'$. In addition, if 1 belongs to the boundary of A′, this means that A is unbounded, hence has points in common with the exterior of a ball containing H; but as that exterior is connected (9.8.4), it is contained in A by definition of a connected component (Section 3.19). This shows that there is a ball V of center 1, such that $\mathrm{V} - \{1\} \subset \mathrm{A}'$, hence 1 is not a frontier point of $\mathbf{C} - \bar{\mathrm{A}}'$, which proves that the frontier of $\mathbf{C} - \bar{\mathrm{A}}'$ is always *contained in* H′. We have to show that the mapping $u \to u/|u|$ of H′ into $\mathbf{U}$ is essential (Ap.2.2). Suppose the contrary; then there would exist a continuous mapping f of H′ into $\mathbf{R}$ such that $u/|u| = e^{if(u)}$ for $u \in \mathrm{H}'$. By the Tietze–Urysohn theorem (4.5.1), f can be extended to a continuous mapping g of $\bar{\mathrm{A}}' \cup \mathrm{H}'$ into $\mathbf{R}$. Define a mapping h of $\mathbf{C}$ into $\mathbf{U}$ by taking $h(u) = u/|u|$ for $u \in \mathbf{C} - \bar{\mathrm{A}}'$, $h(u) = e^{ig(u)}$ for $u \in \bar{\mathrm{A}}'$; it follows at once from the definition of g that h is *continuous* in $\mathbf{C}$. Let $r > 0$ be such that $\bar{\mathrm{A}}'$ is contained in the ball B: $|z| \leqslant r$; the restriction of h to B is inessential (Ap.2.6), and so is therefore the restriction of h to S: $|z| = r$. But the identity mapping $\zeta \to \zeta$ of $\mathbf{U}$ onto itself can be written $h_1 \circ g_1$, where h_1 is the mapping $z \to z/|z|$ of S onto $\mathbf{U}$, and g_1 the mapping $\zeta \to r\zeta$ of $\mathbf{U}$ onto S. However, h_1 is the restriction of h to S, hence inessential, and therefore $h_1 \circ g_1$ would be inessential (Ap.2.2), contradicting (Ap.2.9).

(Ap.3.2) (Janiszewski's theorem) *Let* A, B *be two compact subsets of* $\mathbf{C}$, *a, b two distinct points of* $\mathbf{C} - (\mathrm{A} \cup \mathrm{B})$. *If neither* A *nor* B *separates a and b, and if* $\mathrm{A} \cap \mathrm{B}$ *is connected, then* $\mathrm{A} \cup \mathrm{B}$ *does not separate a and b.*

From the assumption and (Ap.3.1) it follows that the restrictions of $z \to s_{a,b}(z)/|s_{a,b}(z)|$ to A and B are inessential; by (Ap.2.7) the restriction of that mapping to $\mathrm{A} \cup \mathrm{B}$ is also inessential, hence the conclusion by (Ap.3.1).

4. SIMPLE ARCS AND SIMPLE CLOSED CURVES

An *injective* path $t \to \gamma(t)$ in $\mathbf{C}$, defined in $\mathrm{I} = [\alpha, \beta]$, is also called a *simple path*; a subset of $\mathbf{C}$ is called a *simple arc* if it is the set of points $\gamma(\mathrm{I})$ of a simple path. A loop γ defined in I is called a *simple loop* if $\gamma(s) \neq \gamma(t)$

for any pair of distinct points (s, t) of I, one of which is not an extremity of I. A subset of $\mathbf{C}$ is called a *simple closed curve* if it is the set of points of a simple loop. Equivalent definitions are that a simple arc is a subset homeomorphic to $[0, 1]$, and a simple closed curve a subset homeomorphic to the unit circle $\mathbf{U}$ (9.5.7).

(Ap.4.1) *The complement in* $\mathbf{C}$ *of a simple arc is connected* (*in other words, a simple arc does not cut the plane*).

Let γ be a simple path defined in I, and let f be the continuous mapping of $\gamma(\mathrm{I})$ onto I, inverse to γ. Let a, b be two distinct points of $\mathbf{C} - \gamma(\mathrm{I})$. By (Ap.3.1), we have to prove that the restriction φ of $z \to s_{a,b}(z)/|s_{a,b}(z)|$ to $\gamma(\mathrm{I})$ is inessential. But we can write $\varphi = (\varphi \circ \gamma) \circ f$; the continuous mapping $\varphi \circ \gamma$ of I into $\mathbf{U}$ is inessential (Ap.2.6), and so is therefore φ by (Ap.2.2).

(Ap.4.2) (The Jordan curve theorem) *Let* H *be a simple closed curve in* $\mathbf{C}$. *Then:*

(a) $\mathbf{C} - \mathrm{H}$ *has exactly two connected components, one of which is bounded and the other unbounded.*

(b) *The frontier of every connected component of* $\mathbf{C} - \mathrm{H}$ *is* H.

(c) *If* γ *is a simple loop defined in* I *and such that* $\gamma(\mathrm{I}) = \mathrm{H}$, *then* $j(x; \gamma) = 0$ *if* x *is in the unbounded connected component of* $\mathbf{C} - \mathrm{H}$, *and* $j(x; \gamma) = \pm 1$ *if* x *is in the bounded connected component of* $\mathbf{C} - \mathrm{H}$.

The proof is done in several steps.

(Ap.4.2.1) We first prove (b) *without* any assumption on the number of components of $\mathbf{C} - \mathrm{H}$. Let A be a connected component of $\mathbf{C} - \mathrm{H}$; as $\mathbf{C} - \mathrm{H}$ is open, we see as in (Ap.3.1) that the frontier of A is *contained* in H. Let $z \in \mathrm{H}$, and let f be a homeomorphism of $\mathbf{U}$ onto H; let $\zeta = e^{i\theta} \in \mathbf{U}$ be such that $f(\zeta) = z$. Let W be an arbitrary open neighborhood of z in $\mathbf{C}$, $\mathrm{V} \subset \mathrm{W}$ a closed ball of center z; then there is a number ω such that $0 < \omega < \pi$ and that $f(e^{it}) \in \mathrm{V}$ for $\theta - \omega < t < \theta + \omega$; let J be the image of that interval by $t \to f(e^{it})$; then the complement L of J in H is the image by $t \to f(e^{it})$ of the compact interval $[\theta + \omega - 2\pi, \theta - \omega]$ (9.5.7), and is a simple arc by (9.5.7). It follows from (Ap.4.1) that the open set $\mathbf{C} - \mathrm{L} \supset \mathbf{C} - \mathrm{H}$ is *connected*. Therefore (9.7.2) for any $x \in \mathrm{A} \subset \mathbf{C} - \mathrm{L}$, there is a path γ in $\mathbf{C} - \mathrm{L}$, defined in $\mathrm{I} = [a, b]$, such that $\gamma(a) = x$, $\gamma(b) = z$.

The set $\gamma(\mathrm{I}) \cap \mathrm{J}$ is compact and contained in V; let M be its inverse image by γ, which is a compact subset of I, such that $a \notin \mathrm{M}$; let $c = \inf \mathrm{M} > a$. Then the image by γ of the interval $[a, c[$ is a connected set P ((3.19.7) and (3.19.1)), which does not meet J nor L, hence is contained in $\mathbf{C} - (\mathrm{J} \cup \mathrm{L}) = \mathbf{C} - \mathrm{H}$; as P contains x, it is contained in A by definition. But when $t < c$ tends to c, $\gamma(t) \in \mathrm{A}$ tends to $\gamma(c) \in \mathrm{V}$, hence $\gamma(t) \in \mathrm{W}$ as soon as $c - t$ is small enough; this shows that $z \in \bar{\mathrm{A}}$. Q.E.D.

(Ap.4.2.2) We next prove the theorem under the additional assumption that H *contains a segment* S with distinct extremities. Applying to $\mathbf{C}$ a homeomorphism $z \to \lambda z + \mu$, we can suppose S in an interval $[-a, a]$ of the real line $\mathbf{R}$. Let $\rho = d(0, \mathrm{H} - \mathrm{S}) \leqslant a$, and consider an open ball D: $|z| < r$, with $r < \rho$; then $\mathrm{D} \cap (\mathbf{C} - \mathrm{H}) = \mathrm{D} \cap (\mathbf{C} - \mathrm{S})$, and it is clear that $\mathrm{D} \cap (\mathbf{C} - \mathrm{S})$ is the union of the two sets D_1: $|z| < r, \mathscr{I}z > 0$ and D_2: $|z| < r, \mathscr{I}z < 0$, which have no common points. It is immediately verified that the segment joining two points of D_1 (resp. D_2) is contained in D_1 (resp. D_2), hence (3.19.3) that D_1, D_2 are connected. On the other hand, we have seen in (Ap.4.2.1) that every connected component of $\mathbf{C} - \mathrm{H}$ meets D, hence meets D_1 or D_2; but if two connected components of $\mathbf{C} - \mathrm{H}$ meet D_1 (resp. D_2), they are necessarily identical, since D_1 (resp. D_2) is connected and contained in $\mathbf{C} - \mathrm{H}$ (3.19.4). This proves that $\mathbf{C} - \mathrm{H}$ has *at most two* connected components. We prove next that $\mathbf{C} - \mathrm{H}$ *is not connected*, hence has *exactly two* components. Suppose the contrary, and let $x \in \mathrm{D}_1$, $y \in \mathrm{D}_2$; as D is connected, $\mathbf{C} - \mathrm{D}$ does not separate x and y; on the other hand, if $\mathbf{C} - \mathrm{H}$ is connected, H does not separate x and y. But $\mathrm{H} \cap (\mathbf{C} - \mathrm{D})$ is the complement in H of the open interval $]-r, r[$; by (9.5.7), this complement is therefore a simple arc, hence connected. By Janiszewski's theorem (Ap.3.2), the union $\mathrm{H} \cup (\mathbf{C} - \mathrm{D})$ does not separate x and y; but this is absurd, since the complement of $\mathrm{H} \cup (\mathbf{C} - \mathrm{D})$ in $\mathbf{C}$ is $\mathrm{D}_1 \cup \mathrm{D}_2$, and D_1, D_2 are open sets without common points, hence $\mathrm{D}_1 \cup \mathrm{D}_2$ is not connected.

As H is compact, it is contained in a ball of center 0, whose complement in $\mathbf{C}$ is connected, hence contained in a connected component of $\mathbf{C} - \mathrm{H}$; this shows one of these components A is unbounded, and the other B is bounded. Moreover, it is clear that $j(x; \gamma) = 0$ when $x \in \mathrm{A}$ (9.8.5). On the other hand, D_1 is contained in one of the components of $\mathbf{C} - \mathrm{H}$, D_2 in the other; all we need to prove therefore is that $j(x_1; \gamma) - j(x_2; \gamma) = \pm 1$ for *one* point $x_1 \in \mathrm{D}_1$ and *one* point $x_2 \in \mathrm{D}_2$ (9.8.3). Supposing the origin of γ to be the point $a \in \mathrm{S}$, let $\mathrm{J} \subset \mathrm{I}$ be the inverse image by γ of $\mathrm{H} - \mathrm{S}$, which is a compact interval $[\alpha, \beta]$ and let γ_1 be the path $t \to \gamma(t)$ defined in J, of extremities $-a$ and a. By (Ap.1.1) there is a homotopy φ_1 in $\mathbf{C} - \bar{\mathrm{D}}$ of

γ_1 into a road γ_2, such that φ_1 is defined in $\mathrm{J} \times [0, 1]$ and $\varphi_1(\alpha, \xi) = \gamma(\alpha)$, $\varphi_1(\beta, \xi) = \gamma(\beta)$ for any ξ. Define φ in $\mathrm{I} \times [0, 1]$ as equal to φ_1 in $\mathrm{J} \times [0, 1]$ and to $\gamma(t)$ for any $(t, \xi) \in (\mathrm{I} - \mathrm{J}) \times [0, 1]$; then for any $x_1 \in \mathrm{D}_1$ (resp. $x_2 \in \mathrm{D}_2$), φ is a loop homotopy in $\mathbf{C} - \{x_1\}$ (resp. $\mathbf{C} - \{x_2\}$) of γ into a circuit γ_3. We can therefore limit ourselves to proving that $j(x_1; \gamma) - j(x_2; \gamma) = \pm 1$ when γ is a *circuit* defined in I, having the following properties: (1) $\mathrm{S} \subset \gamma(\mathrm{I})$ and if T is the inverse image $\gamma^{-1}(\mathrm{S})$, then T is a subinterval of I and the restriction of γ to T is a homeomorphism of T onto S; (2) $\gamma(\mathrm{I} - \mathrm{T})$ is contained in $\mathbf{C} - \bar{\mathrm{D}}$ (note that perhaps this new γ is *not* a simple loop). Then the inverse image by γ of the interval $[-r, r]$ is a subinterval $[\lambda, \mu]$ of T; suppose for instance that $\gamma(\lambda) = -r$, $\gamma(\mu) = r$. We can suppose (replacing γ by an equivalent circuit) that $\lambda = -\pi$, $\mu = 0$, and moreover that $-r$ is the origin of γ, so that $\mathrm{I} = [-\pi, \omega]$ with $\omega > 0$. Take $x_1 = i\xi$, $x_2 = -i\xi$ with $0 < \xi < r$; let σ be the road $t \to \gamma(t)$, $-\pi \leqslant t \leqslant 0$, δ_2 the road $t \to re^{it}$, $-\pi \leqslant t \leqslant 0$, δ_1 the road $t \to re^{-it}$, $-\pi \leqslant t \leqslant 0$. Then, Cauchy's theorem applied in the half-plane $\mathscr{I}(z) < \xi$ (resp. $\mathscr{I}(z) > -\xi$) which is a star-shaped domain (9.7.1) yields

$$\int_\sigma \frac{dz}{z - i\xi} = \int_{\delta_2} \frac{dz}{z - i\xi} \quad \text{and} \quad \int_\sigma \frac{dz}{z + i\xi} = \int_{\delta_1} \frac{dz}{z + i\xi}.$$

Hence

$$2\pi i(j(x_1; \gamma) - j(x_2; \gamma)) = \int_{\delta_2} \frac{dz}{z - i\xi} - \int_{\delta_1} \frac{dz}{z + i\xi} + \int_0^\omega \frac{2i\xi\gamma'(t)\, dt}{(\gamma(t))^2 + \xi^2}.$$

Now the left-hand side is independent of ξ, and when ξ tends to 0, the right-hand side tends to $2\pi i$, using the fact that $|\gamma(t)| \geqslant r$ for $0 \leqslant t \leqslant \omega$, the mean value theorem (to majorize the last integral), and (8.11.1).

(Ap.4.2.3) We now turn to the case in which H contains *no segment* with distinct extremities. Let a, b be two distinct points of H, S the segment of extremities a, b; we may again suppose that S is a closed interval in $\mathbf{R}$. By assumption, there is at least one point $x \in \mathrm{S} \cap (\mathbf{C} - \mathrm{H})$; let J be the connected component of x in $\mathrm{S} \cap (\mathbf{C} - \mathrm{H})$, which is an open interval $]y, z[$ since $\mathrm{S} \cap (\mathbf{C} - \mathrm{H})$ is open in $\mathbf{R}$ ((3.19.1) and (3.19.5)); moreover its extremities y, z are in H. Let g be a homeomorphism of H onto the unit circle $\mathbf{U}$, and let $g(y) = e^{ic}$, $g(z) = e^{id}$, where we may suppose that $c < d < c + 2\pi$ (9.5.7). Let U_1, U_2 be the simple arcs, images of $t \to e^{it}$, $c \leqslant t \leqslant d$, and $t \to e^{it}$, $d \leqslant t \leqslant c + 2\pi$, and let H_1, H_2 be their images by the homeomorphism f of $\mathbf{U}$ onto H, inverse to g. Using (9.5.7), we see immediately that there is a homeomorphism f_1 (resp. f_2) of U_1 (resp. U_2) onto the closed interval $\bar{J} = [y, z]$, such that $f_1(e^{ic}) = f_2(e^{ic}) = y$, $f_1(e^{id}) = f_2(e^{id}) = z$. Let h_1 (resp. h_2) be the mapping of **U** into **C**, equal to f in U_1 (resp. in U_2), to f_2 in U_2 (resp. to f_1 in U_1); the definition of J implies that h_1, h_2 are homeomorphisms of **U** onto two *simple closed curves* $G_1 = H_1 \cup J$, $G_2 = H_2 \cup J$, each of which contains the segment $\bar{J}$. Let $w \in H_1$, distinct of y and z; there is an open ball D of center w, which does not meet the compact set G_2. From (Ap.4.2.1), each connected component of $\mathbf{C} - G_1$ has points in D; moreover, if w', w'' are two points of D in a same connected component of $\mathbf{C} - G_1$, w' and w'' are not separated by G_1; they are not separated either by G_2, since they belong to $D \subset \mathbf{C} - G_2$ which is connected. But $G_1 \cap G_2 = \bar{J}$ is connected, hence, by Janiszewski's theorem (Ap.3.2), w' and w'' are not separated by $G_1 \cup G_2$, nor of course by $H \subset G_1 \cup G_2$. In other words, w' and w'' belong to the same connected component of $\mathbf{C} - H$. But as $\mathbf{C} - G_1$ has exactly two connected components, and each connected component of $\mathbf{C} - H$ has points in D by (Ap.4.2.1), it follows that $\mathbf{C} - H$ has *at most two* connected components. On the other hand, it follows from (Ap.4.2.2) that there are two points w', w'' in D which are separated by G_1. We show they are separated by H. Otherwise, as they are not separated by G_2, and $G_2 \cap H = H_2$ is connected, they would not be separated by $G_2 \cup H \supset G_1$ (Ap.3.2), contrary to assumption. We have thus shown that $\mathbf{C} - H$ has exactly two connected components; the same argument as in (Ap.4.2.2) proves that one of them, A, is unbounded and the other, B, is bounded.

Finally, we can suppose y is the origin of the loop γ, and, if $I = [\alpha, \beta]$, that $H_1 = \gamma([\alpha, \lambda])$, $H_2 = \gamma([\lambda, \beta])$. Define the loops γ_1 and γ_2 as follows: $\gamma_1(t) = (t - \alpha + 1)(y - z) + z$ for $\alpha - 1 \leqslant t \leqslant \alpha$, $\gamma_1(t) = \gamma(t)$ for $\alpha \leqslant t \leqslant \lambda$; $\gamma_2(t) = \gamma(t)$ for $\lambda \leqslant t \leqslant \beta$, $\gamma_2(t) = y + (t - \beta)(z - y)$ for $\beta \leqslant t \leqslant \beta + 1$. Using (Ap.1.1) it is immediately verified that for any point $x \notin G_1 \cup G_2$, $j(x; \gamma) = j(x; \gamma_1) + j(x; \gamma_2)$. With the same meaning as above for D, let again w', w'' be two points of D separated by G_1; then we have $j(w'; \gamma_2) = j(w''; \gamma_2)$ since w' and w'' are not separated by G_2 (9.8.3), and $j(w'; \gamma_1) - j(w''; \gamma_1) = \pm 1$ by (Ap.4.2.2). From this it follows that $j(w'; \gamma) - j(w''; \gamma) = \pm 1$, which ends the proof.

(Ap.4.3) *Let* H *be a simple closed curve in* **C**, D *the bounded connected component of* $\mathbf{C} - H$. *Then, for any loop* γ *in* D, $j(x; \gamma) = 0$ *for any* $x \in H$.

Let U be an open ball of center x, having no common points with the set $\gamma(I)$ of points of γ. There exists in U a point $z \in \mathbf{C} - (D \cup H) = \mathbf{C} - \bar{D}$ (Ap.4.2), and as U is connected, $j(x; \gamma) = j(z; \gamma)$ (9.8.3). But $j(z; \gamma) = j(y; \gamma)$

for all points y of the unbounded connected component $\mathbf{C} - \bar{\mathrm{D}}$ of H (9.8.3), and there are points $y \in \mathbf{C} - \bar{\mathrm{D}}$ which are exterior to a closed ball containing $\gamma(\mathrm{I})$; for such points, $j(y; \gamma) = 0$ (9.8.5), hence the result.

PROBLEMS

1. Let A be a connected open subset of $\mathbf{C}$; show that for any two points a, b of A, there is a *simple* path γ contained in A, having a and b as extremities, and whose set of points is a broken line (Section 5.1, Problem 4; this amounts to saying that γ is piecewise linear). (Use a similar argument as that in (9.7.2). If a "square" $\mathrm{Q} = \mathrm{I} \times \mathrm{I} \subset \mathrm{A}$ (I closed interval with nonempty interior in $\mathbf{R}$) is such that $a \notin \mathrm{Q}$, and there is a simple path $t \to \gamma_1(t)$ in A, defined in $\mathrm{J} \subset \mathbf{R}$, with origin a and extremity $c \in \mathrm{Q}$, consider the smallest value $t_0 \in \mathrm{J}$ such that $\gamma_1(t_0) \in \mathrm{Q}$, and observe that the segment of extremities $\gamma_1(t_0)$ and any point of Q is contained in Q.)
2. Is Janiszewski's theorem still true when A and B are only supposed to be closed subsets of $\mathbf{C}$, even if $\mathrm{A} \cap \mathrm{B}$ is compact (and connected)? Show that the statement of the theorem remains true in the two following cases: (1) A, B are two closed sets, one of which is compact; (2) A and B are two closed sets without a common point. (If c is a point sufficiently close to a, consider the mapping $z \to 1/(z - c)$, and the images of a, b, A and B under that mapping.)
3. For any simple closed curve H in $\mathbf{C}$, denote by $\beta(\mathrm{H})$ the bounded component of $\mathbf{C} - \mathrm{H}$.
   (a) Let A be a connected open subset of $\mathbf{C}$, H a simple closed curve contained in A. Show that $\mathrm{A} - \mathrm{H}$ has exactly two connected components, which are the intersections of A and of the connected components of $\mathbf{C} - \mathrm{H}$ (use Problem 2).
   (b) More generally, if H_i $(1 \leqslant i \leqslant r)$ are r simple closed curves contained in A, and such that no two of them have common points, the complement of $\bigcup_i \mathrm{H}_i$ in A has exactly $r + 1$ components (use induction on r).
   (c) If H, H′ are two simple closed curves without a common point in $\mathbf{C}$, show that either $\beta(\mathrm{H}) \cap \beta(\mathrm{H}') = \varnothing$, or the closure of one of the sets $\beta(\mathrm{H})$, $\beta(\mathrm{H}')$ is contained in the other. (Observe that if $\mathrm{H} \subset \beta(\mathrm{H}')$, the unbounded component of $\mathbf{C} - \mathrm{H}'$ has no common point with $\beta(\mathrm{H})$, using (3.19.9).)
   (d) Suppose a connected open subset T of $\mathbf{C}$ has a frontier which is the union of r simple closed curves H_i $(1 \leqslant i \leqslant r)$, no two of which have common points. Show that there are only two possibilities: (1) T is unbounded and no two of the sets $\beta(\mathrm{H}_i)$ have common points, their union being the complement of $\overline{\mathrm{T}}$; (2) there is one of the H_i, say H_r, such that the $\overline{\beta(\mathrm{H}_i)}$ are contained in $\beta(\mathrm{H}_r)$ for $1 \leqslant i \leqslant r-1$, no two of the $\overline{\beta(\mathrm{H}_i)}$ $(1 \leqslant i \leqslant r-1)$ have common points, and T is the complement of the union of the $\overline{\beta(\mathrm{H}_i)}$ (for $1 \leqslant i \leqslant r-1$) in $\beta(\mathrm{H}_r)$. (If γ_i is a simple loop whose set of points is H_i $(1 \leqslant i \leqslant r)$, observe that the indices $j(x; \gamma_i)$ are constant for $x \in \mathrm{T}$, and that at most one of them may be $\neq 0$; otherwise, using (c), show that one at least of the H_i would not be contained in the frontier of T.)
4. Let A be a bounded open connected subset of $\mathbf{C}$, such that for any loop γ in A and any $z \in \mathbf{C} - \mathrm{A}$, $j(z; \gamma) = 0$.
   (a) Show that for any simple closed curve $\mathrm{H} \subset \mathrm{A}$, the bounded component $\beta(\mathrm{H})$ is contained in A. (Observe that otherwise it would contain points of $\mathbf{C} - \mathrm{A}$, using (3.19.9) and part (b) of the Jordan curve theorem.)

(b) Let $(z \mid z')$ be the euclidean scalar product $xx' + yy'$ in the plane $\mathbf{C} = \mathbf{R}^2$ (with $z = x + iy$, $z' = x' + iy'$). Let P_0 be the *open hexagon* defined by the relations

$$|(z \mid 1)| < \tfrac{1}{2}, \qquad |(z \mid e^{i\pi/3})| < \tfrac{1}{2}, \qquad |(z \mid e^{-i\pi/3})| < \tfrac{1}{2}.$$

For any number $\alpha > 0$, the set of all hexagons αP_{mn} deduced from αP_0 by all translations of the form $\alpha(me^{i\pi/3} + n)$, where m and n are arbitrary integers in $\mathbf{Z}$, is called an *hexagonal net of width* α; the sets αP_{mn} (resp. $\alpha \overline{P}_{mn}$) are called the *open* (resp. *closed*) *meshes* of the net; the boundary of αP_{mn} is the union of 6 segments (the *sides* of αP_{mn}), whose extremities are called the *vertices* of αP_{mn}; the *nodes* of the hexagonal mesh are all the vertices of the meshes. Every node is a vertex of three meshes, and the other extremities of the three sides issuing from that node are called its *neighboring* nodes. Let B be the union of a finite number of closed meshes of an hexagonal net. Show that if a node belongs to fr(B), there are exactly two neighboring nodes which also belong to fr(B); conclude that fr(B) is the union of a finite number of disjoint simple closed curves, each of which is a union of sides of meshes of the net. (Start with two neighboring nodes a_1, a_2 in fr(B), and show that one may define by induction a finite sequence (a_n) of nodes belonging to fr(B), such that a_n and a_{n+1} are neighboring nodes for every n.)
(c) Let B be the union of a finite number of closed meshes of an hexagonal net of width α, such that fr(B) is a simple closed curve (union of sides of meshes of the net). Let a, b be two neighboring nodes on fr(B); prove that there exists a continuous mapping $(z, t) \to \varphi(z, t)$ of $B \times [0, 1]$ into B such that: (1) $\varphi(z, 0) = z$ in B; (2) $\varphi(z, t) = z$ for every $t \in [0, 1]$ and every z on the segment S of extremities a and b; (3) $\varphi(z, 1) \subset S$ for any $z \in B$. (Use induction on the number N of meshes contained in B; consider one side of extremities c, d, contained in fr(B), such that c and d have the same first coordinate, equal to the supremum of $\mathrm{pr}_1(B)$, and that d has the largest second coordinate among all the nodes in fr(B) having that supremum as first coordinate; show that if $N > 1$, $B = B_1 \cup P$, where P is the unique mesh contained in B and having c and d as vertices, B_1 is the union of $N - 1$ meshes, and has in common with P one, two or three sides; examine the various possibilities.) Prove that the interior of B is *simply connected.*
(d) Let B be the union of all closed meshes of an hexagonal net of width α, which are contained in A; α is taken small enough for B to be nonempty. Let D be one of the (open) connected components of $\mathring{B}$; show that fr(D) is a simple closed curve. (Use (a) and Problem 3(d), to prove that if fr(D) was the union of more than one simple closed curve, there would be simple loops γ in A and points $z \in \mathrm{fr}(A)$ such that $j(z; \gamma) = 1$.)
(e) Conclude that A is *simply connected*, and is the union of an increasing sequence (D_n) of open simply connected subsets, each of which is the bounded component of the complement of a simple closed curve (use (c) and (d)). Conversely, such a union is always simply connected.
(f) Extend the result of (e) to arbitrary simply connected open subsets of $\mathbf{C}$ (for each n, consider the closed hexagons of the hexagonal net of width $1/n$ which are contained in the intersection of A and of the ball $B(0; n)$).
(g) Let A be an open connected subset of $\mathbf{C}$ such that the complement $\mathbf{C} - A$ has no bounded component; show that A is simply connected (use (9.8.5)).
(h) Prove that any connected component of the intersection of a finite number of open simply connected sets in $\mathbf{C}$ is simply connected.

5. Show that the following open subsets of $\mathbf{C}$ are simply connected but that their frontier is not a simple closed curve:
(1) The set A_1 of points $x + iy$ such that $0 < x < 1$, $-2 < y < \sin(1/x)$.
(2) The set A_2 of points $x + iy$ such that $-1 < x < 0$ and $-1 < y < 1$, or $0 \leqslant x < 1$ and $0 < |y| < 1$.

(In both cases, define an increasing sequence of bounded components $\beta(H_n)$, where H_n is a simple closed curve, such that the union of the $\beta(H_n)$ is the given open set. To prove that $fr(A_1)$ is not homeomorphic to **U**, show that it is not locally connected, using **(3.19.1)**; to prove the similar property for $fr(A_2)$ consider the complement of the point $z = 1$ in that set.) Are $fr(A_1)$ and $fr(A_2)$ homeomorphic?

6. Let A be a simply connected open subset of **C**, distinct from **C**. Show that the frontier of A contains at least two distinct points. (Show that otherwise, one would have $A = \mathbf{C} - \{a\}$, using **(3.19.9)** and the fact that $\mathbf{C} - \{a\}$ is connected to prove that there can be no exterior point of A; conclude by using **(9.8.4)** and **(9.8.7)**.)

7. Let γ be a simple loop defined in $I = [0, 2]$, and let $H = \gamma(I)$ be the corresponding simple closed curve. Let α be a simple path defined in $I_2 = [1, 2]$ and such that: (1) $\alpha(1) = \gamma(1)$, $\alpha(2) = \gamma(2) = \gamma(0)$; (2) $\alpha(t) \in \beta(H)$ for every $t \in]1, 2[$; let $L = \alpha(I_2)$. Define the simple loops γ_1, γ_2 in I by the conditions:

$$\gamma_1(t) = \gamma(t) \quad \text{for} \quad 0 \leqslant t \leqslant 1, \qquad \gamma_1(t) = \alpha(t) \quad \text{for} \quad 1 \leqslant t \leqslant 2;$$

$$\gamma_2(t) = \alpha(2 - t) \quad \text{for} \quad 0 \leqslant t \leqslant 1, \qquad \gamma_2(t) = \gamma(t) \quad \text{for} \quad 1 \leqslant t \leqslant 2.$$

Let $H_1 = \gamma_1(I)$, $H_2 = \gamma_2(I)$.

(a) Show that for any $z \in \mathbf{C}$ which does not belong to $H_1 \cup H_2$, $j(z; \gamma) = j(z; \gamma_1) + j(z; \gamma_2)$ (use **(Ap.1.1)**).

(b) Prove that there are points $z_1 \in \beta(H)$ such that $j(z_1; \gamma_1) = 0$, and points $z_2 \in \beta(H)$ such that $j(z_2; \gamma_2) = 0$ (use (b) of the Jordan curve theorem **(Ap.4.2)**).

(c) Deduce from (a) and (b) that $\beta(H)$ is the union of $\beta(H_1)$, $\beta(H_2)$ and $L \cap \beta(H)$, no two of these sets having common points.

8. (a) Let H be a simple closed curve, L_k $(1 \leqslant k \leqslant n)$ n simple arcs, having their extremities in H, and whose points distinct from the extremities are in $\beta(H)$. Suppose in addition that no two of the L_k have common points belonging to $\beta(H)$. Then the interior of the complement of $\bigcup_{k=1}^{n} L_k$ in $\overline{\beta(H)}$ has $n + 1$ connected components, each of which is the bounded component of the complement of a simple closed curve in **C**. (Use induction on n, and Problem 7.)

(b) Let H_1, H_2 be two simple closed curves in **C**, such that $H_1 \cap H_2$ is finite. Show that each connected component of $\beta(H_1) \cap \beta(H_2)$ is the bounded component of the complement in **C** of a simple closed curve (use (a)).

9. Let γ be a simple loop in **C**, defined in $I = [-1, 1]$, let $H = \gamma(I)$, and suppose (for simplicity's sake) that $\gamma(0) = 0$ and the diameter of H is > 2. Define inductively two decreasing sequences of numbers, (α_n) and (ρ_n), tending to 0, such that $\rho_1 = 1$, α_n is the largest number > 0 such that $|\gamma(t)| < \rho_n$ for $|t| < \alpha_n$, and $\rho_{n+1} = \inf\left(\frac{1}{n+1}, \delta_n\right)$, where δ_n is the distance of 0 to the set of points $\gamma(t)$ such that $|t| \geqslant \alpha_n$.

(a) Prove that if z, z' are two points of $\beta(H)$ such that $|z| < \rho_{n+1}$ and $|z'| < \rho_{n+1}$, then there is a path of extremities z, z', contained in the intersection of $\beta(H)$ and of the closed disk of center 0 and radius ρ_n. (Let L be a simple broken line of extremities z, z', contained in $\beta(H)$ (Problem 1). Suppose first that the segment S of extremities z, z' has no point in common with L, distinct from z, z'; then $R = L \cup S$ is a simple closed curve. Prove that if $t \in I$ is such that $\gamma(t) \in \beta(R)$, then $|t| < \alpha_n$: observe that the intersection $R \cap H$ is contained in S, and show that if there was a $t \in I$ such that $\gamma(t) \in \beta(R)$ and $|t| \geqslant \alpha_n$, there would be another $t' \in I$ such that $\gamma(t') \in S$ and $|t'| \geqslant \alpha_n$, contradicting the definition of ρ_{n+1}. Conclude in that case by taking the connected component of the intersection of $\beta(R)$ and the open disk of center 0 and radius ρ_n, which contains points arbitrarily close to S, and applying Problem 8(b) to the frontier of that component. In the general case in which L and S have more than two common points, use induction on the number of these points.)

(b) Prove that for any point $x \in \beta(\mathrm{H})$, there is a simple arc of extremities 0 and x, whose points $\neq 0$ are in $\beta(\mathrm{H})$. ("Schoenflies's theorem." Consider a sequence (z_n) of points of $\beta(\mathrm{H})$ such that $|z_n| < \rho_{n+1}$, and apply (a) to two consecutive points of that sequence.)

CHAPTER X

EXISTENCE THEOREMS

There are of course many kinds of existence theorems in analysis and this chapter only deals with *one* kind, namely, those which are linked to the notion of *completeness*; roughly speaking, the most intuitive result (10.1.3) says that when in a Banach space the identity mapping is "slightly" perturbed by an additional term in the neighborhood of a point, it still remains a homeomorphism around that point. The word "slightly" has to be understood in a precise way, which means more than mere "smallness" of the perturbing function (see Section 10.2, Problem 2), and has to do with a limitation on the *rate of variation* of that function, generally referred to as a condition of "lipschitzian" type. As a consequence, the natural field of application of theorems of that type consists of equations in which some limitation is known on the *derivatives* of the given functions; furthermore, the existence theorems obtained in that way are of a *local* nature. In the next chapter, we will meet different kinds of existence theorems, which can be applied to *global* problems.

The main applications of the general existence theorems of Section 10.1 are: (1) the implicit function theorem (10.2.1) together with its consequence, the rank theorem (10.3.1) which (locally) reduces to a *canonical* form the continuously differentiable mappings of constant rank in finite dimensional spaces; (2) the Cauchy existence theorem for ordinary differential equations (10.4.5) with its various improvements and consequences; both theorems are among the most useful tools of both classical and modern analysis. Of course, what is said of differential equations in this and the next chapter is only a tiny fraction of that vast theory; other parts of it will be examined in Chapters XXIII and XXV; the reader who wants to go farther in that direction is referred to the books of Coddington-Levinson [9], Ince [12] and Kamke [14].

As a last application, we have given a proof of the theorem of Frobenius (10.9.4), which, as we state it, appears as a natural extension of the Cauchy existence theorem to functions of several variables; it is usually formulated in a more geometric way, as an existence theorem of manifolds having at each point a given "tangent space." We will deal with that formulation in Chapter XVIII.

It goes without saying that as usual we have expressed all results for vector valued functions, so that, for instance, we practically never speak of "systems" of equations; it is one of the virtues of the "vector space methods" that one never need consider more than *one* equation, at least for the proofs of the general theorems.

1. THE METHOD OF SUCCESSIVE APPROXIMATIONS

As in Chapter IX, K will denote either the real or the complex field, and whenever a statement is made about Banach spaces without specifying K, it is understood that all the Banach spaces concerned are over the same field.

(10.1.1) *Let* E, F *be two Banach spaces,* U (resp. V) *an open ball in* E (resp. F) *of center* 0 *and radius* α (resp. β). *Let* v *be a continuous mapping of* $U \times V$ *into* F, *such that* $\|v(x, y_1) - v(x, y_2)\| \leqslant k \cdot \|y_1 - y_2\|$ *for* $x \in U$, $y_1 \in V$, $y_2 \in V$, *where* k *is a constant such that* $0 \leqslant k < 1$. *Then, if* $\|v(x, 0)\| < \beta(1 - k)$ *for any* $x \in U$, *there exists a unique mapping* f *of* U *into* V *such that*

(10.1.1.1) $$f(x) = v(x, f(x))$$

for any $x \in U$; *and* f *is continuous in* U.

For any $x \in U$, we will show there exists a sequence (y_n) of points of V such that $y_0 = 0$, $y_n = v(x, y_{n-1})$ for any $n \geqslant 1$. We have to show that if y_p is defined and in V for $1 \leqslant p \leqslant n$, then $v(x, y_n) \in V$. But we have then for $2 \leqslant p \leqslant n$, $y_p - y_{p-1} = v(x, y_{p-1}) - v(x, y_{p-2})$, hence $\|y_p - y_{p-1}\| \leqslant k \cdot \|y_{p-1} - y_{p-2}\|$, and by induction on p we conclude that $\|y_p - y_{p-1}\| \leqslant k^{p-1}\|y_1\|$. Hence

(10.1.1.2) $$\|y_p\| \leqslant (1 + k + k^2 + \cdots + k^{p-1})\|y_1\| \leqslant \|y_1\|/(1 - k) < \beta$$

which proves our contention. Moreover, by induction on n, we can write $y_n = f_n(x)$, where f_n is a continuous mapping of U into V (3.11.5). We have furthermore $\|f_n(x) - f_{n-1}(x)\| \leqslant k^{n-1}\beta(1 - k)$ for $x \in U$, hence the series $(f_n - f_{n-1})$ is *normally convergent* (Section 7.1) in $\mathscr{B}_F(U)$; as F is complete, the series $(f_n(x) - f_{n-1}(x))$ is convergent for any $x \in \mathrm{U}$, and if $f(x)$ is its sum, f is *continuous* in U (7.2.1); moreover, by the principle of extension of inequalities applied to (10.1.1.2), $\|f(x)\| \leqslant \|v(x, 0)\|/(1 - k) < \beta$ for any $x \in \mathrm{U}$, hence f is a mapping of U *into* V. From the relation $f_n(x) = v(x, f_{n-1}(x))$ we deduce (10.1.1.1) by passage to the limit, for every $x \in \mathrm{U}$. Finally, suppose g is another mapping of U into V such that $g(x) = v(x, g(x))$ for any $x \in \mathrm{U}$. Then, from that relation and (10.1.1.1) we deduce

$$\|g(x) - f(x)\| = \|v(x, g(x)) - v(x, f(x))\| \leqslant k \cdot \|g(x) - f(x)\|$$

and this implies $g(x) = f(x)$ since $k < 1$.

(10.1.2) (Fixed point theorem) *Let* F *be a Banach space,* V *an open ball in* F *of center* y_0 *and radius* β. *Let* v *be a mapping of* V *into* F *such that* $\|v(y_1) - v(y_2)\| \leqslant k \cdot \|y_1 - y_2\|$ *for any pair of points* y_1, y_2 *of* V, *where k is a constant such that* $0 \leqslant k < 1$. *Then, if* $\|v(y_0) - y_0\| < \beta(1 - k)$, *there is one and only one point* $z \in \mathrm{V}$ *such that* $z = v(z)$.

Observe that v is continuous in V and apply (10.1.1) to the mapping $(x, y) \to v(y + y_0) - y_0$, which is independent of x.

(10.1.3) *Let* F *be a Banach space,* V *an open ball in* F *of center* 0 *and radius* β. *Let* w *be a mapping of* V *into* F *such that* $\|w(y_1) - w(y_2)\| \leqslant k \cdot \|y_1 - y_2\|$ *for any pair of points of* V, *with k constant and* $0 \leqslant k < 1$. *Then, if* $\|w(0)\| < \frac{1}{2}\beta(1 - k)$, *there is an open neighborhood* $\mathrm{W} \subset \mathrm{V}$ *of* 0, *such that the restriction to* W *of the mapping* $y \to g(y) = y + w(y)$ *is a homeomorphism of* W *onto an open neighborhood of* 0 *in* F.

We apply (10.1.1) to E = F, U being the open ball of center 0 and radius $\alpha = \beta(1 - k) - \|w(0)\|$, and to the mapping $(x, y) \to v(x, y) = x - w(y)$; the conditions of (10.1.1) are then verified, hence there is a continuous mapping f of U into V such that $f(x) = x - w(f(x))$, in other words $g(f(x)) = x$ for $x \in \mathrm{U}$. To prove f is a homeomorphism of U onto $f(\mathrm{U})$, we need merely to show that g is an *injective* mapping of V into $g(\mathrm{V})$ (since f is clearly injective in U); but the relation $g(y_1) = g(y_2)$ implies $\|y_1 - y_2\| = \|w(y_1) - w(y_2)\| \leqslant k\|y_1 - y_2\|$, hence $y_1 = y_2$ since $k < 1$. Therefore g is the homeomorphism of $\mathrm{W} = f(\mathrm{U})$ onto U, inverse to f; moreover $\mathrm{W} = g^{-1}(\mathrm{U})$ is open in F (3.11.4). Finally we have $0 \in \mathrm{W}$, for that condition is equivalent to $\|w(0)\| < \frac{1}{2}\beta(1 - k)$.

PROBLEMS

1. Let A be a compact metric space, d the distance on A, v a mapping of A into itself such that for every pair (x, y) of *distinct* points of A, $d(v(x), v(y)) < d(x, y)$. Show that there exists a point $z \in A$ such that $v(z) = z$. (Use contradiction, by considering the number $c = \inf_{x \in A} d(x, v(x))$ and proving that there exists a point $y \in A$ such that $d(y, v(y)) = c$.)
2. Let B be the ball $\|x\| \leqslant 1$ in the space (c_0) of Banach (Section 5.3, Problem 5). Let u be the continuous linear mapping of (c_0) into itself such that

$$u(e_n) = \left(1 - \frac{1}{2^{n+1}}\right) e_{n+1} \qquad (n \geqslant 0),$$

and let $v(x) = \frac{1}{2}(1 + \|x\|)e_0 + u(x)$. Show that v is a continuous mapping of B into itself such that for any pair (x, y) of distinct points of B, $\|v(x) - v(y)\| < \|x - y\|$, but that there is no point $z \in B$ such that $v(z) = z$ (use the inequality $\prod_{i=1}^{n}(1 - \alpha_i) \geqslant 1 - \sum_{i=1}^{n} \alpha_i$ for $0 \leqslant \alpha_i \leqslant 1$).
3. Let E, F, be two normed vector spaces, u a linear homeomorphism of E, onto a subspace $u(E)$ of F; let $v : u(E) \to E$ be the inverse mapping of u, and let $m = \|v\|$.
(a) Let A be an open subset of E, w a mapping of A into F such that $\|w(x_1) - w(x_2)\| \leqslant k\|x_1 - x_2\|$ for x_1, x_2 in A. Show that if the constant k is such that $km < 1$, then $x \to f(x) = u(x) + w(x)$ is a homeomorphism of A onto $f(A)$. If in addition, E and F are Banach spaces, and $u(E) = F$, show that $f(A)$ is an open subset of F (use (10.1.3).)
(b) Suppose w is a continuous linear mapping of E into F such that $\|w\| < 1/m$. Show that f is then a linear homeomorphism of E onto $f(E)$. Furthermore, for any $y_0 \in u(E)$ such that $\|y_0\| = 1$, show that there exists $y \in f(E)$ such that $\|y - y_0\| \leqslant m\|w\|$; conversely, for any $y \in f(E)$ such that $\|y\| = 1$, show that there exists $y_0 \in u(E)$ such that $\|y - y_0\| \leqslant m\|w\|/(1 - m\|w\|)$.
4. Let E, F be normed spaces, u a continuous linear mapping of E into F, such that $N = u^{-1}(0)$ is a finite dimensional subspace, then there exists a closed topological supplement M of N (Section 5.4) such that the restriction of u to M is a homeomorphism onto $u(M) = u(E)$ (see [6]). Let w be a continuous linear mapping of E into F; show that if $\|w\|$ is small enough, and $f = u + w$, then $f^{-1}(0)$ has finite dimension at most equal to the dimension of $u^{-1}(0)$, and there is a closed topological supplement P of $f^{-1}(0)$, such that the restriction of f to P is a homeomorphism onto $f(P) = f(E)$ (use Problem 3(b)).
5. Let E be a Banach space, F a normed space, u a linear homeomorphism of E onto $u(E)$ such that there is a topological supplement Q of $u(E)$ in F. Show that if w is a continuous linear mapping of E into F with sufficiently small norm $\|w\|$, and $f = u + w$, then Q is still a topological supplement of $f(E)$ in F. (Show that the projection of F onto $u(E)$, restricted to $f(E)$, is a linear homeomorphism onto $u(E)$ when $\|w\|$ is small enough, using Problem 3.)
6. Let E, F be two Banach spaces, u a continuous linear mapping of E into F such that $N = u^{-1}(0)$ has finite dimension p; then N has a topological supplement M such that the restriction of u to M is a homeomorphism into $u(M) = u(E)$. Suppose in addition $u(E)$ has finite codimension q in F. Let w a continuous linear mapping of E into F;

show that if $\|w\|$ is small enough, $f = u + w$ is such that the dimension r of $f^{-1}(0)$ satisfies the inequalities $p - q \leqslant r \leqslant p$, and that the codimension of $f(\mathrm{E})$ in F is equal to $q - p + r$. (Use Problems 4 and 5, as well as (5.9.3).)

7. Let $\mathrm{I} = [0, 1]$, and let P be the subspace of the Banach space $\mathscr{C}_{\mathbf{R}}(\mathrm{I})$ (Section 7.2) consisting of the restriction to I of the *polynomials* $x(t)$ with real coefficients. In the normed space P, let u be the identity mapping $x \to x$, and let w be the linear mapping which to each polynomial $x(t)$ (restricted to I) associates the polynomial $x(t^2)$, restricted to I. For any ε such that $0 < \varepsilon < 1$, the linear mapping $f = u + \varepsilon w$ is a linear homeomorphism of P onto the subspace $f(\mathrm{P})$, but the codimension of $f(\mathrm{P})$ in P is infinite (compare to Problem 6).

8. Let E, F be two Banach spaces, u a continuous linear mapping of E into F such that $u(\mathrm{E}) = \mathrm{F}$; then there exists a number $m > 0$ such that for any $y \in \mathrm{F}$ there is an $x \in \mathrm{E}$ for which $u(x) = y$ and $\|x\| \leqslant m\|y\|$ (12.16.10). Let w be a continuous mapping of an open ball $\mathrm{U} = \mathrm{B}(a; r) \subset \mathrm{E}$ into F, such that $\|w(x_1) - w(x_2)\| \leqslant k\|x_1 - x_2\|$ for x_1, x_2 in U. Prove that if k and $\|w(a)\|$ are small enough, the continuous mapping $x \to f(x) = u(x) + w(x)$ is such that $f(\mathrm{U})$ contains an open ball of center $u(a)$. (Use the same method as in the proof of (10.1.1).)

9. Suppose E, F, U, V, and v satisfy the assumptions of (10.1.1). In addition, let φ be a continuous mapping of U into itself such that $\|\varphi(x)\| \leqslant \|x\|$ for any $x \in \mathrm{U}$. Show that (under the condition $\|v(x, 0)\| < \beta(1 - k)$ for $x \in \mathrm{U}$) there exists a unique mapping f of U into V such that $f(x) = v(x, f(\varphi(x)))$ and that f is continuous in U.

Generalize to equations of the form $f(x) = v(x, f(\varphi_1(x)), \ldots, f(\varphi_p(x)))$.

10. Let E, F, U, V have the same meaning as in (10.1.1). Suppose the continuous mapping v of $\mathrm{U} \times \mathrm{V}$ into F satisfies the following conditions:

$$(1) \qquad \|v(x, y_1) - v(x, y_2)\| \leqslant c(\|x\|^{2\mu} + \|y_1\|^{2\mu} + \|y_2\|^{2\mu})\|y_1 - y_2\|;$$

$$(2) \qquad \|v(x, 0)\| \leqslant c\|x\|^{1+2\mu},$$

where c and μ are constants >0. Let λ be an element of K such that $|\lambda| > 1$. Finally, let $x \to L(x)$ be a continuous linear mapping of E into F, and let $x \to \varphi(x)$ be a continuous mapping of U into itself such that $\|\varphi(x)\| \leqslant \|x\|$. Show that there exists a mapping f of a neighborhood $\mathrm{W} \subset \mathrm{U}$ of 0 into V, having the following properties: (1) f satisfies in W the equation

$$f(x) - \lambda f\left(\frac{x}{\lambda}\right) = v(x, f(\varphi(x)));$$

(2) $\lim_{x \to 0,\, x \neq 0} (f(x) - L(x))/\|x\| = 0$. Furthermore, any two mappings having these properties coincide in a neighborhood of 0. (Reduce the problem to the case in which $L(x) = 0$. Observe that if f satisfies the preceding conditions, then one must have in a neighborhood of 0

$$(*) \qquad f(x) = \sum_{n=0}^{\infty} \lambda^n v\left(\frac{x}{\lambda^n}, f\left(\varphi\left(\frac{x}{\lambda^n}\right)\right)\right)$$

where the series is normally convergent in a neighborhood of 0. Then use the method of (10.1.1) to prove the existence of a solution of $(*)$ in a sufficiently small neighborhood of 0; show, by induction on n, that there exists an $r > 0$ such that, for $\|x\| \leqslant r$, $\|f_n(x)\| \leqslant \|x\|^{1+\mu}$ and $\|f_n(x) - f_{n-1}(x)\| \leqslant \|x\|^{1+n\mu}$).

11. (a) Let $F(x_1, \ldots, x_p, y)$ be an entire function in K^{p+1}, such that in the power series equal to $F(x_1, \ldots, x_p, y)$, all monomials have a total degree $\geqslant 2$. Let φ be a linear mapping of K^p into itself such that $\|\varphi(x)\| \leqslant \|x\|$ for any $x = (x_1, \ldots, x_p) \in K^p$; finally, let $L(x)$ be an arbitrary linear form on K^p. Show that there is a unique solution f of the equation

$$f(x) - \lambda f(x/\lambda) = F(x, f(\varphi(x))) \qquad (|\lambda| > 1)$$

which is defined in a neighborhood of 0 and such that $\lim_{x \to 0} (f(x) - L(x))/\|x\| = 0$. Furthermore, that solution is an entire function in K^p. (Apply Problem 10 in a neighborhood of 0; reduce the problem to the case $K = C$, and apply (9.4.2) and (9.12.1) to prove that f is an entire function.)

(b) Show that there is no solution of the equation $f(x) - \lambda f(x/\lambda) = x$ ($\lambda > 1$) defined in a neighborhood of 0 in $\mathbf{R}$ and such that $f(x)/x$ is bounded in a neighborhood of 0.

12. Let $I = [0, a]$, $H = [-b, b]$, and let f be a real valued continuous function in $I \times H$; put $M = \sup_{(x,y) \in I \times H} |f(x, y)|$, and let $J = [0, \inf(a, b/M)]$.

(a) For any $x \in J$, let $E(x)$ be the set of values of $y \in H$ such that $y = xf(x, y)$. Show that $E(x)$ is a nonempty closed set; if $g_1(x) = \inf(E(x))$, $g_2(x) = \sup(E(x))$, show that $g_1(0) = g_2(0) = 0$, and that $\lim_{x \to 0, x > 0} g_1(x)/x = \lim_{x \to 0, x > 0} g_2(x)/x = f(0, 0)$. If $g_1 = g_2 = g$ in J, g is continuous (cf. Section 3.20, Problem 5).

(b) Suppose $a = b = 1$; let E be the union of the family of the segments $S_n : x = 1/2^n$, $1/4^{n+1} \leqslant y \leqslant 1/4^n$ ($n \geqslant 0$), of the segments $S'_n : y = 1/4$, $1/2^n \leqslant x \leqslant 1/2^{n-1}$ ($n \geqslant 1$) and of the point (0, 0). Define $f(x, y)$ as follows: $f(0, y) = 0$; for $1/2^n < x \leqslant 1/2^{n-1}$ and $y \leqslant 1/4^n$, take $f(x, y) = ((y/x) + d((x, y), E))^+$; for $1/2^n < x \leqslant 1/2^{n-1}$ and $1/4^n \leqslant y \leqslant x^2$, take $f(x, y) = (y/x) - d((x, y), E)$ and finally, for $1/2^n < x \leqslant 1/2^{n-1}$ and $y \leqslant x^2$, take $f(x, y) = x - d((x, x^2), E)$ ($n \geqslant 1$). Show that f is continuous, but that there is no function g, continuous in a neighborhood of 0 in I and such that $g(x) = xf(x, g(x))$ in that neighborhood.

(c) Let u_0 be a continuous mapping of J into H, and define by induction $u_n(x) = xf(x, u_{n-1}(x))$ for $n \geqslant 1$; the functions u_n are continuous mappings of J into H. With the notations of (a), suppose that in an interval $[0, c] \subset J$, $\lim_{n \to \infty} (u_{n+1}(x) - u_n(x)) = 0$ for every x, and $g_1(x) = g_2(x)$; show that $\lim_{n \to \infty} u_n(x) = g_1(x)$ for $0 \leqslant x \leqslant c$. Apply that criterion to the two following cases: (1) there exists $k > 0$ such that $|f(x, z_1) - f(x, z_2)| \leqslant k|z_1 - z_2|$ for $x \in I$, z_1, z_2 in H (compare to (10.1.1)); (2) for $0 < x \leqslant \gamma \leqslant a$ and z_1, z_2 in H, $|f(x, z_1) - f(x, z_2)| < |z_1 - z_2|/x$.

(d) When f is defined as in (b), the sequence $(u_n(x))$ is convergent for every $x \in I$, to a limit which is not continuous.

(e) Take $a = b = 1$, $f(x, y) = y/x$ for $0 < x \leqslant 1$, $|y| \leqslant x^2$, $f(x, y) = x$ for $0 \leqslant x \leqslant 1$, $y \geqslant x^2$, $f(x, y) = -x$ for $0 \leqslant x \leqslant 1$, $y \leqslant -x^2$. Any continuous function g in I such that $|g(x)| \leqslant x^2$ is a solution of $g(x) = xf(x, g(x))$ although $|f(x, z_1) - f(x, z_2)| \leqslant |z_1 - z_2|/x$ for $0 < x \leqslant 1$, z_1, z_2 in H; for any choice of u_0, the sequence (u_n) converges uniformly to such a solution.

(f) Define f as in (e), and let $f_1(x, y) = -f(x, y)$. The function 0 is the only solution of $g(x) = xf_1(x, g(x))$, but there are continuous functions u_0 for which the sequence $(u_n(x))$ is not convergent for any $x \neq 0$, although $|f_1(x, z_1) - f_1(x, z_2)| \leqslant |z_1 - z_2|/x$ for $0 < x \leqslant 1$, z_1, z_2 in H.

13. Generalize the results of Problems 12(a) and 12(c) when H is replaced by a disk of center (0, 0) in $\mathbf{R}^2$ (use the result of Problem 3 of Section 10.2).

2. IMPLICIT FUNCTIONS

(10.2.1) (The implicit function theorem) *Let* E, F, G *be three Banach spaces, f a continuously differentiable mapping* (Section 8.9) *of an open subset* A *of* E × F *into* G. *Let* (x_0, y_0) *be a point of* A *such that* $f(x_0, y_0) = 0$ *and that the partial derivative* $D_2 f(x_0, y_0)$ *be a linear homeomorphism of* F *onto* G. *Then, there is an open neighborhood* U_0 *of* x_0 *in* E *such that, for every open* connected *neighborhood* U *of* x_0, *contained in* U_0, *there is a unique continuous mapping* u *of* U *into* F *such that* $u(x_0) = y_0$, $(x, u(x)) \in A$ *and* $f(x, u(x)) = 0$ *for any* $x \in U$. *Furthermore,* u *is continuously differentiable in* U, *and its derivative is given by*

(10.2.1.1) $$u'(x) = -(D_2 f(x, u(x)))^{-1} \circ (D_1 f(x, u(x))).$$

Let T_0 be the linear homeomorphism $D_2 f(x_0, y_0)$ of F onto G, T_0^{-1} the inverse linear homeomorphism; write the relation $f(x, y) = 0$ under the equivalent form

(10.2.1.2) $$y = y - T_0^{-1} \cdot f(x. y)$$

and write $g(x, y)$ the right-hand side of (10.2.1.2). We are going to prove that it is possible to apply (10.1.1) to the mapping

$$(x', y') \to g(x_0 + x', y_0 + y') - y_0$$

of E × F into F, in a sufficiently small neighborhood of (0, 0). As $T_0^{-1} \circ T_0 = 1$ by definition, we can write, for (x, y_1) and (x, y_2) in A,

$$g(x, y_1) - g(x, y_2) = T_0^{-1} \cdot (D_2 f(x_0, y_0) \cdot (y_1 - y_2) - (f(x, y_1) - f(x, y_2))).$$

Let $\varepsilon' > 0$ be such that $\varepsilon \|T_0^{-1}\| \leqslant \frac{1}{2}$; as f is continuously differentiable in A, it follows from (8.6.2) and (8.9.1) that there is a ball U_0 (resp. V_0) of center x_0 (resp. y_0) and radius α (resp. β) in E (resp. F) such that, for $x \in U_0$, $y_1 \in V_0$, $y_2 \in V_0$, we have

$$\|f(x, y_1) - f(x, y_2) - D_2 f(x_0, y_0) \cdot (y_1 - y_2)\| \leqslant \varepsilon \|y_1 - y_2\|;$$

whence $\|g(x, y_1) - g(x, y_2)\| \leqslant \varepsilon \|T_0^{-1}\| \cdot \|y_1 - y_2\| \leqslant \frac{1}{2}\|y_1 - y_2\|$ for any $x \in U_0$, $y_1 \in V_0$, $y_2 \in V_0$. On the other hand, $g(x, y_0) - y_0 = -T_0^{-1} \cdot f(x, y_0)$; as $f(x_0, y_0) = 0$ and f is continuous, we can suppose ε has been taken small enough to have $\|g(x, y_0) - y_0\| \leqslant \beta/2$ for $x \in U_0$. We can then apply (10.1.1), which yields the existence and uniqueness of a mapping u of U_0 *into* V_0, such that $f(x, u(x)) = 0$ for every $x \in U_0$; as $f(x_0, y_0) = 0$, this gives in particular $u(x_0) = y_0$; finally u is continuous in U_0.

Next we prove that if $U \subset U_0$ is a *connected* open neighborhood of x_0, u is the unique *continuous* mapping of U *into* F such that $u(x_0) = y_0$, $(x, u(x)) \in A$ and $f(x, u(x)) = 0$. Let v be a second mapping verifying these conditions, and consider the subset $M \subset U$ of the points x such that $u(x) = v(x)$. This set contains x_0 by definition and is closed (3.15.1); we need therefore only prove M is *open* (Section 3.19). But by assumption, $x \to D_2 f(x, u(x))$ is continuous in U_0, hence (replacing if necessary U_0 by a smaller neighborhood), we can suppose that $D_2 f(x, u(x))$ is a *linear homeomorphism* of F onto G for $x \in U_0$, by (8.3.2). Let $a \in M$; the first part of the proof shows that there exists an open neighborhood $U_a \subset U$ of a and an open neighborhood $V_a \subset V$ of $b = u(a)$ such that, for any $x \in U_a$, $u(x)$ is the only solution y of the equation $f(x, y) = 0$ *such that* $y \in V_a$. However, as v is continuous at the point a, and $v(a) = u(a)$, there is a neighborhood W of a, contained in U_a and such that $v(x) \in V_a$ for $x \in W$; the preceding remark then shows that $v(x) = u(x)$ for $x \in W$, and this proves M is open, hence $u = v$ in U.

Finally we show that u is continuously differentiable in U_0, provided ε has been taken small enough. For x and $x + s$ in U_0, let us write $t = u(x + s) - u(x)$; by assumption $f(x + s, u(x) + t) = 0$, and t tends to 0 when s tends to 0. Hence, for a given $x \in U_0$, and for any $\delta > 0$, there is $r > 0$ such that the relation $\|s\| \leqslant r$ implies $\|f(x + s, u(x) + t) - f(x, u(x)) - S(x) \cdot s - T(x) \cdot t\| \leqslant \delta(\|s\| + \|t\|)$ where $S(x) = D_1 f(x, u(x))$ and $T(x) = D_2 f(x, u(x))$ (8.9.1). This is equivalent by definition to

$$\|S(x) \cdot s + T(x) \cdot t\| \leqslant \delta(\|s\| + \|t\|)$$

and as $T(x)$ is a linear homeomorphism of F onto G, we deduce from the preceding relation

$$\text{(10.2.1.3)} \qquad \|(T^{-1}(x) \circ S(x)) \cdot s + t\| \leqslant \delta\|T^{-1}(x)\|(\|s\| + \|t\|).$$

Suppose δ has been taken such that $\delta\|T^{-1}(x)\| \leqslant \frac{1}{2}$; then, if we put $a = 2\|T^{-1}(x) \circ S(x)\| + 1$, we deduce from (10.2.1.3) that

$$\|t\| - \frac{a-1}{2}\|s\| \leqslant \frac{1}{2}(\|t\| + \|s\|)$$

i.e., $\|t\| \leqslant a\|s\|$, and therefore

$$\|t + (T^{-1}(x) \circ S(x)) \cdot s\| \leqslant \delta(a + 1)\|T^{-1}(x)\| \cdot \|s\|$$

as soon as $\|s\| \leqslant r$. By definition of t, this proves u is differentiable at the point x and has a derivative given by (10.2.1.1). Using (8.3.2) and (8.3.1), formula (10.2.1.1) then proves u is continuously differentiable in U_0.

We formulate explicitly the most important case of (10.2.1), i.e. the one in which $E = K^m$, $F = G = K^n$ are *finite dimensional spaces*:

(10.2.2) *Let f_i be n scalar functions defined and continuously differentiable in a neighborhood* $U \times V$ *of a point* $(a_1, \dots, a_m, b_1, \dots, b_n)$ *of* $E \times F$, *such that* $f_i(a_1, \dots, a_m, b_1, \dots, b_n) = 0$ *for* $1 \leqslant i \leqslant n$, *and that the jacobian* $\dfrac{\partial(f_1, \dots, f_n)}{\partial(y_1, \dots, y_n)}$ *is not* 0 *at* $(a_1, \dots, a_m, b_1, \dots, b_n)$. *Then there is an open neighborhood* $W_0 \subset U$ *of* $(a_1, \dots, a_m)$ *such that, for any connected open neighborhood* $W \subset W_0$ *of* $(a_1, \dots, a_m)$, *there is a unique system of n scalar functions* g_i $(1 \leqslant i \leqslant n)$, *defined and continuous in* W *and such that* $g_i(a_1, \dots, a_m) = b_i$ *for* $1 \leqslant i \leqslant n$, *and*

$$f_i(x_1, \dots, x_m, g_1(x_1, \dots, x_m), \dots, g_n(x_1, \dots, x_m)) = 0$$

for $1 \leqslant i \leqslant n$ *and any* $(x_1, \dots, x_m) \in W$. *Moreover, the functions* g_i *are continuously differentiable in* W, *and the jacobian matrix* $(D_j g_i(x))$ *is equal to* $-B^{-1}A$, *where* A (resp. B) *is obtained by replacing* y_i *by* $g_i(x_1, \dots, x_m)$ $(1 \leqslant i \leqslant n)$ *in the jacobian matrix* $(\partial f_i / \partial x_k)$ (resp. $(\partial f_i / \partial y_j)$).

(10.2.3) *If the assumptions of* (10.2.1) *are verified, and if in addition f is p times continuously differentiable in a neighborhood of* (x_0, y_0), *then u is p times continuously differentiable in a neighborhood of* x_0.

We prove by induction on k that u is k times continuously differentiable for $1 \leqslant k \leqslant p$; for $k = 1$, this follows from (10.2.1), and moreover $u'(x) = F(x, u(x))$, where $F(x, y) = -(D_2 f(x, y))^{-1} \circ (D_1 f(x, y))$ is $p - 1$ times continuously differentiable by (8.12.9), (8.12.11), and (8.12.10). By (8.12.10), u' is therefore $k - 1$ times continuously differentiable (for $k \leqslant p$) and that means that u is k times continuously differentiable by (8.12.5).

(10.2.4) *Suppose* E, F, G *are finite dimensional, and f is analytic in* A; *then u is analytic in a neighborhood of* x_0.

If the field of scalars K is **C**, the result follows from (10.2.1) and the characterization of analytic functions as continuously differentiable functions (9.10.1). Suppose now $K = \mathbf{R}$, $E = \mathbf{R}^m$, $F = G = \mathbf{R}^n$; then there is an open set $B \subset \mathbf{C}^{m+n}$ such that $B \cap \mathbf{R}^{m+n} = A$ and an analytic mapping g of B into $\mathbf{C}^n$ which extends f (9.4.5). Identifying $D_2 f$ and $D_2 g$ with jacobian matrices shows that $D_2 g(x_0, y_0)$ transforms a basis of $\mathbf{R}^n$ over **R** into a basis of $\mathbf{R}^n$, and these bases are also bases of $\mathbf{C}^n$ over **C**, hence $D_2 g(x_0, y_0)$ is a linear homeomorphism of $\mathbf{C}^n$ onto itself. We therefore can apply (10.2.1) to g, which shows the existence of an analytic mapping v of a neighborhood W of x_0 in $\mathbf{C}^m$ such that $g(z, v(z)) = 0$ and $v(x_0) = y_0$. Moreover, it follows from formula (10.2.1.1) by induction on $|\nu|$ that all the derivatives $D^\nu v$ at the point x_0 map $\mathbf{R}^m$ *into*

$\mathbf{R}^n$ (since all derivatives of g at (x_0, y_0) are equal to the corresponding derivatives of f); hence, by (9.3.5.1), v maps a neighborhood of x_0 *in* $\mathbf{R}^m$ into the space $\mathbf{R}^n$, and the uniqueness part of (10.2.1) therefore proves that the restriction of v to $W \cap \mathbf{R}^m$ is identical to u. Q.E.D.

One of the most important applications of (10.2.1) is the following:

(10.2.5) *Let* E, F *be two Banach spaces, f a continuously differentiable mapping of a neighborhood* V *of $x_0 \in$ E into* F. *If $f'(x_0)$ is a linear homeomorphism of* E *onto* F, *there exists an open neighborhood* $U \subset V$ *of x_0 such that the restriction of f to* U *is a homeomorphism of* U *onto an open neighborhood of $y_0 = f(x_0)$ in* F. *Furthermore, if f is p times continuously differentiable in* U (resp. *analytic in* U, E *and* F *being finite dimensional*), *the inverse mapping g of f*(U) *onto* U *is p times continuously differentiable* (resp. *analytic*) *in f*(U).

Apply (10.2.1) to the function $h(x, y) = f(x) - y$, exchanging the roles of x and y; as $D_1 h(x_0, y_0) = f'(x_0)$, we conclude that there is an open ball W of center y_0 in F and a continuous mapping g of W into E such that $g(W) \subset U$, $f(g(y)) = y$ in W and $g(y_0) = x_0$; furthermore, by (10.2.3) (resp. (10.2.4)), if f is p times continuously differentiable (resp. analytic), g is p times continuously differentiable (resp. analytic). From the identity $f(g(y)) = y$ it follows that g is injective in W, hence is a bijective continuous mapping of W onto $V = g(W) \subset U$; moreover, $g(W) = f^{-1}(W)$ is open in E, and f is a homeomorphism of $V = g(W)$ onto W, which ends the proof.

PROBLEMS

1. Let E, F be two Banach spaces, A an open neighborhood of a point $x_0 \in E$, f a continuous mapping of A into F, which is differentiable at x_0 (but not necessarily at other points of A). Suppose $f'(x_0)$ is a linear homeomorphism of E onto its image in F; show that there is a neighborhood $U \subset A$ of x_0 such that $f(x) \neq f(x_0)$ for every $x \in U$ such that $x \neq x_0$. (Observe that the assumption implies the existence of a constant $c > 0$ such that $\|f'(x_0) \cdot s\| \geqslant c\|s\|$ for all $s \in E$ (5.5.1).)
2. Let $f = (f_1, f_2)$ be the mapping of $\mathbf{R}^2$ into itself defined by $f_1(x_1, x_2) = x_1$; $f_2(x_1, x_2) = x_2 - x_1^2$ for $x_1^2 \leqslant x_2$, $f_2(x_1, x_2) = (x_2^2 - x_1^2 x_2)/x_1^2$ for $0 \leqslant x_2 \leqslant x_1^2$, and finally $f_2(x_1, -x_2) = -f_2(x_1, x_2)$ for $x_2 \geqslant 0$. Show that f is differentiable at every point of $\mathbf{R}^2$; at the point $(0, 0)$, Df is the identity mapping of $\mathbf{R}^2$ onto itself, but Df is not continuous. Show that in every neighborhood of $(0, 0)$, there are pairs of distinct points x', x'' such that $f(x') = f(x'')$ (compare to (10.2.5)).

3. Let B be the unit disc $|z| \leqslant 1$ in $\mathbf{R}^2$ and let $z \to f(z) = z + g(z)$ be a continuous mapping of B into $\mathbf{R}^2$ such that $|g(z)| < |z|$ for every z such that $|z| = 1$. Show that $f(\mathrm{B})$ is a neighborhood of 0 in $\mathbf{R}^2$ ("Brouwer's theorem" for the plane, cf. Chapter XXIV). (Let γ be the loop $t \to f(e^{it})$ defined in $[0, 2\pi]$; show that $j(x; \gamma) = 1$ for all points x in a neighborhood V of 0 (see proof of (9.8.3)); using the fact that, in B, γ is homotopic to 0, deduce that there is no point of V belonging to the complement of $f(\mathrm{B})$.)

4. Let E, F be two Banach spaces, B the unit open ball $\|x\| < 1$ in E; let u_0 be a continuously differentiable homeomorphism of B onto a neighborhood of 0 in F, such that $u_0(0) = 0$; suppose u_0^{-1} is continuously differentiable in a ball $\mathrm{V}_0 : \|y\| < r$ contained in $u_0(\mathrm{B})$, and $\mathrm{D}u_0$ is bounded in B and $\mathrm{D}u_0^{-1}$ is bounded in V_0. Let V be a ball $\|y\| < \beta$, with $\beta < r$.

(a) Show that for any $\alpha < 1$, there is a neighborhood H of u_0 in the space $\mathscr{D}_{\mathrm{F}}^{(1)}(\mathrm{B})$ (Section 8.12, Problem 8) such that for any $u \in \mathrm{H}$, the restriction of u to U: $\|x\| < \alpha$ is a homeomorphism of U onto an open set of F containing V, such that the restriction of u^{-1} to V is a continuously differentiable mapping $\Phi(u)$ of V into E. (Use (10.1.1).)

(b) Show that the mapping $u \to \Phi(u)$ of H into $\mathscr{D}_{\mathrm{E}}^{(1)}(\mathrm{V})$ is differentiable at the point u_0, and that its derivative at u_0 is the linear mapping $s \to -(u_0' \circ \Phi(u_0))^{-1} \cdot (s \circ \Phi(u_0))$.

5. Let E, F be two Banach spaces, f a continuously differentiable mapping of a neighborhood V of $x_0 \in \mathrm{E}$ into F. Suppose there are two numbers $\beta > 0$, $\lambda > 0$ such that: (1) $\|f(x_0)\| < \beta/2\lambda$; (2) in the ball U: $\|x - x_0\| < \beta$, the oscillation of f' is $\leqslant 1/2\lambda$; (3) for every $x \in \mathrm{U}$, $f'(x)$ is a linear homeomorphism of E onto F such that $\|(f'(x))^{-1}\| \leqslant \lambda$. Let (z_n) be an arbitrary sequence of points of U; show that there exists a sequence $(x_n)_{n \geqslant 0}$ of points of U such that $x_{n+1} = x_n - (f'(z_n))^{-1} \cdot f(x_n)$ for $n \geqslant 0$. Prove that the sequence (x_n) converges to a point $y \in \mathrm{U}$, such that y is the only solution of the equation $f(x) = 0$ in U. ("Newton's method of approximation." Use (8.6.2) to prove by induction on n that $\|x_n - x_{n-1}\| < 2^{-n}\beta$ and $\|f(x_n)\| < \beta/2^{n+1}\lambda$).

6. Let E, F be two *finite dimensional* vector spaces over K, A a connected open subset of E, f a continuously differentiable mapping of $\mathrm{A} \times \mathrm{F}$ into F. Suppose that the set Γ of pairs $(x, y) \in \mathrm{A} \times \mathrm{F}$ such $f(x, y) = 0$ is not empty, and that for any $(x, y) \in \Gamma$, $\mathrm{D}_2 f(x, y)$ is an invertible linear mapping of F onto itself.

(a) Show that for every point $(x_0, y_0) \in \Gamma$ there is an open neighborhood V of that point *in* Γ such that the restriction of the projection pr_1 to V is a homeomorphism of V onto an open ball of center x_0 contained in A. (Use the fact that there is an open ball U of center x_0 in A and an open ball W of center y_0 in F such that for each $x \in \mathrm{U}$, the equation $f(x, y) = 0$ has a unique solution $y \in \mathrm{W}$, and apply (10.2.1).)

(b) Deduce from (a) that every connected component G of Γ (Section 3.19) is open in Γ and that $\mathrm{pr}_1(\mathrm{G})$ is open in A. It is not necessarily true that $\mathrm{pr}_1(\Gamma) = \mathrm{A}$ (as the example $\mathrm{A} = \mathrm{E} = \mathrm{F} = \mathbf{R}$, $f(x,y) = xy^2 - 1$ shows), nor that if $\mathrm{pr}_1(\Gamma) = \mathrm{A}$, $\mathrm{pr}_1(\mathrm{G}) = \mathrm{A}$ for every connected component G of Γ (as the example $\mathrm{A} = \mathrm{E} = \mathrm{F} = \mathbf{R}$, $f(x, y) = xy^2 - y$ shows). Prove that if $\mathrm{pr}_2(\Gamma)$ is bounded in F, then $\mathrm{pr}_1(\mathrm{G}) = \mathrm{A}$ for every connected component G of Γ. (If x_0 is a cluster point of $\mathrm{pr}_1(\mathrm{G})$ in A, show that there is a sequence (x_n, y_n) of points of G such that $\lim_{n \to \infty} x_n = x_0$ and that $\lim_{n \to \infty} y_n$ exists in F; apply then (a).)

(c) The notations of *path, loop, homotopy*, and *loop homotopy* in A are defined as in Section 9.6, replacing $\mathbf{C}$ by E. Suppose there is a connected component G of Γ such that $\mathrm{pr}_1(\mathrm{G}) = \mathrm{A}$; if γ is a path in A, defined in $\mathrm{I} = [a, b] \subset \mathbf{R}$, show that there exists a continuous mapping u of I into G such that $\mathrm{pr}_1(u(t)) = \gamma(t)$ for each $t \in \mathrm{I}$ (consider the l.u.b. c in I of the points ξ such that there exists a continuous mapping u_ξ of $[a, \xi]$ into G such that $\mathrm{pr}_1(u_\xi(t)) = \gamma(t)$ for $a \leqslant t \leqslant \xi$ and use (a)). Is that mapping always unique? (Consider the case $\mathrm{E} = \mathrm{F} = \mathbf{C}$, $\mathrm{A} = \mathbf{C} - \{0\}$, $f(x, y) = y^2 - x$.)

Show that if two continuous mappings u, v of I into G are such that $\mathrm{pr}_1(u(t)) = \mathrm{pr}_1(v(t)) = \gamma(t)$ for each $t \in \mathrm{I}$, and if they are equal for one value of $t \in \mathrm{I}$, then $u = v$ (use a similar method).

(d) Under the same assumptions as in (c), let φ be a continuous mapping of $\mathrm{I} \times \mathrm{J}$ into A, where $\mathrm{J} = [c, d] \subset \mathbf{R}$. Let v be a continuous mapping of J into G such that $\mathrm{pr}_1(v(\xi)) = \varphi(a, \xi)$ for $\xi \in \mathrm{J}$; and for each $\xi \in \mathrm{J}$, let u_ξ be the unique continuous mapping of I into G such that $\mathrm{pr}_1(u_\xi(t)) = \varphi(t, \xi)$ for $t \in \mathrm{I}$ and $u_\xi(a) = v(\xi)$. Show that the mapping $(t, \xi) \to u_\xi(t)$ is continuous in $\mathrm{I} \times \mathrm{J}$. (Given $\zeta \in \mathrm{J}$, there is a number $r > 0$ such that for any $t \in \mathrm{I}$, the intersection V_t of Γ and of the closed ball in $\mathrm{E} \times \mathrm{F}$, of center $u_\zeta(t)$ and radius r, is contained in G and such that pr_1 is a homeomorphism of V_t onto the closed ball in E of center $\gamma(t)$ and radius r. If $\mathrm{L} = u_\zeta(\mathrm{I})$, let M be the supremum of $\|(\mathrm{D}_2 f(x, y))^{-1} \circ (\mathrm{D}_1 f(x, y))\|$ for all points $(x, y) \in \mathrm{G}$ at a distance $\leqslant r$ of L. Let $\varepsilon > 0$ be such that $\varepsilon < r/4$ and $\varepsilon \mathrm{M} < r/4$. Show that if δ is such that the relation $|\xi - \zeta| \leqslant \delta$ implies $\|\varphi(t, \xi) - \varphi(t, \zeta)\| \leqslant \varepsilon$ for $t \in \mathrm{I}$, then the relation $|\xi - \zeta| \leqslant \delta$ implies $\|u_\xi(t) - u_\zeta(t)\| \leqslant r/4$ for $t \in \mathrm{I}$; prove this by considering the l.u.b. of the $t \in \mathrm{I}$ for which the inequality holds, and using **(10.2.1)**.)

(e) Conclude from (d) that if the loop γ defined in $\mathrm{I} = [a, b]$ is loop homotopic to a point in A, then any continuous mapping u of I into G such that $\mathrm{pr}_1(u(t)) = \gamma(t)$ for $t \in \mathrm{I}$ is such that $u(b) = u(a)$. In particular, if A is *simply connected* (i.e., if any loop in A is homotopic to a point in A), then pr_1 is a *homeomorphism of* G *onto* A, i.e. there exists a *unique* continuously differentiable mapping g *of* A *into* F such that $f(x, g(x)) = 0$ in A and that $(x, g(x))$ belongs to G for at least one $x \in \mathrm{A}$ (cf. **(16.28.7)**.)

7. With the notations of Problem 6, show that the condition $\mathrm{pr}_1(\mathrm{G}) = \mathrm{A}$ is satisfied for every connected component G of Γ in each of the following cases:

(1) $f(x, y) = f_1(y) - f_2(x, y)$, and there exist numbers $\mathrm{R} > 0, k > 0, h > 0$ and a positive continuous function $x \to \mathrm{H}(x)$ in A such that for $\|y\| \geqslant \mathrm{R}$, $\|f_1(y)\| \geqslant \|y\|^k$ and $\|f_2(x, y)\| \leqslant \mathrm{H}(x)\|y\|^{k-h}$.

(2) $\mathrm{F} = \mathbf{C}$, E is a vector space over $\mathbf{C}$, $f(x, y) = e^y - g(x)$, where g is analytic in A and $g(x) \neq 0$ in A (this last condition already ensures that $\mathrm{pr}_1(\Gamma) = \mathrm{A}$; observe that $f(x, y) = f(x, y')$ implies that $y' - y$ is a multiple of $2\pi i$, hence for any $x \in \mathrm{A}$ there is an open ball U of center x contained in A such that for *any* connected component V of $\mathrm{pr}_1^{-1}(\mathrm{U}) \cap \Gamma$, pr_1 is a homeomorphism of V onto U; if x is a cluster point of $\mathrm{pr}_1(\mathrm{G})$, G must have a common point with one of these components V, hence contains V).

8. (a) If f is a complex valued entire function in $\mathbf{C}^p$, such that $f(x) \neq 0$ for every $x \in \mathbf{C}^p$, show that there exists a complex valued entire function g in $\mathbf{C}^p$ such that $f(x) = e^{g(x)}$ (use Problem 7).

(b) Let f be an arbitrary complex valued entire function in $\mathbf{C}$, which is not identically 0; there is a finite or infinite sequence (a_n) (with $n \geqslant 1$) of complex numbers (which may be empty) such that $|a_n| \leqslant |a_{n+1}|$, $f(a_n) = 0$ and for every $c \in \mathbf{C}$ such that $f(c) = 0$, the number of indices n for which $a_n = c$ is equal to the order $\omega(c; f)$; when the sequence (a_n) is infinite, $\lim_{n \to \infty} |a_n| = +\infty$ **(9.1.5)**. Show (with the notations of Section **9.12**, Problem 1) that there exists an entire function g such that

$$f(z) = e^{g(z)} \prod_{n=1}^{\infty} \mathrm{E}\left(\frac{z}{a_n}, n - 1\right), \qquad \text{(“Weierstrass decomposition”).}$$

9. Let A and B be two open neighborhoods of 0 in $\mathrm{E} = \mathbf{C}^p$, A being *connected*; let $(x, y) \to U(x, y)$ be an analytic mapping of $\mathrm{A} \times \mathrm{B}$ into $\mathscr{L}(\mathrm{E}; \mathrm{E})$ (identified to the space of $p \times p$ matrices with complex elements).

(a) Suppose there exists a sequence (u_n) of analytic mappings of A *into* B such that $u_0(x)=0$ in A and $u_n(x)=U(x, u_{n-1}(x))\cdot x$ in A for $n\geqslant 1$. Suppose in addition that for every compact subset L of A, the restrictions of the u_n to L form a relatively compact subset of $\mathscr{C}_{\mathrm{E}}(\mathrm{L})$. Prove that the sequence (u_n) converges uniformly in any compact subset of A to an analytic mapping v of A into B such that $v(x)=U(x, v(x))\cdot x$ in A; furthermore, v is the unique mapping satisfying that equation (use **(10.2.1)** and **(9.13.2)**).

(b) Suppose that in E, A and B are the open balls of center 0 and radii a and b. Let φ be a continuous mapping of $[0, a[\times[0, b[$ into $\mathbf{R}$ such that $\eta\to\varphi(\xi, \eta)$ is increasing in $[0, b[$ for every $\xi\in[0, a]$ and suppose that $\|U(x, y)\|\leqslant\varphi(\|x\|, \|y\|)$ in $\mathrm{A}\times\mathrm{B}$. Suppose in addition that there exists a continuous mapping θ of $[0, a[$ into $[0, b[$ such that $\theta(\xi)=\varphi(\xi, \theta(\xi))\xi$ in $[0, a]$. Prove that under these conditions there is a unique analytic mapping v of A into B such that $v(x)=U(x, v(x))\cdot x$ in A, and that $\|v(x)\|\geqslant\theta(\|x\|)$ in A (use (a); prove the existence of the mappings u_n by induction on n).

(c) Suppose A and B are defined as in (b): let $\psi(\eta)$ be the l.u.b. of $\|U(x, y)\|$ for $\|x\|<a$, $\|y\|<\eta$, when $\eta>0$, and take $\psi(0)=\psi(0+)$. Suppose that $\psi(0)>0$ and that the function $\eta\to\eta/\psi(\eta)$ is increasing in some interval $[0, \gamma[$, where $\gamma\leqslant b$, and $\gamma/\psi(\gamma-)\leqslant a$. Then there is a unique analytic mapping v of the open ball P of center 0 and radius $\gamma/\psi(\gamma-)$ into B, such that $v(x)=U(x, v(x))\cdot x$ in P.

10. Let f, g be two complex valued analytic functions defined in a neighborhood of the closed polydisk $\mathrm{P}\subset\mathbf{C}^2$ of center $(0, 0)$ and radii a, b. Let M (resp. N) be the l.u.b. of $|f(x, y)|$ (resp. $|g(x, y)|$) for $|x|=a$ and $|y|\leqslant b$ (resp. for $|x|\leqslant a$ and $|y|=b$). Then, there exist two uniquely determined functions $u(s, t)$, $v(s, t)$, analytic for $|s|<a/\mathrm{M}$ and $|t|<b/\mathrm{N}$, such that $(u(s, t), v(s, t))\in\mathrm{P}$ for (s, t) in the polydisk Q defined by the previous inequalities and that

$$u(s, t)-sf(u(s, t), v(s, t))=0 \qquad\text{and}\qquad v(s, t)-tg(u(s, t), v(s, t))=0$$

in Q. Furthermore, let

$$\Delta(x, y, s, t)=\begin{vmatrix} 1-s\dfrac{\partial f}{\partial x} & -s\dfrac{\partial f}{\partial y} \\ -t\dfrac{\partial g}{\partial x} & 1-t\dfrac{\partial g}{\partial y}\end{vmatrix}$$

and let $h(x, y, s, t)$ be an arbitrary analytic function in $\mathrm{P}\times\mathrm{Q}$; show that

$$\frac{h(u(s, t), v(s, t), s, t)}{\Delta(u(s, t), v(s, t), s, t)}=\sum_{m\geqslant 0, n\geqslant 0} c_{mn}s^m t^n$$

for $(s, t)\in\mathrm{Q}$, where c_{mn} is the value for $x=y=0$ of the function

$$\frac{1}{m!\,n!}\frac{\partial^{m+n}}{\partial x^m\,\partial y^n}[h(x, y, s, t)(f(x, y))^m(g(x, y))^n]$$

and the series on the right-hand side is convergent in Q; note that c_{mn} depends on s and t if h does. ("Lagrange's inversion formula." First apply Rouché's theorem **(9.17.3)** to $x-sf(x, y)$, considered as a function of x; this defines an analytic function $w(s, y)$ such that $w(s, y)-sf(w(s, y), y)=0$, by **(10.2.4)**; next apply similarly Rouché's theorem to $y-tg(w(s, y), y)$ considered as a function of y. Finally, let γ, δ be the circuits $\theta\to ae^{i\theta}$, $\theta\to be^{i\theta}$ in $\mathbf{C}$ $(0\leqslant\theta\leqslant 2\pi)$. Consider the repeated integral

$$\int_\delta dy \int_\delta \frac{h(x, y, s, t)\, dx}{(x - sf(x, y))(y - tg(x, y))}.$$

On one hand, find the value of that integral by repeated application of the theorem of residues (9.16.1); and on the other hand, consider the power series development of $(1-\xi)^{-1}(1-\eta)^{-1}$ in which ξ is replaced by $sf(x, y)/x$ and η by $tg(x, y)/y$.)
Generalize to any number of complex variables. From the inversion formula for one variable, deduce the formula

$$h(u(s)) = h(0) + \sum_{n=1}^{\infty} \frac{s^n}{n!} \mathrm{D}^{n-1}(h'(0)(f(0))^n)$$

where $u(s) - sf(u(s)) = 0$ and $|s| < a/\mathrm{M}$, with $\mathrm{M} = \sup_{|x| \leqslant a} |f(x)|$, h being analytic for $|x| < a$.

3. THE RANK THEOREM

Let E, F be two *finite dimensional* vector spaces of dimensions n and m, A an open subset of E, f a continuously differentiable mapping of A into F, The *rank* of the linear mapping $f'(x)$ at a point $x \in \mathrm{A}$ is the largest number p such that there is at least a minor of order p in the matrix of $f'(x)$ with respect to two bases of E and F, which is not 0 (A.7.3). As these minors are continuous functions of x, it follows that if the rank of $f'(x_0)$ is p, there is a neighborhood of x_0 in which the rank of $f'(x)$ is *at least* p; but it can be $>p$ at every point $x \neq x_0$ of that neighborhood, as the example of the mapping $(x, y) \to (x^2 - y^2, xy)$ shows at the point (0, 0).

(10.3.1) (Rank theorem) *Let* E *be an n-dimensional space,* F *an m-dimensional space,* A *an open neighborhood of a point* $a \in \mathrm{E}$, *f a continuously differentiable mapping* (resp. *q times continuously differentiable mapping*, resp. *indefinitely differentiable mapping*, resp. *analytic mapping*) *of* A *into* F, *such that in* A *the rank of* $f'(x)$ *is a* constant *number p. Then there exists:*

(1) *an open neighborhood* $\mathrm{U} \subset \mathrm{A}$ *of a, and a homeomorphism u of* U *onto the unit ball* $\mathrm{I}^n : |x_i| < 1$ $(1 \leqslant i \leqslant n)$ *in* K^n, *which is continuously differentiable* (resp. *q times continuously differentiable*, resp. *indefinitely differentiable*, resp. *analytic*) *as well as its inverse;*

(2) *an open neighborhood* $\mathrm{V} \supset f(\mathrm{U})$ *of* $b = f(a)$ *and a homeomorphism v of the unit ball* $\mathrm{I}^m : |y_i| < 1$ $(1 \leqslant i \leqslant m)$ *of* K^m *onto* V, *which is continuously differentiable* (resp. *q times continuously differentiable*, resp. *indefinitely differentiable*, resp. *analytic*) *as well as its inverse;*

—such that $f = v \circ f_0 \circ u$, *where* f_0 *is the mapping*

$$(x_1, \ldots, x_n) \to (x_1, \ldots, x_p, 0, \ldots, 0)$$

of I^n *into* I^m.

We write the proof for continuously differentiable mappings, the modifications in the other cases being obvious.

We may suppose $a = 0, b = 0$, replacing f by the mapping $x \to f(a + x) - b$. Let M be the kernel of the linear mapping $f'(0)$, which is an $(n - p)$-dimensional subspace of E, and let N be a (p-dimensional) supplement of M in E; we take as a basis of E a system $(c_i)_{1 \leqslant i \leqslant n}$ of n vectors such that $c_1, \ldots, c_p$ form a basis of N, $c_{p+1}, \ldots, c_n$ a basis of M, and we write $x = \sum_{i=1}^{n} \varphi_i(x) c_i$ for any $x \in$ E, the φ_i being linear forms. If $e_1, \ldots, e_n$ is the canonical basis of K^n, we denote by $x \to G(x)$ the linear mapping $x \to \sum_{i=p+1}^{n} \varphi_i(x) e_i$ of E onto the subspace K^{n-p} of K^n generated by the e_i of index $i > p$.

Let P be the image of E (and of N) by the linear mapping $f'(0)$; it is a p-dimensional subspace of F, having the elements $d_i = f'(0) \cdot c_i$ $(1 \leqslant i \leqslant p)$ as a basis; we take a basis $(d_j)_{1 \leqslant j \leqslant m}$ of F, of which the preceding basis of P form the first p elements, and we write $y = \sum_{j=1}^{m} \psi_j(y) d_j$ for any $y \in$ F, the ψ_j being linear forms. We denote by $y \to H(y)$ the linear mapping $y \to \sum_{j=1}^{p} \psi_j(y) e_j$ of F onto the subspace K^p of K^n generated by the e_i of index $i \leqslant p$.

We now consider the mapping $x \to g(x) = H(f(x)) + G(x)$ of A into K^n which is continuously differentiable. Moreover, by (8.1.3) and (8.2.1), we have $g'(x) \cdot s = H(f'(x) \cdot s) + G(s)$ for any $s \in$ E, hence $g'(0) \cdot c_i = e_i$ for $1 \leqslant i \leqslant n$ (i.e. $g'(0)$ is represented by the unit matrix with respect to the bases (c_i) and (e_i)). Using (10.2.5), we conclude that there is an open neighborhood $U_0 \subset$ A of 0 such that the restriction of g to U_0 is a homeomorphism of U_0 onto an open neighborhood of 0 in K^n, and that the inverse homeomorphism g^{-1} is continuously differentiable in $g(U_0)$. Let $r > 0$ be such that the ball $|x_i| < r$ $(1 \leqslant i \leqslant n)$ is contained in $g(U_0)$, and let U be the inverse image of that ball by g, which is an open neighborhood of 0; our mapping u will be the restriction to U of the mapping $x \to \frac{1}{r} g(x)$.

Up to now we have not used the assumption that the rank of $f'(x)$ is *constant* in A; this implies that the image P_x of E by $f'(x)$ has dimension p for any $x \in$ A. Now we may suppose U_0 has been taken small enough so that $g'(x)$ is a linear *bijection* of E onto K^n for $x \in U_0$ (8.3.2); as we have $g'(x) \cdot s = H(f'(x) \cdot s)$ for $s \in$ N, the restriction of $f'(x)$ to N must be a bijection of that p-dimensional space onto P_x, and the restriction of H to P_x a *bijection* of P_x onto K^p. Denote by L_x the bijection of K^p onto P_x, inverse of the preceding mapping; we can thus write $f'(x) = L_x \circ H \circ f'(x)$.

Now consider K^n as the product $E_1 \times E_2$ with $E_1 = K^p$, $E_2 = K^{n-p}$; we are going to prove that the mapping $(z_1, z_2) \to f_1(z_1, z_2) = f(u^{-1}(z_1, z_2))$ of I^n into F *does not depend on* z_2, i.e. that $D_2 f_1(z_1, z_2) = 0$ in I^n (8.6.1). By definition, we can write $f(x) = f_1\left(\frac{1}{r} H(f(x)), \frac{1}{r} G(x)\right)$, hence by (8.9.2)

$$rf'(x) \cdot t = D_1 f_1\left(\frac{1}{r} H(f(x)), \frac{1}{r} G(x)\right) \cdot H(f'(x) \cdot t)$$
$$+ D_2 f_1\left(\frac{1}{r} H(f(x)), \frac{1}{r} G(x)\right) \cdot G(t)$$

for any $t \in E$. This yields

(10.3.11) $$D_2 f_1\left(\frac{1}{r} H(f(x)), \frac{1}{r} G(x)\right) \cdot G(t) = S_x \cdot H(f'(x) \cdot t)$$

where $S_x = rL_x - D_1 f_1\left(\frac{1}{r} H(f(x)), \frac{1}{r} G(x)\right)$ is a linear mapping of $K^p = E_1$ into F. We prove that $S_x = 0$ for any $x \in U_0$. Indeed, if $t \in N$, we have $G(t) = 0$ by definition, hence $S_x \cdot H(f'(x) \cdot t) = 0$ by (10.3.1.1). But $t \to H(f'(x) \cdot t) = g'(x) \cdot t$ is a *bijection* of N onto E_1 for $x \in U_0$, and this proves $S_x = 0$. From (10.3.1.1) we then deduce

$$D_2 f_1\left(\frac{1}{r} H(f(x)), \frac{1}{r} G(x)\right) \cdot G(t) = 0$$

for *any* $t \in E$; but G maps E *onto* E_2, hence by definition,

$$D_2 f_1\left(\frac{1}{r} H(f(x)), \frac{1}{r} G(x)\right),$$

which is a linear mapping of E_2 into F, is 0 for any $x \in U_0$. The relation $D_2 f_1(z_1, z_2) = 0$ in I^n then follows from the fact that

$$x \to \left(\frac{1}{r} H(f(x)), \frac{1}{r} G(x)\right)$$

is a homeomorphism of U_0 onto an open set containing I^n.

We can now write $f_1(z_1)$ instead of $f_1(z_1, z_2)$ and consider f_1 as a continuously differentiable mapping of $E_1 = K^p$ into F; we then have $f(x) = f_1\left(\frac{1}{r} H(f(x))\right)$ for $x \in U$; in other words, $y = f_1\left(\frac{1}{r} H(y)\right)$ for $y \in f(U)$. This proves that $y \to \frac{1}{r} H(y)$ is a homeomorphism of $f(U)$ *onto* $I^p \subset E_1$, and $z_1 \to f_1(z_1)$ the inverse homeomorphism.

Consider now K^m as the product $E_1 \times E_3$ with $E_3 = K^{m-p}$. Let T be the linear bijection of E_3 onto the supplement Q of P in F generated by $d_{p+1}, \dots, d_m$, which maps the canonical basis of K^{m-p} onto $d_{p+1}, \dots, d_m$. We define $v(z_1, z_3) = f_1(z_1) + T(z_3)$ for $z_1 \in I^p$, $z_3 \in I^{m-p}$; it is obviously (8.9.1) a continuously differentiable mapping. By definition, we have $H(v(z_1, z_3)) = H(f_1(z_1)) = rz_1$; hence the relation $v(z_1, z_3) = v(z_1', z_3')$ implies $z_1' = z_1$, and then boils down to $T(z_3) = T(z_3')$, which yields $z_3 = z_3'$; therefore v is *injective*. The relation $S_x = 0$ proved above shows that for any $z_1 \in I^p$, $f_1'(z_1) = rL_x$ where x is any point in U such that $f(x) = f_1(z_1)$; the derivative of v at (z_1, z_3) is therefore the linear mapping $(t_1, t_3) \to rL_x \cdot t_1 + T(t_3)$ ((8.9.1) and (8.1.3)). But as the restriction of H to P_x is injective, P_x is a supplement of Q in F, hence $v'(z_1, z_3)$ is a *linear homeomorphism* of K^m onto F. For any point $(z_1, z_3) \in I^m$, there is therefore an open neighborhood W of that point in I^m such that the restriction of v to W is a homeomorphism of W onto an open subset $v(W)$ of F, by (10.2.5). As in addition v is injective, it is a homeomorphism of I^m onto the open subset $V = v(I^m)$, whose inverse is continuously differentiable in V. The relation $f = v \circ f_0 \circ u$ then follows from the definitions.

(10.3.2) *If the rank of $f'(a)$ is equal to n* (resp. *to m*), *then the conclusion of* (10.3.1) *holds with $p = n$* (resp. $p = m$).

Indeed, at the beginning of this section we have seen that there exists then a neighborhood of a in which the rank of $f'(x)$ is $\geqslant n$ (resp. $\geqslant m$), hence equal to n (resp. to m) since it is always at most equal to $\inf(m, n)$ (A.4.18).

PROBLEMS

1. Let E, F be two Banach spaces, A an open neighborhood of a point $x_0 \in E$, f a continuously differentiable mapping of A into F.
(a) Suppose $f'(x_0)$ is a linear homeomorphism of E onto its image in F; show that there exists a neighborhood $U \subset A$ of x_0 such that f is a homeomorphism of U onto $f(U)$ (use Problem 3 of Section 10.1).
(b) Suppose $f'(x_0)$ is surjective; then there exists a number $a > 0$ having the following property: if N is the kernel of $f'(x_0)$, for every $s \in E$, one has $\|f'(x_0) \cdot s\| \geqslant a \cdot \inf_{t \in N} \|t + s\|$ (12.16.12). Show that there exists a neighborhood $V \subset A$ of x_0 such that $f(V)$ is a neighborhood of $f(x_0)$ in F (use Problem 8 of Section 10.1).
2. Let A be an open subset of $\mathbf{C}^p$, and f an analytic mapping of A into $\mathbf{C}^p$. Show that if f is *injective*, then the rank of $Df(x)$ is equal to p for every $x \in A$. (Use contradiction, and induction on p; for $p = 1$, apply Rouché's theorem (9.17.3). Assume $Df(a)$ has a rank $< p$ for some $a \in A$; show first that after performing a linear transformation in F, one may assume that, if $f(z) = (f_1(z), \dots, f_p(z))$, then $D_1 f_1(a) = 0$, and if $g(z) = (f_2(z), \dots, f_p(z))$, the rank of $Dg(a)$ is exactly $p - 1$; then there is a neighborhood

$U \subset A$ of a such that $Dg(x)$ has rank $p-1$ for $x \in U$. Using the rank theorem (10.3.1), reduce the proof to the case in which $a = 0$, $f_k(z) = z_k$ for $2 \leqslant k \leqslant p$.) Is the result still true when **C** is replaced by **R**?

3. (a) Let A be a simply connected open subset of **C**, distinct from **C**, and let a, b be two distinct points of fr(A). (Appendix to Chapter IX, Problem 6.) There exists a complex-valued analytic function h in A such that $(h(z))^2 = (z-a)/(z-b)$ (Section 10.2, Problem 7); h is an analytic homeomorphism of A onto a simply connected open subset B of **C** (Problem 2 and (10.3.1)); furthermore, $B \cap (-B) = \varnothing$, hence there are points of **C** exterior to B.

(b) Deduce from (a) that there exists an analytic homeomorphism of A onto a simply connected open subset of **C** contained in the disc $U: |z| < 1$, and containing 0.

4. (a) Let A be a simply connected open subset of **C** contained in the unit disk $U: |z| < 1$, containing 0, and let H be the set of all complex valued analytic functions g in A, such that g is an *injective* mapping of A into **C**, $|g(z)| < 1$, $g(0) = 0$ and $g'(0)$ is a real number >0. For each compact subset L of A, the set H_L of the restrictions to L of the functions of H is relatively compact in $\mathscr{C}_{\mathbf{C}}(L)$ (9.13.2). Show that the set of real numbers $g'(0)$ (for $g \in H$) is bounded (cf. proof of (9.13.1)); let λ be the l.u.b. of that set. Show that there is a function $g_0 \in H$ such that $g_0(0) = \lambda$ (use the result of Section 9.17, Problem 5).

(b) Suppose $g \in H$ is such that $g(A) \neq U$, and let $c \in U - g(A)$. Replacing g by g_1 defined by $g_1(z) = e^{-i\theta} g(ze^{i\theta})$, one can assume, for a suitable choice of θ, that c is real and >0. There exists a function h which is analytic in A and such that

$$h((z))^2 = (c - g(z))/(1 - cg(z))$$

and $h(0) = \sqrt{c} > 0$ (same argument as in Problem 3(a)); show that the function g_2 defined by

$$h(z) = (\sqrt{c} - g_2(z))/(1 - \sqrt{c}g_2(z))$$

belongs to H, and that $g_2'(0) > g'(0)$.

(c) Conclude from (a) and (b) that the function g_0 defined in (a) is an analytic homeomorphism of A *onto* U; using Problem 3(b), this implies that for any simply connected open subset D of **C**, distinct from **C**, there is an analytic homeomorphism of D onto U ("Riemann's conformal mapping theorem").

5. (a) Let f be a complex valued analytic function in the unit disk $U: |z| < 1$ such that $f(0) = 1$ and $|f(z)| < M$ in U; show that for $|z| \leqslant 1/M$, $|f(z) - 1| \leqslant M|z|$ (apply Schwarz's lemma (Section 9.5, Problem 7) to the function $g(z) = M(f(z) - 1)/(M^2 - f(z))$).

(b) Let f be a complex valued analytic function in U such that $f(0) = 0$, $f'(0) = 1$, $|f'(z)| \leqslant M$ in U; show that for $|z| \leqslant 1/M$, $|f(z) - z| \leqslant M|z|^2/2$ (apply (a) to f').

(c) Show that under the assumptions of (b), the restriction of f to the disk B(0; 1/M) is an analytic homeomorphism of that disk onto an open subset containing the disk B(0; 1/2M) (apply Rouché's theorem ((9.17.3), using the result of (b)).

(d) For any complex number $a \in U$, let $u(z) = (z - a)/(\bar{a}z - 1)$; for any complex valued function f analytic in U, show that, if $g(z) = f(u(z))$, then $|g'(z)|(1 - |z|^2) = |f'(u(z))|(1 - |u(z)|^2)$ for any $z \in U$.

(e) Show that there is a real number ("Bloch's constant") $b > 1/3\sqrt{3}$ having the following property: for any complex valued function f analytic in U and such that $f'(0) = 1$, there exists $z_0 \in U$ such that, if $x_0 = f(z_0)$, the open disk B of center x_0 and radius b is contained in $f(U)$ and there is a function g, analytic in B and such that $g(B) \subset U$ and $f(g(z)) = z$ for $z \in B$. (Consider first the case in which f is analytic in a neighborhood of $\bar{U}$, and take for z_0 a point where $|f'(z)|(1 - |z|^2)$ reaches its maximum; use then (d) to reduce the problem to the case in which $z_0 = 0$, and apply in that case the result of (c) to a function of the form $a + f(Rz)$, where a and R are suitable complex numbers. In the general case consider the function $f((1 - \varepsilon)z)/(1 - \varepsilon)$, where $\varepsilon > 0$ is arbitrarily small.)

6. (a) Let $\mathfrak{M}$ be the set of all complex valued functions f analytic in the unit disk U: $|z| < 1$, such that $f(U)$ does not contain the points 0 and 1. For any function $f \in \mathfrak{M}$, there is a unique analytic function g in U such that $\exp(2\pi i g(z)) = f(z)$ in U and $|\mathscr{I}(g(0))| < \pi$ (Section **10**.2, Problem 7); $g(U)$ does not contain any positive or negative integer. Furthermore (same reference) there is an analytic function h in U such that $g(z)/(g(z) - 1) = ((1 + h(z))/(1 - h(z)))^2$; $h(U)$ does not contain any of the points 0, 1, $c'_n = (\sqrt{n} + \sqrt{n-1})^2$ and $c''_n = (\sqrt{n} - \sqrt{n-1})^2$ (n integer $\geqslant 1$). Finally, there is an analytic function φ in U such that $\exp(\varphi(z)) = h(z)$; $\varphi(U)$ does not contain any of the points $\log c'_n + 2k\pi i$, $\log c''_n + 2k\pi i$ (k positive or negative integer, $n \geqslant 1$). Show that no disk of radius >4 can be contained in $\varphi(U)$; using Problem 5(e), deduce from that result that

$$|\varphi'(x)| \leqslant 4/b(1 - |x|)$$

for $|x| < 1$ (consider the function $t \to c\varphi(x + (1 - |x|)t)$, for a suitably chosen constant c). Conclude that there is a function $F(u, v)$, finite and continuous in $(\mathbf{C} - \{0, 1\}) \times [0, 1[$, such that for every function $f \in \mathfrak{M}$, $\log|f(z)| \leqslant F(f(0), r)$ for any $|z| \leqslant r < 1$.

(b) Let $f \in \mathfrak{M}$ be such that either $|f(0)| < 1/2$ or $|f(0) - 1| < 1/2$. Given r such that $0 \leqslant r < 1$, show that either $|f(z)| \leqslant 5/2$ for $|z| \leqslant r$, or there exists a point x such that $|x| < r$ and $|f(x)| \geqslant 1/2$, $|f(x) - 1| \geqslant 1/2$ and $|1/f(x)| \geqslant 1/2$. Applying the result of (a) to the function $f((z - x)/(\bar{x}z - 1))$, conclude that there is a function $F_1(u, v)$, continuous and finite in $[0, +\infty[\times [0, 1[$, such that for any function $f \in \mathfrak{M}$, the relations $|f(0)| \leqslant s$ and $|z| \leqslant r$ imply $|f(z)| \leqslant F_1(s, r)$ ("Schottky's theorem").

7. Let A be an open connected subset of **C**, and (f_n) a sequence of functions of the set $\mathfrak{M}$ (Problem 6). Show that for any compact subset L of A, there exists a subsequence (f_{n_k}) such that either that subsequence is uniformly convergent in L, or the sequence $(1/f_{n_k})$ converges uniformly to 0 in L. (Using Schottky's theorem, prove that the points $x \in A$ such that $\lim_{n \to \infty} (1/f_n(x)) = 0$ form an open and closed subset of A, hence equal to A or empty; in the second case, show, using the compactness of L, that there is a subsequence of (f_n) which is bounded in a compact neighborhood of L, and apply (**9.13.1**); in the first case, use similarly (**9.13.1**) applied to the sequence $(1/f_n)$.)

8. (a) Let f be a complex valued function, analytic in the open set $V: 0 < |z - a| < r$, and suppose a is an essential singularity of f (Section **9.15**). Show that $\mathbf{C} - f(V)$ is empty or reduced to a single point ("Picard's theorem". Let W be the open subset of V defined by $r/2 < |z - a| < r$ and consider in W the family of analytic functions $f_n(z) = f(z/2^n)$; if there are at least two distinct points in $\mathbf{C} - f(V)$, apply Problem 7 to the sequence (f_n), and derive a contradiction with Problem 2 of Section **9.15**, using (**9.15.2**).)

(b) Deduce from (a) that if g is an entire function in **C**, which is not a constant, then $\mathbf{C} - g(\mathbf{C})$ is empty or reduced to a single point (consider $g(1/z)$ in $\mathbf{C} - \{0\}$).

9. (a) Show that there is an entire function $f(x, y)$ in $\mathbf{C}^2$ satisfying the identity

$$f(4x, 4y) - 4f(x, y) = -5(f(2x, -2y))^2 + 2(f(2x, -2y))^5$$

and such that the term of degree $\leqslant 1$ in the Taylor development of f at the point (0, 0) are $x + y$ (Section **10.1**, Problem 11).

(b) Let $g(x, y) = f(2x, -2y)$, and let $J(x, y) = \partial(f, g)/\partial(x, y)$; show that $J(2x, -2y) = J(x, y)$, and conclude that $J(x, y) = -4$ in $\mathbf{C}^2$ (express $f(x, y)$ and $g(x, y)$ in terms of $f(2x, -2y)$ and $g(2x, -2y)$). Prove that the analytic mapping $u : (x, y) \to (f(x, y), g(x, y))$ of $\mathbf{C}^2$ into itself is injective (if it was not, it would not be injective in a neighborhood of $(0, 0)$, owing to the preceding expressions).

(c) Show that there is a neighborhood of $(1, 1)$ which is not contained in $u(\mathbf{C}^2)$. (Observe that there exists ε such that $0 < \varepsilon < 1$ and that the relations $|f(2x, -2y) - 1| \leqslant \varepsilon, |g(2x, -2y) - 1| \leqslant \varepsilon$ imply $|f(x, y) - 1| \leqslant \varepsilon$ and $|g(x, y) - 1| \leqslant \varepsilon$; conclude that the relations $|f(x, y) - 1| \leqslant \varepsilon$ and $|g(x, y) - 1| \leqslant \varepsilon$ would imply $|f(0, 0) - 1| \leqslant \varepsilon$ and $|g(0, 0) - 1| \leqslant \varepsilon$, a contradiction) (compare to Problem 8(b).)

4. DIFFERENTIAL EQUATIONS

Let E be a Banach space, I an open set in the field K, H an open subset of E, f a *continuously differentiable* mapping of $I \times H$ into E. A differentiable mapping u of an open ball $J \subset I$ into H is called a *solution of the differential equation*

(10.4.1) $$x' = f(t, x)$$

if, for any $t \in J$, we have

(10.4.2) $$u'(t) = f(t, u(t)).$$

It follows at once from (10.4.2) that u is then *continuously differentiable* in J (hence *analytic* if $K = \mathbf{C}$, by (9.10.1)).

(10.4.3) *In order that, in the ball* $J \subset I$ *of center* t_0, *the mapping* u *of* J *into* H *be a solution of* (10.4.1) *such that* $u(t_0) = x_0 \in H$, *it is necessary and sufficient that* u *be continuous* (resp. *analytic*) *in* J *if* $K = \mathbf{R}$ (resp. $K = \mathbf{C}$), *and such that*

(10.4.4) $$u(t) = x_0 + \int_{t_0}^{t} f(s, u(s))\, ds$$

(where, if $K = \mathbf{C}$, the integral is taken along the linear path $\xi \to t_0 + \xi(t - t_0)$, $0 \leqslant \xi \leqslant 1$).

This follows from the definition of a primitive, for (when $K = \mathbf{C}$) if f is continuously differentiable and u is analytic, then $s \to f(s, u(s))$ is analytic (9.10.1).

(10.4.5) (Cauchy's existence theorem) *If f is continuously differentiable in* $I \times H$, *for any* $t_0 \in I$ *and any* $x_0 \in H$ *there exists an open ball* $J \subset I$ *of center* t_0 *such that there is in* J *a solution* u *of* (10.4.1) *such that* $u(t_0) = x_0$.

We first prove a lemma:

(10.4.5.1) *Let* A *be a compact metric space,* F *a metric space,* B *a compact subset of* F, g *a continuous mapping of* A × F *into a metric space* E. *Then there is a neighborhood* V *of* B *in* F *such that* $g(A \times V)$ *is bounded in* E.

For any $t \in A$ and any $z \in B$, there is a ball $S_{t,z}$ of center t in A and a ball $U_{t,z}$ of center z in F such that $g(S_{t,z} \times U_{t,z})$ is bounded, since g is continuous. For any $z \in B$, cover A by a finite number of balls $S_{t_i,z}$ and let V_z be the ball $U_{t_i,z}$ of smallest radius. Then $g(A \times V_z)$ is bounded (3.4.4). Cover now B by finitely many balls V_{z_j}; the union V of the V_{z_i} satisfies the requirements (3.4.4.).

(a) Suppose first $K = \mathbf{R}$. Let J_a be a compact ball of center t_0 and radius a, contained in I. By (10.4.5.1) there is an open ball B of center x_0 and radius b, contained in H, and such that $M = \sup_{(t,x) \in J_a \times B} \|f(t, x)\|$ and $k = \sup_{(t,x) \in J_a \times B} \|D_2 f(t, x)\|$ are finite. Let J_r for $r < a$ be the closed ball of center t_0 and radius r, and let F_r be the space of continuous mappings y of J_r into E, which is a Banach space for the norm $\|y\| = \sup_{t \in J_r} \|y(t)\|$ (7.2.1) Let V_r be the open ball in F_r, having center x_0 (identified to the constant mapping $t \to x_0$) and radius b. For any $y \in V_r$, the mapping $t \to x_0 + \int_{t_0}^{t} f(s, y(s))\, ds$ is defined and continuous in J_r, since $y(s) \in B$ by definition, for $y \in V_r$; let $g(y)$ be that mapping; g is thus a mapping of V_r into F_r. We will prove that for r small enough, g verifies the conditions of (10.1.2); applying that theorem and (10.4.3) will then end the proof, with $J = \mathring{J}_r$.

Now, for any two points y_1, y_2 in V_r, we have, by (8.5.4)

$$\|f(s, y_1(s)) - f(s, y_2(s))\| \leqslant k \cdot \|y_1(s) - y_2(s)\| \leqslant k \cdot \|y_1 - y_2\|$$

for any $s \in J_r$; therefore, by (8.7.7), for any $t \in J_r$,

$$\left\| \int_{t_0}^{t} (f(s, y_1(s)) - f(s, y_2(s)))\, ds \right\| \leqslant kr \|y_1 - y_2\|$$

hence $\|g(y_1) - g(y_2)\| \leqslant kr\|y_1 - y_2\|$. On the other hand, for any $y \in V_r$, $\|f(s, y(s))\| \leqslant M$ for any $s \in J_r$, hence $\left\| \int_{t_0}^{t} f(s, y(s))\, ds \right\| \leqslant Mr$ by (8.7.7) and therefore $\|g(x_0) - x_0\| \leqslant Mr$. We thus see that in order to be able to apply (10.1.2), we should have $kr < 1$ and $Mr < b(1 - kr)$, and both inequalities will be satisfied as soon as $r < b/(M + kb)$.

(b) Suppose now $K = \mathbf{C}$; define J_a, J_r, B, M, and k as above, and let F_r be the space of mappings y of J_r into E which are *continuous in* J_r and *analytic in* $\mathring{J}_r$. This is again a *Banach space* for the norm $\|y\| = \sup_{t \in J_r} \|y(t)\|$, by (7.2.1) and (9.12.1). For $y \in V_r$, the mapping $t \to x_0 + \int_{t_0}^{t} f(s, y(s))\, ds$ again belongs to F_r, for it is analytic in $\mathring{J}_r$ since $s \to f(s, y(s))$ is (9.7.3); and its continuity in J_r at once follows from (8.11.1). We therefore have defined a mapping g of V_r into F_r, and the end of the proof is then unchanged.

(10.4.6) *Remark.* The proof of (10.4.5) shows that the result is still valid when $K = \mathbf{R}$ and when f satisfies the following weaker hypotheses: (a) for every continuous mapping $t \to w(t)$ of I into H, $t \to f(t, w(t))$ is a *regulated* function in I (Section 7.6); (b) for any point $(t, x) \in I \times H$, there is a ball J of center t in I and a ball B of center x in H such that f is *bounded* in $J \times B$, and there exists a constant $k \geqslant 0$ (depending on J and B) such that $\|f(s, y_1) - f(s, y_2)\| \leqslant k\|y_1 - y_2\|$ for $s \in J$, y_1, y_2 in B. Such a function f is said to be *locally lipschitzian* in $I \times H$; equation (10.4.2) is then to be understood as holding only in *the complement of an at most denumerable subset* of J. This last remark also enables one to replace the open intervals I and J by *any* kind of interval in $\mathbf{R}$.

5. COMPARISON OF SOLUTIONS OF DIFFERENTIAL EQUATIONS

We say that a differentiable mapping u of an open ball $J \subset I$ into H is an *approximate solution of* (10.4.1) *with approximation* ε if we have

$$\|u'(t) - f(t, u(t))\| \leqslant \varepsilon$$

for any $t \in J$.

(10.5.1) *Suppose* $\|D_2 f(t, x)\| \leqslant k$ *in* $I \times H$. *If* u, v *are two approximate solutions of* (10.4.1) *in an open ball* J *of center* t_0, *with approximations* $\varepsilon_1, \varepsilon_2$, *then, for any* $t \in J$, *we have*

(10.5.1.1) $$\|u(t) - v(t)\| \leqslant \|u(t_0) - v(t_0)\| e^{k|t-t_0|} + (\varepsilon_1 + \varepsilon_2)\frac{e^{k|t-t_0|} - 1}{k}.$$

(For $k = 0$, $(e^{k|t-t_0|} - 1)/k$ is to be replaced by $|t - t_0|$). We immediately are reduced to the case $K = \mathbf{R}$, $t_0 = 0$ and $t \geqslant 0$ by putting $t = t_0 + a\xi$, $|a| = 1$, $\xi \geqslant 0$; then if $u_1(\xi) = u(t_0 + a\xi)$, $v_1(\xi) = v(t_0 + a\xi)$, u_1 and v_1 are approximate solutions of $x' = af(t_0 + a\xi, a^{-1}x)$, whence our assertion. From the relation $\|u'(s) - f(s, u(s))\| \leqslant \varepsilon_1$ in the interval $0 \leqslant s \leqslant t$, we deduce by (8.7.7)

$$\left\| u(t) - u(0) - \int_0^t f(s, u(s))\, ds \right\| \leqslant \varepsilon_1 t$$

and similarly

$$\left\| v(t) - v(0) - \int_0^t f(s, v(s))\, ds \right\| = \varepsilon_2 t$$

whence

$$\|u(t) - v(t)\| \leqslant \|u(0) - v(0)\| + \left\| \int_0^t (f(s, u(s)) - f(s, v(s)))\, ds \right\| + (\varepsilon_1 + \varepsilon_2)t.$$

From the assumption on $D_2 f$ and from (8.5.4) and (8.7.7) this yields

(10.5.1.2.)
$$w(t) \leqslant w(0) + (\varepsilon_1 + \varepsilon_2)t + k \int_0^t w(s)\, ds$$

where $w(t) = \|u(t) - v(t)\|$. Theorem (10.5.1) is then a consequence of the following lemma:

(10.5.1.3) (Gronwall's lemma) *If, in an interval* $[0, c]$, φ *and* ψ *are two regulated functions* $\geqslant 0$, *then for any regulated function* $w \geqslant 0$ *in* $[0, c]$ *satisfying the inequality*

(10.5.1.4)
$$w(t) \leqslant \varphi(t) + \int_0^t \psi(s) w(s)\, ds$$

we have in $[0, c]$

(10.5.1.5)
$$w(t) \leqslant \varphi(t) + \int_0^t \varphi(s)\psi(s) \exp\left(\int_s^t \psi(\xi)\, d\xi\right) ds.$$

Write $y(t)) = \int_0^t \psi(s) w(s)\, ds$; y is continuous, and from (10.5.1.4) it follows that, in the complement of a denumerable subset of $[0, c]$, we have

(10.5.1.6)
$$y'(t) - \psi(t) y(t) \leqslant \varphi(t)\psi(t)$$

by Section 8.7. Write $z(t) = y(t) \exp(-\int_0^t \psi(s)\, ds)$; relation (10.5.1.6) is equivalent to

$$z'(t) \leqslant \varphi(t)\psi(t) \exp\left(-\int_0^t \psi(s)\, ds\right).$$

By (8.5.3) and using the fact that $z(0) = 0$, we get, for $t \in [0, c]$

$$z(t) \leqslant \int_0^t \varphi(s)\psi(s) \exp\left(-\int_0^s \psi(\xi)\, d\xi\right) ds$$

whence by definition

$$y(t) \leqslant \int_0^t \varphi(s)\psi(s) \exp\left(\int_s^t \psi(\xi)\, d\xi\right) ds$$

and (10.5.1.5) now follows from the relation $w(t) \leqslant \varphi(t) + y(t)$.

(10.5.2) *Suppose f is continuously differentiable in* $\mathrm{I} \times \mathrm{H}$. *If u, v are two solutions of* (10.4.1), *defined in an open ball* J *of center t_0 and such that $u(t_0) = v(t_0)$, then $u = v$ in* J.

It is enough to prove that u and v coincide in every compact ball L of center t_0 contained in J. This follows from (10.5.1) applied to u and v, provided we know that $\mathrm{D}_2 f$ is *bounded* in some set $\mathrm{L} \times \mathrm{H}'$, where H' is an open subset of H containing both $u(\mathrm{L})$ and $v(\mathrm{L})$. But the existence of such a set follows at once from (10.4.5.1).

(10.5.3) *Suppose* E *is finite dimensional and f is analytic in* $\mathrm{I} \times \mathrm{H}$. *Then any solution of* (10.4.1) *in an open ball* $\mathrm{J} \subset \mathrm{I}$ *is analytic.*

This is immediate by definition if $\mathrm{K} = \mathbf{C}$. Suppose $\mathrm{K} = \mathbf{R}$, and let $\mathrm{E} = \mathbf{R}^m$; then for any point $(t_0, x_0) \in \mathrm{I} \times \mathrm{H}$ there is a ball $\mathrm{L}_0 \subset \mathbf{C}$ of center t_0 and a ball $\mathrm{P} \subset \mathbf{C}^m$ of center x_0 such that $\mathrm{L}_0 \cap \mathbf{R} \subset \mathrm{I}$ and $\mathrm{P} \cap \mathbf{R}^m \subset \mathrm{H}$, and an analytic mapping g of $\mathrm{L}_0 \times \mathrm{P}$ into $\mathbf{C}^m$ whose restriction to $(\mathrm{L}_0 \cap \mathbf{R}) \times (\mathrm{P} \cap \mathbf{R}^m)$ coincides with f (9.4.5). There is by (10.4.5) an open ball $\mathrm{L} \subset \mathrm{L}_0$ of center t_0 in $\mathbf{C}$ such that there exists a solution v of the differential equation $z' = g(t, z)$, taking the value x_0 at the point t_0, and v is analytic in L. Using the relation $v'(t) = g(t, v(t))$, and the definition of g and v, it is immediately verified by induction on n that all derivatives $v^{(n)}(t_0)$ belong to $\mathbf{R}^m$; hence (9.3.5.1) $v(t)$ belongs to $\mathbf{R}^m$ for $t \in \mathrm{L} \cap \mathbf{R}$. This proves that the restriction u of v to $\mathrm{L} \cap \mathbf{R}$ is a solution of (10.4.1) (see Section 8.4, *Remarks*), such that $u(t_0) = x_0$. But by (10.5.2), any solution w of (10.4.1) in a ball M of center t_0 such that $w(t_0) = x_0$ coincides with u in $\mathrm{L} \cap \mathrm{M}$, hence is analytic at the point t_0. Q.E.D.

(10.5.4) *Remark.* When $\mathrm{K} = \mathbf{R}$, the proof of (10.5.1) shows that the inequality (10.5.1.1) is still valid when f is *lipschitzian* in $\mathrm{I} \times \mathrm{H}$ for a constant $k \geqslant 0$, i.e. such that condition (a) of (10.4.6) is satisfied and that $\|f(t, x_1) - f(t, x_2)\| \leqslant k \cdot \|x_1 - x_2\|$ for any $t \in \mathrm{I}$, x_1, x_2 in H; J can then be taken as an interval of origin (or extremity) t_0, containing t_0, u and v are primitives of regulated functions in J, and the relations $\|u'(t) - f(t, u(t))\| \leqslant \varepsilon_1$, $\|v'(t) - f(t, v(t))\| \leqslant \varepsilon_2$ are only supposed to hold *in the complement of an at most denumerable subset* of J. The uniqueness result (10.5.2) holds likewise (when $\mathrm{K} = \mathbf{R}$) under the only assumption that f is *locally lipschitzian* (10.4.6) in $\mathrm{I} \times \mathrm{H}$, when one takes for J an interval having t_0 as origin or extremity, and one only requires that the relations $u'(t) = f(t, u(t))$, $v'(t) = g(t, v(t))$ hold in the complement of an at most denumerable subset of J.

(10.5.5) *Let f be continuously differentiable in* $I \times H$ *if* $K = \mathbf{C}$, *locally lipschitzian in* $I \times H$ *if* $K = \mathbf{R}$. *Suppose v is a solution of* (10.4.1) *defined in an open ball* $J: |t - t_0| < r$, *such that* $\bar{J} \subset I$, *that* $\overline{v(J)} \subset H$, *and that* $t \to f(t, v(t))$ *is bounded in* J. *Then there exists a ball* $J' : |t - t_0| < r'$ *contained in* I, *with* $r' > r$, *and a solution of* (10.4.1) *defined in* J' *and coinciding with v in* J.

(a) $K = \mathbf{R}$. By assumption, we have $\|f(t, v(t))\| \leqslant M$ for $t \in J$, hence $\|v'(t)\| \leqslant M$ in the complement of an at most denumerable subset of J. This implies $\|v(s) - v(t)\| \leqslant M|s - t|$ for s, t in J by the mean value theorem (8.5.2). From the Cauchy convergence criterion (3.14.6) we conclude that the limits $v((t_0 - r)+)$ and $v((t_0 + r)-)$ exist and belong to $\overline{v(J)} \subset H$. By (10.4.6), there exists a solution w_1 (resp. w_2) of $x' = f(t, x)$ defined in an open ball U_1 (resp. U_2) of center $t_0 + r$ (resp. $t_0 - r$), contained in I, and taking the value $v((t_0 + r)-)$ (resp. $v((t_0 - r)+)$) at this point; from (10.5.4) it follows in addition that w_1 (resp. w_2) coincides with v in $U_1 \cap J$ (resp. $U_2 \cap J$), and the proof is therefore concluded in that case. (One may observe that *it has not been necessary* to check the existence of derivatives on the left or on the right for v (extended by continuity) nor for w_1 and w_2, at the points $t_0 - r$ and $t_0 + r$.)

(b) $K = \mathbf{C}$. For any complex number ζ such that $|\zeta| = 1$, put $t = t_0 + \zeta s$, with $s \geqslant 0$, and $v_\zeta(s) = v(t_0 + \zeta s)$. Then the same argument as in (a) proves that $v_\zeta(r-)$ exists and is in H; hence there exists a solution w_ζ of $x' = f(t, x)$ defined in an open ball V_ζ of center $t_0 + \zeta r$, contained in J, such that $w_\zeta(t_0 + \zeta r) = v_\zeta(r-)$. From (10.5.4) it follows that w_ζ and v coincide in the intersection of $J \cap V_\zeta$ with the segment of extremities t_0 and $t_0 + \zeta r$; as these functions are *analytic* in $J \cap V_\zeta$, they *coincide* in $J \cap V_\zeta$ by (9.4.4). Now cover the compact set $|t - t_0| = r$ with finitely many balls V_{ζ_i} $(1 \leqslant i \leqslant m)$; if $V_{\zeta_i} \cap V_{\zeta_j} \neq \varnothing$, the functions w_{ζ_i} and w_{ζ_j} *coincide in* $V_{\zeta_i} \cap V_{\zeta_j}$, for both coincide with v in the nonempty open set $J \cap V_{\zeta_i} \cap V_{\zeta_j}$, and we have only to apply (9.4.2) (to show that the preceding intersection is not empty, remark that the assumption implies $r|\zeta_i - \zeta_j| < \rho_i + \rho_j$, where ρ_i, ρ_j are the radii of V_{ζ_i} and V_{ζ_j}; hence there is $\lambda \in]0, 1[$ such that $r\lambda|\zeta_i - \zeta_j| < \rho_i$ and and $r(1 - \lambda)|\zeta_i - \zeta_j| < \rho_j$; it follows that the point $t_0 + r((1 - \lambda)\zeta_i + \lambda\zeta_j)$ belongs to $J \cap V_{\zeta_i} \cap V_{\zeta_j}$). There is therefore a solution of $x' = f(t, x)$ equal to v in J, to w_{ζ_i} in each of the V_{ζ_i}, and there is an open ball of center t_0 and radius $r' > r$ contained in the union of these sets (3.17.11), which ends the proof.

(10.5.5.1) It follows from (10.5.5) that if r_0 is the l.u.b. of all numbers r such that $\bar{J} \subset I$ and $\overline{v(J)} \subset H$, either $r_0 = +\infty$, or, if J_0 is the open ball $|t - t_0| < r_0$, one of the two relations $\bar{J}_0 \not\subset I$, $\overline{v(J_0)} \not\subset H$ holds.

(10.5.6) *Let f, g be two continuously differentiable mappings of* $I \times H$ *into* E, *and suppose that, in* $I \times H$, $\|f(t, x) - g(t, x)\| \leqslant \alpha$ *and* $\|D_2 g(t, x)\| \leqslant k$. *Let* (t_0, x_0) *be a point of* $I \times H$, μ, β *two numbers* > 0, *and* $\varphi(\xi) = \mu e^{k\xi} + (\alpha + \beta)\dfrac{e^{k\xi} - 1}{k}$ *for* $\xi \geqslant 0$. *Let u be an approximate solution of* $x' = g(t, x)$, *with approximation* β, *defined in an open ball* $J : |t - t_0| < b$ *contained in* I, *and such that* $u(t_0) = x_0$ *and for any* $t \in J$, *the closed ball of center* $u(t)$ *and radius* $\varphi(|t - t_0|)$ *is contained in* H. *Then, for any* $y \in H$ *such that* $\|y - x_0\| \leqslant \mu$ *there, exists a unique solution v of* $x' = f(t, x)$, *defined in* J, *taking its values in* H *and such that* $v(t_0) = y$; *furthermore* $\|u(t) - v(t)\| \leqslant \varphi(|t - t_0|)$ *for* $t \in J$.

Let A be the set of numbers r such that $0 < r \leqslant b$ and that there exists a solution v_r of $x' = f(t, x)$ with values in H, defined in the ball $J_r : |t - t_0| < r$ and such that $v_r(t_0) = y$. By Cauchy's existence theorem (10.4.5), A is not empty. Moreover, we have, in J_r, $\|v_r'(t) - g(t, v_r(t))\| \leqslant \alpha$; in other words v_r is an approximate solution of $x' = g(t, x)$ with approximation α, and by (10.5.1.1) we conclude that $\|u(t) - v_r(t)\| \leqslant \varphi(|t - t_0|)$ in J_r. If r, r' are in A and such that $r < r'$, then v_r and $v_{r'}$ *coincide in* J_r, by (10.5.2) and (10.5.4).

Let c be the l.u.b. of A; we have to prove $c = b$. Suppose the contrary; there is then a unique solution v of $x' = f(t, x)$ in J_c, equal to v_r in each of the balls J_r with $r < c$, taking its values in H and such that $\|u(t) - v(t)\| \leqslant \varphi(|t - t_0|)$ in J_c. We therefore have $\|g(t, v(t)))\| \leqslant \|g(t, u(t))\| + k\varphi(|t - t_0|)$ in J_c, and as $t \to g(t, u(t))$ is continuous in $\bar{J}_c$, it is bounded in that compact ball; from which it follows that $t \to g(t, v(t))$ is *bounded* in J_c. On the other hand, any cluster point z of $v(J_c)$ is the limit of a sequence $(v(t_n))$ where $t_n \in J_c$ and t_n tends to $t_0 + c\zeta$ with $|\zeta| \leqslant 1$; by continuity, we have $\|z - u(t_0 + c\zeta)\| \leqslant \varphi(c|\zeta|)$, hence $z \in H$ by assumption. We thus can apply (10.5.5) and obtain a solution of $x' = f(t, x)$ defined in a ball $J_{r'}$ with $r' > c$ and taking the value y at t_0, which contradicts the definition of c.

When $K = \mathbf{R}$, one may, in the statement of (10.5.6), replace J by an open interval $]c, d[$ containing the point t_0.

(10.5.6.1) We again remark that if $\mathbf{K} = \mathbf{R}$, we can relax in (10.5.6) the hypotheses on f and g, supposing merely that g is lipschitzian for the constant k, and f locally lipschitzian in $I \times H$.

PROBLEMS

1. Let $f(t, x)$ be a real valued continuous function defined in the set $|t| \leqslant a$, $|x| \leqslant b$ in $\mathbf{R}^2$, such that $f(t, x) < 0$ for $tx > 0$, and $f(t, x) > 0$ for $tx < 0$. Show that $x = 0$ is the unique solution of the differential equation $x' = f(t, x)$ defined in a neighborhood

of 0 and such that $x(0) = 0$ (use contradiction, and consider, in a compact interval containing 0, the points where a solution reaches its maximum or minimum).

2. Let $f(t, x)$ be the real valued continuous function defined in $\mathbf{R}^2$ by the following conditions: $f(t, x) = -2t$ for $x \geqslant t^2$, $f(t, x) = -2x/t$ for $|x| < t^2$, $f(t, x) = 2t$ for $x \leqslant -t^2$. Let (y_n) be the sequence of functions defined by $y_0(t) = t^2$, $y_n(t) = \int_0^t f(u, y_{n-1}(u))\,du$ for $n \geqslant 1$. Show that the sequence $(y_n(t))$ is not convergent for any $t \neq 0$, although the differential equation $x' = f(t, x)$ has a unique solution such that $x(0) = 0$ (Problem 1).

3. For any pair of real numbers $\alpha > 0$, $\beta > 0$, the function equal to $-(t-\alpha)^2$ for $t < \alpha$, to 0 for $\alpha \leqslant t \leqslant \beta$, to $(t-\beta)^2$ for $t > \beta$, is a solution of the differential equation $x' = 2|x|^{1/2}$ such that $x(0) = 0$.
Let u_0 be an arbitrary continuous function defined in a compact interval $[a, b]$, and define by induction $u_n(t) = 2\int_a^t |u_{n-1}(s)|^{1/2}\,ds$ for $t \in [a, b]$. Show that if γ is the largest number in $[a, b]$ such that $u_0(t) = 0$ in $[a, \gamma]$, the sequence (u_n) converges uniformly in $[a, b]$ to the solution of $x' = 2|x|^{1/2}$ which is equal to 0 for $a \leqslant t \leqslant \gamma$, to $(t-\gamma)^2$ for $\gamma \leqslant t \leqslant b$. (Consider first the case in which $u_0(t) = 0$ for $t \leqslant \gamma$, $u_0(t) = k(t-\gamma)^2$ for $\gamma \leqslant t \leqslant b$. Next remark that, replacing if necessary u_0 by u_1, one may suppose that u_0 is increasing in $[a, b]$; observe that for any number $\varepsilon > 0$, there are two numbers $k_1 > 0$, $k_2 > 0$ such that in $[a, b]$

$$k_1 v_0(t-\gamma-\varepsilon) \leqslant u_0(t) \leqslant k_2 v_0(t-\gamma+\varepsilon)$$

where $v_0(t) = 0$ if $t \leqslant 0$, $v_0(t) = t^2$ if $t \geqslant 0$.)

4. The notations being those of Section **10.4**, suppose $\mathrm{K} = \mathbf{R}$, f is continuous and bounded in $\mathrm{I} \times \mathrm{H}$, and let $\mathrm{M} = \sup_{(t,x) \in \mathrm{I} \times \mathrm{H}} \|f(t, x)\|$. Let x_0 be a point of H, S an open ball of center x_0 and radius r, contained in H.
(a) Suppose in addition f is uniformly continuous in $\mathrm{I} \times \mathrm{S}$ (a condition which is automatically satisfied if E is finite dimensional and I is contained in a compact interval I_0 such that f is continuous in $\mathrm{I}_0 \times \mathrm{H}$). Prove that for any $\varepsilon > 0$, and any compact interval $[t_0, t_0 + h]$ (resp. $[t_0 - h, t_0]$) contained in I and such that $h < r/(\mathrm{M} + \varepsilon)$, there exists in that interval an approximate solution of $x' = f(t, x)$ with approximation ε, taking the value x_0 for $t = t_0$. (Suppose $\delta > 0$ is such that the relations $|t_1 - t_2| \leqslant \delta$, $\|x_1 - x_2\| \leqslant \delta$ imply $\|f(t_1, x_1) - f(t_2, x_2)\| \leqslant \varepsilon$; consider a subdivision of the interval $[t_0, t_0 + h]$ in intervals of length at most equal to $\inf(\delta, \delta/\mathrm{M})$, and define the approximate solution on each successive subinterval, starting from t_0.)
(b) Suppose E is *finite dimensional* and $\mathrm{I} =]t_0 - a, t_0 + a[$. Prove that there exists a solution of $x' = f(t, x)$, defined in the interval $[t_0, t_0 + c]$ (resp. $[t_0 - c, t_0]$) with $c = \inf(a, r/\mathrm{M})$, taking its values in S, and equal to x_0 for $t = t_0$. ("Peano's theorem": for each n, let u_n be an approximate solution with approximation $1/n$, defined in $\mathrm{J}_n = [t_0, t_0 + c - (1/n)]$, whose existence is given by (a). Observe that for each m, the restrictions of the functions u_n (for $n \geqslant m$) to J_m form a relatively compact subset of the normed normed space $\mathscr{C}_{\mathrm{E}}(\mathrm{J}_m)$ (**7.5.7**), and use the "diagonal process" as in the proof of (**9.13.2**); finally apply (**10.4.3**) and (**8.7.8**).)

5. Let f be the mapping of the space (c_0) of Banach (Section **5.3**, Problem 5) into itself, such that, for $x = (x_n)$, $f(x) = (y_n)$, with $y_n = |x_n|^{1/2} + \dfrac{1}{n+1}$. Show that f is continuous in (c_0), but that there is no solution of the differential equation $x' = f(x)$, defined in a neighborhood of 0 in $\mathbf{R}$, taking its values in (c_0), and equal to 0 for $t = 0$. (If there was such a solution $u(t)=(u_n(t))$, compute the value of each $u_n(t)$ by straightforward integration, and show that the sequence $(u_n(t))_{n\geq 0}$ does not tend to 0 for $t\neq 0$.)

6. (a) The notations being those of Section 10.4, let f be analytic in $\mathrm{I}\times\mathrm{H}$ if $\mathrm{K}=\mathbf{C}$, locally lipschitzian in $\mathrm{I}\times\mathrm{H}$ if $\mathrm{K}=\mathbf{R}$. Let I_0 be an open ball of center t_0 and radius a, contained in I, and S an open ball of center x_0 and radius r, contained in H. Let $h(s,z)$ be a continuous function defined in $[0,a[\times[0,r[\subset\mathbf{R}^2$, such that $h(s,z)\geqslant 0$ and that, for every $s\in[0,a[$, the function $z\to h(s,z)$ is increasing in $[0,r[$. Suppose that: (1) $\|f(t,x)\|\leqslant h(|t-t_0|,\|x-x_0\|)$ in $\mathrm{I}_0\times\mathrm{S}$; (2) there exists an interval $[0,\alpha]$ with $\alpha<a$, and a function φ, which is a primitive of a regulated function φ' in $[0,\alpha]$, and is such that $\varphi(0)=0$, $\varphi(s)\in[0,r[$ and $\varphi'(s)>h(s,\varphi(s))$ in the interval $[0,\alpha]$, with the exception of an at most denumerable set of values of s. Show that there is a solution u of $x'=f(t,x)$, defined in the open ball J of center t_0 and radius α, taking its values in S and such that $u(t_0)=x_0$; furthermore, in J, $\|u(t)-x_0\|\leqslant\varphi(|t-t_0|)$. (Use (10.5.5) to prove that there is a largest open ball J_0 of center t_0, contained in I_0, and in which there is a solution v of $x'=f(t,x)$, taking its values in S and such that $\|v(t)-x_0\|\leqslant\varphi(|t-t_0|)$ in J_0, and furthermore that solution is unique; use then the mean value theorem to prove by contradiction that $\mathrm{J}\subset\mathrm{J}_0$.)

(b) Suppose that $\mathrm{H}=\mathrm{E}$, and that there is a function $h(z)>0$ defined, continuous and increasing in $[0,+\infty[$, and such that $\int_0^{+\infty}\frac{dz}{h(z)}=+\infty$, and that $\|f(t,x)\|\leqslant h(\|x\|)$ in $\mathrm{I}_0\times\mathrm{E}$. Show that every solution of $x'=f(t,x)$ defined in a neighborhood of t_0, is defined in I_0 (use (a)).

(c) If $\|f(t,x)\|\leqslant\mathrm{M}$ in $\mathrm{I}_0\times\mathrm{S}$, then there exists a solution u of $x'=f(t,x)$ in the ball J of center t_0 and radius $\inf(a,r/\mathrm{M})$, taking its values in S and such that $u\ t_0)=x_0$ (take $h(s,z)=\mathrm{M}$). Suppose $\mathrm{K}=\mathrm{E}=\mathbf{C}$, and $a\geqslant r/\mathrm{M}$; show that, unless f is a constant, there is an open ball $\mathrm{J}'\supset\bar{\mathrm{J}}$ in which u can be extended to a solution of $x'=f(t,x)$ taking its values in S. (Observe that, due to the maximum principle (9.5.9), $|u'(t)|<\mathrm{M}$ for $t\in\mathrm{J}$; for any ζ such that $|\zeta|=1$, consider the function $u_\zeta(s)=u(t_0+\zeta s)$; arguing as in (10.5.5), prove that the assumptions of (10.5.5) are satisfied.) It is not possible to take for the radius of J' a number depending only on a, r and M, and not on f itself, as the example $f(t,x)=((1+x)/2)^{1/n}$ (Section 9.5, Problem 8), with $t=x_0=0$, $a=r=\mathrm{M}=1$, shows (n arbitrary integer >1).

7. Let f be a real valued bounded continuous function in the open polydisk P: $|t-t_0|<a$, $|x-x_0|<b$ in $\mathbf{R}^2$, and let $\mathrm{M}=\sup_{(t,x)\in\mathrm{P}}|f(t,x)|$; let $r=\inf(a,b/\mathrm{M})$, and let $\mathrm{I}=]t_0-r,t_0+r[$. Let Φ be the set of all solutions u of $x'=f(t,x)$, defined in I, taking their values in the open interval $]x_0-b,x_0+b[$ and equal to x_0 for $t=t_0$; the set Φ is not empty (Problem 4(b)). For each $t\in\mathrm{I}$, let $v(t,t_0,x_0)=\inf_{u\in\Phi}u(t)$, $w(t,t_0,x_0)=\sup_{u\in\Phi}u(t)$; show that v and w belong to Φ (Section 7.5, Problem 11); v (resp. w) is called the *minimal* (resp. *maximal*) *solution* of $x'=f(t,x)$ in I, corresponding to the point (t_0,x_0).

For each $\tau\in\mathrm{I}$, let $\xi=v(\tau,t_0,x_0)$. Show that $v(t,\tau,\xi)=v(t,t_0,x_0)$ in an interval of the form $[\tau,\tau+h[$, if $\tau>t_0$, of the form $]\tau-h,\tau]$ if $\tau<t_0$ (with $h>0$). Conclude that there is a largest open interval $]t_1,t_2[$ contained in $]t_0-a,t_0+a[$ and containing t_0, such that $v(t,t_0,x_0)$ can be extended to a continuous function g defined in $]t_1,t_2[$, taking its values in $]x_0-b,x_0+b[$, and such that, for every $t\in]t_1,t_2[$, $g(s)=v(s,t,g(t))$ in an interval of the form $[t,t+h[$ if $t>t_0$, of the form $]t-h,t]$ if $t<t_0$ with $h>0$). (If g_1 is another such extension of $v(t,t_0,x_0)$ in an interval $]t_1',t_2'[$, show that g and g_1 coincide in the intersection of $]t_1,t_2[$ and $]t_1',t_2'[$ by considering the l.u.b. (resp. g.l.b.) of the points s in that intersection such that g and g_1 coincide in $[t_0,s[$ (resp. in $]s,t_0]$). Furthermore, either $t_1=t_0-a$ (resp. $t_2=t_0+a$), or $g(t_1+)=x_0\pm b$ (resp. $g(t_2-)=x_0\pm b$).

8. (a) Generalize Gronwall's lemma (10.5.1.3) to the inequalities

$$w(t) \leqslant \varphi(t) + \theta(t)\int_0^t \psi(s)w(s)\,ds$$

$$w(t) \leqslant \varphi(t) + \theta_1(t)\int_0^t \psi_1(s)w(s)\,ds + \theta_2(t)\int_0^t \psi_2(s)w(s)\,ds, \quad \text{etc.,}$$

where $\varphi, \psi_1, \psi_2, \theta_1, \theta_2$ are regulated functions $\geqslant 0$. (Use induction on the number of integrals on the right-hand side.)

(b) Let $K(t, s)$ be a continuously differentiable function $\geqslant 0$ defined in $[0, c] \times [0, c]$. Suppose there are two regulated functions g, h, defined and $\geqslant 0$ in $[0, c]$, such that $\partial K(t, s)/\partial t \leqslant g(t)h(s)$. Show that the inequality

$$w(t) \leqslant \varphi(t) + \int_0^t K(t, s)w(s)\,ds$$

for a regulated function $w \geqslant 0$ implies

$$w(t) \leqslant \varphi_1(t) + \theta_1(t)\int_0^t h(s)w(s)\,ds$$

where φ_1 and θ_1 are functions which one can explicitly compute when the functions φ, g and $r(t) = K(t, t)$ are known (consider the function $y(t) = \int_0^t K(t, s)w(s)\,ds$ and majorize its derivative).

(c) Apply (a) or (b) to the inequality

$$w(t) \leqslant t + \lambda^2 t\int_0^t e^{-\lambda s}w(s)\,ds + \int_0^t w(s)\,ds,$$

where $\lambda > 0$.

9. Let w be a real function defined in an open interval $I \subset R$, and suppose w is the primitive of a regulated function w' whose points of discontinuity are isolated in I, and such that in each of these points $w'(t+) > w'(t-)$; suppose in addition that if E is the set of points of discontinuity of w', the second derivative w'' exists in $I - E$ and $w''(x) \geqslant w(x)$ in $I - E$.

(a) Show that if a, b are two points of I such that $w(a) = w(b) = 0$, then $w(x) \leqslant 0$ for $a < x < b$ (use contradiction). Conclude that for any three points $x_1 < x < x_2$ in I one has

$$w(x) \leqslant \frac{w(x_1)\sinh(x_2 - x) + w(x_2)\sinh(x - x_1)}{\sinh(x_2 - x_1)}$$

(consider the difference $w(x) - u(x)$, where u is a solution of the equation $u''(x) - u(x) = 0$ taking the same values as w at the points x_1 and x_2).

6. LINEAR DIFFERENTIAL EQUATIONS

The existence theorem (10.4.5) can be improved in special cases:

(10.6.1) *Let* $I \subset K$ *be an open ball of center* t_0 *and radius* r. *Let* f *be continuous in* $I \times E$ *if* $K = \mathbf{R}$, *continuously differentiable in* $I \times E$ *if* $K = \mathbf{C}$, *and such that*

$\|f(t, x_1) - f(t, x_2)\| \leqslant k(|t - t_0|)\|x_1 - x_2\|$ *for* $t \in \mathrm{I}$, x_1, x_2 *in* E, *where* $\xi \to k(\xi)$ *is a regulated function in* $[0, r[$. *Then for every* $x_0 \in \mathrm{E}$, *there exists a unique solution u of* (10.4.1), defined in I, *and such that* $u(t_0) = x_0$.

We only have to prove that, if c is the l.u.b. of the numbers ρ such that $0 < \rho < r$ and that there exists a solution of (10.4.1) defined in $|t - t_0| < \rho$ and taking the value x_0 at t_0, then $c = r$ (by (10.5.4)). Suppose the contrary; then, by (10.5.4), there is a solution v of (10.4.1) defined in $\mathrm{J} : |t - t_0| < c$ and such that $v(t_0) = x_0$. We are going to show that the conditions of (10.5.5) are satisfied; applying (10.5.5) then yields a contradiction and ends the proof.

As here H = E, the condition $\overline{v(\mathrm{J})} \subset \mathrm{H}$ is trivially verified, so we have only to check that $t \to f(t, v(t))$ is *bounded* in J. Now, in the compact interval $[0, c]$, k is bounded and so is the continuous function $t \to \|f(t, x_0)\|$ in the compact set $\bar{\mathrm{J}}$; hence there exist two numbers $m > 0$, $h > 0$ such that $\|f(t, x)\| \leqslant m\|x\| + h$ for $t \in \mathrm{J}$ and $x \in \mathrm{E}$. This implies $\|v'(t)\| \leqslant m\|v(t)\| + h$ for $t \in \mathrm{J}$; if we write $w(\xi) = \|v(t_0 + \lambda\xi)\|$ with $|\lambda| = 1$, the mean value theorem shows that $w(\xi) \leqslant \|x_0\| + hc + m\int_0^\xi w(\zeta)\, d\zeta$. We therefore can apply Gronwall's lemma (10.5.1.3), which shows that $\|v(t)\| \leqslant ae^{m|t - t_0|} + b$ in J (a and b constants), hence v is bounded in J, and so is $\|f(t, v(t))\| \leqslant m\|v(t)\| + h$.

(10.6.1.1) Here again, when $\mathrm{K} = \mathbf{R}$, the condition of continuity on f can be relaxed to condition (a) of *Remark* (10.4.6).

A *linear differential equation* is an equation (10.4.1) of the special form

(10.6.2) $$x' = A(t) \cdot x + b(t) \qquad (= f(t, x))$$

where A is a mapping of I into the Banach space $\mathscr{L}(\mathrm{E}; \mathrm{E})$ of continuous linear mappings of E into itself (Section 5.7), and b a mapping of I into E. We have here H = E, and by (5.7.4)

$$\|f(t, x_1) - f(t, x_2)\| \leqslant \|A(t)\| \cdot \|x_1 - x_2\|$$

for all $t \in \mathrm{I}$, x_1, x_2 in E. Applying (10.6.1) and (10.6.1.1) we therefore get:

(10.6.3) *Let* $\mathrm{I} \subset \mathrm{K}$ *be an open ball of center* t_0. *Suppose A and b are regulated in* I *if* $\mathrm{K} = \mathbf{R}$, *analytic in* I *if* $\mathrm{K} = \mathbf{C}$. *Then, for every* $x_0 \in \mathrm{E}$, *there exists a unique solution u of* (10.6.2), defined in I *and such that* $u(t_0) = x_0$.

Observe that if $b = 0$, and $x_0 = 0$, the solution u of (10.6.2) is equal to 0.

From (10.6.3) we easily deduce the apparently more general result:

(10.6.4) *The assumptions being the same as in* (10.6.3), *for every* $s \in \mathrm{I}$ *and every* $x_0 \in \mathrm{E}$, *there is a unique solution* u *of* (10.6.2) *defined in* I *and such that* $u(s) = x_0$.

Replacing t by $t - t_0$, we may assume that $t_0 = 0$. Suppose I is a ball of radius r; the mapping

$$t \to r^2 \frac{t - s}{\bar{s}t - r^2}$$

is an analytic homeomorphism of I onto itself, mapping s on 0: indeed, one has

$$t' = r^2 \frac{t - s}{\bar{s}t - 1} = \frac{r^2}{\bar{s}} \left(1 - \frac{r^2 - |s|^2}{r^2 - \bar{s}t}\right)$$

hence, if $|t| \leqslant r$, we have

$$|r^2 - \bar{s}t| \leqslant r(r + |s|)$$

whence

$$|t'| \leqslant \frac{r^2}{|s|} \left(1 - \frac{r^2 - |s|^2}{r(r + |s|)}\right) = r;$$

our assertion follows from the fact that, conversely,

$$t = r^2 \frac{t' - s}{\bar{s}t' - 1}.$$

Now, if

$$A_1(t) = \frac{(\bar{s}t - r^2)^2}{r^2(|s|^2 - r^2)} A\left(r^2 \frac{t - s}{\bar{s}t - r^2}\right),$$

and

$$b_1(t) = \frac{(\bar{s}t - r^2)^2}{r^2(|s|^2 - r^2)} b\left(r^2 \frac{t - s}{\bar{s}t - r^2}\right),$$

one sees at once that if v is the unique solution of the differential equation

$$x' = A_1(t) \cdot x + b_1(t)$$

defined in I and such that $v(0) = x_0$, then

$$u(t) = v\left(r^2 \frac{t - s}{\bar{s}t - r^2}\right)$$

is the unique solution of (10.6.2), defined in I and such that $u(s) = x_0$.

When $\mathrm{E} = \mathrm{K}^n$, $A(t) = (a_{ij}(t))$ is an $n \times n$ matrix, $b(t) = (b_i(t))$ a vector, the $a_{ij}(t)$ and $b_i(t)$ being regulated in I if $\mathrm{K} = \mathbf{R}$, analytic if $\mathrm{K} = \mathbf{C}$; if $x = (x_i)_{1 \leqslant i \leqslant n}$, equation (10.6.2) is equivalent to the *system of scalar linear differential equations*

(10.6.5) $$x_i' = \sum_{j=1}^{n} a_{ij}(t)x_j + b_i(t) \qquad (1 \leqslant i \leqslant n).$$

The (scalar) *linear differential equations of order* $n > 1$

(10.6.6) $$\mathrm{D}^n x - a_1(t)\mathrm{D}^{n-1}x - \cdots - a_{n-1}(t)\mathrm{D}x - a_n(t)x = b(t)$$

are equivalent to special systems of type (10.6.5); one has only to write $x_1 = x$, $x_p = \mathrm{D}^{p-1}x$ for $2 \leqslant p \leqslant n$, and (10.6.6) is equivalent to

(10.6.7) $$\begin{cases} x_k' = x_{k+1} & \text{for} \quad 1 \leqslant k \leqslant n-1 \\ x_n' = a_1(t)x_n + a_2(t)x_{n-1} + \cdots + a_n(t)x_1 + b(t). \end{cases}$$

7. DEPENDENCE OF THE SOLUTION ON PARAMETERS

(10.7.1) *Let* E *be a Banach space over* K, I *an open subset of* K, H *an open subset of* E, P *a metric space, f a mapping of* $\mathrm{I} \times \mathrm{H} \times \mathrm{P}$ *into* E. *Suppose that:* (1) *for any* $z \in \mathrm{P}$, $(t, x) \to f(t, x, z)$ *is a continuously differentiable mapping of* $\mathrm{I} \times \mathrm{H}$ *into* E; (2) f *and* $\mathrm{D}_2 f$ *are continuous in* $\mathrm{I} \times \mathrm{H} \times \mathrm{P}$. *Then, for any point* $(t_0, x_0, z_0) \in \mathrm{I} \times \mathrm{H} \times \mathrm{P}$, *there exists an open ball* $\mathrm{J} \subset \mathrm{I}$ *of center* t_0 *and an open ball* $\mathrm{T} \subset \mathrm{P}$ *of center* z_0 *such that, for each* $z \in \mathrm{T}$, *there exists in* J *one and only one solution* $t \to u(t, z)$ *of the equation* $x' = f(t, x, z)$ *such that* $u(t_0, z) = x_0$. *Moreover the mapping* $(t, z) \to u(t, z)$ *is bounded and continuous in* $\mathrm{J} \times \mathrm{T}$.

The proof is very similar to that of (10.4.5). Let J_a be a compact ball of center t_0 and radius a contained in I. By (10.4.5.1), there is an open ball B of center x_0 and radius b contained in H, and an open ball T of center z_0 in P, such that $\|f(t, x, z)\| \leqslant \mathrm{M}$ and $\|\mathrm{D}_2 f(t, x, z)\| \leqslant k$ in $\mathrm{J}_a \times \mathrm{B} \times \mathrm{T}$. For $r < a$, let J_r be the closed ball of center t_0 and radius r. If $\mathrm{K} = \mathbf{R}$, we define F_r to be the space of bounded continuous mappings y of $\mathrm{J}_r \times \mathrm{T}$ into E, which is a Banach space. If $\mathrm{K} = \mathbf{C}$, we define F_r as the space of mappings y of $\mathrm{J}_r \times \mathrm{T}$ into E which are bounded and continuous in J_r and such that, for any $z \in \mathrm{T}$, $t \to y(t, z)$ is analytic in $\mathring{\mathrm{J}}_r$; this is again a Banach space by (9.12.1). The remainder of the proof of (10.4.5) is then unchanged.

For linear differential equations, there is a better result:

(10.7.2) *Let* $\mathrm{I} \subset \mathrm{K}$ *be an open ball of center* t_0*; suppose* A *and* b *continuous in* $\mathrm{I} \times \mathrm{P}$, *and, if* $\mathrm{K} = \mathbf{C}$, *such that for each* $z \in \mathrm{P}$, $t \to A(t, z)$ *and* $t \to b(t, z)$ *are analytic in* I. *For any* $x \in \mathrm{E}$, *let* $t \to u(t, z)$ *be the solution of* $x' = A(t, z) \cdot x + b(t, z)$ *defined in* I *and such that* $u(t_0, z) = x_0$; *then* u *is continuous in* $\mathrm{I} \times \mathrm{P}$.

Let $z_0 \in \mathrm{P}$, and consider an arbitrary compact ball $\mathrm{J} \subset \mathrm{I}$ of center t_0 and radius r; it will be enough to prove that u is continuous at each point (t, z_0) where $t \in \mathrm{J}$. As $t \to u(t, z_0)$ is continuous in J, it is bounded in that compact set, let $\|u(t, z_0)\| \leqslant \mathrm{M}$ in J. By (10.4.5.1), there is a neighborhood U of z_0 in P such that $\|A(t, z)\| \leqslant k$ for $z \in \mathrm{U}$ and $t \in \mathrm{J}$. Given arbitrarily an $\varepsilon > 0$, let us show next that there exists a neighborhood $\mathrm{V} \subset \mathrm{U}$ of z_0 in P such that $\|A(t, z) - A(t, z_0)\| \leqslant \varepsilon$ and $\|b(t, z) - b(t, z_0)\| \leqslant \varepsilon$ for $t \in \mathrm{J}$ and $z \in \mathrm{V}$. We only have to remark that for any $s \in \mathrm{J}$ there is a neighborhood W_s of s in J and a neighborhood $\mathrm{V}_s \subset \mathrm{U}$ of z_0 in P such that the preceding inequalities hold in $\mathrm{W}_s \times \mathrm{V}_s$; then we cover J by a finite number of neighborhoods W_{s_i}, and take for V the intersection of the V_{s_i}. We can now write

$$u'(t, z) - u'(t, z_0)$$
$$= A(t, z) \cdot (u(t, z) - u(t, z_0)) + (A(t, z) - A(t, z_0)) \cdot u(t, z_0) + b(t, z) - b(t, z_0)$$

hence, for $t \in \mathrm{J}$ and $z \in \mathrm{V}$

$$\|u'(t, z) - u'(t, z_0)\| \leqslant k \cdot \|u(t, z) - u(t, z_0)\| + \varepsilon(\mathrm{M} + 1).$$

Put $t = t_0 + \lambda\xi$ with $|\lambda| = 1, 0 \leqslant \xi \leqslant r$, and

$$w(\xi) = \|u(t_0 + \lambda\xi, z) - u(t_0 + \lambda\xi, z_0)\|;$$

then by the mean value theorem, we have $w(\xi) \leqslant \varepsilon(\mathrm{M} + 1)r + k \int_0^\xi w(\zeta)\, d\zeta$ for $0 \leqslant \xi \leqslant r$, and using (10.5.1.3), we obtain $w(\xi) \leqslant \varepsilon(\mathrm{M} + 1)re^{kr}$ for $0 \leqslant \xi \leqslant r$, in other words, we have $\|u(t, z) - u(t, z_0)\| \leqslant \varepsilon(\mathrm{M} + 1)re^{kr}$ for $t \in \mathrm{J}$ and $z \in \mathrm{V}$; as ε is arbitrary, this ends the proof (since $t \to u(t, z_0)$ is continuous in J).

(10.7.3) *In addition to the assumptions of* (10.7.1), *suppose that* P *is an open subset of a Banach space* G, *and that* (1) *if* $\mathrm{K} = \mathbf{R}$, f *is continuously differentiable in* $\mathrm{I} \times \mathrm{H} \times \mathrm{P}$; (2) *if* $\mathrm{K} = \mathbf{C}$, f *is twice continuously differentiable in* $\mathrm{I} \times \mathrm{H} \times \mathrm{P}$ *(when* E *and* G *are finite dimensional, this is equivalent to saying that* f *is analytic in* $\mathrm{I} \times \mathrm{H} \times \mathrm{P}$ (9.10)). *Let* $\mathrm{J}_1 \subset \mathrm{I}$ *be an open ball of center* t_0 *and* $\mathrm{T}_1 \subset \mathrm{P}$ *an open ball of center* z_0 *such that, for every* $z \in \mathrm{T}_1$, *there is a solution* $t \to u(t, z)$ *of* $x' = f(t, x, z)$ *(necessarily unique by* (10.5.2)) *defined in* J_1 *and such that* $u(t_0, z) = x_0$. *Then, for any open ball* J *of center* t_0, *such that* $\bar{\mathrm{J}} \subset \mathrm{J}_1$, *there exists an open ball* $\mathrm{T} \subset \mathrm{T}_1$ *of center* z_0 *such that* $(t, z) \to u(t, z)$ *is continuously differentiable in* $\mathrm{J} \times \mathrm{T}$. *Furthermore, for any* $z \in \mathrm{T}$, $t \to \mathrm{D}_2 u(t, z)$ *is equal in* J *to the solution* $U(t, z)$ *of the linear differential equation*

(10.7.3.1) $$U' = A(t, z) \circ U + B(t, z)$$

such that $U(t_0, z) = 0$, *where* $A(t, z) = \mathrm{D}_2 f(t, u(t, z), z)$ *and* $B(t, z) = \mathrm{D}_3 f(t, u(t, z), z)$.

Let J be an open ball of center t_0 and radius r, such that $\bar{\mathrm{J}} \subset \mathrm{J}_1$. By (10.4.5.1), there is an open ball $\mathrm{S} \subset \mathrm{H}$ of center x_0 and an open ball $\mathrm{T} \subset \mathrm{T}_1$ of center z_0 such that $\mathrm{D}_2 f$ and $\mathrm{D}_3 f$ are bounded in $\mathrm{J} \times \mathrm{S} \times \mathrm{T}$, let $\|\mathrm{D}_2 f(t, x, z)\| \leqslant a$ and $\|\mathrm{D}_3 f(t, x, z)\| \leqslant b$. Then, by (8.5.2) and (8.9.1), we have,

(10.7.3.2) $$\|f(t, x_1, z_1) - f(t, x_2, z_2)\| \leqslant a\|x_1 - x_2\| + b\|z_1 - z_2\|$$

for $t \in \mathrm{J}$, x_1, x_2 in S, z_1, z_2 in T. Taking (10.7.3.2) into account, we see that, by (10.5.1), we have, for $t \in \mathrm{J}$ and z_1, z_2 in T

(10.7.3.3) $$\|u(t, z_1) - u(t, z_2)\| \leqslant c\|z_1 - z_2\|$$

with $c = b(e^{ar} - 1)/a$. We next prove that, given a point $z \in \mathrm{T}$ and $\varepsilon > 0$, there exists $\rho > 0$ such that, for any $w \in \mathrm{P}$ such that $z + w \in \mathrm{T}$ and $\|w\| \leqslant \rho$, and *any* $t \in \bar{\mathrm{J}}$, we have

(10.7.3.4) $$\begin{aligned}\|f(t, u(t, z + w), z + w) - f(t, u(t, z), z) \\ - A(t, z)\cdot(u(t, z + w) - u(t, z)) - B(t, z)\cdot w\| \\ \leqslant \varepsilon\|w\|.\end{aligned}$$

Indeed, using (8.6.2), (8.9.1), the continuity of $\mathrm{D}_2 f$ and $\mathrm{D}_3 f$ in $\mathrm{I} \times \mathrm{H} \times \mathrm{P}$, and relation (10.7.3.3), for any $s \in \bar{\mathrm{J}}$, there is a neighborhood W_s of s in J_1 and a number $\rho(s) > 0$ such that relation (10.7.3.4) holds for $t \in \mathrm{W}_s$ and $\|w\| \leqslant \rho(s)$; covering $\bar{\mathrm{J}}$ by finitely many W_{s_i}, we need only take for ρ the smallest of the $\rho(s_i)$ to have (10.7.3.4). Due to the definition of $u(t, z)$, (10.7.3.4) can also be written

(10.7.3.5)

$$\begin{aligned}\|\mathrm{D}_1 u(t, z + w) - \mathrm{D}_1 u(t, z) - A(t, z)\cdot(u(t, z + w) - u(t, z)) - B(t, z)\cdot w\| \\ \leqslant \varepsilon\|w\|.\end{aligned}$$

Now the existence of $U(t, z)$ in $\mathrm{J} \times \mathrm{T}$ is guaranteed by (10.6.3), since $D_2 f$ and $D_3 f$ are continuously differentiable when $\mathrm{K} = \mathbf{C}$. Put $v(t, z, w) = u(t, z + w) - u(t, z) - U(t, z) \cdot w$; this function has a derivative with respect to t equal to

$$D_1 v(t, z, w) = D_1 u(t, z + w) - D_1 u(t, z) - A(t, z) \cdot (U(t, z) \cdot w) - B(t, z) \cdot w,$$

by (10.7.3.1). Relation (10.7.3.5) therefore can be written

$$\|D_1 v(t, z, w) - A(t, z) \cdot v(t, z, w)\| \leqslant \varepsilon \|w\|,$$

for *any* $t \in \mathrm{J}$ and any w such that $z + w \in \mathrm{T}$ and $\|w\| \leqslant \rho$. In other words, $v(t, z, w)$ is an *approximate solution*, with approximation $\varepsilon \|w\|$, of the linear differential equation

$$y' = A(t, z) \cdot y. \tag{10.7.3.6}$$

Furthermore, we have $v(t_0, z, w) = 0$ by definition; as $\|A(t, z)\| \leqslant a$ in $\mathrm{J} \times \mathrm{T}$, we conclude from (10.5.1) (since 0 is a solution of (10.7.3.6)) that

$$\|v(t, z, w)\| \leqslant c_0 \varepsilon \|w\|$$

where $c_0 = (e^{ar} - 1)/a$, this inequality being valid for *any* $t \in \mathrm{J}$ and any w such that $z + w \in \mathrm{T}$ and $\|w\| \leqslant \rho$. As ε is arbitrary, the definition of the derivative of a function shows that u is differentiable with respect to z at any point $(t, z) \in \mathrm{J} \times \mathrm{T}$ and that $D_2 u(t, z) = U(t, z)$.

Finally, from the assumptions and (10.7.2), it follows that U is continuous in $\mathrm{J} \times \mathrm{T}$; on the other hand, $D_1 u(t, z) = f(t, u(t, z), z)$ is continuous in $\mathrm{J} \times \mathrm{T}$ by (10.7.1). Therefore, by (8.9.1), u is continuously differentiable in $\mathrm{J} \times \mathrm{T}$, and this ends the proof of (10.7.3).

(10.7.4) *Suppose* $\mathrm{K} = \mathbf{R}$, *and* f *is* p *times continuously differentiable* (resp. E *and* G *are finite dimensional and* f *is indefinitely differentiable*) *in* $\mathrm{I} \times \mathrm{H} \times \mathrm{P}$. *Then, for each open interval* J *of center* t_0 *such that* $\bar{\mathrm{J}} \subset \mathrm{J}_1$, *it is possible to take* T *such that* u *is* p *times continuously differentiable* (resp. *indefinitely differentiable*) *in* $\mathrm{J} \times \mathrm{T}$.

If $p = 1$, this is (10.7.3). Using induction on p, suppose we have proved the result for $(p - 1)$ times continuously differentiable mappings. Then, in the right-hand side of (10.7.3.1), A and B are $p - 1$ times continuously differentiable mappings in $\mathrm{J} \times \mathrm{T}$ (by (8.12.10)); therefore, by (10.7.3) (applied to $U(t, z)$), $D_2 u(t, z)$ is $p - 1$ times continuously differentiable in $\mathrm{J} \times \mathrm{T}$ (when T has been conveniently chosen). On the other hand $D_1 u(t, z) = f(t, u(t, z), z)$ is also $p - 1$ times continuously differentiable in $\mathrm{J} \times \mathrm{T}$ by the induction hypothesis and (8.12.10); therefore $Du(t, z)$ is $p - 1$ times continuously differentiable in $\mathrm{J} \times \mathrm{T}$ by (8.9.1), (8.12.9), and (8.12.10); but this implies that u is p times continuously differentiable in $J \times T$, by (8.12.5). When E and G are finite dimensional and f is indefinitely differentiable, it follows from (3.17.10) that in the preceding argument one may choose T *independently of* p, since all derivatives of f are continuous; therefore u is indefinitely differentiable in $J \times T$.

Observe that in (10.7.4), one may replace J_1 by *any* open interval containing the point t_0, and J by any open interval containing t_0 and such that $\bar{J} \subset J_1$.

(10.7.5) *Suppose that the Banach spaces* E *and* G *are finite dimensional and that f is analytic in* $I \times H \times P$. *Then, for any open ball* J *of center* t_0, *such that* $\bar{J} \subset J_1$, *it is possible to take* T *such that u is analytic in* $J \times T$.

If $K = \mathbf{C}$, this follows immediately from (10.7.1), (10.7.3), (9.10.1), and (9.9.4). If $K = \mathbf{R}$, we apply an argument exactly similar to that of (10.5.3), which we accordingly suppress.

(10.7.6) *Remarks.* There are several improvements and variants of the preceding theorems. For instance, in (10.7.3), when $K = \mathbf{R}$, the existence of $D_1 f$ is not required to insure that $D_2 u(t, z)$ exists: we need only the continuity of $D_2 f$ and $D_3 f$ as functions of (x, z), and their boundedness in $J \times S \times T$, as well as the fact that $t \to f(t, h(t), z)$ is regulated in I for any function h continuous in I and similarly for $D_2 f$ and $D_3 f$.

PROBLEMS

1. The notations being those of Section 10.4, let I be an open ball in K of center t_0 and radius a, S an open ball in E of center x_0 and radius r, G the normed space $\mathscr{C}_E^\infty(I \times S)$ (Section 7.2). For each $M > 0$, let G_M be the ball $\|f\| \leqslant M$ in G. Let L be the subset of G consisting of all continuous *lipschitzian* mappings of $I \times S$ into E (10.5.4); for each $M > 0$, let J_M be the open ball of center t_0 and radius $\inf(a, r/M)$; for each function $f \in L \cap G_M$, there is a unique solution $u = U(f)$ of $x' = f(t, x)$ taking its values in S, defined in J_M and such that $u(t_0) = x_0$ (Section 10.5, Problem 6(c)).
(a) Let (f_n) be a sequence of functions belonging to $L \cap G_M$, and suppose f_n converges uniformly in $I \times S$ to a function f; show that in the space $\mathscr{C}_E^\infty(J_M)$, every cluster value of the sequence of functions $u_n = U(f_n)$ is a solution of $x' = f(t, x)$, taking its values in S, and equal to x_0 for $t = t_0$ (use (10.4.3) and (8.7.8)). Give an example in which the sequence (u_n) has *no* cluster value in $\mathscr{C}_E^\infty(J_M)$ (see Section 10.5, Problem 5).

(b) Suppose in addition that E is *finite dimensional*; using the result of (a), give a new proof of Peano's theorem (Section **10.5**, Problem 4(b); use Ascoli's theorem **(7.5.7)** and the Weierstrass approximation theorem **(7.4.1)**).

2. (a) In the polydisk P: $|t-t_0|<a$, $|x-x_0|<b$ in $\mathbf{R}^2$, let g, h be two real valued continuous functions such that $g(t,x)<h(t,x)$ in P. Let u (resp. v) be a solution of $x'=g(t,x)$ (resp. $x'=h(t,x)$) defined in an interval $[t_0, t_0+c[$, taking its values in $]x_0-b, x_0+b[$ and such that $u(t_0)=x_0$ (resp. $v(t_0)=x_0$); show that $u(t)<v(t)$ for $t_0<t<t_0+c$ (consider the l.u.b. of the points s in $[t_0, t_0+c[$ such that $u(t)<v(t)$ for $t_0<t<s$).
(b) Let g be continuous and real valued in P, and let u be the maximal solution of $x'=g(t\ x)$ corresponding to (t_0, x_0) (Section **10.5**, Problem 7); suppose u is defined (at least,) in an interval $[t_0, t_0+c[$ and takes its values in $]x_0-b, x_0+b[$. Show that in every compact interval $[t_0, t_0+d]$ contained in $[t_0, t_0+c[$, the maximal and minimal solutions of $x'=g(t,x)+\varepsilon$ are defined and take their values in $]x_0-b, x_0+b[$ as soon as $\varepsilon>0$ is small enough, and converge uniformly to u when ε tends to 0. (Given $\varepsilon_0>0$, there exists an $s>t_0$ such that the maximal and minimal solutions of all the equations $x'=g(t,x)+\varepsilon$ for $0\leqslant\varepsilon\leqslant\varepsilon_0$, corresponding to (t_0, x_0), are defined and take their values in $]x_0-b, x_0+b[$ for t in $[t_0, s]$; observe that all these functions form an equicontinuous set in $[t_0, s]$, and prove the uniform convergence to u in $[t_0, s]$ by applying the result of (a), Ascoli's theorem **(7.5.7)**, **(10.4.3)**, and **(8.7.8)**. Finally, show that the l.u.b. of the numbers d having the stated property is necessarily equal to c, using in particular the last statement of Section **10.5**, Problem 7.)
(c) In the polydisk P, let g and h be two continuous real valued functions such that $g(t,x)\leqslant h(t,x)$ in P. Let $[t_0, t_0+c]$ be an interval in which a solution u of $x'=g(t,x)$ such that $u(t_0)=x_0$, and the maximal solution v of $x'=h(t,x)$ corresponding to (t_0, x_0) are defined and take their values in $]x_0-b, x_0+b[$. Show that $u(t)\leqslant v(t)$ for $t_0\leqslant t\leqslant t_0+c$ (apply (a) and (b)).

3. (a) Show that the conclusions of Problem 6(a) of Section **10.5** are still valid when E is *finite dimensional*, and the assumptions are modified as follows: (1) f is supposed to be continuous in I × H (when K = R), but not necessarily locally lipschitzian; (2) φ is the maximal solution (Section **10.5**, Problem 7) of the equation $z'=h(s,z)$ in $[0,\alpha]$, corresponding to the point (0, 0). (Use the results of Problems 1(a) and 2(b), and apply the diagonal process as in Problem 4(b) of Section **10.5**.)
(b) Suppose in addition that there exists a sequence $(Y_n)_{n\geqslant 0}$ of real valued functions, continuous in $[0,\alpha]$, taking their values in $[0,r]$, such that for $n\geqslant 1$, $Y_n(s)=\int_0^s h(\xi, Y_{n-1}(\xi))\,d\xi$ for $0\leqslant s\leqslant\alpha$. Let y_0 be continuous in J if K = R, analytic in J if K = C, with values in S, and such that $\|y_0(t)-x_0\|\leqslant Y_0(|t-t_0|)$ in J. Show that there exists a sequence $(y_n)_{n\geqslant 1}$ of mappings of J into S, which are continuous if K = R, analytic if K = C, and such that $y_n(t)=x_0+\int_0^s f(\theta, y_{n-1}(\theta))\,d\theta$, and that $\|y_n(t)-x_0\|\leqslant Y_n(|t-t_0|)$ in J for every $n\geqslant 1$. When K = C, conclude that the sequence (y_n) converges in J (uniformly in every compact subset of J) to the unique solution u of $x'=f(t,x)$. (Use **(9.13.2)** and the proof of **(10.4.5)**.) Is this last statement still true when K = R and f is not supposed to be locally lipschitzian (cf. Section **10.5**, Problem 2)?

4. (a) Let $I=[t_0, t_0+c[\subset\mathbf{R}$, and let ω be a real valued continuous function $\geqslant 0$, defined in I × R. Let S be an open ball of center x_0 in E, and let f be a continuous mapping of I × S into E such that for $t\in I$, $x_1\in S$ and $x_2\in S$, $\|f(t,x_1)-f(t,x_2)\|\leqslant\omega(t, \|x_1-x_2\|)$. Let u, v be two solutions of $x'=f(t,x)$, defined in

I, taking their values in S, and such that $u(t_0) = x_1$, $v(t, x_0) = x_2$; let w be the *maximal* solution (Section 10.5, Problem 7) of $z' = \omega(t, z)$ corresponding to $(t_0, \|x_1 - x_2\|)$, and suppose w is defined in I; show that in I, $\|u(t) - v(t)\| \leqslant w(t)$. (For small $\varepsilon > 0$, consider the maximal solution $w(t, \varepsilon)$ of $z' = \omega(t, z) + \varepsilon$ corresponding to $(t_0, \|x_1 - x_2\|)$, which is defined in $[t_0, t_0 + d]$ if $d < c$, as soon as ε is small enough (Problem 2); show that for $t_0 \leqslant t \leqslant t_0 + d$, $\|u(t) - v(t)\| \leqslant w(t, \varepsilon)$, using contradiction: consider the g.l.b. t_1 of the points t such that $\|y(t)\| > w(t, \varepsilon)$, where $y(t) = u(t) - v(t)$, and observe that for $t > t_1$

$$\|y(t)\| - \|y(t_1)\| \leqslant \|y(t) - y(t_1)\| \leqslant \sup_{t_1 < s < t} \|y'(s)\| \cdot (t - t_1).)$$

(b) Let $I' =]t_0 - c, t_0]$, and suppose that the assumptions of (a) are verified when I is replaced throughout by I′. Let now w be the *minimal* solution of $z' = \omega(t, z)$ corresponding to $(t_0, \|x_1 - x_2\|)$, and suppose it is defined in I′; show that in I′, $\|u(t) - v(t)\| \geqslant w(t)$ (same method).

5. (a) Let I be the *open* interval $]0, a[$ in **R**, and let ω be a continuous function in $[0, +\infty[$, such that $\omega(t, z) \geqslant 0$, and $\omega(t, 0) = 0$ for $t \in I$; ω can be extended to $I \times \mathbf{R}$ by the condition $\omega(t, -z) = \omega(t, z)$ for $z < 0$. We suppose that if w is a solution of $z' = \omega(t, z)$ defined in an open interval $]0, \alpha[\subset I$, such that w can be extended by continuity to the half-open interval $[0, \alpha[$ by taking $w(0) = 0$, and that in addition $w'(0)$ is then defined and equal to 0, then necessarily $w(t) = 0$ identically in $]0, \alpha[$. Let now S be an open ball of center x_0 in a real Banach space E, f a continuous mapping of $[0, a[\times S$ into E, such that, for $0 < t < a$ and x_1, x_2 in S, $\|f(t, x_1) - f(t, x_2)\| \leqslant \omega(t, \|x_1 - x_2\|)$. Show that in an interval $[0, \alpha]$ with $\alpha < a$, there is *at most* one solution u of $x' = f(t, x)$ such that $u(0) = x_0$. (Use contradiction: if v is a second solution such that $v(0) = x_0$, minorize $\|u(t) - v(t)\|$ in $]0, \alpha]$, using Problem 4(b).)

(b) Let $\theta(t)$ be a continuous function defined in $]0, a[$ and such that $\theta(t) \geqslant 0$. Show that if the integral $\int_0^a \frac{\theta(t)}{t}\, dt$ is convergent, the result of (a) applies to $\omega(t, z) = \frac{1 + \theta(t)}{t} z$; if, on the contrary, $\int_0^a \frac{\theta(t)}{t}\, dt = +\infty$, give an example of a continuous real valued function f in $[0, a[\times \mathbf{R}$, such that

$$|f(t, x_1) - f(t, x_2)| \leqslant \frac{1 + \theta(t)}{t} |x_1 - x_2|,$$

and that the equation $x' = f(t, x)$ has an infinity of solutions in $[0, a[$, equal to 0 for $t = 0$. (Let

$$\varphi(t) = \exp\left(-\int_t^a \frac{1 + \theta(s)}{s}\, ds\right);$$

define $f(t, x)$ as equal to $(1 + \theta(t))x/t$ for $|x| \leqslant \varphi(t)$, and independent of x for $|x| \geqslant \varphi(t)$.)

6. Let I be an open interval in **R**, H an open subset of a Banach space E over **R**. Let t_0 be a point of I.

(a) Suppose f is continuous in $I \times H$, and that there is a number k such that $0 < k < 1$ and that, for any $t \neq t_0$, and x_1, x_2 arbitrary in H,

$$\|f(t, x_1) - f(t, x_2)\| \leqslant \frac{k}{|t - t_0|} \|x_1 - x_2\|.$$

There is then at most one solution of $x' = f(t, x)$ taking a given value $x_0 \in \mathrm{H}$ for $t = t_0$ and defined in a neighborhood of t_0 (Problem 5(a)). But in addition, if u, v are two approximate solutions of $x' = f(t, x)$ in an open ball J of center t_0, contained in I, with approximations $\varepsilon_1, \varepsilon_2$, and such that $u(t_0) = v(t_0) = x_0$, then, for any $t \in \mathrm{J}$

$$\|u(t) - v(t)\| \leqslant \frac{\varepsilon_1 + \varepsilon_2}{1 - k} |t - t_0|.$$

(Use the same method as in **(10.5.1)**.)

(b) Let $\mathrm{I} =]-1, 1[$, $\mathrm{H} = \mathrm{E} = \mathbf{R}$, and let Φ be the set of all real valued functions f, continuous in $\mathrm{I} \times \mathrm{H}$, and such that, for $t \neq 0$ in I, $|f(t, x_1) - f(t, x_2)| \leqslant |x_1 - x_2|/|t|$. There is then at most one solution of $x' = f(t, x)$ taking a given value for $t = t_0$ and defined in a neighborhood of t_0 (Problem 5(a)). But prove that there is *no* function $\varphi(t, \varepsilon) \geqslant 0$ such that, for *any* pair (u, v) of approximate solutions, with approximation ε, of *any* equation $x' = f(t, x)$ with $f \in \Phi$, such that u and v are defined in I and $u(t_0) = v(t_0)$, the relation $\|u(t) - v(t)\| \leqslant \varphi(|t|, \varepsilon)$ would hold for every $t \in \mathrm{I}$. (For any $\alpha \in]0, 1[$, let f be the continuous function equal to x/t for $|x| \leqslant t^2/(\alpha - t)$, $0 \leqslant t < \alpha$, and for $t \geqslant \alpha$, and independent of x for the other values of (t, x) such that $t \geqslant 0$; define $f(t, x) = f(-t, x)$ for $t \leqslant 0$. Take $u = 0$; let $v(t) = \varepsilon t$ for $|t| \leqslant \alpha$, and take for v a solution of $x' = f(t, x) + \varepsilon$ for the other values of t.)

7. The notations being those of Section **10.4**, suppose E is *finite dimensional* and f is continuous in $\mathrm{I} \times \mathrm{H}$; let (t_0, x_0) be a point of $\mathrm{I} \times \mathrm{H}$, J an open ball of center t_0 contained in I, S an open ball of center x_0 such that $\mathrm{S} \subset \mathrm{H}$. Suppose f is bounded in $\mathrm{J} \times \mathrm{S}$, and the following conditions are verified:

(1) There is *at most one* solution of $x' = f(t, x)$ defined in an open interval contained in J and containing t_0, and taking the value x_0 for $t = t_0$.

(2) There exists a sequence $(u_n)_{n \geqslant 0}$ of continuous mappings of J into S such that

$$u_n(t) = x_0 + \int_{t_0}^{t} f(s, u_{n-1}(s))\, ds \qquad \text{for} \quad n \geqslant 1 \quad \text{and} \quad t \in \mathrm{J}.$$

(3) For every $t \in \mathrm{J}$, $u_{n+1}(t) - u_n(t)$ converges to 0 when n tends to $+\infty$.

Show that in every compact interval $\mathrm{J}' \subset \mathrm{J}$ containing t_0 the sequence (u_n) converges uniformly to a solution of $x' = f(t, x)$ equal to x_0 for $t = t_0$. (Observe that the sequence (u_n) is equicontinuous; use Ascoli's theorem **(7.5.7)**, as well as **(3.16.4)** and **(8.7.8)**.)

8. Suppose E is *finite dimensional*, ω and f verify the conditions of Problem 5(a), and in addition, for every $t \in]0, a[$, the function $z \to \omega(t, z)$ is *increasing* in $[0, +\infty[$. There is then *at most one* solution of $x' = f(t, x)$ defined in an interval $[0, \alpha[\subset [0, a[$ and taking the value x_0 for $t = 0$ (Problem 5(a)). Suppose in addition that there exists, in an interval $\mathrm{J} = [0, \alpha] \subset [0, a[$, a sequence $(u_n)_{n \geqslant 0}$ of continuous mappings of J into S such that

$$u_n(t) = x_0 + \int_0^t f(s, u_{n-1}(s))\, ds \qquad \text{for} \quad n \geqslant 1 \quad \text{and} \quad t \in \mathrm{J}.$$

(a) For every $t \in \mathrm{J}$, let $y_n(t) = \|u_{n+1}(t) - u_n(t)\|$, $z_n(t) = \sup_{k \geqslant 0} y_{n+k}(t)$, and $w(t) = \inf_{k \geqslant 0} z_n(t)$. Show that the functions z_n and w are continuous in J (use Problem 11 of Section **7.5**).

(b) Let $t, t - h$ be two points of J ($h > 0$); show that, for every $\delta > 0$, there is an N such that, for $n \geqslant \mathrm{N}$,

$$|y_n(t) - y_n(t - h)| \leqslant \int_{t-h}^{t} \omega(s, w(s) + \delta)\, ds.$$

(Use the mean value theorem (8.5.1), as well as (7.5.5).)
(c) Deduce from (b) that, for $n \geqslant N$

$$|z_n(t) - z_n(t-h)| \leqslant \int_{t-h}^{t} \omega(s, w(s) + \delta)\, ds$$

(consider in succession the cases $z_n(t) \leqslant z_n(t-h)$ and $z_n(t) \geqslant z_n(t-h)$). Hence

$$|w(t) - w(t-h)| \leqslant \int_{t-h}^{t} \omega(s, w(s))\, ds \qquad \text{(by (8.7.8))}.$$

(d) Conclude that $w(t) = 0$ in J (same argument as in Problems 4(b) and 5(a)), and using Problem 7, prove that the sequence (u_n) converges uniformly in J to a solution of $x = f(t, x)$ taking the value x_0 for $t = 0$.

9. The notations being those of Section 10.4, suppose E is *finite dimensional*, and f is continuous and bounded in $I \times H$. Suppose in addition there is *at most one* solution of $x' = f(t, x)$ defined in any open interval $J \subset I$ containing t_0, and equal to $x_0 \in H$ for $t = t_0$. Suppose that, for any integer $n > 0$, there exists an approximate solution u_n of $x' = f(t, x)$, with approximation $1/n$, defined in I and taking its values in H, and such that $u_n(t_0) = x_0$. Show that in any compact interval contained in I, the sequence (u_n) is uniformly convergent to a solution u of $x' = f(t, x)$, taking its values in H and such that $u(t_0) = x_0$. (Use the same argument as in Problem 7.)

8. DEPENDENCE OF THE SOLUTION ON INITIAL CONDITIONS

(10.8.1) *Let f be locally lipschitzian* (10.5.4) *in $I \times H$ if $K = \mathbf{R}$, analytic in $I \times H$ if $K = \mathbf{C}$. Then, for any point $(a, b) \in I \times H$:*

(a) *There is an open ball $J \subset I$ of center a and an open ball $V \subset H$ of center b such that, for every point $(t_0, x_0) \in J \times V$, there exists a unique solution $t \to u(t, t_0, x_0)$ of* (10.4.1) *defined in J, taking its values in H and such that $u(t_0, t_0, x_0) = x_0$.*

(b) *The mapping $(t, t_0, x_0) \to u(t, t_0, x_0)$ is uniformly continuous in $J \times J \times V$.*

(c) *There is an open ball $W \subset V$ of center b such that, for any point $(t, t_0, x_0) \in J \times J \times W$, the equation $x_0 = u(t_0, t, x)$ has a unique solution $x = u(t, t_0, x_0)$ in V.*

(a) By assumption, there is a ball $J_0 \subset I$ of center a and a ball $B_0 \subset H$ of center b and radius r such that in $J_0 \times B_0$, $\|f(t, x)\| \leqslant M$, and $\|f(t, x_1) - f(t, x_2)\| \leqslant k \cdot \|x_1 - x_2\|$ for $t \in J_0$, x_1, x_2 in B_0. By (10.4.5) and (10.5.2) there is an open ball $J_1 \subset J_0$ of center t_0 and a unique solution v of (10.4.1) defined in J_1, taking its values in H and such that $v(a) = b$. We are going to see that the open ball V of center b and radius $r/2$, and the open ball J of center a and radius ρ, answer our specifications *as soon as ρ is small enough.* Apply

(10.5.6) to the case $\alpha = \beta = 0$; this shows that there exists a solution of (10.4.1) *defined in* J, with values in B_0, taking the value $x_0 \in V$ at the point $t_0 \in J$, provided we have

(10.8.1.1)
$$\|v(t) - b\| + \|v(t_0) - x_0\|e^{k|t-t_0|} < r$$

for every $t \in J$. But by the mean value theorem, we have $\|v(t) - b\| \leqslant M\,|t - a| \leqslant M\rho$ for every $t \in J$; as by assumption $\|x_0 - b\| \leqslant r/2$, the inequality (10.8.1.1) will be satisfied if ρ is such that

(10.8.1.12)
$$M\rho + \left(M\rho + \frac{r}{2}\right)e^{2k\rho} < r$$

which certainly will be satisfied for small values of $\rho > 0$, since the left-hand side of (10.8.1.2) tends to $r/2$ when ρ tends to 0.

(b) From the mean value theorem, we have

(10.8.1.3)
$$\|u(t_1, t_0, x_0) - u(t_2, t_0, x_0)\| \leqslant M\,|t_2 - t_1|$$

for t_0, t_1, t_2 in J, x_0 in V. By (10.5.1), we have

(10.8.1.4)
$$\|u(t, t_0, x_1) - u(t, t_0, x_2)\| \leqslant e^{2k\rho}\,|x_2 - x_1|$$

for t, t_0 in J, x_1, x_2 in V. Finally, (10.8.1.3) for $t_0 = t_2$ yields by definition

$$\|u(t_1, t_2, x_0) - x_0\| \leqslant M\,|t_2 - t_1|$$

and as $t \to u(t, t_2, x_0)$ is the unique solution of (10.4.1) in J which is equal to $u(t_1, t_2, x_0)$ at the point t_1, we have, by (10.5.1)

(10.8.1.5)
$$\|u(t, t_1, x_0) - u(t, t_2, x_0)\| \leqslant Me^{2k\rho}\,|t_2 - t_1|$$

for t, t_1, t_2 in J, $x_0 \in V$. The three inequalities (10.8.1.3), (10.8.1.4), and (10.8.1.5) prove that u is uniformly continuous in $J \times J \times V$.

(c) By (10.8.1.3), we have $\|u(t, t_0, x_0) - x_0\| \leqslant M|t - t_0| \leqslant 2M\rho$ in $J \times J \times V$. Suppose ρ satisfies (10.8.1.2) and in addition the inequality $2M\rho < r/4$; then, if W is the open ball of center b and radius $r/4$, we have $u(t, t_0, x_0) \in V$ for t, t_0 in J and $x_0 \in W$. Let $x = u(t, t_0, x_0)$ for such values of t, t_0, x_0; then $s \to u(s, t, x)$ is defined in J and is the unique solution of (10.4.1) with values in H which takes the value x at the point t; but as $s \to u(s, t_0, x_0)$ has these properties, we have $u(s, t, x) = u(s, t_0, x_0)$ for $s \in J$; in particular $x_0 = u(t_0, t_0, x_0) = u(t_0, t, x)$. Suppose now $y \in V$ is such that $u(t_0, t, y) = x_0$; then $s \to u(s, t, y)$ is a solution of (10.4.1) defined in J and taking the value x_0 for $s = t_0$; therefore $u(s, t, y) = u(s, t_0, x_0)$ for any $s \in J$, and in particular, for $s = t$, $y = u(t, t_0, x_0) = x$, which ends the proof.

(10.8.2) *With the notations of* (10.8.1), *suppose* f *is* p *times continuously differentiable* (resp. E *is finite dimensional and* f *is indefinitely differentiable*, resp. E *is finite dimensional and* f *is analytic*) *in* $I \times H$. *Then it is possible to choose* J *and* V *such that the function* $(t, t_0, x_0) \to u(t, t_0, x_0)$ *is* p *times continuously differentiable* (resp. *indefinitely differentiable*, resp. *analytic*) *in* $J \times J \times V$.

Indeed, if we write $v(s, t_0, x_0) = u(t_0 + s, t_0, x_0) - x_0$, we see that $s \to v(s, t_0, x_0)$ is a solution of the equation

$$z' = f(t_0 + s, x_0 + z)$$

which takes the value 0 at the point $s = 0$; the result then follows from (10.7.4) and (10.7.5).

For *linear* differential equations, there are much more precise results. The equation

$$x' = A(t) \cdot x \tag{10.8.3}$$

is called the *homogeneous* linear differential equation associated to (10.6.2); the difference of any two solutions of (10.6.2) in I is a solution of (10.8.3) in I, and the solutions of (10.8.3) in I constitute a vector subspace $\mathscr{H}$ of the space $\mathscr{C}_E(I)$ of all continuous mappings of I into E.

(10.8.4) *For each* (s, x_0), *let* $t \to u(t, s, x_0)$ *be the unique solution of* (10.8.3) *defined in* I *and such that* $u(s, s, x_0) = x_0$.

(1) *For each* $t \in I$, *the mapping* $x_0 \to u(t, s, x_0)$ *is a linear homeomorphism* $C(t, s) \in \mathscr{L}(E)$ *of* E *onto itself.*

(2) *The mapping* $t \to C(t, s)$ *of* I *into the Banach space* $\mathscr{L}(E)$ *is equal to the solution of the linear homogeneous differential equation*

$$U' = A(t) \circ U \tag{10.8.4.1}$$

which is equal to I_E (*identity mapping of* E) *for* $t = s$.

(3) *For any three points* r, s, t *in* I

$$C(r, t) = C(r, s) \circ C(s, t) \quad \textit{and} \quad C(s, t) = (C(t, s))^{-1}. \tag{10.8.4.2}$$

It is clear that $u(t, s, x_1) + u(t, s, x_2)$ (resp. $\lambda u(t, s, x_0)$) is a solution of (10.8.3) which is equal to $x_1 + x_2$ (resp. λx_0) for $t = s$; hence (10.6.4) it is equal to $u(t, s, x_1 + x_2)$ (resp. $u(t, s, \lambda x_0)$) in I, which proves that the mapping $x_0 \to u(t, s, x_0)$ is linear; let us write it $C(t, s)$ (we have not yet proved that this mapping is continuous in E).

Now the bilinear mapping $(X, Y) \to X \circ Y$ of $\mathscr{L}(\mathrm{E}) \times \mathscr{L}(\mathrm{E})$ into $\mathscr{L}(\mathrm{E})$ is continuously differentiable (8.1.4); denote by $R(t)$ the continuous linear mapping $U \to A(t) \circ U$ of $\mathscr{L}(\mathrm{E})$ into itself. From (5.7.5) it follows at once that

$$\|R(t) - R(t')\| \leqslant \|A(t) - A(t')\|$$

hence, if $\mathrm{K} = \mathbf{R}$, $t \to R(t)$ is regulated if $t \to A(t)$ is regulated. On the other hand, if $t \to A(t)$ is differentiable, so is $t \to R(t)$, and its derivative at the point t (identified (Section 8.4) to an element of $\mathscr{L}(\mathrm{E})$) is the mapping $U \to A'(t) \circ U$ ((8.1.3) and (8.2.1)); hence if $t \to A'(t)$ is continuous, so is $t \to R'(t)$. We can therefore conclude that if $\mathrm{K} = \mathbf{C}$ and if $t \to A(t)$ is analytic in I, so is $t \to R(t)$ (9.10.1). In any case, we may apply (10.6.4) to the equation (10.8.4.1); let $V(t)$ be the solution of that equation equal to I_{E} for $t = s$. We have, for any $t \in \mathrm{I}$ ((8.1.3) and (8.2.1))

$$\mathrm{D}(V(t) \cdot x_0) = V'(t) \cdot x_0 = A(t) \cdot (V(t) \cdot x_0)$$

and furthermore, for $t = s$, $V(s) \cdot x_0 = I_{\mathrm{E}} \cdot x_0 = x_0$; it therefore follows from (10.6.4) applied to (10.8.3) that $C(t, s) \cdot x_0 = V(t) \cdot x_0$ for any $x_0 \in \mathrm{E}$, hence $C(t, s) = V(t)$ for $t \in \mathrm{I}$. This proves that $C(t, s) \in \mathscr{L}(\mathrm{E})$ and that $t \to C(t, s)$ is the solution of (10.8.4.1) which is equal to I_{E} for $t = s$.

Finally, the function $t \to C(t, r) \cdot x_0$ is the solution of (10.8.3) equal to $C(s, r) \cdot x_0$ for $t = s$; hence, by definition

$$C(t, r) \cdot x_0 = C(t, s) \cdot (C(s, r) \cdot x_0) = (C(t, s) \circ C(s, r)) \cdot x_0$$

for any $x_0 \in \mathrm{E}$, which proves the first relation (10.8.4.2); as $C(t, t) = I_{\mathrm{E}}$, that relation yields $C(t, s) \circ C(s, t) = I_{\mathrm{E}}$. This shows that $C(s, t)$ is a *bijective* linear mapping of E, whose inverse mapping is $C(t, s)$ (hence also belongs to $\mathscr{L}(\mathrm{E})$). With this we reach the end of the proof of (10.8.4).

The operator $C(t, s)$ is called the *resolvent* of (10.8.3) (or of (10.6.2)) in I.

(10.8.5) *The mapping* $(s, t) \to C(s, t)$ *of* $\mathrm{I} \times \mathrm{I}$ *into* $\mathscr{L}(\mathrm{E})$ *is continuous.*

We may indeed write $C(s, t) = C(s, t_0) \circ (C(t, t_0))^{-1}$, and the result then follows from (10.8.4), (5.7.5), and (8.3.2).

The knowledge of $C(s, t)$ enables one to give the explicit solution of (10.6.2) taking the value x_0 for $t = t_0$:

(10.8.6) *The function*

$$u(t) = C(t, t_0) \cdot x_0 + \int_{t_0}^{t} (C(t, s) \cdot b(s))\, ds$$

is the solution of (10.6.2) *in* I *which is equal to* x_0 *for* $t = t_0$ (if K = **C**, the integral is to be taken along the segment of origin t_0 and extremity t).

Indeed, one may write, by (10.8.4.2)

$$\int_{t_0}^{t} (C(t, s) \cdot b(s))\, ds = C(t, t_0) \cdot \left(\int_{t_0}^{t} (C(t_0, s) \cdot b(s))\, ds\right)$$

using (8.7.6); therefore, we have $u(t) = C(t, t_0) \cdot z(t)$, where

$$z(t) = x_0 + \int_{t_0}^{t} (C(t_0, s) \cdot b(s))\, ds.$$

Hence ((8.1.4) and (8.2.1))

$$u'(t) = C'(t, t_0) \cdot z(t) + C(t, t_0) \cdot z'(t).$$

But by (10.8.4.1), $C'(t, t_0) = A(t) \circ C(t, t_0)$, and on the other hand, $z'(t) = C(t_0, t) \cdot b(t)$ by definition; hence

$$u'(t) = A(t) \cdot u(t) + b(t)$$

and as $u(t_0) = x_0$, this ends our proof.

When E = K^n, and the equation (10.6.2) is then written as a system of scalar linear differential equations (10.6.5), the resolvent $C(s, t)$ is an *invertible* $n \times n$ matrix $(c_{ij}(s, t))$ whose elements are continuous in I × I, and $t \to c_{ij}(t, s)$ is a primitive of a regulated function in I if K = **R**, an analytic function in I if K = **C**.

PROBLEM

(a) Suppose, in the linear differential equation (10.6.2), that A and b are analytic functions in the *simply connected* open subset H ⊂ **C**. Show that, for any $t_0 \in$ H and any $x_0 \in$ E, there is a unique solution u of (10.6.2), *defined in* H and such that $u(t_0) = x_0$. (Use the same kind of argument as in (9.6.3): (10.6.3) allows one to define a solution of (10.6.2) along a broken line (Section 5.1, Problem 4) in H, and the argument of (9.6.3), along with local uniqueness, yields the result.)
(b) Show that the result of (a) is not valid for the scalar differential equation $x' = t/x$: given *any* simply connected open subset H ⊂ **C**, and any $t_0 \in$ H, there exists an $x_0 \in$ E, such that $x_0 \neq 0$ and that there is *no* solution of the equation *defined in* H and equal to x_0 for $t = t_0$.

9. THE THEOREM OF FROBENIUS

Let E, F be two Banach spaces over K, A (resp. B) an open subset of E (resp. F), U a mapping of A × B *into the Banach space* $\mathscr{L}$(E; F) (Section 5.7).

A differentiable mapping u of A into B is a *solution of the total differential equation*

(10.9.1) $$y' = U(x, y)$$

if, for any $x \in A$, we have

(10.9.2) $$u'(x) = U(x, u(x)).$$

When $E = K$, $\mathscr{L}(E; F)$ is identified to F (5.7.6), and a total differential equation is thus an ordinary differential equation (10.4.1). When $E = K^n$ is finite dimensional, a linear mapping U of E into F is defined by its value at each of the n basis vectors of E, and, by definition, (10.9.2) is thus equivalent to the system of n "partial differential equations"

(10.9.3) $$D_i y = f_i(x_1, \ldots, x_n, y) \qquad (1 \leqslant i \leqslant n).$$

In general, such a system will have no solution when $n > 1$, even if the right-hand sides f_i are continuously differentiable functions. We say that an equation (10.9.1) is *completely integrable* in $A \times B$ if, *for every point* $(x_0, y_0) \in A \times B$, *there is an open neighborhood* S *of* x_0 *in* A *such that there is a unique solution* u *of* (10.9.1), *defined in* S, *with values in* B, *and such that* $u(x_0) = y_0$.

We will suppose in what follows that U is *continuously differentiable* in $A \times B$; for each $(x, y) \in A \times B$, $D_1 U(x, y)$ (resp. $D_2 U(x, y)$) is an element of $\mathscr{L}(E; \mathscr{L}(E; F))$ (resp. $\mathscr{L}(F; \mathscr{L}(E; F))$), which can be identified to the continuous bilinear mapping $(s_1, s_2) \to (D_1 U(x, y) \cdot s_1) \cdot s_2$ of $E \times E$ into F, written $(s_1, s_2) \to D_1 U(x, y) \cdot (s_1, s_2)$ (resp. the continuous bilinear mapping $(t, s) \to (D_2 U(x, y) \cdot t) \cdot s$ of $F \times E$ into F, written $(t, s) \to D_2 U(x, y) \cdot (t, s)$) (5.7.8); furthermore, the linear mapping $s_1 \to (D_1 U(x, y) \cdot s_1) \cdot s_2$ of E into F, for each $s_2 \in E$, is the derivative at the point (x, y) of the mapping $x \to U(x, y) \cdot s_2$ of E into F, by (8.2.1) and (8.1.3); similarly, the linear mapping $t \to (D_2 U(x, y) \cdot t) \cdot s$ of F into F, for each $s \in E$, is the derivative at the point (x, y) of the mapping $y \to U(x, y) \cdot s$ of F into F.

(10.9.4) (Frobenius's theorem) *Suppose U is continuously differentiable in $A \times B$ if $K = \mathbf{R}$, twice continuously differentiable if $K = \mathbf{C}$. In order that* (10.9.1) *be completely integrable in $A \times B$, it is necessary and sufficient that, for each $(x, y) \in A \times B$, the relation*

(10.9.4.1) $$D_1 U(x, y) \cdot (s_1, s_2) + D_2 U(x, y) \cdot (U(x, y) \cdot s_1, s_2) = D_1 U(x, y) \cdot (s_2, s_1) + D_2 U(x, y) \cdot (U(x, y) \cdot s_2, s_1)$$

holds for any pair (s_1, s_2) in $E \times E$.

(a) *Necessity.* Suppose u is a solution of (10.9.1) in an open ball $S \subset A$ of center x_0 such that $u(x_0) = y_0$; then, from (10.9.2) and the assumption it follows that $u'(x)$ is differentiable in S; moreover, for any $s_2 \in E$, the derivative at the point x_0 of the mapping $x \to u'(x) \cdot s_2$ is $s_1 \to u''(x_0) \cdot (s_1, s_2)$ by (8.12.1). But by (10.9.2), that derivative is also (using (8.2.1), (8.1.3), and (8.9.1))

$$s_1 \to (D_1 U(x_0, y_0) \cdot s_1) \cdot s_2 + (D_2 U(x_0, y_0) \cdot (u'(x_0) \cdot s_1)) \cdot s_2 .$$

Using the relation (10.9.2) again, and expressing that the second derivative of u at the point x_0 is a *symmetric* bilinear mapping (8.12.2), we obtain (10.9.4.1) at the point (x_0, y_0). But by assumption that point may be taken arbitrarily in $A \times B$, hence the result.

(b) *Sufficiency.* Let $S_0 \subset A$ be an open ball of center x_0 and radius α $T_0 \subset B$ an open ball of center y_0 and radius β, such that U is bounded in $S_0 \times T_0$, let $\|U(x, y)\| \leqslant M$. We consider for a vector $z \in E$ the (ordinary) differential equation (where $\xi \in K$)

(10.9.4.2) $$w' = U(x_0 + \xi z, w) \cdot z = f(\xi, w, z)$$

and observe that if u satisfies (10.9.2) in a neighborhood $\|x - x_0\| < \rho$ of x_0, $\xi \to u(x_0 + \xi z)$ for $\|z\| < \rho$ is a solution of (10.9.4.2) in the ball $|\xi| < 1$, in K, taking the value y_0 for $\xi = 0$ (which already proves uniqueness of u by (10.5.2)). Now the right-hand side of (10.9.4.2) is continuously differentiable for $|\xi| \leqslant 2$, $\|w - y_0\| < \beta$ and $\|z\| < \alpha/2$, and we have $\|f(\xi, w, z)\| \leqslant M\|z\|$ for such values. Applying (10.5.6) to f and to $g = 0$, we conclude that for any $z \in E$ such that $\|z\| < \beta/2M$, there is a unique solution $\xi \to v(\xi, z)$ of (10.9.4.2) defined for $|\xi| < 2$, taking its values in H and such that $v(0, z) = y_0$. We are going to prove that *the function* $u(x) = v(1, x - x_0)$ *is a solution of* (10.9.1) *in the ball* $\|x - x_0\| < \beta/2M$.

Now, for $\|z\| < \beta/2M$ and $|\xi| < 2$, we know from (10.7.3) that v is continuously differentiable, and that $\xi \to D_2 v(\xi, z)$ is, for $|\xi| < 2$, the solution of the linear differential equation

$$V' = D_2 f(\xi, v(\xi, z), z) \circ V + D_3 f(\xi, v(\xi, z), z)$$

taking the value 0 for $\xi = 0$. For any $s_1 \in E$, write $g(\xi) = D_2 v(\xi, z) \cdot s_1$; we have $g'(\xi) = D_2 f(\xi, v(\xi, z), z) \cdot g(\xi) + D_3 f(\xi, v(\xi, z), z) \cdot s_1$ and from the definition of f, this can be written

$$g'(\xi) = A(\xi) \cdot (g(\xi), z) + B(\xi) \cdot s_1 + \xi C(\xi) \cdot (s_1, z)$$

with $A(\xi) = D_2 U(x_0 + \xi z, v(\xi, z))$, $B(\xi) = U(x_0 + \xi z, v(\xi, z))$, $C(\xi) = D_1 U(x_0 + \xi z, v(\xi, z))$. We want to prove that $g(\xi) = \xi U(x_0 + \xi z, v(\xi, z)) \cdot s_1$

and we therefore consider the difference $h(\xi) = g(\xi) - \xi U(x_0 + \xi z, v(\xi, z)) \cdot s_1 = g(\xi) - \xi B(\xi) \cdot s_1$. We have

$$h'(\xi) = A(\xi) \cdot (g(\xi), z) + B(\xi) \cdot s_1 + \xi C(\xi) \cdot (s_1, z)$$
$$- B(\xi) \cdot s_1 - \xi C(\xi) \cdot (z, s_1) - \xi A(\xi) \cdot (B(\xi) \cdot z, s_1)$$

using the relation $D_1 v(\xi, z) = U(x_0 + \xi z, v(\xi, z)) \cdot z = B(\xi) \cdot z$. But relation (10.9.4.1) yields in particular

$$C(\xi) \cdot (z, s_1) + A(\xi) \cdot (B(\xi) \cdot z, s_1) = C(\xi) \cdot (s_1, z) + A(\xi) \cdot (B(\xi) \cdot s_1, z)$$

hence

$$h'(\xi) = A(\xi) \cdot (g(\xi) - \xi B(\xi) \cdot s_1, z) = A(\xi) \cdot (h(\xi), z).$$

Furthermore, $h(0) = 0$; but the only solution of the linear differential equation $r' = A(\xi) \cdot (r, z)$ which vanishes for $\xi = 0$ is $r(\xi) = 0$ (10.6.3), hence $h(\xi) = 0$ for $|\xi| < 2$, which proves the relation

$$D_2 v(\xi, z) \cdot s_1 = \xi U(x_0 + \xi z, v(\xi, z)) \cdot s_1$$

for any $s_1 \in E$, i.e. $D_2 v(\xi, z) = \xi U(x_0 + \xi z, v(\xi, z))$. This holds for $|\xi| < 2$ and $\|z\| < \beta/2M$; in particular, for $\xi = 1$, and putting $x = x_0 + z$, we obtain $u'(x) = U(x, u(x))$ for $\|x - x_0\| < \beta/2M$, which ends the proof.

(10.9.5) *Suppose U is continuously differentiable in* $A \times B$ *if* $K = \mathbf{R}$, *twice continuously differentiable if* $K = \mathbf{C}$, *and verifies the Frobenius condition* (10.9.4.1). *Then, for each point* $(a, b) \in A \times B$, *there is an open ball* $S \subset A$ *of center a and an open ball* $T \subset B$ *of center b, having the following properties:* (1) *for any point* $(x_0, y_0) \in S \times T$, *there is a unique solution* $x \to u(x, x_0, y_0)$ *of* (10.9.1), *defined in* S *and such that* $u(x_0, x_0, y_0) = y_0$; (2) *u is continuously differentiable in* $S \times S \times T$. *If in addition* E *and* F *are finite dimensional and U is p times continuously differentiable* (resp. *indefinitely differentiable*, resp. *analytic*) *in* $A \times B$, *then u is p times continuously differentiable* (resp. *indefinitely differentiable*, resp. *analytic*) *in* $S \times S \times T$.

Finally, there is an open ball $W \subset T$ *of center b such that, for every point* $(x, x_0, y_0) \in S \times S \times W$, *the equation* $y_0 = u(x_0, x, y)$ *has a unique solution* $y = u(x, x_0, y_0)$ *in* T.

Let $S_0 \subset A$ be an open ball of center a and radius α, $T_0 \subset B$ an open ball of center b and radius β, such that $\|U(x, y)\| \leqslant M$ in $S_0 \times T_0$. Consider the ordinary differential equation

(10.9.5.1) $$w' = U(x_0 + \xi z, y_0 + w) \cdot z = f(\xi, w, z, x_0, y_0).$$

As in the proof of (10.9.4) we see that there is a unique solution $\xi \to v(\xi, z, x_0, y_0)$ of that equation, defined for $|\xi| < 2$ and such that $v(0, z, x_0, y_0) = 0$, provided $\|x_0 - a\| < \alpha/8$, $\|z\| < \inf(\alpha/4, \beta/2M)$, $\|y_0 - b\| < \beta$. Furthermore, (10.7.3) shows that v is continuously differentiable for these values of ξ, z, x_0, y_0 provided α and β have been taken such that the derivative of U is bounded in $S_0 \times T_0$. Then (10.9.4) shows that $u(x, x_0, y_0) = y_0 + v(1, x - x_0, x_0, y_0)$ is the unique solution of (10.9.1), *defined in* $S: \|x - a\| \leqslant \alpha/8$, taking the value y_0 for $x = x_0$, hence $(x, x_0, y_0) \to u(x, x_0, y_0)$ is continuously differentiable in $S \times S \times T_0$. If E and F are finite dimensional, the proof that u is p times continuously differentiable (resp. indefinitely differentiable, resp. analytic) when U has the corresponding property, is done in the same way, using (10.7.4) (resp. (10.7.5)) instead of (10.7.3). Finally, the last statement of the theorem is proved by the same argument as part (c) of (10.8.1).

When $E = K^n$, the Frobenius condition (10.9.4.1) of complete integrability is equivalent, for the system (10.9.3), to the relations

(10.9.6)
$$\frac{\partial}{\partial x_j} f_i(x_1, \ldots, x_n, y) + \frac{\partial}{\partial y} f_i(x_1, \ldots, x_n, y) \cdot f_j(x_1, \ldots, x_n, y)$$
$$= \frac{\partial}{\partial x_i} f_j(x_1, \ldots, x_n, y) + \frac{\partial}{\partial y} f_j(x_1, \ldots, x_n, y) \cdot f_i(x_1, \ldots, x_n, y)$$

(where it must be remembered that $\frac{\partial}{\partial y} f_i(x_1, \ldots, x_n, y)$ is an element of $\mathscr{L}(F; F)$ (a matrix if F is finite dimensional), and $f_j(x_1, \ldots, x_n, y)$ an element of F).

CHAPTER XI

ELEMENTARY SPECTRAL THEORY

The choice of the subject matter of this chapter has been dictated by two considerations: (1) it is the first step in one of the main branches of modern functional analysis, the so-called " spectral theory "; (2) it draws practically on *every* preceding chapter for the formulation of its concepts and the proof of its theorems, and thus may convince the student that the " abstract " developments of these chapters were not purposeless generalizations.

General spectral theory, being closely linked to the general theory of integration, falls outside the scope of this first volume, and the reader will not find any results of that theory in this chapter, with the exception of the proof of the existence of the spectrum (**11.1.3**) and a few elementary properties of the adjoint of an operator (Section **11.5**). We have concentrated on the theory of *compact* linear operators, which can again be considered as " slight " perturbations of general operators, although in a sense quite different from the one which was prevalent in Chapter X; here what is considered as " negligible " is what happens in *finite dimensional* subspaces, and the substance of the main theorem (**11.3.3**) on compact operators is that when we add such an operator to the identity, what we get is again a linear homeomorphism, provided it is restricted to a suitable subspace of *finite codimension.* Compact self-adjoint operators in Hilbert space have a special interest, not only because it is possible to have much more precise information on their spectrum than for general compact operators (**11.5.7**), but also because their general theory immediately applies to Fredholm integral equations with hermitian kernel (Section **11.6**), and in particular to the classical Sturm–Liouville problem, which we have chosen as a particularly beautiful illustration of the power of the methods of functional analysis (Section **11.7**).

For more information on spectral theory, and on its powerful applications, we strongly recommend Courant–Hilbert's classic [10] for its delightful style and its wealth of information. General spectral theory will be developed in Chapter XV, and its most important applications in Chapters XXI (representations of compact groups), XXII (harmonic analysis), and XXIII (linear functional equations).

1. SPECTRUM OF A CONTINUOUS OPERATOR

Let E be a *complex* normed space; a linear mapping u of E into itself is often called an *operator* in E. The set $\mathscr{L}(\mathrm{E}; \mathrm{E})$ of *continuous* operators (which we will write simply $\mathscr{L}(\mathrm{E})$) is a complex normed space (Section 5.7); it is also a noncommutative *algebra* over $\mathbf{C}$, the "product" being the mapping $(u, v) \to u \circ v$, also written $(u, v) \to uv$. The identity mapping of E is the unit element of $\mathscr{L}(\mathrm{E})$, written 1_{E}. The mappings $(u, v) \to u + v$ and $(u, v) \to u \circ v$ are *continuous* in $\mathscr{L}(\mathrm{E}) \times \mathscr{L}(\mathrm{E})$ (5.7.5).

We say that a complex number ζ is a *regular value* for a continuous operator u if $u - \zeta \cdot 1_{\mathrm{E}}$ has an *inverse* v_ζ in $\mathscr{L}(\mathrm{E})$ (i.e. is a *linear homeomorphism* of E *onto* itself). The complex numbers ζ which are not regular for u are called *spectral values* of u and the set of spectral values of u is called the *spectrum* $\mathrm{sp}(u)$ of u.

If $\zeta \in \mathbf{C}$ is such that the kernel of $u - \zeta \cdot 1_{\mathrm{E}}$ is not reduced to 0, then ζ is a spectral value of u; such spectral values are called *eigenvalues* of u; any vector $x \neq 0$ in the kernel of $u - \zeta \cdot 1_{\mathrm{E}}$, i.e. such that $u(x) = \zeta x$, is called an *eigenvector* of u corresponding to the eigenvalue ζ; these eigenvectors and 0 form a closed vector subspace of E, the kernel of $u - \zeta \cdot 1_{\mathrm{E}}$, also called the *eigenspace* of u corresponding to the eigenvalue ζ, and written $\mathrm{E}(\zeta)$ or $\mathrm{E}(\zeta; u)$.

When E has *finite* dimension n, elementary linear algebra shows that any spectral value of an operator u is an eigenvalue of u (A.4.19); the spectrum of u is a finite set of at most n elements, which are the roots of the *characteristic polynomial* $\det(u - \zeta \cdot 1_{\mathrm{E}})$ of u, of degree n (A.6.9). But if E is infinite dimensional, there may exist spectral values which *are not* eigenvalues.

Example

(11.1.1) Let E be a complex Hilbert space, $(a_n)_{n \geqslant 1}$ a total orthonormal system in E (6.6.1). To each vector $x = \sum_n \zeta_n a_n$ in E (with $\|x\|^2 = \sum_n |\zeta_n|^2$) we associate the vector $u(x) = \sum_n \zeta_n a_{n+1}$; it is readily verified that u is linear and $\|u(x)\| = \|x\|$, hence (5.5.1) u is continuous. Moreover, $u(\mathrm{E})$ is the subspace of E orthogonal to a_1, hence u is not surjective, and this shows that $\zeta = 0$ is a spectral value of u; but $u(x) = 0$ implies $x = 0$, hence 0 is not an eigenvalue of u.

(11.1.2) *Suppose* E *is a complex* Banach *space, u a continuous operator in* E. *The set* R_u *of regular elements* $\zeta \in \mathbf{C}$ *for u is open in* $\mathbf{C}$ *and the mapping* $\zeta \to (u - \zeta \cdot 1_E)^{-1}$ *of* R_u *into* $\mathscr{L}(E)$ *is analytic.*

Suppose $\zeta_0 \in R_u$, and let $v_0 = (u - \zeta_0 \cdot 1_E)^{-1}$. For any $\zeta \in \mathbf{C}$, we may write, in $\mathscr{L}(E)$,

$$u - \zeta \cdot 1_E = u - \zeta_0 \cdot 1_E - (\zeta - \zeta_0) \cdot 1_E = (u - \zeta_0 \cdot 1_E)(1 - (\zeta - \zeta_0)v_0).$$

But, by (8.3.2.1), for $|\zeta - \zeta_0| < \|v_0\|^{-1}$, $1_E - (\zeta - \zeta_0)v_0$ has an inverse in $\mathscr{L}(E)$, equal to the sum of the absolute convergent series $\sum_{n=0}^{\infty} (\zeta - \zeta_0)^n v_0^n$; hence, for these values of ζ, $u - \zeta \cdot 1_E$ is invertible in $\mathscr{L}(E)$, and its inverse, equal to $(1_E - (\zeta - \zeta_0)v_0)^{-1}v_0$, can be written $(u - \zeta \cdot 1_E)^{-1} = \sum_{n=0}^{\infty} (\zeta - \zeta_0)^n v_0^{n+1}$, the series being absolutely convergent for $|\zeta - \zeta_0| < \|v_0\|^{-1}$; which ends the proof.

(11.1.3) *If* E *is a complex* Banach *space, the spectrum of any continuous operator u in* E *is a nonempty compact subset of* $\mathbf{C}$ *contained in the ball* $|\zeta| \leqslant \|u\|$.

First observe that for $\zeta \neq 0$, $u - \zeta \cdot 1_E = -\zeta(1_E - \zeta^{-1}u)$, and therefore $u - \zeta \cdot 1_E$ is invertible in $\mathscr{L}(E)$ for $|\zeta| > \|u\|$, by (8.3.2.1). Furthermore, for $|\zeta| > \|u\|$,

$$(u - \zeta \cdot 1_E)^{-1} = -\sum_{n=0}^{\infty} \zeta^{-n-1} u^n,$$

where the series is absolutely convergent, and

$$\|(u - \zeta \cdot 1_E)^{-1}\| \leqslant \sum_{n=0}^{\infty} |\zeta|^{-n-1} \|u\|^n = (|\zeta| - \|u\|)^{-1};$$

as soon as $|\zeta| \geqslant 2\|u\|$, we have therefore $\|(u - \zeta \cdot 1_E)^{-1}\| \leqslant \|u\|^{-1}$. Now, if we had $R_u = \mathbf{C}$, $(u - \zeta \cdot 1_E)^{-1}$ would be an entire function (9.9.6), bounded in $\mathbf{C}$ since it is bounded in the compact set $|\zeta| \leqslant 2\|u\|$ and bounded in its complement; by Liouville's theorem (9.11.1) $(u - \zeta \cdot 1_E)^{-1}$ would be a constant, hence also its inverse $u - \zeta \cdot 1_E$, which is absurd. The first part of the proof shows in addition that $(u - \zeta \cdot 1_E)^{-1}$ exists and is analytic for $|\zeta| > \|u\|$, therefore the spectrum of u, which is closed in $\mathbf{C}$, is compact and contained in the ball $|\zeta| \leqslant \|u\|$.

It is possible to give examples of operators for which the spectrum is an *arbitrary* compact subset of $\mathbf{C}$ (see Problem 3).

PROBLEMS

1. Let E be a complex Banach space, u an element of $\mathscr{L}(\mathrm{E})$, $\mathrm{sp}(u)$ its spectrum.
(a) Show that if a complex number ζ is such that, for an integer $p > 1$, $|\zeta|^p > \|u^p\|$, then ζ is regular for u. (Use (11.1.3), and from the convergence of the series $\sum_{n=0}^{\infty} \zeta^{-np} u^{np}$, conclude that the series $\sum_{n=0}^{\infty} \zeta^{-n} u^n$ is also convergent.)
(b) Show that the number $\rho(u) = \inf_n \|u^n\|^{1/n}$ is equal to the radius of the smallest disk of center 0 containing $\mathrm{sp}(u)$, and furthermore that the sequence $(\|u^n\|^{1/n})$ has a limit equal to $\rho(u)$. (Use (a), Problem 1 of Section 9.1, and (9.9.4).) (For an example in which $\rho(u) \neq \|u\|$, see Section 11.4, Problem 4.)
2. Let u, v be two elements of $\mathscr{L}(\mathrm{E})$, where E is a complex Banach space. Show that, with the notations of Problem 1, the intersections of $\mathrm{sp}(uv)$ and $\mathrm{sp}(vu)$ with $\mathbf{C} - \{0\}$ are the same. (Observe that if f, g are two elements of $\mathscr{L}(\mathrm{E})$ such that $1_{\mathrm{E}} - fg$ is invertible, and $h = (1_{\mathrm{E}} - fg)^{-1}$, then $1_{\mathrm{E}} + ghf$ is the inverse of $1_{\mathrm{E}} - gf$.)
3. Let E be a separable complex Hilbert space, $(e_n)_{n \geqslant 1}$ a Hilbert basis of E. Let S be an arbitrary infinite compact subset of $\mathbf{C}$, and let (ρ_n) be a denumerable set of points of S, which is dense in S (3.10.9). Show that there is a unique element $u \in \mathscr{L}(\mathrm{E})$ such that $u(e_n) = \rho_n e_n$ for every $n \geqslant 1$; prove that the spectrum of u is equal to S, whereas the eigenvalues of u are the ρ_n. If $\zeta \in \mathrm{S}$, ζ is not equal to any of the ρ_n, and $v_\zeta = u - \zeta \cdot 1_{\mathrm{E}}$, show that $v_\zeta(\mathrm{E})$ is dense in E but not equal to E (use (6.5.3) to prove the first statement).
4. Show that the spectrum of the operator u defined in (11.1.1) is the disk $|\zeta| \leqslant 1$ in $\mathbf{C}$; u has no eigenvalue. If $v_\zeta = u - \zeta \cdot 1_{\mathrm{E}}$, show that for $|\zeta| < 1$, $v_\zeta(\mathrm{E})$ is not dense in E, but for $|\zeta| = 1$, $v_\zeta(\mathrm{E})$ is dense in E and distinct from E (cf. (6.5.3)).
5. Let E be a complex Banach space, E_0 a dense subspace of E. Show that for any element $u \in \mathscr{L}(\mathrm{E}_0)$, the spectrum of u contains the spectrum of its unique continuous extension $\tilde{u}$ to E (5.5.4). Give an example in which these spectra are distinct and an example of an operator $u \in \mathscr{L}(\mathrm{E}_0)$ and of a spectral value ζ of u such that, if $v_\zeta = u - \zeta \cdot 1_{\mathrm{E}}$, v_ζ is a *bijective* mapping of E_0 onto itself (in Problem 3, consider the subspace E_0 of E consisting of the (finite) linear combinations of the vectors e_n). Note that this is impossible if E_0 is a *Banach* space, for every continuous bijective linear mapping of E_0 onto itself is then a homeomorphism (12.16.8).
6. Let E be a complex separable Hilbert space, $(e_n)_{n \geqslant 1}$ a Hilbert basis of E; let u be a continuous operator in E such that, for every pair of indices h, k, one has $(u(e_h) \mid e_k) \geqslant 0$.
(a) Show that the number $\rho(u)$ (Problem 1(b)) belongs to $\mathrm{sp}(u)$. (Note that for $|\zeta| > \rho(u)$, if $v_\zeta = (u - \zeta \cdot 1_{\mathrm{E}})^{-1}$, one has

$$(v_\zeta(e_h) \mid e_k) = -\sum_{n=0}^{\infty} (u^n(e_h) \mid e_k) \zeta^{-n-1}$$

and use Problem 7(b) of Section 9.15.)
(b) Suppose in addition that for some integer $n \geqslant 1$, there exist an integer $k \geqslant 1$ such that $(u^n(e_k) \mid e_k) = d > 0$. Prove then that $\rho(u) \geqslant d^{1/n}$ (observe that for every integer $m \geqslant 1$, $(u^{nm}(e_k) \mid e_k) \geqslant d^m$).
(c) Suppose $\rho(u) > 0$ and that the point $\rho(u)$ is a *pole* of the function $\zeta \to v_\zeta$. Prove that there exists then an eigenvector $x = \sum_{n=1}^{\infty} \xi_n e_n$ of u corresponding to $\rho(u)$, such that $\xi_n \geqslant 0$ for every n. (Let N be the order of the pole $\rho(u)$ of v_ζ, and let

$$w_{\mathrm{N}} = \lim_{\zeta \to \rho(u)} (\zeta - \rho(u))^{\mathrm{N}} v_\zeta.$$

Show that $(w_N(e_h) \mid e_k) \leqslant 0$ for every pair h, k, and $w_N \neq 0$ by assumption, and use the fact that $uw_N = \rho(u)w_N$.)

(d) Suppose that $(u(e_k) \mid e_k) > 0$ for every pair of indices h, k (this, by (b), implies $\rho(u) > 0$), and in addition suppose that $\rho(u)$ is a pole of v_ζ. Show that $\rho(u)$ is then a *simple* pole of v_ζ. (Observe that $(d/d\zeta) - v_\zeta = v_\zeta^2$ and prove that, if one had $N > 1$, then one would have $w_N^2 = 0$; this would imply $(w_N(e_k) \mid e_k) = 0$ for every k; using the relation $uw_N = \rho(u)w_N$, observe that if $(w_N(e_k) \mid e_h) = 0$ for *one* index h, then $w_N(e_k) = 0$.) Prove that there exists an eigenvector $z = \sum_n \zeta_n e_n$ of u corresponding to $\rho(u)$ and such that $\zeta_n > 0$ for every n. Next show that if $y = \sum_n \eta_n e_n$ is an eigenvector of the adjoint u^* corresponding to $\rho(u)$ (cf. Section 11.5), one has $\eta_n \geqslant 0$ for every n, or $\eta_n \leqslant 0$ for every n (otherwise, one would get the contradictory inequality $\sum_n \zeta_n \mid \eta_n \mid < \sum_u \zeta_n \mid \eta_n \mid$, using a majoration of each η_n derived from $\rho(u)\eta_n = \sum_k \eta_k(u(e_k) \mid e_n)$). Conclude finally that *all* eigenvectors of u corresponding to $\rho(u)$ are scalar multiples of z (exchange u and u^*). ("Theorem of Frobenius–Perron.")

2. COMPACT OPERATORS

Let E, F be two normed (real or complex) spaces; we say that a linear mapping u of E into F is *compact* if, for any *bounded* subset B of E, $u(B)$ is *relatively compact* in F. An equivalent condition is that for any bounded sequence (x_n) in E, there is a subsequence (x_{n_k}) such that the sequence $(u(x_{n_k}))$ converges in F. As a relatively compact set is bounded in F (3.17.1), it follows from (5.5.1) that a compact mapping is *continuous*.

Examples

(11.2.1) If E or F is finite dimensional, every continuous linear mapping of E into F is compact (by (5.5.1), (3.17.6), (3.20.16), and (3.17.9)).

(11.2.2) If E is an infinite dimensional normed space, the identity operator in E is *not* compact, by F. Riesz's theorem (5.9.4).

(11.2.3) Let $I = [a, b]$ be a compact interval in $\mathbf{R}$, $E = \mathscr{C}_C(I)$ the Banach space of continuous complex-valued functions in I (Section 7.2), $(s, t) \to K(s, t)$ a continuous complex-valued function in $I \times I$. For any function $f \in E$, the mapping $t \to \int_a^b K(s, t) f(s)\, ds$ is continuous in I by (8.11.1); denote this function by Uf. Then the mapping $f \to Uf$ of E into itself is linear; we prove that it is *compact*. Indeed, if $g = Uf$, we can write, for $t_0 \in \mathrm{I}$, $t \in \mathrm{I}$,

(11.2.3.1) $$g(t) - g(t_0) = \int_a^b (\mathrm{K}(s, t) - \mathrm{K}(s, t_0))f(s)\, ds.$$

As K is uniformly continuous in $\mathrm{I} \times \mathrm{I}$ (3.16.5), for any $\varepsilon > 0$ there is a $\delta > 0$ such that the relation $|t - t_0| \leqslant \delta$ implies $|\mathrm{K}(s, t) - \mathrm{K}(s, t_0)| \leqslant \varepsilon$ for any $s \in \mathrm{I}$; hence, for any f in E

(11.2.3.2) $$|g(t) - g(t_0)| \leqslant \varepsilon(b - a)\|f\|$$

by the mean-value theorem. This shows that the image $U(\mathrm{B})$ of any bounded set B in E is *equicontinuous* at every point t_0 of I (Section 7.5); on the other hand, for any $t \in \mathrm{I}$, we have similarly $|g(t)| \leqslant k\|f\|$ if $|\mathrm{K}(s, t)| \leqslant k/(b - a)$ in $\mathrm{I} \times \mathrm{I}$. By Ascoli's theorem (7.5.7), $U(\mathrm{B})$ is relatively compact in E.

(11.2.4) With the same notations and assumptions on K as in (11.2.3), let now F be the space of complex-valued *regulated functions* in I (Section 7.6), which is again a Banach space, when considered as a subspace of the space $\mathscr{B}_{\mathrm{C}}(\mathrm{I})$; Uf is then defined as in (11.2.3) for any $f \in \mathrm{F}$, and the inequality (11.2.3.2) still holds. The argument in (11.2.3) then proves that U is a *compact mapping of* F *into* E.

(11.2.5) *If u, v are two compact mappings of* E *into* F, *$u + v$ is compact.*

Let (x_n) be a bounded sequence in E; by assumption, there is a subsequence (x_n') of (x_n) such that $(u(x_n'))$ converges in F. As the sequence (x_n') is bounded in E, there is a subsequence (x_n'') of (x_n') such that $(v(x_n''))$ converges in F. Then by (3.13.10) and (5.1.5), the sequence $(u(x_n'') + v(x_n''))$ converges in F. Q.E.D.

(11.2.6) *Let* E, F, E_1, F_1 *be normed spaces, f a continuous linear mapping of* E_1 *into* E, *g a continuous linear mapping of* F *into* F_1. *Then, for any compact mapping u of* E *into* F, *$u_1 = g \circ u \circ f$ is a compact mapping of* E_1 *into* F_1.

For if B_1 is bounded in E_1, $f(\mathrm{B}_1)$ is bounded in E by (5.5.1), $u(f(\mathrm{B}_1))$ is relatively compact in F by assumption, and $g(u(f(\mathrm{B}_1)))$ is relatively compact in F_1 by (3.17.9).

(11.2.7) *If u is a compact mapping of* E *into* F, *the restriction of u to any vector subspace* E_1 *of* E *is a compact mapping of* E_1 *into* $\overline{u(E_1)}$.

For by (11.2.6), that restriction is a compact mapping of E_1 into F. If B is a bounded subset of E_1, $\overline{u(B)}$ is then a compact subset of F, and as $\overline{u(B)} \subset \overline{u(E_1)}$, $u(B)$ is relatively compact in $\overline{u(E_1)}$.

Example

(11.2.8) With the same notations and assumptions on the function K as in (11.2.3), let now G be the prehilbert space defined by the scalar product $(f|g) = \int_a^b f(t)g(t)\,dt$ on the set $\mathscr{C}_{\mathbf{C}}(\mathrm{I})$ (6.5.1); we write the norm $(f|f)^{1/2} = \|f\|_2$ to distinguish it from the norm $\|f\| = \sup_{t \in \mathrm{I}} |f(t)|$, and we still denote by E the space $\mathscr{C}_{\mathbf{C}}(\mathrm{I})$ with the norm $\|f\|$; the identity mapping $f \to f$ of E into G is continuous, since $\|f\|_2 \leqslant (b-a)^{1/2} \cdot \|f\|$ by the mean value theorem; but it is not bicontinuous, nor is G a Banach space. The Cauchy–Schwarz inequality (6.2.1) is written here

(11.2.8.1) $$\left| \int_a^b f(t)\overline{g(t)}\,dt \right|^2 \leqslant \left(\int_a^b |f(t)|^2\,dt \right)\left(\int_a^b |g(t)|^2\,dt \right).$$

With the same notations as in (11.2.3), we therefore deduce from (11.2.3.1) and (11.2.8.1) that $|t_1 - t_2| \leqslant \delta$ implies

(11.2.8.2) $$|g(t_1) - g(t_2)| \leqslant \varepsilon(b-a)^{1/2} \cdot \|f\|_2,$$

and similarly $|g(t)| \leqslant k(b-a)^{1/2} \cdot \|f\|_2$ for any $t \in \mathrm{I}$. Hence, by the same argument as in (11.2.3), $f \to Uf$ is a compact mapping *of* G *into* E; and as the identity mapping of E into G is continuous, $f \to Uf$ is also a compact mapping *of* G *into* G by (11.2.6).

(11.2.9.) *Let* E, F *be two Banach spaces,* E_0 (resp. F_0) *a dense subspace of* E (resp. F), *u a compact mapping of* E_0 *into* F_0, *$\tilde{u}$ its unique continuous extension as a mapping of* E *into* F (5.5.4). *Then* $\tilde{u}(E) \subset F_0$, *and $\tilde{u}$ is a compact mapping of* E *into* F_0.

It is immediate that any ball $\|x\| \leqslant r$ in E is contained in the closure of any ball of center 0 and radius $> r$ in E_0 (3.13.13) hence any bounded set in E is contained in the closure of a bounded set B in E_0. But $\tilde{u}(\bar{B})$ is contained in the closure *in* F of the set $\tilde{u}(B) = u(B)$ by (3.11.4); now, $u(B)$

is relatively compact in F_0, i.e. its closure *in* F_0 is compact, hence closed *in* F, and therefore equal to its closure *in* F. This shows that $\tilde{u}(\bar{B})$ is contained in F_0 and relatively compact in that space. Q.E.D.

(11.2.10) *Let* E *be a normed space,* F *a* Banach *space,* (u_n) *a sequence of mappings in* $\mathscr{L}(E; F)$ (Section 5.7) *which converges to* u *in* $\mathscr{L}(E; F)$. *Then, if every* u_n *is compact,* u *is compact.*

Let B be any bounded set in E; as F is complete, all we have to do is to prove that $u(B)$ is precompact (3.17.5). Now B is contained in a ball $\|x\| \leqslant a$; for any $\varepsilon > 0$, there is n_0 such that $n \geqslant n_0$ implies $\|u - u_n\| \leqslant \varepsilon/2a$, and therefore (by (5.7.4)) $\|u(x) - u_n(x)\| \leqslant \varepsilon/2$ for any $x \in B$. But as $u_{n_0}(B)$ is precompact, it can be covered by finitely many balls of centers y_j $(1 \leqslant j \leqslant m)$ and radius $\varepsilon/2$. For any $x \in B$, there is therefore a j such that $\|u_{n_0}(x) - y_j\| \leqslant \varepsilon/2$, hence $\|u(x) - y_j\| \leqslant \varepsilon$, and the balls of centers y_j and radius ε cover $u(B)$. Q.E.D.

In particular, any limit in $\mathscr{L}(E; F)$ of a sequence of mappings of *finite rank* is compact by (11.2.1) and (11.2.10). Whether conversely any compact mapping is equal to such a limit is still an open problem (see Problem 4).

PROBLEMS

1. Let E be a Banach space, A a bounded open subset of E, F a finite dimensional vector space. Show that for any $p \geqslant 1$, the identity mapping $f \to f$ of the Banach space $\mathscr{D}_F^{(p)}(A)$ (Section 8.12, Problem 8) into $\mathscr{D}_F^{(p-1)}(A)$ (the latter being replaced by $\mathscr{C}_F^{\infty}(A)$ for $p = 1$) is a *compact* operator. (Use the mean value theorem and Ascoli's theorem.)
2. Let u be a compact mapping of an infinite dimensional Banach space E into a normed space F. Show that there is in E a sequence (x_n) such that $\|x_n\| = 1$ for every n, and $\lim_{n \to \infty} u(x_n) = 0$. (Observe that there is a number $\alpha > 0$ and a sequence (y_n) in E such that $\|y_n\| = 1$ for every n, and $\|y_m - y_n\| \geqslant \alpha$ for $m \neq n$ (Section 5.9, Problem 3, and (3.16.1)), and consider the sequence $(u(y_n))$.)

   Conclude that if the image by u of the sphere S: $\|x\| = 1$ is closed in F, it contains 0.
3. Let E be a separable Hilbert space, (e_n) a Hilbert basis of E. If u is a compact mapping of E into a normed space F, show that the sequence $(u(e_n))$ tends to 0. (Use contradiction, and show that it is impossible that the sequence $(u(e_n))$ should have a limit $b \neq 0$ in F.) If, conversely, F is a Banach space and the series of general term $\|u(e_n)\|^2$ is convergent, show that u is compact (use the Cauchy–Schwarz inequality to prove that the image of the ball $\|x\| \leqslant 1$ by u is precompact).
4. Let F be a normed space having the following property: there exists a constant $c > 0$ such that, for any *finite* subset $(a_i)_{1 \leqslant i \leqslant n}$ of F, and any $\varepsilon > 0$, there exists a decomposition $E = M + N$ of E into a direct sum of two closed subspaces, such that M is finite dimensional, $d(a_i, M) \leqslant \varepsilon$ for $1 \leqslant i \leqslant n$, and if for any $x \in F$, $x = p(x) + q(x)$, where

$p(x) \in \mathrm{M}$ and $q(x) \in \mathrm{N}$, then $\|q(x)\| \leqslant c \cdot d(x, \mathrm{M})$. Show that, under that assumption, any compact linear mapping of a normed space E into F is a limit in $\mathscr{L}(\mathrm{E}; \mathrm{F})$ of a sequence of linear mappings of finite rank (use the definition of precompact spaces). Show that any Hilbert space satisfies the preceding condition, as well as the spaces (c_0) (Section 5.3, Problem 5) and l^1 (Section 5.7, Problem 1).

5. Let $\mathrm{I} = [a, b]$ be a compact interval in **R**, $\mathrm{K}(s, t)$ a complex valued function defined in $\mathrm{I} \times \mathrm{I}$, and satisfying the assumptions of Section 8.11, Problem 4. Show that if U is defined as in (11.2.3), U is still a compact mapping of $\mathrm{E} = \mathscr{C}_{\mathrm{C}}(\mathrm{I})$ into itself.

3. THE THEORY OF F. RIESZ

We will need repeatedly the following lemma:

(11.3.1) *Let u be a continuous operator in a normed space* E, $v = 1_{\mathrm{E}} - u$, L, M *two closed vector subspaces of* E *such that* $\mathrm{M} \subset \mathrm{L}$, $\mathrm{M} \neq \mathrm{L}$, *and* $v(\mathrm{L}) \subset \mathrm{M}$. *Then there is a point* $a \in \mathrm{L} \cap \complement \mathrm{M}$ *such that* $\|a\| \leqslant 1$ *and that, for any* $x \in \mathrm{M}$, $\|u(a) - u(x)\| \geqslant \frac{1}{2}$.

By assumption, there is $b \in \mathrm{L}$ such that $b \notin \mathrm{M}$, hence $d(b, \mathrm{M}) = \alpha > 0$. Let $y \in \mathrm{M}$ be such that $\|b - y\| \leqslant 2\alpha$, and take $a = (b - y)/\|b - y\|$; we have $\|a\| = 1$, and, for any $z \in \mathrm{M}$, $a - z = (b - y - \|b - y\|z)/\|b - y\|$; but as $y + \|b - y\|z \in \mathrm{M}$, we have $\|b - y - \|b - y\|z\| \geqslant \alpha$, hence $\|a - z\| \geqslant \frac{1}{2}$ for any $z \in \mathrm{M}$. But, for $x \in \mathrm{M}$, we have $u(a) - u(x) = a - (x + v(a) - v(x))$, and by assumption, $x + v(a) - v(x) \in \mathrm{M}$; hence our conclusion.

(11.3.2) *Let u be a compact operator in a normed space* E, *and let* $v = 1_{\mathrm{E}} - u$. *Then:*

(a) *the kernel* $v^{-1}(0)$ *is finite dimensional;*

(b) *the image* $v(\mathrm{E})$ *is closed in* E;

(c) $v(\mathrm{E})$ *has finite codimension in* E;

(d) *if* $v^{-1}(0) = \{0\}$, *then* v *is a linear homeomorphism of* E *onto* $v(\mathrm{E})$ (cf. (11.3.4)).

(a) For any $x \in \mathrm{N} = v^{-1}(0)$, we have $u(x) = x$, hence the image of the ball B: $\|x\| \leqslant 1$ *in* N by u is B itself; by assumption $u(\mathrm{B})$ is relatively compact in E, hence in N since N is closed in E. But this implies that N is finite dimensional by Riesz's theorem (5.9.4).

(b) Suppose $y \in \overline{v(\mathrm{E})}$; there is then a sequence (x_n) in E, such that $y = \lim_{n \to \infty} v(x_n)$ (3.13.13). Suppose first that the sequence $(d(x_n, \mathrm{N}))$ is unbounded; then, by extracting a subsequence, we may suppose that

$\lim_{n\to\infty} d(x_n, \mathrm{N}) = +\infty$. Let $z_n = x_n/d(x_n, \mathrm{N})$; it is immediate that $d(z_n, \mathrm{N}) = 1$, and therefore there is $t_n \in \mathrm{N}$ such that $\|z_n - t_n\| \leqslant 2$. Let $s_n = z_n - t_n$, and observe that by definition we have $v(s_n) = v(z_n) = v(x_n)/d(x_n, \mathrm{N})$, and $d(s_n, \mathrm{N}) = 1$. From the assumptions we deduce at once that $\lim_{n\to\infty} v(s_n) = 0$. But the sequence (s_n) is bounded in E; as u is compact, there is a subsequence (s_{n_k}) such that $(u(s_{n_k}))$ converges to a point $a \in \mathrm{E}$. As $\lim_{n\to\infty} (s_n - u(s_n)) = 0$, we also have $\lim_{n\to\infty} s_{n_k} = a$, hence, as $x \to d(x, \mathrm{N})$ is continuous, $d(a, \mathrm{N}) = 1$. But $v(a) = \lim_{k\to\infty} v(s_{n_k}) = 0$, and this contradicts the definition of N.

We therefore can suppose that the sequence $(d(x_n, \mathrm{N}))$ is bounded by a number $\mathrm{M} - 1$; there is then a sequence x'_n such that $x_n - x'_n \in \mathrm{N}$ and $\|x'_n\| \leqslant \mathrm{M}$; as $v(x'_n) = v(x_n)$, we may suppose that $\|x_n\| \leqslant \mathrm{M}$. Then as u is compact there is a subsequence (x_{n_k}) such that $(u(x_{n_k}))$ converges to a point $b \in \mathrm{E}$; as $x_{n_k} - u(x_{n_k}) = v(x_{n_k})$ tends to y, (x_{n_k}) tends to $b + y$ and by continuity we have $v(b + y) = y$, which proves that $y \in v(\mathrm{E})$, hence $v(\mathrm{E})$ is closed.

(c) To say that $v(\mathrm{E})$ has an infinite codimension in E means that there exists an infinite sequence (a_n) of points of E such that a_n does not belong to the subspace V_{n-1} generated by $v(\mathrm{E})$ and by $a_1, \ldots, a_{n-1}$ for every n. Now each V_n is closed since $v(\mathrm{E})$ is closed (using (5.9.2)). By (11.3.1) we can define by induction a sequence (b_n) such that $b_n \in \mathrm{V}_n$, $b_n \notin \mathrm{V}_{n-1}$, $\|b_n\| \leqslant 1$, and $\|u(b_n) - u(b_j)\| \geqslant \frac{1}{2}$ for any $j \leqslant n - 1$. This implies that the sequence $(u(b_n))$ has no cluster point, contradicting the assumption that u is compact.

(d) In order to prove that v is a homeomorphism of E onto $v(\mathrm{E})$ when $v^{-1}(0) = \{0\}$, it is only necessary to show that for any closed set $\mathrm{A} \subset \mathrm{E}$, $v(\mathrm{A})$ is closed in E (hence in $v(\mathrm{E})$) (3.11.4). But this is proved by exactly the same argument as in (b), replacing throughout E by A (and N by $\{0\}$).

(11.3.3) *Under the same assumptions as in* (11.3.2), *define inductively* $\mathrm{N}_1 = v^{-1}(0)$, $\mathrm{N}_k = v^{-1}(\mathrm{N}_{k-1})$ *for* $k > 1$, $\mathrm{F}_1 = v(\mathrm{E})$, $\mathrm{F}_k = v(\mathrm{F}_{k-1})$ *for* $k > 1$. *Then*:

(a) *The* N_k *form an increasing sequence of finite dimensional subspaces, the* F_k *a decreasing sequence of finite codimensional closed subspaces.*

(b) *There is a smallest integer* n *such that* $\mathrm{N}_{k+1} = \mathrm{N}_k$ *for* $k \geqslant n$; *then* $\mathrm{F}_{k+1} = \mathrm{F}_k$ *for* $k \geqslant n$, *E is the topological direct sum* (Section 5.4) *of* F_n *and* N_n, *and the restriction of* v *to* F_n *is a linear homeomorphism of* F_n *onto itself.*

(a) Define by induction $v_1 = v$, $v_k = v_{k-1} \circ v$; I claim that $v_k = 1_{\mathrm{E}} - u_k$, where u_k is *compact*: this is shown by induction on k, for $v_k = (1_E - u_{k-1}) \circ (1_E - u) = 1_E - u_{k-1} - u + u_{k-1} \circ u$, and the result follows at once from the inductive hypothesis and from (11.2.6) and (11.2.5). Then by definition $N_k = v_k^{-1}(0)$ and $F_k = v_k(E)$, and our assertion follows from (11.3.2).

(b) Suppose $N_k \neq N_{k+1}$ for every k. We have $v(N_{k+1}) \subset N_k$ for $k \geqslant 1$; by (11.3.1), there would exist an infinite sequence (x_k) of points of E such that $x_k \in N_k$, $x_k \notin N_{k-1}$, $\|x_k\| \leqslant 1$ for $k > 1$ and $\|u(x_k) - u(x_j)\| \geqslant \frac{1}{2}$ for any $j < k$. This implies that the sequence $(u(x_k))$ has no cluster point, contradicting the assumption that u is compact.

Similarly, suppose $F_{k+1} \neq F_k$ for every k. We have $v(F_k) \subset F_{k+1}$ for $k \geqslant 1$; by (11.3.1), there would exist an infinite sequence (x_k) of points of E such that $x_k \in F_k$, $x_k \notin F_{k+1}$, $\|x_k\| \leqslant 1$ for $k \geqslant 1$, and $\|u(x_k) - u(x_j)\| \geqslant \frac{1}{2}$ for any $j > k$. This again implies contradiction, hence there exists a smallest integer m such that $F_{k+1} = F_k$ for $k \geqslant m$.

Next we prove that $N_n \cap F_n = \{0\}$: if $y \in F_n \cap N_n$, then there is $x \in E$ such that $y = v_n(x)$, and on the other hand $v_n(y) = 0$; but this implies that $v_{2n}(x) = 0$, hence $x \in N_{2n} = N_n$, and $y = v_n(x) = 0$.

By definition, we have $F_m \subset F_n$ and $v(F_m) = F_m$; let us prove that $F_n = F_m$. Otherwise, we would have $m > n$; let z be such that $z \in F_{m-1} \subset F_n$, and $z \notin F_m$; as $v(z) \in F_m = v(F_m)$, there is a $t \in F_m$ such that $v(z) = v(t)$, i.e. $z - t \in N_1 \subset N_n$; but as $z - t \in F_n$, we conclude that $z = t$, and our initial assumption has led to a contradiction.

For each $x \in E$ we have $v_n(x) \in F_n = F_m$, and as $v_n(F_n) = F_n$ by definition of m, there is $y \in F_n$ such that $v_n(x) = v_n(y)$, hence $x - y \in N_n$, and therefore $E = F_n + N_n$. This last sum is direct since $F_n \cap N_n = \{0\}$; F_n is closed and N_n is finite dimensional, therefore (5.9.3) E is the *topological direct sum* of F_n and N_n. Finally, the restriction of v to F_n is surjective and its kernel is $F_n \cap N_1 \subset F_n \cap N_n = \{0\}$, hence it is also injective. By (11.3.2(d)) that restriction is a linear homeomorphism of F_n onto itself, and this ends the proof.

(11.3.4) *Under the same assumptions as in* (11.3.2), *if v is injective* (i.e. $v^{-1}(0) = \{0\}$), *then v is surjective, hence a linear homeomorphism of* E *onto itself.*

For the assumptions imply that $N_k = \{0\}$ for every k, hence $n = 1$ and N_1 is reduced to 0, therefore $F_1 = E$ by (11.3.3) and the result follows from (11.3.3).

PROBLEMS

1. Let E, F be two Banach spaces, f a continuous linear mapping of E into F such that $f(\mathrm{E}) = \mathrm{F}$; then, there exists a number $m > 0$ such that for any $y \in \mathrm{F}$, there is an $x \in \mathrm{E}$ for which $f(x) = y$ and $\|x\| \leqslant m\|y\|$ (12.16.12).
(a) If (y_n) is a sequence of points of F which converges to a point b, show that there exists a subsequence (y_{n_k}), and a sequence (x_k) of points of E, which converges to a point a and is such that $f(x_k) = y_{n_k}$ for every k. (Take (y_{n_k}) such that the series of general term $\|y_{n_{k+1}} - y_{n_k}\|$ is convergent.)
(b) Let u be a compact mapping of E into F, and let $v = f - u$. Show that $v(\mathrm{E})$ is closed in F and has finite codimension in F. (Follow the same pattern as in the proof of (11.3.2), using (a).)
(c) Define inductively $\mathrm{F}_1 = v(\mathrm{E})$, $\mathrm{F}_{k+1} = v(f^{-1}(\mathrm{F}_k))$ for $k \geqslant 1$; show that there is an integer n such that $\mathrm{F}_{k+1} = \mathrm{F}_k$ for $k \geqslant n$ (same method).
(d) Take $\mathrm{E} = \mathrm{F}$ to be a separable Hilbert space, and let $(e_n)_{n \geqslant 1}$ be a Hilbert basis of E. Define f and u such that $f(e_n) = e_{n-3}$ for $n \geqslant 4$, $f(e_n) = 0$ for $n \leqslant 3$, $u(e_n) = e_{n-2}/n$ for $n \geqslant 6$, $u(e_1) = u(e_3) = 0$, $u(e_2) = -e_2$, $u(e_4) = e_1$, $u(e_5) = e_2 + (e_3/5)$. Define inductively $\mathrm{N}_1 = v^{-1}(0)$, $\mathrm{N}_{k+1} = v^{-1}(f(\mathrm{N}_k))$ for $k \geqslant 1$; show that the N_k are all distinct and finite dimensional.
2. Let E, F be two normed spaces, f a linear homeomorphism of E onto a closed subspace $f(\mathrm{E})$ of F, u a compact mapping of E into F, and let $v = f - u$.
(a) Show that $v^{-1}(0)$ is finite dimensional and $v(\mathrm{E})$ is closed in F; furthermore, if $v^{-1}(0) = \{0\}$, v is a linear homeomorphism of E onto $v(\mathrm{E})$. (Follow the same method as in (11.3.2).)
(b) Define inductively $\mathrm{N}_1 = v^{-1}(0)$, $\mathrm{N}_{k+1} = v^{-1}(f(\mathrm{N}_k))$ for $k \geqslant 1$; show that there is an integer n such that $\mathrm{N}_{k+1} = \mathrm{N}_k$ for $k \geqslant n$.
(c) Give an example in which, when $\mathrm{F}_1 = v(\mathrm{E})$, and $\mathrm{F}_{k+1} = v(f^{-1}(\mathrm{F}_k))$ for $k \geqslant 1$, the F_k are all distinct (take for $\mathrm{E} = \mathrm{F}$ a separable Hilbert space, and for f and u the *adjoints* (Section 11.5) of the mappings noted f and u in Problem 1(d)).
3. Let E be a Banach space, g a continuous linear mapping of E onto itself such that $\|g\| < \frac{1}{2}$; then $f = 1_{\mathrm{E}} - g$ is a linear homeomorphism of E onto itself (8.3.2.1). Let u be a compact operator in E, and let $v = f - u$; then the statements in (11.3.2) and (11.3.3) are all valid. (First prove the following result, corresponding to (11.3.1): if $\mathrm{M} \subset \mathrm{L}$, $\mathrm{M} \neq \mathrm{L}$ and $v(\mathrm{L}) \subset \mathrm{M}$, there is an $a \in \mathrm{L} \cap \complement \mathrm{M}$ such that $\|a\| \leqslant 1$ and for any $x \in \mathrm{M}$ such that $\|x\| \leqslant 1$, $\|u(a) - u(x)\| \geqslant (1 - 2\|g\|)/2$.)
4. In the space $\mathrm{E} = l^1$ (Section 5.7, Problem 1; we keep the notations of that problem), let f be the automorphism of E such that $f(e_{2k}) = e_{2k+2}$ $(k \geqslant 0)$, $f(e_1) = e_0$, $f(e_{2k+1}) = e_{2k-1}$ for $k \geqslant 1$, and let u be the compact mapping such that $u(e_n) = 0$ for $n \neq 1$, and $u(e_1) = e_0$. If $v = f - u$, and the F_k and N_k are defined as in (11.3.3), show that $\mathrm{N}_{k+1} \neq \mathrm{N}_k$ and $\mathrm{F}_{k+1} \neq \mathrm{F}_k$ for every k.

4. SPECTRUM OF A COMPACT OPERATOR

(11.4.1) *Let u be a compact operator in a complex normed space* E. *Then:*

(a) *The spectrum* S *of u is an at most denumerable compact subset of* $\mathbf{C}$, *each point of which, with the possible exception of* 0, *is isolated;* 0 *belongs to* S *if* E *is infinite dimensional.*

(b) *Each number* $\lambda \neq 0$ *in the spectrum is an eigenvalue of* u.

(c) *For each* $\lambda \neq 0$ *in* S, *there is a unique decomposition of* E *into a topological direct sum of two subspaces* $F(\lambda)$, $N(\lambda)$ (*also written* $F(\lambda; u)$, $N(\lambda; u)$) *such that*:

(i) $F(\lambda)$ *is closed*, $N(\lambda)$ *is finite dimensional*;

(ii) $u(F(\lambda)) \subset F(\lambda)$, *and the restriction of* $u - \lambda \cdot 1_E$ *to* $F(\lambda)$ *is a linear homeomorphism of that space onto itself*;

(iii) $u(N(\lambda)) \subset N(\lambda)$ *and there is a smallest integer* $k = k(\lambda)$, *called the order of* λ (*also written* $k(\lambda; u)$), *such that the restriction to* $N(\lambda)$ *of* $(u - \lambda \cdot 1_E)^k$ *is* 0.

(d) *The eigenspace* $E(\lambda)$ *of* u *corresponding to the eigenvalue* $\lambda \neq 0$ *is contained in* $N(\lambda)$ (*hence finite dimensional*).

(e) *If* λ, μ *are two different points of* S, *distinct from* 0, *then* $N(\mu) \subset F(\lambda)$.

(f) *If* E *is a Banach space, the function* $\zeta \to (u - \zeta \cdot 1_E)^{-1}$, *which is defined and analytic in* $\mathbf{C} - S$, *has a pole of order* $k(\lambda)$ *at each point* $\lambda \neq 0$ *of* S.

Let $\lambda \neq 0$ be any complex number; as $\lambda^{-1}u$ is compact, we can apply the Riesz theory (Section 11.3). By (11.3.4), if λ is not an eigenvalue of u, $1_E - \lambda^{-1}u$ is a linear homeomorphism of E onto itself, and the same is true of course of $u - \lambda \cdot 1_E = -\lambda(1_E - \lambda^{-1}u)$, i.e. λ is regular for u, which proves b). Suppose on the contrary λ is an eigenvalue of u; then the existence of the decomposition $F(\lambda) + N(\lambda)$ of E with properties (i), (ii), (iii), follows from (11.3.3), as well as (d) ($E(\lambda)$ is the kernel noted N_1 in (11.3.3)). To end the proof of (c), we need only show the uniqueness of $F(\lambda)$ and $N(\lambda)$. Suppose there is a second decomposition $E = F' + N'$ having the same properties, and write $v = u - \lambda \cdot 1_E$. Then, any $x \in N'$ can be written $x = y + z$ where $y \in F(\lambda)$, $z \in N(\lambda)$; by assumption there is $h > 0$ such that $v^h(x) = 0$, hence $v^h(y) = 0$; as the restriction to $F(\lambda)$ of v^h is a homeomorphism by assumption, $y = 0$ and $x \in N(\lambda)$. This proves that $N' \subset N(\lambda)$, and a similar argument proves $N(\lambda) \subset N'$. Next, if $x = y + z \in F'$ with $y \in F(\lambda)$, $z \in N(\lambda)$, we have $v^k(x) = v^k(y)$, hence $v^k(F') \subset F(\lambda)$; but as $v(F') = F'$, this implies $F' \subset F(\lambda)$,

Denote by u_1, u_2 the restrictions of u to $F(\lambda)$ and $N(\lambda)$, respectively. From the relation $(u_2 - \lambda \cdot 1_{N(\lambda)})^k = 0$, it follows by linear algebra (A.6.10 and A.6.12) that there is a basis of $N(\lambda)$ such that the matrix of $u_2 - \lambda \cdot 1_{N(\lambda)}$ with respect to that basis is triangular with diagonal 0; if $d = \dim(N(\lambda))$, the determinant of $u_2 - \zeta \cdot 1_{N(\lambda)}$ is therefore equal to $(\lambda - \zeta)^d$ and this proves that $u_2 - \zeta \cdot 1_{N(\lambda)}$ is invertible if $\zeta \neq \lambda$. Let us prove on the other hand that $u_1 - \zeta \cdot 1_{F(\lambda)}$ is invertible for $\zeta - \lambda$ small enough: we can write $u_1 - \zeta \cdot 1_{F(\lambda)} = v_1 + (\lambda - \zeta) \cdot 1_{F(\lambda)}$ with $v_1 = u_1 - \lambda \cdot 1_{F(\lambda)}$. We know by (c) that v_1 is invertible; by (5.7.4), we therefore have $\|v_1^{-1}(x)\| \leqslant \|v_1^{-1}\| \cdot \|x\|$ in $F(\lambda)$, which can also be written $\|v_1(x)\| \geqslant c \cdot \|x\|$ with $c = \|v_1^{-1}\|^{-1}$. Now if $\zeta \neq 0$ and

$u_1 - \zeta \cdot 1_{F(\lambda)}$ is not invertible, this implies, by (b) (applied to $F(\lambda)$ and u_1, using (11.2.7)) that there would exist an $x \neq 0$ in $F(\lambda)$ such that $u_1(x) = \zeta x$, hence $|\zeta - \lambda| \cdot \|x\| = \|v_1(x)\| \geqslant c \cdot \|x\|$, which is impossible if $|\zeta - \lambda| < c$. This shows that for $\zeta \neq 0$, $\zeta \neq \lambda$, and $|\zeta - \lambda| < c$, $u - \zeta \cdot 1_E$ is invertible (since its restrictions to $F(\lambda)$ and $N(\lambda)$ are), i.e. ζ is not in S; therefore all points $\lambda \neq 0$ in S are isolated, and S is at most denumerable. By (b), for each $\lambda \neq 0$ in S, there is $x \neq 0$ in E such that $u(x) = \lambda x$, hence $|\lambda| \cdot \|x\| \leqslant \|u\| \cdot \|x\|$ by (5.7.4), and $|\lambda| \leqslant \|u\|$, which proves S is compact. To end the proof of (a), suppose E is infinite dimensional; if u were a homeomorphism of E onto itself, the image $u(B)$ of the ball B: $\|x\| \leqslant 1$ would be a neighborhood of 0 in E, and as it is relatively compact in E, this violates Riesz's theorem (5.9.4).

If μ is a point of S distinct from 0 and λ, and $x \in N(\mu)$, we can write $x = y + z$ with $y \in F(\lambda)$, $z \in N(\lambda)$. We have seen above that the restriction of $w = u - \mu \cdot 1_E$ to $N(\lambda)$ is a homeomorphism; as $w^h(x) = 0$ for h large enough, and $w^h(y) \in F(\lambda)$, $w^h(z) \in N(\lambda)$, we must have $w^h(y) = w^h(z) = 0$, which proves statement (e).

If E is a Banach space, the analyticity of $(u - \zeta \cdot 1_E)^{-1}$ in $\mathbf{C} - S$ follows from (11.1.2). With the same notations as above, λ is not in the spectrum of u_1, hence (by (11.2.7)) $(u_1 - \zeta \cdot 1_{F(\lambda)})^{-1}$ is analytic in a neighborhood of λ; in particular, there are numbers $\rho > 0$ and $M > 0$ such that

$$\|(u_1 - \zeta \cdot 1_{F(\lambda)})^{-1}(x)\| \leqslant M \cdot \|x\|$$

for $x \in F(\lambda)$ and $|\zeta - \lambda| \leqslant \rho$. On the other hand, we can write $u_2 - \zeta \cdot 1_{N(\lambda)} = (\lambda - \zeta) \cdot 1_{N(\lambda)} + v_2$ with $v_2 = u_2 - \lambda \cdot 1_{N(\lambda)}$, and we know that for $\zeta \neq \lambda$, $u_2 - \zeta \cdot 1_{N(\lambda)}$ is invertible; moreover, we can write

(11.4.1.1) $$(u_2 - \zeta \cdot 1_{N(\lambda)})^{-1} = -\sum_{h=1}^{k} (\zeta - \lambda)^{-h} v_2^{h-1}$$

since $v_2^k = 0$. From this it follows that there is a number $M' > 0$ such that $|\zeta - \lambda|^k \cdot \|(u_2 - \zeta \cdot 1_{N(\lambda)})^{-1}(x)\| \leqslant M'\|x\|$ for $|\zeta - \lambda| < \rho$, $\zeta \neq \lambda$ and for any $x \in N(\lambda)$. Now any $x \in E$ can be written $x = y + z$ with $y \in F(\lambda)$, $z \in N(\lambda)$, and there is a constant $a > 0$ such that $\|y\| \leqslant a\|x\|$ and $\|z\| \leqslant a\|x\|$ (5.9.3); therefore we see that, for $|\zeta - \lambda| \leqslant \rho$, $\zeta \neq \lambda$, and any $x \in E$, we have

$$|\zeta - \lambda|^k \cdot \|(u - \zeta \cdot 1_E)^{-1}(x)\| \leqslant a(M\rho^k + M')\|x\|.$$

In other words, $|\zeta - \lambda|^k \cdot \|(u - \zeta \cdot 1_E)^{-1}\| \leqslant a(M\rho^k + M')$ for $\zeta \neq \lambda$ and $|\zeta - \lambda| \leqslant \rho$; by (9.1.5.2), this implies that λ is a pole of order $\leqslant k$ for $(u - \zeta \cdot 1_E)^{-1}$. But by definition there is an $x \in N(\lambda)$ such that $v_2^{k-1}(x) \neq 0$, hence $(\zeta - \lambda)^{k-1}((u - \zeta \cdot 1_E)^{-1}(x))$ is not bounded when $\zeta \neq \lambda$ tends to λ, and this proves that λ is a pole of order k, and ends the proof of (11.4.1).

We say that the dimension of $N(\lambda)$ is the *algebraic multiplicity* of the eigenvalue λ of u, the dimension of the eigenspace $E(\lambda)$ its *geometric multiplicity*; they are equal if and only if $k(\lambda) = 1$; when E is a Banach space, this is equivalent to saying that λ is a *simple pole* of $(u - \zeta \cdot 1_E)^{-1}$.

(11.4.2) *Let* E *be a Banach space,* E_0 *a dense subspace of* E, u *a compact operator in* E_0, $\tilde{u}$ *its unique continuous extension to* E. *Then the spectra of* u *and* $\tilde{u}$ *are the same, and for each eigenvalue* $\lambda \neq 0$ *of* u, $N(\lambda, u) = N(\lambda, \tilde{u})$, $E(\lambda, u) = E(\lambda, \tilde{u})$ *and* $k(\lambda, u) = k(\lambda, \tilde{u})$.

We know that $\tilde{u}$ is compact and maps E *into* E_0, by (11.2.9); if $\lambda \neq 0$ is an eigenvalue of $\tilde{u}$, any eigenvector x corresponding to λ is such that $x = \lambda^{-1}\tilde{u}(x) \in E_0$, hence λ is an eigenvalue of u, and $E(\lambda, \tilde{u}) \subset E(\lambda, u)$; the converse being obvious, we have $\text{sp}(\tilde{u}) = \text{sp}(u)$ and $E(\lambda, u) = E(\lambda, \tilde{u}) \subset E_0$ for each eigenvalue $\lambda \neq 0$. Considering similarly the kernels of $(u - \lambda \cdot 1_{E_0})^k$ and of its extension $(\tilde{u} - \lambda \cdot 1_E)^k$ we see that they are equal, hence $k(\lambda, u) = k(\lambda, \tilde{u})$ and $N(\lambda, u) = N(\lambda, \tilde{u}) \subset E_0$.

PROBLEMS

1. Let E be a complex *Banach* space, u a compact operator in E; we keep the notations of (11.4.1), and in addition, we write p_λ (or $p_{\lambda, u}$) and $q_\lambda = 1_E - p_\lambda$ the projections of E onto $N(\lambda)$ and $F(\lambda)$ in the decomposition of E as direct sum $F(\lambda) + N(\lambda)$.
(a) Show that $-p_\lambda$ is the residue of the meromorphic function $(u - \zeta \cdot 1_E)^{-1}$ at the pole λ, for every $\lambda \in \text{sp}(u)$ such that $\lambda \neq 0$.
(b) If $\lambda_1, \ldots, \lambda_r$ are distinct points of the spectrum $\text{sp}(u)$, show that the projections p_{λ_j} $(1 \leqslant j \leqslant r)$ commute, and that $p_{\lambda_1} + \cdots + p_{\lambda_r}$ is the projection of E onto $N(\lambda_1) + \cdots + N(\lambda_r)$ in the decomposition of E as direct sum of that subspace and of $F(\lambda_1) \cap F(\lambda_2) \cap \cdots \cap F(\lambda_r)$.
2. Let E be an infinite dimensional complex Banach space, u a compact operator in E, $(u_n)_{n \geqslant 1}$ a sequence of compact operators in E, which converges to u in the Banach space $\mathscr{L}(E)$.
(a) Prove that for any bounded subset B of E, the union $\bigcup_n u_n(B)$ is relatively compact in E. (Show that it is precompact.)
(b) If $\lambda \in \mathbf{C}$ does not belong to $\text{sp}(u)$, show that there is an open disk D of center λ and an integer n_0 such that, for $n \geqslant n_0$, the intersection $\text{sp}(u_n) \cap D = \varnothing$ (use (8.3.2.1)) and $(u_n - \zeta \cdot 1_E)^{-1}$ converges *uniformly* to $(u - \zeta \cdot 1_E)^{-1}$ for $\zeta \in D$.
(c) Let (μ_n) be a sequence of complex numbers such that $\mu_n \in \text{sp}(u_n)$ for every n; such a sequence is always bounded. If λ is a cluster point of (μ_n), show that $\lambda \in \text{sp}(u)$. (One can assume that $\lambda = \lim_{n \to \infty} \mu_n \neq 0$; there is then $x_n \in E$ such that $\|x_n\| = 1$ and $u_n(x_n) = \lambda_n x_n$; use then (a).)

(d) Conversely, let $\lambda \neq 0$ be in $\mathrm{sp}(u)$. Show that for each n there is (at least) a number $\mu_n \in \mathrm{sp}(u_n)$ such that $\lambda = \lim_{n\to\infty} \mu_n$. (Otherwise, one can assume that there is an open disk D of center λ and radius r, such that $D \cap \mathrm{sp}(u) = \{\lambda\}$ and $D \cap \mathrm{sp}(u_n) = \varnothing$ (extract from (u_n) a suitable subsequence). Let then γ be the road $t \to \lambda + re^{it}$ defined in $[0, 2\pi]$; consider the integral

$$\int_\gamma (u_n - \zeta \cdot 1_E)^{-1}(\zeta - \lambda)^k \, d\zeta = 0 \qquad \text{for} \quad k \geqslant 0$$

and use (b) to obtain a contradiction.)

(e) Let $\lambda \neq 0$ be in $\mathrm{sp}(u)$, and let D be an open disk of center λ and radius r such that $D \cap \mathrm{sp}(u) = \{\lambda\}$; there exists n_0 such that, for $n \geqslant n_0$ the intersection of $\mathrm{sp}(u_n)$ and of the circle $|\zeta - \lambda| = r$ is empty (use (c)). Let $\mu_1, \dots, \mu_r$ be the points of $D \cap \mathrm{sp}(u_n)$, and write $k_n = \sum_{j=1}^{r} k(\mu_j; u_n)$. Show that there exists n_1 such that, for $n \geqslant n_1$, $k_n \geqslant k(\lambda; u)$. (Use the same method as in (d), multiplying $(u_n - \zeta \cdot 1_E)^{-1}$ by a suitable polynomial in ζ of degree k_n.) Give an example in which $k_n > k(\lambda; u)$ for every n.

(f) With the notations of (e), let $p = p_{\lambda,u}$, $p_n = \sum_{j=1}^{r} p_{\mu_j, u_n}$; show that $\lim_{n\to\infty} p_n = p$ in the Banach space $\mathscr{L}(E)$ (use (b), and Problem 1). Deduce from that result that there exists n_2 such that, for $n \geqslant n_2$, $N_n = N(\mu_1; u_n) + \dots + N(\mu_r; u_n)$ is a supplement to $F(\lambda; u)$ in E. (Suppose n is such that $\|p - p_n\| \leqslant 1/2$; if there was a point $x_n \in F(\lambda) \cap N_n$ such that $\|x_n\| = 1$, then the relations $p(x_n) = 0$, $p_n(x_n) = x_n$ would contradict the preceding inequality. Prove similarly that the intersection of $N(\lambda; u)$ and of the subspace $F(\mu_1; u_n) \cap \dots \cap F(\mu_r; u_n)$ is reduced to 0.)

3. Let u be a compact operator in an infinite dimensional complex Banach space E, and let $P(\zeta)$ be a polynomial without constant term; put $v = P(u)$. Show that the spectrum $\mathrm{sp}(v)$ is identical to the set of numbers $P(\lambda)$, where $\lambda \in \mathrm{sp}(u)$; furthermore, for every $\mu \in \mathrm{sp}(v)$, $N(\mu; v)$ is the (direct) sum of the subspaces $N(\lambda_k; u)$ such that $P(\lambda_k) = \mu$, and $F(\mu; v)$ the intersection of the corresponding subspaces $F(\lambda_k; u)$. (Let V be any closed subspace of E, such that $u(V) \subset V$, and let u_V be the restriction of u to V. Show that there is a constant M independent of V and n, such that $\|(P(u_V))^n\| \leqslant M^n \|u_V^n\|$. Apply that remark and Problem 1 of Section **11.1**, taking for V a suitable intersection of a finite number of subspaces of the form $F(\lambda; u)$.)

4. Let E be a separable Hilbert space, $(e_n)_{n\geqslant 0}$ a Hilbert basis of E. Show that the operator u defined by $u(e_n) = e_{n+1}/(n+1)$ for $n \geqslant 0$ is compact and that $\mathrm{sp}(u)$ is reduced to 0 (more precisely, u has *no eigenvalue*).

5. Let u be a continuous operator in a complex Banach space E. A *Riesz point* for u is a point λ in the spectrum $\mathrm{sp}(u)$ such that: (1) λ is isolated in $\mathrm{sp}(u)$; (2) E is the direct sum of a closed subspace $F(\lambda)$ and of a finite dimensional subspace $N(\lambda)$ such that $u(F(\lambda)) \subset F(\lambda)$, $u(N(\lambda)) \subset N(\lambda)$, the restriction of $u - \lambda \cdot 1_E$ to $F(\lambda)$ is a linear homeomorphism and the restriction of $u - \lambda \cdot 1_E$ to $N(\lambda)$ is nilpotent.

(a) If λ and μ are two distinct Riesz points in $\mathrm{sp}(u)$, show that $N(\mu) \subset F(\lambda)$, and $F(\lambda)$ is the direct sum of $N(\mu)$ and $F(\lambda) \cap F(\mu)$.

(b) A *Riesz operator* u is defined as a continuous operator such that *all* points $\neq 0$ in the spectrum $\mathrm{sp}(u)$ are Riesz points. For any $\varepsilon > 0$, the set of points $\lambda \in \mathrm{sp}(u)$ such that $|\lambda| \geqslant \varepsilon$ is then a finite set $\{\mu_1, \dots, \mu_r\}$; let p_i be the projection of E onto $N(\mu_i)$ in the decomposition of E into the direct sum $N(\mu_i) + F(\mu_i)$ $(1 \leqslant i \leqslant r)$, and let $v = u - \sum_{i=1}^{r} u \circ p_i$. Show that $\mathrm{sp}(v)$ is contained in the disk $|\zeta| \leqslant \varepsilon$, hence (Section **11.1**, Problem 1) that $\lim_{n\to\infty} \|v^n\|^{1/n} \leqslant \varepsilon$.

(c) In the Banach space $\mathscr{L}(E)$, let $\mathscr{K}$ be the closed (11.2.10) subspace of all compact operators. Show that, in order that $u \in \mathscr{L}(E)$ be a Riesz operator, it is necessary and sufficient that $\lim_{n\to\infty} (d(u^n, \mathscr{K}))^{1/n} = 0$. (To prove that the condition is necessary, use (b), observing that $u^n = v^n + w_n$, where w_n is an operator of *finite* rank, hence compact. To prove that the condition is sufficient, use the result of Problem 3 of Section 11.3, which can be interpreted in the following way: if $\|g\| < \frac{1}{2}$, then either $\lambda = 1$ does not belong to $\text{sp}(g + u)$ or is a Riesz point for $g + u$.)

5. COMPACT OPERATORS IN HILBERT SPACES

Let E be a *prehilbert* space, u an operator in E. We say u has an *adjoint* if there exists an operator u^* in E such that

$$(u(x) \mid y) = (x \mid u^*(y)) \tag{11.5.1}$$

for any pair of points x, y in E. It is immediate that the adjoint u^* is unique (when it exists), and (by Section 6.1(V)) that then $(u^*)^*$ exists and is equal to u. It is similarly verified that when the operators u and v have adjoints, then $u + v$, λu, and uv have adjoints respectively equal to $u^* + v^*$, $\bar{\lambda} u^*$, and $v^* u^*$.

(11.5.2) *If u is continuous and has an adjoint, then u^* is continuous and $\|u^*\| = \|u\|$ in $\mathscr{L}(E)$. If E is a Hilbert space, every continuous operator in E has an adjoint.*

From (11.5.1) and the Cauchy–Schwarz inequality (6.2.4) we deduce

$$|(x \mid u^*(y))| \leqslant \|u(x)\| \cdot \|y\| \leqslant \|u\| \cdot \|x\| \cdot \|y\|$$

for any pair x, y; taking $x = u^*(y)$, we get $\|u^*(y)\| \leqslant \|u\| \cdot \|y\|$ for any $y \in E$, which proves the continuity of u^* and the inequality $\|u^*\| \leqslant \|u\|$; the converse inequality is proved by interchanging u and u^* in the argument. If E is a Hilbert space and u is continuous, then, for any $y \in E$, the linear form $x \to (u(x) \mid y)$ is continuous, and by (6.3.2) there exists a unique vector $u^*(y)$ such that (11.5.1) holds. From the uniqueness of $u^*(y)$, we conclude that u^* is linear, hence the adjoint of u. The second statemento f (11.5.2) does not extend to prehilbert spaces.

An operator u in a prehilbert space E is called *self-adjoint* (or *hermitian*) if it has an adjoint and if $u^* = u$; the mapping $(x, y) \to (u(x) \mid y) = \overline{(u(y) \mid x)}$ is then a *hermitian form* on E; the self-adjoint operator u is called *positive* (resp. *nondegenerate*) if the corresponding hermitian form is positive (resp. nondegenerate); one writes then $u \geqslant 0$. For any operator u having an adjoint, $u + u^*$ and $i(u - u^*)$ are self-adjoint operators.

(11.5.3) (i) *If a continuous operator u in a prehilbert space* E *has an adjoint, then u^*u and uu^* are self-adjoint positive operators, and* $\|u^*u\| = \|uu^*\| = \|u\|^2 = \|u^*\|^2$. *In particular, if u is self-adjoint,* $\|u^2\| = \|u\|^2$.

(ii) *If P is the orthogonal projection of* E *on a complete vector subspace* F (Section 6.3), *P is a positive hermitian operator. Conversely, if* E *is a Hilbert space, every continuous operator P in* E *which is hermitian and idempotent* (i.e. $P^2 = P$) *is the orthogonal projection of* E *on the closed subspace* $P(\mathrm{E})$ (these operators are called the *orthogonal projectors* in $\mathscr{L}(\mathrm{E})$).

(i) The fact that u^*u and uu^* are self-adjoint follows from the relations $(u^*)^* = u$ and $(uv)^* = v^*u^*$; moreover $(u^*u(x) \mid x) = (u(x) \mid u(x)) \geqslant 0$ for any $x \in \mathrm{E}$, and it is proved similarly that uu^* is positive. Further this last relation shows that $\|u(x)\|^2 \leqslant \|u^*u(x)\| \cdot \|x\|$ by Cauchy–Schwarz, hence (by (5.7.4)) $\|u\|^2 \leqslant \|u^*u\|$. On the other hand, $\|u^*u\| \leqslant \|u^*\| \cdot \|u\| = \|u\|^2$ by (5.7.5) and (11.5.2), and this concludes the proof of (i).

(ii) If P is the orthogonal projection of E on a complete subspace F, then $(P \cdot x \mid y - P \cdot y) = 0$ for $x \in \mathrm{E}$, $y \in \mathrm{E}$, hence $(P \cdot x \mid y) = (P \cdot x \mid P \cdot y) = (x \mid P \cdot y)$, which proves that P is hermitian, and it is positive since $(P \cdot x \mid x) = (P \cdot x \mid P \cdot x) \geqslant 0$. Conversely, suppose E is a Hilbert space, and $P^2 = P = P^*$; then, for all x, y in E, $(P \cdot x \mid y - P \cdot y) = (x \mid P \cdot y - P^2 \cdot y) = 0$; as the relation $y = P \cdot x$ implies $P \cdot y = P^2 \cdot x = P \cdot x = y$, $P(\mathrm{E})$ is the kernel of $1_{\mathrm{E}} - P$, hence is a closed vector subspace; furthermore, for any $y \in \mathrm{E}$, $y - P \cdot y$ is orthogonal to every $P \cdot x$, in other words to $P(\mathrm{E})$, which proves (ii).

(11.5.4) *If* E *is a Hilbert space, the adjoint of any compact operator u in* E *is a compact operator.*

As E is complete, it will be enough to prove that the image $u^*(\mathrm{B})$ of the ball $\mathrm{B}: \|y\| \leqslant 1$ is *precompact*. Let $\mathrm{F} = \overline{u(\mathrm{B})}$, which is a compact subspace of E, and consider, in the space $\mathscr{C}_{\mathbf{C}}(\mathrm{F})$ (Section 7.2) the set H of the restrictions to F of the linear continuous mappings $x \to (x \mid y)$ of E into $\mathbf{C}$, where $y \in \mathrm{B}$; we prove that H is *relatively compact* in $\mathscr{C}_{\mathbf{C}}(\mathrm{F})$. Indeed, we have $|(x - x' \mid y)| \leqslant \|x - x'\|$ by the Cauchy–Schwarz inequality, since $\|y\| \leqslant 1$, which shows that H is *equicontinuous*; on the other hand F is contained in the ball $\|x\| \leqslant \|u\|$, hence $|(x \mid y)| \leqslant \|u\|$ for any $y \in \mathrm{B}$ and any $x \in \mathrm{F}$; Ascoli's theorem (7.5.7) then proves our contention. Therefore, for any $\varepsilon > 0$, there exist a finite number of points y_j $(1 \leqslant j \leqslant m)$ in B such that for any $y \in \mathrm{B}$, there is an index j such that $|(u(x) \mid y - y_j)| \leqslant \varepsilon$ for *any* $x \in \mathrm{B}$. But by (11.5.1) this last inequality is written $|(x \mid u^*(y) - u^*(y_j))| \leqslant \varepsilon$, and either $u^*(y) = u^*(y_j)$ or we can take $x = z/\|z\|$, where $z = u^*(y) - u^*(y_j)$; we therefore conclude that $\|u^*(y) - u^*(y_j)\| \leqslant \varepsilon$, and this ends the proof.

Note that the proof that $u^*(B)$ is precompact still holds when E is not complete; but it can happen that in a prehilbert space E, a compact operator has an adjoint which is not compact.

(11.5.5) *Let u be a compact operator in a complex prehilbert space* E, *having an adjoint u^* which is compact. Then:*

(a) *The spectrum* $\mathrm{sp}(u^*)$ *is the image of* $\mathrm{sp}(u)$ *by the mapping* $\xi \to \bar{\xi}$.

(b) *For each $\lambda \neq 0$ in* $\mathrm{sp}(u)$, $k(\lambda; u) = k(\bar{\lambda}; u^*)$.

(c) *If $v = u - \lambda \cdot 1_E$, then $v^*(E)$ is the orthogonal supplement* (Section 6.3) *of* $v^{-1}(0) = E(\lambda; u)$, *and the dimensions of the eigenspaces* $E(\lambda; u)$ *and* $E(\bar{\lambda}; u^*)$ *are equal.*

(d) *The subspace* $F(\bar{\lambda}; u^*)$ *is the orthogonal supplement of* $N(\lambda; u)$, *and the dimensions of* $N(\lambda; u)$ *and* $N(\bar{\lambda}; u^*)$ *are equal.*

We have $v^* = u^* - \bar{\lambda} \cdot 1_E$, hence $(v(x) \mid y) = (x \mid v^*(y))$ from (11.5.1), and therefore the relation $v(x) = 0$ implies that x is orthogonal to the subspace $v^*(E)$. Now by (11.4.1) applied to u^*, $v^*(E)$ is the topological direct sum of $F(\bar{\lambda}; u^*)$ and of the subspace $v^*(N(\bar{\lambda}; u^*))$ of $N(\bar{\lambda}; u^*)$, and from linear algebra (A.4.17) it follows that the *codimension* of $v^*(E)$ is equal to the dimension of $v^{*-1}(0) = E(\bar{\lambda}; u^*)$; hence we have $\dim E(\lambda; u) \leqslant \dim E(\bar{\lambda}; u^*)$. But $u = (u^*)^*$, hence we have $\dim E(\lambda; u) = \dim E(\bar{\lambda}; u^*)$; furthermore, the orthogonal supplement of $E(\lambda; u)$ contains $v^*(E)$ and has the same codimension as $v^*(E)$, hence both are equal, which proves (c). This also shows that for any eigenvalue $\lambda \neq 0$ of u, $\bar{\lambda}$ is an eigenvalue of u^*, and as the converse follows from the relation $u = (u^*)^*$, we have also proved (a).

The same argument may be applied to the successive iterates v^h of v, and shows that the image of E by $v^{*h} = (v^h)^*$ is the orthogonal supplement of the kernel of v^h. Using (11.3.2), (11.4.1), and the relation $u = (u^*)^*$, this immediately proves (b) and (d).

Theorems (11.4.1) and (11.5.5) can be translated into a criterion for the solutions of the equation $u(x) - \lambda x = y$:

(11.5.6) *Under the assumptions of* (11.5.5):

(a) *If λ is not in the spectrum of u, the equation $u(x) - \lambda x = y$ has a unique solution in* E *for every* $y \in E$.

(b) *If $\lambda \neq 0$ is in the spectrum of u, a necessary and sufficient condition for $y \in E$ to be such that the equation $u(x) - \lambda x = y$ have a solution in* E *is that y be orthogonal to the solutions of the equation $u^*(x) - \bar{\lambda} x = 0$.*

For a finite dimensional space, this reduces to the classical criterion for existence of a solution of a system of scalar linear equations.

(11.5.7) *Let u be a compact* self-adjoint *operator in a complex* Hilbert *space* E. *Then:*

(a) *Every element of the spectrum* $\mathrm{sp}(u)$ *is real and* $k(\lambda) = 1$ *for every eigenvalue* $\lambda \neq 0$ *of* u.

(b) *If* λ, μ *are two distinct eigenvalues of* u, *the eigenspaces* $\mathrm{E}(\lambda)$ *and* $\mathrm{E}(\mu)$ *are orthogonal.*

(c) *Let* (μ_n) *be the strictly decreasing (finite or infinite) sequence of eigenvalues* >0, (ν_n) *the strictly increasing (finite or infinite) sequence of eigenvalues* <0. *For each* k *such that* μ_k (*resp.* ν_k) *is defined, let* F'_k (resp. F''_k) *be the orthogonal supplement of* $\mathrm{E}(\mu_1) + \cdots + \mathrm{E}(\mu_{k-1})$ (resp. $\mathrm{E}(\nu_1) + \cdots + \mathrm{E}(\nu_{k-1})$); *then* μ_k (resp. ν_k) *is the largest* (resp. *smallest*) *value of the function* $x \to (u(x) \mid x)$ *on the sphere* $\|x\| = 1$ *in* F'_k (resp. F''_k), *and the points of that sphere where* $(u(x) \mid x) = \mu_k$ (resp. $(u(x) \mid x) = \nu_k$) *are the points which belong to* $\mathrm{E}(\mu_k)$ (resp. $\mathrm{E}(\nu)_k$). *Furthermore,* $\|u\| = \sup(\mu_1, -\nu_1)$.

(d) *The space* E *is the Hilbert sum* (Section 6.4) *of the subspaces* $\mathrm{E}(\mu_n)$, $\mathrm{E}(\nu_n)$, *and* $\mathrm{E}(0) = u^{-1}(0)$.

(It may happen that either the μ_n or the ν_n are absent, but from (c) it follows that the only case in which there are *no* eigenvalues $\neq 0$ is the case $u = 0$.)

For any eigenvalue $\lambda \neq 0$ of u, we have, for an eigenvector x corresponding to λ, $(u(x) \mid x) = \lambda(x \mid x)$, but $(u(x) \mid x) = (x \mid u(x)) = \overline{(u(x) \mid x)}$ is *real* for any $x \in \mathrm{E}$, hence, as $(x \mid x)$ is real and $\neq 0$, λ is real. If $v = u - \lambda \cdot 1_{\mathrm{E}}$, we therefore have $v^* = v$, hence $v(\mathrm{E})$ is the orthogonal supplement of $\mathrm{E}(\lambda) = v^{-1}(0)$ by (11.5.5); this implies that the restriction of v to $v(\mathrm{E})$ is injective, hence, by definition (see (11.3.3)) $\mathrm{N}(\lambda) = \mathrm{E}(\lambda)$, $\mathrm{F}(\lambda) = v(\mathrm{E})$ and therefore $k(\lambda) = 1$. This proves statement (a), and as $\mathrm{E}(\mu) = \mathrm{N}(\mu) \subset \mathrm{F}(\lambda)$ for any eigenvalue $\mu \neq \lambda$ by (11.4.1), we also have proved (b).

We first prove the last part of statement (c). Let $\rho = \sup(\mu_1, -\nu_1)$. Then by (11.1.2) the mapping $\zeta \to (u - \zeta \cdot 1_{\mathrm{E}})^{-1}$ is analytic for $|\zeta| > \rho$, whence it follows at once that the mapping $\xi \to (1_{\mathrm{E}} - \xi u)^{-1}$ is analytic for $|\xi| < 1/\rho$. Now, for ξ in a sufficiently small neighborhood of 0, the power series $\sum_{n=0}^{\infty} \xi^n u^n$ converges to $(1_{\mathrm{E}} - \xi u)^{-1}$ in $\mathscr{L}(\mathrm{E})$ (8.3.2.1); by (9.9.4) that power series converges for every ξ such that $|\xi| < 1/\rho$. Furthermore, for each r such that $0 < r < 1/\rho$, if M is the maximum of $\|(1_{\mathrm{E}} - \xi u)^{-1}\|$ for $|\xi| = r$, the Cauchy inequalities (9.9.5) yield $\|u^n\| \leqslant \mathrm{M}/r^n \leqslant \mathrm{M}\rho^n$. In particular, if we use (11.5.3), we get here $\|u\|^{2^n} \leqslant M\rho^{2^n}$ for every $n \geqslant 1$; taking 2^nth roots and letting n tend to $+\infty$, we get, by Section **4.3**, $\|u\| \leqslant \rho$. On the other hand we have $\rho \leqslant \|u\|$ by **(11.1.3)**, hence $\|u\| = \rho$.

Let us now write (ρ_n) for the strictly decreasing sequence of the absolute values of the eigenvalues of u, so that $\rho_1 = \rho = \sup(\mu_1, -\nu_1)$; and let G_n be equal to the sum of the $E(\lambda)$ such that $|\lambda| = \rho_n$ (there are of course either only one or two such eigenvalues λ). Next let F_n be the orthogonal supplement of $G_1 + \cdots + G_{n-1}$; we have $u(F_n) \subset F_n$ by (a), and we prove that the restriction u_n of u to F_n is such that $\|u_n\| < \rho_{n-1}$. Otherwise, by what has just been seen above (and by **(11.2.7)**) there would be in F_n an eigenvector x such that $u(x) = \lambda x$ with $|\lambda| \geqslant \rho_{n-1}$, which contradicts the definition of F_n. Write now $x = y + z$ for every $x \in F_n$, with $y \in F_{n+1}$ and $z \in G_n$; we have, by Cauchy–Schwarz,

$$-\|u_{n+1}\| \cdot \|y\|^2 + (u(z) \mid z) \leqslant (u(x) \mid x) \leqslant \|u_{n+1}\| \cdot \|y\|^2 + (u(z) \mid z).$$

Suppose $\rho_n = \mu_h = -\nu_k$, and write therefore $z = z_1 + z_2$ with $z_1 \in E(\mu_h)$ and $z_2 \in E(\nu_k)$; this yields $(u(z) \mid z) = \rho_n(\|z_1\|^2 - \|z_2\|^2)$. As $\|x\|^2 = \|y\|^2 + \|z_1\|^2 + \|z_2\|^2$, we see at once, using the preceding inequality and the inequality $\|u_{n+1}\| < \rho_n$, that on the sphere $\|x\| = 1$ in F_n, the largest value of $(u(x) \mid x)$ is ρ_n and is reached at the points of $E(\mu_h)$ only, and the smallest value is $-\rho_n$, and is reached at the points of $E(\nu_k)$ only. The results are similar and simpler if either there is no k such that $\rho_n = -\nu_k$, or no h such that $\rho_n = \mu_h$. Finally, if we remark that $F'_h = F_n + E(\nu_1) + \cdots + E(\nu_s)$ if $\mu_h = \rho_n$ and s is the largest value of k such that $\rho_n < -\nu_k$, and similarly

$$F''_k = F_n + E(\mu_1) + \cdots + E(\mu_r)$$

if $\nu_k = -\rho_n$ and r is the largest value of h such that $\rho_n < \mu_h$, an almost identical argument ends the proof of (c).

Let now F_∞ be the closed subspace, intersection of all the F_n; by definition, $u(F_\infty) \subset F_\infty$, and there can be *no* eigenvalue $\neq 0$ of the restriction of u to F_∞; by (c) this implies that $u(x) = 0$ in F_∞. Furthermore, if a vector $x \in E$ is orthogonal to F_∞ and to all the $E(\mu_k)$ and $E(\nu_k)$, by definition it is orthogonal to all the G_n, hence belongs to F_∞, and being orthogonal to F_∞, it is 0. This proves (by **(6.3.1)**) that the algebraic sum of the subspaces $E(\mu_k)$, $E(\nu_k)$, and F_∞ is dense in E; hence, by **(6.4.2)**, E is the *Hilbert sum* of those spaces. Any $x \in E$ can therefore be written uniquely $x = \sum_k x'_k + \sum_k x''_k + x_0$, where x'_k, x''_k, and x_0 are the *orthogonal projections* of x on $E(\mu_k)$, $E(\nu_k)$, and F_∞, respectively, the sums being convergent series in E when the sets of indices are infinite (*canonical decomposition* of x); we conclude that

$$u(x) = \sum_k \mu_k x'_k + \sum_k \nu_k x''_k,$$

and by the uniqueness of that expression, we see that $u(x) = 0$ implies $x \in F_\infty$; in other words, $F_\infty = u^{-1}(0)$, which ends the proof of (11.5.7).

Remarks

(11.5.8) Let E_0 be a prehilbert space which is a dense subspace of a Hilbert space E (it can be proved that for any prehilbert space E_0 there is a Hilbert space E having that property; we have proved in (6.6.2) the special case of that theorem in which E_0 is separable). Let u be a compact self-adjoint operator in E_0; then the results (a), (b), and (c) of theorem (11.5.7) *hold without change* for u. For it follows from the principle of extension of identities that the unique continuous extension $\tilde{u}$ of u to E is self-adjoint, and it is readily verified that $\|\tilde{u}\| = \|u\|$; our assertion then follows from (11.4.2) and from the following remark: if F_0 is a finite dimensional subspace of E_0, G_0 its orthogonal supplement in E_0, G its orthogonal supplement in E, then G_0 is dense in G; this is a consequence of the fact that if $v = 1_E - P_{F_0}$ in $\mathscr{L}(E)$ (notations of Section 6.3), v is continuous and $v(E) = G$, $v(E_0) = G_0$ (see (3.11.3)). With respect to the part (d) of (11.5.7), it is clear that the kernel of u is the intersection of E_0 with the kernel of $\tilde{u}$, hence is the subspace of vectors of E_0 orthogonal to all eigenspaces $E(\lambda)$ with $\lambda \neq 0$. But if we consider the canonical decomposition $x = \sum_k x_k' + \sum_k x_k'' + x_0$ of an element $x \in E_0$, the sums on the right-hand side and the element x_0 *do not necessarily belong to* E_0.

(11.5.9) If $x = \sum_k x_k' + \sum_k x_k'' + x_0$, $y = \sum_k y_k' + \sum_k y_k'' + y_0$ are the canonical decompositions of two vectors x, y of E, then

$$(u(x) \mid y) = \sum_k \mu_k(x_k' \mid y_k') + \sum_k \nu_k(x_k'' \mid y_k'')$$

the series on the right-hand side being absolutely convergent (Section 6.4). This formula at once shows that the self-adjoint operator u is *positive* if and only if there are *no negative eigenvalues* ν_k, and that it is *nondegenerate* if and only if $u^{-1}(0) = \{0\}$. If u is nondegenerate, and if in each eigenspace $E(\lambda)$ ($\lambda \neq 0$), we take a Hilbert basis B_λ (consisting of a finite number of vectors), then the union of the B_λ is a denumerable set which constitutes a *Hilbert basis* in E (Section 6.5).

(11.5.10) Under the assumptions of (11.5.8), it should be observed that it is quite possible that the self-adjoint compact operator u in E_0 is *nondegenerate*, whereas its continuous extension $\tilde{u}$ to E is *degenerate* (in other words, the kernel of u is not necessarily dense in the kernel of $\tilde{u}$); this may happen even if u is a positive self-adjoint operator.

For compact self-adjoint operators in a *Hilbert* space E, (11.5.7) yields a formula for the solutions of the equation $u(x) - \lambda x = y$ in E:

(11.5.11) *Let* $y = \sum_k y'_k + \sum_k y''_k + y_0$ *be the canonical decomposition of* y *in* E. *Then:*

(a) *If* λ *is not in* $\mathrm{sp}(u)$, *the unique solution* x *of the equation* $u(x) - \lambda x = y$ *is given by its canonical decomposition*

(11.5.11.1)
$$x = \sum_k \frac{1}{\mu_k - \lambda} y'_k + \sum_k \frac{1}{\nu_k - \lambda} y''_k - \frac{1}{\lambda} y_0 .$$

(b) *If* λ *is one of the eigenvalues* μ_k (resp. ν_k), *then, in order that the equation* $u(x) - \lambda x = y$ *have a solution, it is necessary and sufficient that* $y'_k = 0$ (resp. $y''_k = 0$). *The solutions are then given by formula* (11.5.11.1) *in which the term corresponding to* μ_k (resp. ν_k) *is replaced by an arbitrary element of* $\mathrm{E}(\mu_k)$ (resp. $\mathrm{E}(\nu_k)$).

(c) *In order that the equation* $u(x) = y$ *have a solution, it is necessary and sufficient that* $y_0 = 0$ *and that the series* $\sum_k (1/\mu_k^2)\|y'_k\|^2$ *and* $\sum_k (1/\nu_k^2)\|y''_k\|^2$ *be convergent; the solutions are then given by*

(11.5.11.2)
$$x = \sum_k \frac{1}{\mu_k} y'_k + \sum_k \frac{1}{\nu_k} y''_k + x_0$$

with x_0 *arbitrary in* $u^{-1}(0)$.

Results (a) and (b) at once follow from (11.5.7) and (11.5.6), the formulae being obtained by using the uniqueness of the canonical decomposition. The same argument proves that if there are solutions to $u(x) = y$, they are necessarily given by (11.5.11.2), hence the necessity of the conditions; and if these conditions are satisfied, then the right-hand side of (11.5.11.2) is an element of E (by Section 6.4) which satisfies $u(x) = y$.

PROBLEMS

1. Let E be the vector space of all indefinitely differentiable complex valued functions defined in the interval [0, 1] of **R** (Section 8.12); E is made into a prehilbert space by the hermitian form

$$(x \mid y) = \int_0^1 x(t)\overline{y(t)}\, dt.$$

Let u be the linear mapping of E into itself such that $u(x) = ix'$. Show that u is self-adjoint, but is not continuous in E. (Consider the sequence (x_n) where $x_n(t) = (\sin nt)/n$.)

2. Let F be a separable Hilbert space, (e_n) $(n \geqslant 1)$ a Hilbert basis of F, v the compact operator in F such that $v(e_n) = (e_1 + e_n)/n$ (Section **11.2**, Problem 3). Let $E = v(F)$, and let u be the restriction of v to E, which is such that $u(E) \subset E$. Show that *in the prehilbert space* E, u is a compact operator which has no adjoint.

3. (a) Let E be a complex Hilbert space, f a continuous hermitian form on $E \times E$; show that there is a constant c such that $|f(x, y)| \leqslant c \|x\| \cdot \|y\|$ (cf. (**5.5.1**)), and show that there exists a unique continuous hermitian operator U in E such that $f(x, y) = (Ux \mid y)$.

(b) Suppose E is separable, and let $(e_n)_{n \geqslant 1}$ be a Hilbert basis for E; let V be the continuous linear operator in E defined by $Ve_1 = \sum_{n=1}^{\infty} e_n/n$, $Ve_i = 0$ for $i > 1$, and let $W = VV^*$. Let E_0 be the subspace of E consisting of the (finite) linear combinations of the e_n, and let f be the restriction to $E_0 \times E_0$ of the mapping $(x, y) \to (Wx \mid y)$. Show that f is a continuous hermitian form on $E_0 \times E_0$, but that there is no linear operator U *in* E_0 such that $f(x, y) = (Ux \mid y)$ in $E_0 \times E_0$.

(c) If u is the operator defined in Problem 1, show that the hermitian form $(x, y) \to (u(x) \mid y)$ is not continuous in $E \times E$.

4. Let E be a complex Hilbert space, u a hermitian operator in E. Prove that u is necessarily *continuous*. (Assume the contrary, and show that it is possible to define by induction a sequence (x_n) of points of E such that $\|x_n\| = 1$ for every n, and an orthonormal sequence (e_n) such that: (1) x_n is orthogonal to $u(e_1), \dots, u(e_{n-1})$; (2) if y_n is the orthogonal projection of $u(x_n)$ on the subspace V_n orthogonal to $e_1, \dots, e_{n-1}$, then $\|y_n\| \geqslant 2n^3$ and $\|y_n\| \geqslant 2n^2 \left|\left(u\left(\sum_{k=1}^{n-1} x_k/k^2\right) \middle| e_n\right)\right|$; (3) $e_n = y_n/\|y_n\|$. Then consider the point $x = \sum_{n=1}^{\infty} x_n/n^2$ in E and obtain a contradiction by showing that $|(u(x) \mid e_n)| \geqslant n$ for every n; to do this, decompose x into $x_n' + (x_n/n^2) + x_n''$, with $x_n' = \sum_{k=1}^{n-1} x_k/k^2$ and $x_n'' = \sum_{k=n+1}^{\infty} x_k/k^2$, and use throughout the identity $(u(y) \mid z) = (y \mid u(z))$ ("method of the gliding hump").) Compare to Problem 3(c) and to (**12.16.7**).

5. Let E be a complex prehilbert space; if U, V are two hermitian operators in E, we write $U \geqslant V$ if the hermitian operator $U - V$ is positive, i.e. if $(Ux \mid x) \geqslant (Vx \mid x)$ for any $x \in E$.

(a) Suppose E is a *Hilbert* space, and there is a number $m > 0$ such that $U \geqslant m \cdot 1_E$. Show that U is a linear homeomorphism of E onto itself. (First remark that $\|Ux\| \geqslant m \|x\|$ for any $x \in E$, hence (Problem 4) that U is a linear homeomorphism of E onto a closed subspace M of E; next observe that if a point $x \in E$ is orthogonal to M, then $x = 0$.)

(b) Let F be the subspace of the prehilbert space E defined in Problem 1, consisting of the restrictions to [0, 1] of all *polynomials* with complex coefficients. Let U be the operator which associates to any polynomial $x \in F$ the polynomial $(1 + t)x(t)$. Show that U is a continuous hermitian operator in F such that $U \geqslant 1_E$, but that $U(F)$ is dense in F and distinct from F.

6. (a) If U is a positive hermitian operator in a complex prehilbert space E, show that, for any $x \in E$,

$$\|Ux\|^4 \leqslant (Ux \mid x)(U^2x \mid Ux)$$

(consider the positive hermitian form $(x, y) \to (Ux \mid y)$ and use (**6.2.1**)).

(b) Suppose in addition U is continuous (cf. Problems 3(c) and 4). Deduce from (a) that $\|U\| = \sup_{\|x\| \leqslant 1} (Ux \mid x)$.

7. Let F, G be two separable complex Hilbert spaces, (a_n) (resp. (b_n)) $(n \geqslant 1)$ a Hilbert basis of F (resp. G), L the Hilbert sum (Section 6.4) of F and G. Let v be the continuous operator in L defined by $v(a_n) = 0$, $v(b_n) = a_n/n$, and let $E = v(G) + v^*(v(G))$. Let u be the restriction of v to E. Show that u is compact and has an adjoint, but that u^* is not compact. (Observe that $v(G)$ is dense in F but not closed in F; if (x_n) is a bounded sequence of points of $v(G)$ converging to a point in F, but not in $v(G)$, show that the sequence $(u^*(x_n))$ converges to a point in L which is not in E, using the fact that the restriction of v^* to F is injective.)

8. The notations and assumptions are those of (11.5.7). Let (λ_n) be the decreasing sequence of numbers >0 such that, for each k, the number of indices n such that $\lambda_n = \mu_k$ is equal to $\dim(E(\mu_k))$; let (a_n) be an orthonormal system in E such that, for the indices n for which $\lambda_n = \mu_k$, the a_n constitute a basis of $E(\mu_k)$. We say that (λ_n) is the *full sequence* of strictly positive eigenvalues of u.

(a) Show that λ_n is the maximum value of $(u(x) \mid x)$ when x varies in the subset of E defined by the relations $\|x\| = 1$, $(x \mid a_k) = 0$ for $1 \leqslant k \leqslant n-1$; furthermore, that maximum value is attained for $x = a_n$ (use (11.5.7(d))).

(b) Let $z_1, \ldots, z_{n-1}$ be arbitrary vectors in E, and denote by $\rho_u(z_1, \ldots, z_{n-1})$ the l.u.b. of $(u(x) \mid x)$ when x varies in the subset of E defined by the relations $\|x\| = 1$, $(x \mid z_k) = 0$ for $1 \leqslant k \leqslant n-1$. Show that $\lambda_n = \rho_u(a_1, \ldots, a_{n-1}) \leqslant \rho_u(z_1, \ldots, z_{n-1})$ (the "maximinimal principle"; take x in the subspace generated by $a_1, \ldots, a_n$ and verifying the relations $(x \mid z_k) = 0$ for $1 \leqslant k \leqslant n-1$).

(c) Let u', u'' be two compact self-adjoint operators, and suppose $u = u' + u''$; let (λ'_n), (λ''_n) be the full sequences of strictly positive eigenvalues of u' and u'', respectively, (a'_n) and (a''_n) the corresponding orthonormal systems. Show that if λ'_p, λ''_q and λ_{p+q-1} are defined, then $\lambda_{p+q-1} \leqslant \lambda'_p + \lambda''_q$ (consider $\rho_u(a'_1, \ldots, a''_{p-1}, a'_1, \ldots, a''_{q-1})$). If the sequence (λ''_n) is finite and has N terms, and if λ'_p and λ_{p+N} are defined, then $\lambda_{p+N} \leqslant \lambda'_p$ (same method, observing that $(u''(x) \mid x) \leqslant 0$ if $(x \mid a''_j) = 0$ for $1 \leqslant j \leqslant N$).

(d) Under the same assumptions as in (c), show that if λ'_p and λ_p are defined, then $|\lambda_p - \lambda'_p| \leqslant \|u''\|$ (use the relation $\lambda_p = \rho_u(a_1, \ldots, a_{p-1})$). Furthermore, if $u'' \geqslant 0$ (resp. $u'' \leqslant 0$), then $\lambda_p \geqslant \lambda'_p$ (resp. $\lambda_p \leqslant \lambda'_p$) (same method).

(e) When E is finite dimensional, transcribe the results of (b), (c), (d) for hermitian forms on E $\times$ E (see Problem 3). Apply to the following problem: let f_i $(1 \leqslant i \leqslant n)$ be regulated functions in a compact interval $I = [a, b]$, and let $I' = [c, d]$ be an interval contained in I; let $\Delta = \det\left(\int_a^b f_i \bar{f}_j \, dt\right)$, $\Delta' = \det\left(\int_c^d f_i \bar{f}_j \, dt\right)$ be the Gram determinants corresponding to I and I'; show that $\Delta' \leqslant \Delta$, by expressing the Gram determinants as products of eigenvalues.

9. (a) Let u be a compact self-adjoint operator in a complex Hilbert space E. Let H be a closed subspace of E, and p the orthogonal projection of E onto H (Section 6.3). Show that the restriction v to H of $p \circ u$ (or of $p \circ u \circ p$) is compact and self-adjoint and that $(v(y) \mid y) = (u(y) \mid y)$ for $y \in H$ (use the relation $p^* = p$). Let (λ_n), (μ_n) be the full sequences of strictly positive eigenvalues of u and v respectively. Show that if λ_n and μ_n are defined, then $\mu_n \leqslant \lambda_n$ (use Problem 8(b)).

(b) Suppose in addition u is positive. Show that for any finite sequence $(x_k)_{1 \leqslant k \leqslant n}$ of points of E, $\det((u(x_i) \mid x_j)) \leqslant \lambda_1 \lambda_2 \cdots \lambda_n \det((x_i \mid x_j))$ (apply (a) to the subspace H generated by $x_1, \ldots, x_n$).

10. (a) Let u be a hermitian operator in a complex prehilbert space E. Show that for any integer $n > 0$, and any $x \in E$, $\|u^n(x)\|^2 \leqslant \|u^{n-1}(x)\| \cdot \|u^{n+1}(x)\|$ (use Cauchy–Schwarz).

(b) Suppose E is a Hilbert space, and u is a compact self-adjoint operator. If $u(x) \neq 0$, show that $u^n(x) \neq 0$ for any integer $n > 0$, and that the sequence of positive numbers $\alpha_n = \|u^{n+1}(x)\| / \|u^n(x)\|$ is increasing and tends to a limit, which is equal to the absolute value of an eigenvalue of u. Characterize that eigenvalue in terms of the canonical decomposition of x; when does the sequence of vectors $u^n(x)/\|u^n(x)\|$ have a limit in E? (Use (11.5.7).)

11. Let u be a compact self-adjoint operator in a complex Hilbert space E, and let f be a complex valued function defined and continuous in the spectrum sp(u). Show that there is a unique continuous operator v such that (with the notations of (11.5.7)), the restriction of v to $E(\mu_k)$ (resp. $E(\nu_k)$, E(0)) is the homothetic mapping $y \to f(\mu_k)y$ (resp. $y \to f(\nu_k)y$, $y \to 0$). This operator is written $f(u)$; one has $(f(u))^* = \bar{f}(u)$. If g is a second function continuous in sp(u), and $h = f + g$ (resp. $h = fg$), then $h(u) = f(u) + g(u)$ (resp. $h(u) = f(u)g(u)$). In order that $f(u)$ be self-adjoint (resp. positive and self-adjoint), it is necessary and sufficient that $f(\xi)$ be real in sp(u) (resp. $f(\zeta) \geqslant 0$ in sp(u)); in order that $f(u)$ be compact, it is necessary and sufficient that $f(0) = 0$.

12. Let u be a compact positive hermitian operator in a complex Hilbert space E. Show that there exists a unique compact positive hermitian operator v in E such that $v^2 = u$; v is called the *square root* of u.

13. Let E be a separable complex Hilbert space, $(e_n)_{n \geqslant 1}$ a Hilbert basis of E. Let u be the compact operator in E defined by $u(e_1) = 0$, $u(e_n) = e_{n-1}/n$ for $n > 1$. Show that there exists *no* continuous operator v in E such that $v^2 = u$. (Observe first that $H = \overline{u^*(E)}$ is a closed hyperplane orthogonal to e_1, and that it is contained in $H' = \overline{v^*(E)}$; as H′ is orthogonal to $x_1 = v(e_1)$, conclude that necessarily $x_1 = 0$; next consider $x_2 = v(e_2)$, and observe that $u(v(e_2)) = 0$, hence necessarily $x_2 = \lambda e_1$, where λ is a scalar; but this implies $x_2 = 0$, hence $u(e_2) = 0$, a contradiction.)

14. Let E be a separable complex Hilbert space, $(e_n)_{n \geqslant 0}$ a Hilbert basis, u the compact positive hermitian operator in E defined by $u(e_0) = 0$, $u(e_n) = e_n/n$ for $n \geqslant 1$. The point $a = \sum_{n=1}^{\infty} (e_n/n)$ does not belong to u(E). Let E_0 be the dense subspace of E which is the direct sum of u(E) and of the one-dimensional subspace $\mathbf{C}(e_0 + a)$. Show that the restriction v of u to E_0 is a compact positive hermitian operator which is nondegenerate, although its continuous extension $\tilde{v} = u$ to E is degenerate; furthermore, in the canonical decomposition (11.5.8) of the vector $e_0 + a \in E_0$, the summands do not all belong to E_0.

15. (a) Let U be a compact operator in a complex Hilbert space E, and denote by R and L the respective square roots (Problem 12) of the compact positive hermitian operators U^*U and UU^*, respectively. Show that there exists a unique continuous operator V in E, whose restriction to $F = \overline{R(E)}$ is an isometry onto $\overline{U(E)}$, whose restriction to the orthogonal supplement F′ to F is 0, and which is such that $U = VR$ (observe that $\|Ux\| = \|Rx\|$ for each $x \in E$). Prove that $R = V^*U = RV^*V$, and $L = VRV^*$.
(b) Let (α_n) the full sequence of strictly positive eigenvalues of R, and (a_n) a corresponding orthonormal system (Problem 8). If $b_n = Va_n$, show that (b_n) is an orthonormal system, and that, for any $x \in E$, $Ux = \sum_n \alpha_n(x \mid a_n)b_n$, where the series on the right-hand side is convergent (if $R_n x = \sum_{k=1}^{n} \alpha_k(x \mid a_k)a_k$, show, using the proof of (11.5.7), that $\lim_{n\to\infty} \|R - R_n\| = 0$, and apply (a)). Deduce from that result that (α_n) is also the full sequence of strictly positive eigenvalues of L, and that (b_n) is a corresponding orthonormal system. The sequence (α_n) is also called the full sequence of *singular values* of U.

(c) Let (μ_n) be the sequence of *distinct* eigenvalues $\neq 0$ of U, arranged in such an order that $|\mu_n| \geqslant |\mu_{n+1}|$ for every n for which μ_{n+1} is defined; let d_n be the dimension of $\mathrm{N}(\mu_n)$, and let (λ_n) be a sequence such that $\lambda_1 = \mu_1, |\lambda_n| \geqslant |\lambda_{n+1}|$ for every n for which λ_{n+1} is defined, and for each k for which μ_k is defined, the indices n for which $\lambda_n = \mu_k$ form an interval of $\mathbf{N}$ having d_k elements. Show that, for each index n such that λ_n and α_n are defined, $\prod_{i=1}^{n} |\lambda_i| \leqslant \prod_{i=1}^{n} \alpha_i$. (Let V be the (direct) sum of the subspaces $\mathrm{N}(\mu_k)$ for $1 \leqslant k \leqslant r$, and let U_{V} be the restriction of U to V; show that there is in V a Hilbert basis $(e_j)_{1 \leqslant j \leqslant m}$ such that $(U(e_j) \mid e_k) = 0$ for $k > j$; for $n \leqslant m$, if W_n is the subspace of V having $e_1, \dots, e_n$ as a basis, let U_n be the restriction of U to W_n, and let P_n be the orthogonal projection of E on W_n. Show that $\prod_{j=1}^{n} |\lambda_j|^2$ is equal to the determinant of $U_n^* U_n = P_n U^* U P_n$, and apply Problem 9(a).)
(d) Let T be an arbitrary continuous operator in E, and let (γ_n) (resp. (δ_n)) be the full sequence of singular values of UT (resp. TU). Show that $\gamma_n \leqslant \alpha_n \|T\|$ (resp. $\delta_n \leqslant \alpha_n \|T\|$) for all values of n for which α_n, γ_n and δ_n are defined (if $S = TU$, observe that $S^*S \leqslant \|T\|^2 U^* U$ and use Problem 8(d)).
(e) Suppose T is also a compact operator, and let (β_n) be the full sequence of its singular values. Show that $\prod_{j=1}^{n} \gamma_j \leqslant \left(\prod_{j=1}^{n} \alpha_j\right)\left(\prod_{j=1}^{n} \beta_j\right)$ for all values of n for which α_n, β_n, and γ_n are defined (apply Problem 9(b)).

16. Let E be a complex Hilbert space, (a_n) a sequence of points of E, (λ_n) a sequence of real numbers. Show that if the series $u(x) = \sum_n \lambda_n (x \mid a_n) a_n$ is convergent in E for every $x \in \mathrm{E}$, u is a hermitian operator in E. The convergence condition is always satisfied if the series of general term $\lambda_n \|a_n\|^2$ is absolutely convergent. If in addition (a_n) is an orthonormal system, the convergence condition is satisfied if the sequence (λ_n) is bounded. When the λ_n are $\geqslant 0$ and the convergence condition is satisfied, u is a positive hermitian operator.

17. Let E be a complex Hilbert space, E_0 a dense vector subspace of E; $(x \mid y)$ and $\|x\|$ denote the scalar product and the norm in E. Suppose a second norm $\|x\|_0$ is given on E_0, for which E_0 is a Banach space, and is such that, for $x \in \mathrm{E}_0$, one has $\|x\| \leqslant a \cdot \|x\|_0$, where a is a constant (in other words, the identity mapping 1_{E_0} of E_0 with the norm $\|x\|_0$, into E_0 with the norm $\|x\|$, is continuous).
(a) Let U be a hermitian operator in E_0 (which *a priori* is not assumed to be continuous); show that if U is continuous for the norm $\|x\|_0$, it is also continuous for the norm $\|x\|$. (If $\|U\|_0$ is the norm in $\mathscr{L}(\mathrm{E}_0)$ when E_0 is given the norm $\|x\|_0$, show that, for every integer n, one has, for $x \in \mathrm{E}_0$,

$$\frac{\|Ux\|}{\|x\|} \leqslant \left(\frac{a\,\|x\|_0}{\|x\|}\right)^{2^{-n}} \|U\|_0 .$$

Use the inequality $\|U^k x\|^2 \leqslant \|x\| \cdot \|U^{2k} x\|$ (Problem 10(a)).)
(b) Let $\tilde{U}$ be the continuous extension of U to E, which is a hermitian operator in E. Show that the spectrum of $\tilde{U}$ is contained in the spectrum of U (when U is considered as an endomorphism of the Banach space E_0 for the norm $\|x\|_0$). (If ζ is a regular value for U, observe that $(U - \zeta \cdot 1_{\mathrm{E}_0})^{-1}$ can be extended by continuity to E, using (a).)
(c) Every eigenvalue λ of U is real; if $V = U - \lambda \cdot 1_{\mathrm{E}_0}$, and if $\mathrm{E}(\lambda) = V^{-1}(0)$ is finite dimensional in E_0, $V(\mathrm{E}_0)$ is supplementary and orthogonal to $\mathrm{E}(\lambda)$ in the prehilbert space E_0, and in addition it is closed for the norm $\|x\|_0$; it follows from (12.16.8) that the restriction of V to $V(\mathrm{E}_0) = \mathrm{F}(\lambda)$ is a linear homeomorphism of

$F(\lambda)$ onto itself for the norm $\|x\|_0$. Show that if $\tilde{V} = \tilde{U} - \lambda \cdot 1_E$, then $\tilde{V}^{-1}(0) = E(\lambda)$ and $\tilde{V}(E) = \overline{F(\lambda)}$ in E (apply (a) to the inverse of the restriction of V to $F(\lambda)$).

(d) Deduce from (c) that if U (or a power of U) is a compact operator in E_0 (for the norm $\|x\|_0$), then $\tilde{U}$ is a compact operator. (If (λ_n) is the sequence of eigenvalues of U, deduce from (b) and (c) that the subspace of E orthogonal to all the subspaces $E(\lambda_n)$ is the kernel of $\tilde{U}$.)

18. Let E be an infinite dimensional complex Hilbert space. For a *positive* hermitian operator T in E, the following conditions are equivalent: (1) $T(E)$ is dense in E; (2) $T^{-1}(0) = \{0\}$; (3) $(Tx \mid x) > 0$ for any $x \neq 0$ (use the Cauchy–Schwarz inequality applied to $(Tx \mid y)$); (4) T is *nondegenerate*. We say that a continuous operator U in E is *quasi-hermitian* if there exists a *nondegenerate* positive hermitian operator T such that $TU = U^*T$.

(a) Show that every eigenvalue of U is real; if $V = U - \lambda \cdot 1_E$ and if $V^{-1}(0)$ is finite dimensional, then E is a direct topological sum of $V(E)$ and $V^{-1}(0)$, and λ is a simple pole of $(U - \zeta \cdot 1_E)^{-1}$. (Consider the Hilbert space obtained by completing E for the scalar product $(Tx \mid y)$, and apply Problem 17.)

(b) Let (α_n) be an infinite sequence of distinct real numbers such that $\sum_n \alpha_n^2 = 1$. Let E be the Hilbert sum of a sequence of finite dimensional Hilbert spaces E_n such that $\dim(E_n) = n$ $(n \geqslant 1)$. In E_n, let $(e_{in})_{1 \leqslant i \leqslant n}$ be a Hilbert basis, U_n an operator in E_n such that $U_n e_{in} = \alpha_i e_{in} + e_{i+1,n}$ for $i \leqslant n-1$ and $U_n e_{nn} = \alpha_n e_{nn}$. Prove that $\|U_n\| \leqslant 2$, but for any complex number ζ such that $|\zeta| = 1$, $\|(U_n + \zeta \cdot 1_{E_n})^{-1}\| \geqslant \frac{1}{2}\sqrt{n}$. There is a unique continuous operator U on E whose restriction to each E_n is U_n; show that U is quasi-hermitian and that the α_n are its eigenvalues, but that its spectrum contains the circle $|\zeta| = 1$.

(c) Let U be a *compact* quasi-hermitian operator. Prove that if $U \neq 0$, the spectrum of U cannot be reduced to the point 0, the eigenvalues $\lambda_n \neq 0$ of U are simple poles of $(U - \zeta \cdot 1_E)^{-1}$ and $N(\lambda_n; U) = E(\lambda_n; U)$ and $T(E(\lambda_n; U)) = E(\lambda_n; U^*)$. Furthermore, the intersection of the subspaces $F(\lambda_n; U)$ is equal to $U^{-1}(0)$, and the intersection of $U^{-1}(0)$ and $U(E)$ is reduced to 0 (method of (a)).

(d) Suppose E is separable, and let U be a compact continuous operator in E having the following property: there is a sequence (λ_n) of real eigenvalues of U^* such that the sum of the $E(\lambda_n; U^*)$ is dense in E. Prove that U is quasi-hermitian. (Show that there is in E a total sequence (b_n) such that $U^* b_n = \lambda_{k(n)} b_n$ (for a suitable $k(n)$), and define T such that $Tx = \sum_n \alpha_n (x \mid b_n) b_n$ with suitable $\alpha_n > 0$; cf. Problem 16.)

(e) Suppose E is separable, and let U be a compact operator in E satisfying the following conditions: (1) all the eigenvalues λ_n of U are real and $k(\lambda_n; U) = 1$ for every n; (2) the intersection of the subspaces $F(\lambda_n; U)$ is equal to $U^{-1}(0)$; (3) the intersection of $U^{-1}(0)$ and $U(E)$ is $\{0\}$. Prove that U is quasi-hermitian (use (11.5.5) and (d)).

(f) Suppose E is separable, and let $(e_n)_{n \geqslant 0}$ be a Hilbert basis for E. Prove that the operator U defined by

$$Ue_{2n} = 0, \qquad Ue_{2n+1} = \frac{1}{n+1}\left(e_{2n} + \frac{1}{n+1} e_{2n+1}\right)$$

for all $n \geqslant 0$, is compact and quasi-hermitian, but the sum $U^{-1}(0) + U(E)$ (which is an algebraic direct sum) is not a topological direct sum (cf. Section 6.5, Problem 2).

(g) With the same notations as in (f), let U be the operator defined by $Ue_0 = \sum_{n=1}^{\infty} e_n/n$, $Ue_n = e_n/n^2$ for $n \geqslant 1$; using (e), show that U is compact and quasi-hermitian, but the sum $U^{-1}(0) + U(E)$ is not dense in E; conclude that U^* *is not quasi-hermitian.*

19. Let E be a Hilbert space, U a continuous operator in E. Suppose there is an element $a \neq 0$ in E such that: (1) the elements $a_n = U^n a$ for $n \geqslant 0$ (with $U^0 a = a$) form a total sequence in E; (2) the image of E by the hermitian operator $V = U + U^*$ is the one-dimensional subspace $D = Ka$.

Let E_0 be a closed vector subspace of E not reduced to 0 and such that $U(E_0) \subset E_0$; let U_0 be the restriction of U to E_0, and P_0 the orthogonal projection of E onto E_0.

(a) Show that E_0 cannot be orthogonal to D. (Observe that for any y orthogonal to D, $Uy = -U^*y$, and conclude that if E_0 was orthogonal to D, one would have $U^n y = (-1)^n U^{*n} y$ for every $y \in E_0$; show that this contradicts the assumption that the $U^n a$ form a total sequence in E.)

(b) Prove that for any $x \in E_0$, $U_0^* x = P_0 U_0^* x = P_0 U^* x$.

(c) Prove that the image of E_0 by $V_0 = U_0 + U_0^*$ is not reduced to 0, hence is the subspace $D_0 = P_0(D)$ of dimension 1 (use the fact that $P_0 a \neq 0$ and the result of (b)).

(d) Prove that the elements $U_0^n(P_0 a)$ constitute a total sequence in E_0. (Let F_0 be the closed vector subspace of E_0 generated by that sequence, and F_0' the orthogonal supplement of F_0 in E_0. Prove that F_0' is orthogonal to D and that $U_0(F_0') = U(F_0') \subset F_0'$; conclude as in (a).)

20. Let E be a separable Hilbert space, U a compact operator in E whose spectrum consists of 0 and of an infinite sequence (λ_n) of distinct eigenvalues $\neq 0$ such that $k(\lambda_n) = 1$ and that $E(\lambda_n)$ is one dimensional for every n. For each n, let a_n be an eigenvector of U corresponding to λ_n, and b_n an eigenvalue of U^* corresponding to $\bar{\lambda}_n$ (see (11.5.5)); a_n and b_n are chosen in such a way that $(a_n \mid b_n) = 1$.

(a) Let A and B be the closed vector subspaces of E respectively generated by the a_n and the b_n, B′ and A′ the orthogonal supplements of B and A, respectively. Show that B′ is stable for U, contains $U^{-1}(0)$ and that the restriction of U to B′ has a spectrum reduced to 0.

(b) Suppose the series of general term $|\lambda_n| \cdot \|a_n\| \cdot \|b_n\|$ is convergent. Show then that for any $x \in A$, $Ux = \sum_n \lambda_n (x \mid b_n) a_n$, where the series is convergent in E; $U^{-1}(0)$ then contains $A \cap B'$.

(c) Give an example in which $A \cap B'$ is infinite dimensional and $U(A \cap B') = A \cap B'$. The following method may be used: let E be a Hilbert sum of three Hilbert spaces of infinite dimension F, R, S, having respective Hilbert bases (f_n), (r_n), and (s_n); define a sequence (a_n) in F + R such that f_n is the projection of a_n in F and the closed vector subspace generated by the a_n is F + R. To do this, observe that in a Hilbert space H with a Hilbert basis $(e_n)_{n \geqslant 0}$, the closed vector subspace generated by the $e_0 + e_n$ for $n \geqslant 1$ is equal to H, and take for F + R the Hilbert sum of a sequence of Hilbert spaces all equal to H. Define U such that $Ua_n = \lambda_n a_n$, $Ur_n = \mu_n r_{n-1}$ for $n \geqslant 1$, $Ur_1 = 0$, $Us_n = \mu_n s_{n+1}$, where the sequences (λ_n) and (μ_n) converge rapidly enough to 0 (cf. Section 11.2, Problem 3). One thus gets B = F, A = F + R, and $A \cap B' = R$.

6. THE FREDHOLM INTEGRAL EQUATION

We now apply the preceding theory to the example (11.2.8). We consider here the prehilbert space G of continuous complex-valued functions in $I = [a, b]$, with $(f \mid g) = \int_a^b f(t)\overline{g(t)}\, dt$, and the operator U such that Uf is the function

$$t \to \int_a^b K(s, t)f(s)\, ds.$$

We say that the operator U is defined by the *kernel function* K.

(11.6.1) *The compact operator U in* G *has a compact adjoint which is defined by the kernel function* K^* *such that* $K^*(s, t) = \overline{K(t, s)}$.

We prove for $a \leqslant x \leqslant b$ the identity

(11.6.1.1) $$\int_a^x \overline{g(t)}\, dt \int_a^b K(s, t)f(s)\, ds = \int_a^b f(s)\, ds \overline{\int_a^x \overline{K(s, t)}g(t)\, dt}$$

which, for $x = b$, will yield the result by definition. Both sides of (11.6.1.1) are differentiable functions of x in $[a, b]$, by (8.7.3) and Leibniz's rule (8.11.2); they vanish for $x = a$, and their derivatives are equal at each $x \in [a, b]$ by (8.7.3) and (8.11.2), hence they are equal everywhere in $[a, b]$ (8.6.1).

We leave to the reader the expression of the criterion (11.5.6) for that particular case (the "Fredholm alternative").

If $\overline{K(t, s)} = K(s, t)$ (in which case the kernel K is called *hermitian*), the compact operator U is *self-adjoint*. As the prehilbert space G is separable ((7.4.3) or (7.4.4)), it can be considered as a dense subspace of a *Hilbert space* $\bar{G}$ (6.6.2), and therefore we can apply to the operator U the results of (11.5.8). We shall denote by (λ_n) the sequence of the (positive or negative) eigenvalues of U, each being repeated a number of times equal to its *multiplicity*, and ordered in such a way that $|\lambda_n| \geqslant |\lambda_{n+1}|$; and we will denote by (φ_n) an orthonormal system in G such that, if the values of n for which $\lambda_n = \mu_k$ (resp. $\lambda_n = \nu_k$) are $m, m + 1, \ldots, m + r$, then $\varphi_m, \varphi_{m+1}, \ldots, \varphi_{m+r}$ constitute a basis for the eigenspace $E(\mu_k)$ (resp. $E(\nu_k)$); we therefore have $U(\varphi_n) = \lambda_n \varphi_n$ for each n. The φ_n are called *eigenfunctions* of the kernel K.

(11.6.2) *If* K *is a hermitian kernel, the series* $\sum_n \lambda_n^2$ *is convergent and*

$$\sum_n \lambda_n^2 \leqslant \int_a^b dt \int_a^b |K(s, t)|^2\, ds.$$

Indeed, if we apply the Bessel inequality (6.5.2) to the function $s \to K(s, t)$ and to the orthonormal system (φ_n), we obtain, for any N

$$\sum_{n=1}^{N} \left| \int_a^b K(s, t)\varphi_n(s)\, ds \right|^2 \leqslant \int_a^b |K(s, t)|^2\, ds$$

i.e.

(11.6.2.1) $$\sum_{n=1}^{N} \lambda_n^2 |\varphi_n(t)|^2 \leqslant \int_a^b |K(s, t)|^2 \, ds$$

for every $t \in I$. Integrating both sides in I and using the relations $(\varphi_n \mid \varphi_n) = 1$ and (11.6.1.1) yields the result.

The *canonical decomposition* in $\bar{G}$ of any function $f \in G$ (11.5.7) can here be written $f = \sum_n c_n \varphi_n + f_0$, where $c_n = (f \mid \varphi_n) = \int_a^b f(t)\overline{\varphi_n(t)}\, dt$; but, as already observed, f_0 may fail to be in G; on the other hand, the series $\sum_n c_n \varphi_n$ converges *in the Hilbert space* $\bar{G}$, but *not* in general in the Banach space $E = \mathscr{C}_C(I)$ (the series $\sum_n c_n \varphi_n(t)$ will not necessarily converge for every $t \in I$). However:

(11.6.3) *If K is a hermitian kernel, and $f = Ug$ for a function $g \in G$ (i.e. $f(t) = \int_a^b K(s, t) g(s)\, ds$), then the series $\sum_n c_n \varphi_n(t)$ converges absolutely and uniformly to $f(t)$ in* I.

We have *in* $\bar{G}$ the canonical decomposition $g = \sum_n d_n \varphi_n + g_0$; as U is a continuous linear mapping of G into $E = \mathscr{C}_C(I)$ (11.2.8), U can be extended to a continuous linear mapping of $\bar{G}$ into E, and $Ug_0 = 0$, hence we have $f = Ug = \sum_n \lambda_n d_n \varphi_n$, where now the convergence is *in* E; i.e. the series $\sum_n \lambda_n d_n \varphi_n(t)$ converges uniformly to $f(t)$ in E; as $c_n = (f \mid \varphi_n) = (Ug \mid \varphi_n) = (g \mid U\varphi_n) = \lambda_n (g \mid \varphi_n) = \lambda_n d_n$, we have proved (11.6.3) except for the statement on absolute convergence. But for any integer N, we have, by Cauchy–Schwarz (for finite dimensional spaces)

$$\left(\sum_{n=1}^{N} |c_n \varphi_n(t)|\right)^2 \leqslant \left(\sum_{n=1}^{N} |d_n|^2\right)\left(\sum_{n=1}^{N} \lambda_n^2 |\varphi_n(t)|^2\right)$$

and the right-hand side is bounded by a number independent of N, by Bessel's inequality (6.5.2) and (11.6.2.1).

(11.6.4) *If K is hermitian, and $\lambda \neq 0$ is not in the spectrum of U, the unique solution f of the equation $Uf - \lambda f = g$, for any $g \in G$, is such that*

$$f(t) = -\frac{1}{\lambda} g(t) + \sum_n \frac{\lambda_n}{\lambda(\lambda_n - \lambda)} d_n \varphi_n(t),$$

where the series is absolutely and uniformly convergent in I, *and* $d_n = (g \mid \varphi_n)$.

We know that the unique solution of $Uf - \lambda f = g$ in $\bar{\mathrm{G}}$ belongs to G since $g \in \mathrm{G}$ (11.5.6), and by (11.5.11) we have $c_n = (f \mid \varphi_n) = 1/(\lambda_n - \lambda)$. As $g + \lambda f = Uf$, we can apply (11.6.3), and this proves the result.

(11.6.5) *Under the same assumptions as in* (11.6.4), *the unique solution of* $Uf - \lambda f = g$ *can be written*

$$f(t) = -\frac{1}{\lambda} g(t) + \int_a^b \mathrm{R}(s, t; \lambda) g(s)\, ds,$$

with

$$\mathrm{R}(s, t; \lambda) = -\frac{1}{\lambda^2} \mathrm{K}(s, t) + \sum_n \frac{\lambda_n^2}{\lambda^2(\lambda_n - \lambda)} \overline{\varphi_n(s)} \varphi_n(t),$$

where the series is absolutely and uniformly convergent for $(s, t) \in \mathrm{I} \times \mathrm{I}$.

By the proof of (11.6.3), we have $\sum_n \lambda_n d_n \varphi_n(t) = Ug(t)$, the series converging absolutely and uniformly in I. As

$$\frac{1}{\lambda(\lambda_n - \lambda)} + \frac{1}{\lambda^2} = \frac{\lambda_n}{\lambda(\lambda_n^2 - \lambda)}$$

the formula in (11.6.4) gives

$$f(t) = -\frac{1}{\lambda} g(t) - \frac{1}{\lambda^2} \int_a^b \mathrm{K}(s, t) g(s)\, ds + \sum_n \frac{\lambda_n^2}{\lambda^2(\lambda_n - \lambda)} \varphi_n(t) \int_a^b g(s) \overline{\varphi_n(s)}\, ds.$$

The theorem will follow when we have proved the uniform convergence of the series $\sum_n \lambda_n^2 |\varphi_n(s)|^2$: for there is a $\delta > 0$ such that $|\lambda_n - \lambda| \geqslant \delta$ for each n, hence

$$\begin{aligned}\sum_{n=p}^{q} \frac{\lambda_n^2}{|\lambda| \cdot |\lambda_n - \lambda|} |\varphi_n(s)\varphi_n(t)| &\leqslant \frac{1}{\delta |\lambda|} \sum_{n=p}^{q} \lambda_n^2 |\varphi_n(s)\varphi_n(t)| \\ &\leqslant \frac{1}{\delta |\lambda|} \left(\left(\sum_{n=p}^{q} \lambda_n^2 |\varphi_n(s)|^2 \right) \left(\sum_{n=p}^{q} \lambda_n^2 |\varphi_n(t)|^2 \right) \right)^{1/2}\end{aligned}$$

by Cauchy–Schwarz, and this will prove that the series

$$\sum_n \frac{\lambda_n^2}{\lambda(\lambda_n - \lambda)} \overline{\varphi_n(s)} \varphi_n(t)$$

is absolutely and uniformly convergent in $\mathrm{I} \times \mathrm{I}$; the conclusion then results from (8.7.8).

Now consider the function $H(s, t) = \int_a^b K(u, s)K(t, u)\, du$; for each fixed $t \in I$, we can apply to it (11.6.3), and we see that $H(s, t) = \sum_n \lambda_n^2 \varphi_n(s)\overline{\varphi_n(t)}$ where the series is convergent for any pair $(s, t) \in I \times I$. In particular $H(s, s) = \sum_n \lambda_n^2 |\varphi_n(s)|^2$ for all $s \in I$, and $H(s, s)$ is continuous; by Dini's theorem (7.2.2), the convergence is uniform in I. Q.E.D.

(11.6.6) *If* K *is hermitian, then*

$$\lim_{n\to\infty} \int_a^b \left| K(s, t) - \sum_{k=1}^n \lambda_k \overline{\varphi_k(s)}\varphi_k(t) \right|^2 dt = 0$$

uniformly for $s \in I$.

With the notations of the proof of (11.6.5), we have

(11.6.6.1) $$\lim_{n\to\infty} \left(H(s, s) - \sum_{k=1}^n \lambda_k^2 \overline{\varphi_k(s)}\varphi_k(s) \right) = 0$$

uniformly for $s \in I$; if we evaluate the integral in the statement of (11.6.6), using the fact that the φ_k are eigenvectors of U, and that they are orthogonal, we obtain the expression in the left-hand side of (11.6.6.1), whence the result.

In general, the series $\sum_n \lambda_n \overline{\varphi_n(s)}\varphi_n(t)$ *will not be convergent* for all $(s, t) \in I \times I$; but we have the special result:

(11.6.7) (Mercer's theorem) *Suppose the compact operator* U *defined by the hermitian kernel* $K(s, t)$ *is positive. Then we have* $K(s, t) = \sum_n \lambda_n \varphi_n(s)\overline{\varphi_n(t)}$, *where the series is absolutely and uniformly convergent in* $I \times I$.

We recall that we have here $\lambda_n > 0$ for every n (11.5.9). We first prove that for each $s \in I$, the series $\sum_n \lambda_n |\varphi_n(s)|^2$ is convergent. For any $s \in I$, we have $K(s, s) \geqslant 0$. Otherwise, there would exist a neighborhood V of s in I such that $\mathscr{R}(K(s', t)) \leqslant -\delta < 0$ for $(s', t) \in V \times V$. Let φ be a continuous mapping of I into [0, 1], equal to 1 at the point s, to 0 in I − V (4.5.2). Then we have

$$\int_a^b \overline{\varphi(t)}\, dt \int_a^b K(s, t)\varphi(s)\, ds \leqslant -\delta\left(\int_a^b \varphi(t)\, dt\right)^2 < 0$$

by (8.5.3). But the left-hand side is $(U\varphi \mid \varphi)$, and this violates the assumption that U is a positive operator.

Remark now that for any finite number of eigenvalues λ_k $(1 \leqslant k \leqslant n)$ $\mathrm{K}_n(s, t) = \mathrm{K}(s, t) - \sum_{k=1}^{n} \lambda_k \varphi_k(s)\overline{\varphi_k(t)}$ is the kernel function of a *positive* operator U_n, for we have

$$(U_n f \mid f) = (Uf \mid f) - \sum_{k=1}^{n} \lambda_k |(f \mid \varphi_k)|^2;$$

but the right-hand side of that equation can be written $(Ug \mid g)$ with $g = f - \sum_{k=1}^{n} (f \mid \varphi_k)\varphi_k$, as is readily verified, hence is positive by assumption. Therefore, by (5.3.1) it follows from $\mathrm{K}_n(s, s) \geqslant 0$ that the series $\sum_n \lambda_n |\varphi_n(s)|^2$ is convergent, and we have $\sum_n \lambda_n |\varphi_n(s)|^2 \leqslant \mathrm{K}(s, s)$ for all $s \in \mathrm{I}$. By Cauchy–Schwarz, we conclude that

(11.6.7.1)
$$\sum_{n=p}^{q} \lambda_n |\varphi_n(s)\varphi_n(t)| \leqslant \left(\left(\sum_{n=p}^{q} \lambda_n |\varphi_n(s)|^2\right)\left(\sum_{n=p}^{q} \lambda_n |\varphi_n(t)|^2\right)\right)^{1/2}$$
$$\leqslant \left(\mathrm{K}(t, t)\left(\sum_{n=p}^{q} \lambda_n |\varphi_n(s)|^2\right)\right)^{1/2},$$

for all $(s, t) \in \mathrm{I} \times \mathrm{I}$. Hence, as $\mathrm{K}(t, t)$ is bounded in I, for *fixed* $s \in \mathrm{I}$, the series $\sum_n \lambda_n \varphi_n(s)\overline{\varphi_n(t)}$ is *uniformly convergent* for $t \in \mathrm{I}$. By (11.6.6), (8.7.8), and (8.5.3), we conclude that $\sum_n \lambda_n \varphi_n(s)\overline{\varphi_n(t)} = \mathrm{K}(s, t)$ for all $(s, t) \in \mathrm{I} \times \mathrm{I}$ since $t \to \left|\mathrm{K}(s, t) - \sum_n \lambda_n \varphi_n(s)\overline{\varphi_n(t)}\right|^2$ is continuous in I and its integral in I is 0. In particular, we have $\mathrm{K}(s, s) = \sum_n \lambda_n |\varphi_n(s)|^2$; by Dini's theorem (7.2.2) the series $\sum_n \lambda_n |\varphi_n(s)|^2$ is therefore *uniformly convergent* in I, and (11.6.7.1) proves that the series $\sum_n \lambda_n \varphi_n(s)\overline{\varphi_n(t)}$ is absolutely and uniformly convergent in $\mathrm{I} \times \mathrm{I}$, which ends the proof.

Remarks

(11.6.8) The result (11.6.7) is still true when we only suppose that U has a *finite* number of eigenvalues $\nu_k < 0$ $(1 \leqslant k \leqslant m)$. For (11.5.7(c)) shows then that in the space F'_{m+1}, orthogonal supplement of $\mathrm{E}(\nu_1) + \cdots + \mathrm{E}(\nu_m)$ in G, the restriction of the operator U is *positive*, and we apply (11.6.7) to that operator, which, as is readily verified, corresponds to the kernel function $K(s, t) - \sum_h \lambda_h \varphi_h(s)\overline{\varphi_h(t)}$, where h runs through all the indices (in finite number) such that $\lambda_h < 0$. The conclusion is then immediate.

(11.6.9) We can consider the operator U in a larger prehilbert space, namely the space F_+ of regulated functions (Section 7.6) which are *continuous on the right* (i.e. such that $f(t+) = f(t)$ for $a \leqslant t < b$) and such that $f(b) = 0$; for such a function the relation $\int_a^b |f(t)|^2 \, dt = 0$ implies $f(t) = 0$ everywhere in $I = [a, b]$, for it implies $f(t) = 0$ except at the points of a denumerable subset D (by (8.5.3)), and every t such that $a \leqslant t < b$ is limit of a decreasing sequence of points of $I - D$. The space G may be identified to a subspace of F_+, by changing eventually the value of a continuous function $f \in G$ at the point b; it is easily proved (using (7.6.1)) that G is *dense* in F_+. The argument of (11.2.8) then shows that U is a *compact mapping of* F_+ *into the Banach space* $E = \mathscr{C}_C(I)$ (and *a fortiori* a compact mapping of the prehilbert space F_+ into itself). *All* the results proved for the operator U in G are still valid (with their proofs) when G is replaced by F_+.

PROBLEMS

1. Extend the results of Section 11.6 (with the exception of (11.6.7)) to the case in which $K(s, t)$ satisfies the assumptions of Section 8.11, Problem 4 (use that problem, as well as Section 11.2, Problem 5).
2. In the prehilbert space G of Section 11.6, let (f_n) be a total orthonormal system (Section 6.5); let

$$K_n(s, t) = \sum_{k=1}^{n} f_k(s)\overline{f_k(t)} \quad \text{and} \quad H_n(s) = \int_a^b |K_n(s, t)| \, dt$$

(the "nth Lebesgue function" of the orthonormal system (f_n)). For any function $g \in G$, let $s_n(g) = \sum_{k=1}^{n} (g \mid f_k) f_k$, so that $s_n(g)(x) = \int_a^b K_n(x, t) g(t) \, dt$ for any $x \in I$.

(a) Prove that if, for an $x_0 \in I$, the sequence $(H_n(x_0))$ is unbounded, then there exists a function $g \in G$ such that the sequence $(s_n(g)(x_0))$ is *unbounded*. (Use contradiction, and show that under the contrary assumption it is possible to define a strictly increasing sequence of integers (n_k), and a sequence (g_k) of functions of G, with the following properties: (1) let $c_h = \sup_n \left| \int_a^b K_n(x_0, t) g_h(t) \, dt \right|$ (a number which is finite by assumption), let $d_k = c_1 + c_2 + \cdots + c_{k-1}$, let $m_k = \int_a^b |K_{n_k}(x_0, t)| \, dt$, and let $q_k = \sup(m_1, \ldots, m_{k-1})$; then $m_k \geqslant 2^{k+1}(q_k + 1)(d_k + k)$; (2) let φ_k be a continuous function such that $\varphi_k(a) = \varphi_k(b) = 0$, $|\varphi_k(t)| \leqslant 1$ in I and $\left| \int_a^b K_{n_k}(x_0, t) \varphi_k(t) \, dt \right| \geqslant m_k/2$ (see Section 8.7, Problem 8); then $g_k = \varphi_k / (2^k(q_k + 1))$. Then show that the function $g = \sum_{k=1}^{\infty} g_k$ is continuous in I and contradicts the assumption: to evaluate the integral

$\int_a^b K_{n_k}(x_0, t)g(t)\,dt$, split g into $\sum_{i<k} g_i + g_k + \sum_{i>k} g_i$, minorize the second integral and majorize the two other ones ("method of the gliding hump").)

(b) Show that for the trigonometric system (Section 6.5) in $I = [-1, 1]$, the nth Lebesgue function is a *constant* h_n, and that $\lim_{n\to\infty} h_n = +\infty$ (observe that

$$\int_{(k-1)/n}^{k/n} \left|\frac{\sin n\pi t}{\sin \pi t}\right| dt \geqslant \frac{2}{k\pi}$$

for $2 \leqslant k \leqslant n$). Conclude that, for any $x_0 \in I$, there exists a continuous function g in I, such that $g(-1) = g(1) = 0$, for which the partial sums $\sum_{k=-n}^{n} \left(\int_{-1}^{1} g(t)e^{-ik\pi t}\,dt\right) e^{ik\pi x}/2$ of the "Fourier series" of g are *unbounded* for $x = x_0$. (Cf. Section 13.17, Problem 2.)

3. Let g be a continuous complex valued function defined in $I = [-1, 1]$ and such that $g(-1) = g(1) = 0$; g is extended to a continuous function of period 2 in **R**. Let $K(s, t)$ be the restriction of $g(s - t)$ to $I \times I$; if $g(-t) = \overline{g(t)}$, the compact operator U defined by the kernel function $K(s, t)$ is self-adjoint. Show that the functions $\varphi_n(t) = e^{n\pi i t}/\sqrt{2}$ are eigenvectors of U, the corresponding eigenvalue being the "Fourier coefficient" $a_n = \int_{-1}^{1} g(t)e^{-n\pi i t}\,dt$ of g.

Using that result and Problem 2, give examples of a hermitian kernel function K for which the series of general term $\lambda_n \overline{\varphi_n(s)}\varphi_n(t)$ has unbounded partial sums for certain values of s and t, and of a positive hermitian kernel function K for which there is a function $f \in G$ such that the series $\sum_{n=1}^{\infty} (f \mid \varphi_n)\varphi_n(t)$ has unbounded partial sums for certain values of t.

4. Let $I = [-2\pi, 2\pi]$, and define $K(s, t)$ in $I \times I$ to be equal to the absolutely convergent series $\sum_{n=1}^{\infty} \frac{1}{n^2} \sin ns \cdot \sin nt$ for $0 \leqslant s \leqslant 2\pi$, $0 \leqslant t \leqslant 2\pi$, and to 0 for other values of (s, t) in $I \times I$. Give an example of a function $f \in G$ such that in the canonical decomposition of f, f_0 does not belong to G. (The eigenfunctions of K are the functions φ_n such that $\varphi_n(t) = 0$ for $-2\pi \leqslant t \leqslant 0$, $\varphi_n(t) = \pi^{-1/2} \sin nt$ for $0 \leqslant t \leqslant 2\pi$. Take for f a continuous function in I equal to $2\pi - t$ in $[0, 2\pi]$, and show that the series $\sum_{n=1}^{\infty} (f \mid \varphi_n)\varphi_n(t)$ converges everywhere in I, but has a discontinuous sum.)

5. With the general notations of Section 11.6, let K be a hermitian kernel defined in $I \times I$, and let U be the corresponding self-adjoint compact operator in G. Show that for every $h > 0$, U^h corresponds to the hermitian kernel K_h, which is defined inductively by $K_1 = K$, and

$$K_h(s, t) = \int_a^b K_{h-1}(s, u)K(u, t)\,du.$$

Prove that for $h \geqslant 2$, $K_h(s, t) = \sum_{n=1}^{\infty} \lambda_n^h \overline{\varphi_n(s)}\varphi_n(t)$, the series being absolutely and uniformly convergent in $I \times I$. Show in addition that

$$A_h = \int_a^b ds \int_a^b |K_h(s, t)|^2\,dt = \sum_{n=1}^{\infty} |\lambda_n|^{2h},$$

and that the sequence (A_{h+1}/A_h) is increasing, and has a limit equal to $|\lambda_1|^2$, where λ_1 is an eigenvalue of K of maximum absolute value (use Cauchy–Schwarz).

6. With the notations of Section 11.6, let K be an arbitrary continuous kernel function in I × I, and let U be the corresponding compact operator in G. Let M be a finite dimensional subspace of G such that $U(\mathrm{M}) \subset \mathrm{M}$; let $(\psi_h)_{1 \leqslant h \leqslant n}$ be an orthonormal basis of the space M, and write $U\psi_h = \sum_{k=1}^{n} a_{hk}\psi_k$. Show that

$$\sum_{h,k} |a_{hk}|^2 \leqslant \int_a^b dt \int_a^b |\mathrm{K}(s, t)|^2 \, ds.$$

(For each $t \in \mathrm{I}$, apply Bessel's inequality (6.5.2) to the function $s \to \mathrm{K}(s, t)$ and the orthonormal system (ψ_h) in G.)

Let (λ_n) be the sequence defined (for the operator U) in Section 11.5, Problem 15(c). Prove that the series $\sum_{n=1}^{\infty} |\lambda_n|^2$ is convergent, and

$$\sum_{n=1}^{\infty} |\lambda_n|^2 \leqslant \int_a^b dt \int_a^b |\mathrm{K}(s, t)|^2 \, ds.$$

(Apply the preceding result to any sum of subspaces $\mathrm{N}(\mu_k)$, with the notations of Section 11.5, Problem 15(c).)

7. Give an example of an hermitian kernel $\mathrm{K}(s, t)$, such that, if U is the corresponding compact operator in G, and V the square root of U^2 (Section 11.5, Problem 12), there is no hermitian kernel to which corresponds the compact operator V. (If there existed such a kernel, Mercer's theorem (11.6.7) could be applied to it; take then for K the first example in Problem 3.)

8. In order that the compact operator U defined by an hermitian kernel $\mathrm{K}(s, t)$ be positive, show that a necessary and sufficient condition is that K be (in I × I) a *function of positive type* (Section 6.3, Problem 4; to prove that the condition is necessary, write the inequality

$$\int_a^b \overline{f(t)} \, dt \int_a^b \mathrm{K}(s, t) f(s) \, ds \geqslant 0$$

for a function f which is 0 outside arbitrary small neighborhoods of a finite number of points x_i of I $(1 \leqslant i \leqslant n)$. To prove that the condition is sufficient, use the same method as in Section 8.7, Problem 1). Conclude from that property and from Section 6.3, Problem 8 and Section 6.6, Problem 5, a new proof of Mercer's theorem.

9. (a) A kernel function $\mathrm{K}(s, t)$ defined in I × I (with $\mathrm{I} = [a, b]$) and satisfying the assumptions of Section 8.11, Problem 4, is called a *Volterra kernel* if $\mathrm{K}(s, t) = 0$ for $s > t$. Let $\mathrm{M} = \sup_{(s,t) \in \mathrm{I} \times \mathrm{I}} |\mathrm{K}(s, t)|$. If U is the compact operator in G corresponding to K (Problem 1), show that U^n corresponds to a Volterra kernel K_n such that $|\mathrm{K}_n(s, t)| \leqslant \mathrm{M}^n (t - s)^{n-1}/(n-1)!$ for $n > 1$ and $s \leqslant t$ (use induction on n). Deduce from that result that the spectrum of U is reduced to 0, and that for any $\zeta \in \mathbf{C}$, $\|(1_\mathrm{E} - \zeta U)^{-1} - 1_\mathrm{E}\| \leqslant \mathrm{M}|\zeta| e^{\mathrm{M}(b-a)|\zeta|}$.

(b) Take $a = 0$, $b = 1$, $\mathrm{K}(s, t) = 1$ for $s \leqslant t$, $\mathrm{K}(s, t) = 0$ for $s > t$. Show that for that kernel, the function $\mathrm{R}(s, t; \lambda)$ in (11.6.5) is equal to $\lambda^{-2} \exp((t - s)/\lambda)$ for $s \leqslant t$, and to 0 for $s > t$. (Use (8.14.2) to compute U^n.)

10. Let F_+ be the prehilbert space defined in (11.6.9) for the interval $\mathrm{I} = [0, 1]$, and let U be the operator defined in Problem 9(b), so that for every function $x \in \mathrm{F}_+$, $y = Ux$ is the function $t \to \int_0^t x(s) \, ds$. The space F_+ is a dense subspace in a Hilbert space E (6.6.2); U is extended by continuity to a compact operator in E, again written U (11.2.9). The closed subspaces E_0 of E, distinct from 0 and E, and such that $U(\mathrm{E}_0) \subset \mathrm{E}_0$ will be determined in this problem.

(a) Show (using (7.4.1)) that the operator U satisfies the condition of Section 11.5, Problem 19, with a equal to the constant function of value 1 in I; let $a_0 \in E_0$ be such that $P_0 a = s_0 a_0$ with $s_0 > 0$ and $\|a_0\| = 1$, so that $0 < s_0 < 1$. For every $x \in E_0$, $V_0 x = s_0^2(x \mid a_0)a_0$ (notations of Section 11.5, Problem 19).
(b) For every $\zeta \in \mathbf{C}$ not 0, let $f(\zeta) = 1 - s_0^2((U_0 - \zeta I)^{-1}a_0 \mid a_0)$. Prove that for $\zeta \neq 0$, $f(-\zeta)\overline{f(\bar{\zeta})} = 1$. (To compute that product, use the relation

$$V_0(U_0 + \zeta I)^{-1}a_0 = s_0^2((U_0 + \zeta I)^{-1}a_0 \mid a_0)a_0$$

deduced from (a), and transform the expression

$$(U_0^* - \zeta I)^{-1}(U_0 + U_0^*)(U_0 + \zeta I)^{-1}.)$$

Deduce from that relation and from Problem 9(a) that $f(\zeta^{-1})$ is an *entire function with no zeros* in $\mathbf{C}$. Using the majoration of Problem 9(a), and Section (10.2), Problem 8(c), conclude that $f(\zeta) = \exp(s_0^2\zeta)$.
(c) Conclude from (b) and from Problem 9(b) that a_0 is the function equal to 0 for $0 \leqslant t < 1 - s_0^2$, to 1 for $1 - s_0^2 \leqslant t \leqslant 1$, and that E_0 is the closure in E of the subspace generated by the functions of F_+ which are 0 in the interval $0 \leqslant t < 1 - s_0^2$.

11. For any two real continuous functions f, g defined in [0, 1], note $f * g$ the function h defined in [0, 1] by $h(x) = \int_0^x f(x-y)g(y)\,dy$. Prove that $f * g$ is continuous and equal to $g * f$; if f_1, f_2, f_3 are three continuous functions defined in [0, 1], prove that $(f_1 * f_2) * f_3 = f_1 * (f_2 * f_3)$, which is written $f_1 * f_2 * f_3$. For every integer $n > 0$, one defines by induction f^{*n} by $f^{*n} = f * (f^{*(n-1)})$; then $f^{*m} * f^{*n} = f^{*(m+n)}$.

Suppose f is continuous in [0, 1] and $f(0) \neq 0$. Prove that if, for a continuous function g defined in [0, 1], $f * g = 0$, then $g = 0$ ("Titchmarsh's theorem"). Observe that, with the notations of Problem 10, $Uf = a * f$, and conclude from Problem 10 that there exists s such that $0 \leqslant s \leqslant 1$ and that the closure in E of the subspace generated by f and the $U^n f$ for $n \geqslant 1$ is also the closure of the set of continuous functions which are 0 in $[0, s]$; the assumption $f(0) \neq 0$ implies $s = 0$. Observe finally that $t \to g(1-t)$ belongs to E and is orthogonal to every $U^n f$ for $n \geqslant 0$.

7. THE STURM–LIOUVILLE PROBLEM

We consider, in a compact interval $I = [a, b]$ of $\mathbf{R}$, a *linear differential equation of the second order*

(11.7.1) $$y'' - q(x)y + \lambda y = f(x)$$

where $q(x)$ is a *real-valued continuous* function in I, $f(x)$ a *complex-valued regulated* function in I, which is continuous except at a *finite* number of interior points, and λ a complex number. By a *solution* of (11.7.1) is meant a continuously differentiable complex-valued function $y(x)$, such that $y'(x)$ is the primitive of a regulated function with only finitely many discontinuities, and that the relation

$$y''(x) - q(x)y(x) + \lambda y(x) = f(x)$$

holds in the complement in $\mathring{I}$ of a *finite* subset of $\mathring{I}$. The *Sturm–Liouville problem* consists in finding solutions which also satisfy the two *boundary conditions*

(11.7.2) $$h_1 y(a) + k_1 y'(a) = 0, \qquad h_2 y(b) + k_2 y'(b) = 0$$

where h_1, k_1, h_2, k_2 are real numbers, and h_i, k_i are not both 0 $(i = 1, 2)$.

We assume in the following the elementary theory of linear differential equations (see Section 10.8). We first consider the *homogeneous* equation

(11.7.3) $$y'' - q(x)y + \lambda y = 0.$$

Note that y'' is *continuous* in I for any solution of (11.7.3).

(11.7.4) *There exists a number $r > 0$ such that, for λ real and $\leqslant -r$, the only solution of* (11.7.3) *satisfying the boundary conditions* (11.7.2) *is* 0.

As q, λ, the h_i, k_i are real, it is clear that if a solution of (11.7.3) verifies (11.7.2), its real and imaginary parts are also solutions verifying the same boundary conditions; we therefore can restrict ourselves to *real* solutions. Suppose first that $k_1 k_2 \neq 0$, so that we can suppose $k_1 = k_2 = -1$. Then we can also suppose $y(a) \neq 0$, otherwise we would have $y'(a) = 0$, and by the existence theorem, our theorem would be proved. Multiplying y by a suitable constant, we may therefore assume that $y(a) = 1$, $y'(a) = h_1$. Note that if we put $z = y'/y$ for $y(x) \neq 0$, we have

(11.7.4.1) $$z' = q(x) - \lambda - z^2.$$

Let $\mathrm{M} = \sup_{x \in \mathrm{I}} |q(x)|$, and suppose $\lambda \leqslant -\mathrm{M} - h_1^2 - 1$; then we have $z'(a) = q(a) - \lambda - h_1^2 \geqslant 1$, and therefore z is strictly increasing in a neighborhood of a in I. I claim that $y(x) \neq 0$ in I and that $z(x) > h_1$ for all $x > a$. Suppose first that $y(x)$ vanishes in I, and let x_1 be the smallest solution $> a$ of $y(x) = 0$. Then $y(x) > 0$ for $a \leqslant x < x_1$, hence $y'(x_1) < 0$ (it cannot be 0, or else y would be identically 0 in I) and as $q(x) - \lambda > 0$ for all $x \in \mathrm{I}$, $y''(x) > 0$ for $a \leqslant x < x_1$ by (11.7.3), hence y' is increasing for $a \leqslant x < x_1$, and therefore is <0 in that interval; it follows that when $x < x_1$ tends to x_1, $z(x)$ would tend to $-\infty$. As z is continuous for $a \leqslant x < x_1$, there would be in that interval a smallest $x_2 > a$ such that $z(x_2) = h_1$ and $h_1 < z(x)$ for $a < x < x_2$. This implies that $z'(x_2) \leqslant 0$; but we have $z'(x_2) = q(x_2) - \lambda - h_1^2 \geqslant 1$ and we obtain a contradiction, which proves both our assertions. In a similar way, we see that if we have $\lambda \leqslant -\mathrm{M} - h_2^2 - 1$, then $z(x) \leqslant h_2$ in I. The function z would thus be such that $|z(x)| \leqslant c = \sup(|h_1|, |h_2|)$ in I, where c is independent of λ. Now from (11.7.4.1) we deduce $z'(x) \geqslant -\mathrm{M} - \lambda - c^2 = \mu$, hence, by the mean value theorem, $h_2 - h_1 = z(b) - z(a) \geqslant \mu(b - a)$. If we take λ such that

$$\lambda \leqslant -\mathrm{M} - c^2 - \frac{|h_2 - h_1|}{b - a} - 1$$

we obtain a contradiction, and this ends the proof of (11.7.4), when $k_1 k_2 \neq 0$.

Suppose next $k_1 = 0$, $k_2 \neq 0$ (hence we can suppose $k_2 = -1$). We can now, by multiplying y with a suitable constant, suppose $y(a) = 0$, $y'(a) = 1$; then z tends to $+\infty$ when $x > a$ tends to a. Suppose $\lambda \leqslant -\mathrm{M} - 2$; then I claim first that $y'(x) \geqslant 1$ in I. As $y''(x) > 0$ by (11.7.3) for $x > a$ in a neighborhood of a, we have $y'(x) > 1$ for $x > a$ in that neighborhood. Suppose that $y'(x) = 1$ for some $x > a$, and let x_1 be the smallest solution of that equation. Then $y'(x) \geqslant 1$ for $a < x \leqslant x_1$, hence $y(x) > 0$ in that interval, and $y''(x) > 0$ by (11.7.3); but we should have $y''(x_1) \leqslant 0$, which is a contradiction. We thus see that y is strictly increasing in I, hence z is finite for $a < x \leqslant b$. I claim that $z(x) > (-\mathrm{M} - \lambda - 1)^{1/2}$; otherwise, there would be a smallest x_2 such that $z(x_2) = (-\mathrm{M} - \lambda - 1)^{1/2}$, and at that point we would have $z'(x_2) \leqslant 0$. But from (11.7.4.1) we deduce $z'(x_2) \geqslant -\mathrm{M} - \lambda - z^2(x_2) \geqslant 1$, and we have again reached a contradiction. If now we suppose λ taken such that $h_2^2 < -\mathrm{M} - \lambda - 1$, we find that the relation $z(b) = h_2$ is impossible, hence the theorem is proved in that case. The case $k_2 = 0$, $k_1 \neq 0$ is treated similarly. Finally, if $k_1 = k_2 = 0$, we may again suppose $y(a) = 0$, $y'(a) = 1$, and the preceding argument shows that y is strictly increasing in I as soon as $\lambda \leqslant -\mathrm{M} - 2$; this of course is in contradiction with the condition $y(b) = 0$, and the proof is complete.

Replacing if necessary $q(x)$ by $q(x) + r$, and λ by $\lambda + r$, we can from now on suppose that there is *no nontrivial solution of* (11.7.3) satisfying *both* boundary conditions (11.7.2), *for* $\lambda \leqslant 0$.

We will use the following identity

(11.7.5) $$\int_a^b (u''v - v''u)\,dt = (u'(b)v(b) - u(b)v'(b)) - (u'(a)v(a) - u(a)v'(a))$$

which is an immediate consequence of the particular case $p = 2$ of (8.14.1) (u'' and v'' are supposed to be regulated functions in I).

(11.7.6) *For any t such that $a < t < b$, there exists a real-valued continuous function $x \to \mathrm{K}_t(x)$ defined in I and having the following properties:*

(a) *In each of the intervals $a \leqslant x < t$, $t < x \leqslant b$, K_t is twice continuously differentiable and is a solution of $y'' - q(x)y = 0$.*

(b) K_t *satisfies the boundary conditions* (11.7.2).

(c) *At the point $x = t$, $\mathrm{K}_t'(x)$ has a limit on the right and a limit on the left, and $\mathrm{K}_t'(t+) - \mathrm{K}_t'(t-) = -1$.*

By the elementary theory of linear differential equations, there exists a solution $u_1 \neq 0$ (resp $u_2 \neq 0$) of $y'' - q(x)y = 0$ satisfying the condition $h_1 u_1(a) + k_1 u_1'(a) = 0$ (resp $h_2 u_2(b) + k_2 u_2'(b) = 0$), and u_1 and u_2 *are not proportional* (otherwise there would be a nontrivial solution of (11.7.3) with $\lambda = 0$ satisfying both boundary conditions (11.7.2)); hence *any* solution of $y'' - q(x)y = 0$ can be written in a unique way $y = c_1 u_1 + c_2 u_2$ with constant coefficients c_1, c_2, and the function $u_1(x)u_2'(x) - u_2(x)u_1'(x)$ is a *constant* $d \neq 0$ (by (8.14.1)). We now have only to choose the constants c_1, c_2 such that the function K_t equal to $c_1 u_1$ for $a \leqslant x \leqslant t$, to $c_2 u_2$ for $t \leqslant x \leqslant b$, should be defined and continuous at the point t, and satisfy condition (c), which yields the relations

$$c_1 u_1(t) - c_2 u_2(t) = 0$$
$$c_1 u_1'(t) - c_2 u_2'(t) = 1$$

and therefore gives $c_1 = -u_2(t)/d$, $c_2 = -u_1(t)/d$ as the solution of our problem.

We say (by abuse of language) that K_t is the *elementary solution* of $y'' - q(x)y = 0$ corresponding to the singularity t (cf. Chap. XXIII); the function $(t, x) \to K_t(x)$ is also written $K(t, x)$ and called the *Green function* corresponding to the Sturm–Liouville problem under consideration. It is only defined for $a < t < b$, $a \leqslant x \leqslant b$, equal to $-u_2(t)u_1(x)/d$ for $x \leqslant t$, to $-u_1(t)u_2(x)/d$ for $x \geqslant t$, hence is *continuous*, and moreover can be extended by continuity for $t = a$ and $t = b$ by taking $K(a, x) = -u_1(a)u_2(x)/d$ and $K(b, x) = -u_2(b)u_1(x)/d$; in addition it has the *symmetry property*

(11.7.7) $$K(t, x) = K(x, t)$$

as follows at once from its expression.

(11.7.8) *In order that a function $y(x)$ be a solution of the equation $y'' - q(x)y = f(x)$ and verify the boundary conditions* (11.7.2), *it is necessary and sufficient that* $y(x) = -\int_a^b K(t, x)f(t)\,dt$ (f being a complex-valued regulated function in I, which is continuous except at a finite number of points of $\mathring{I}$).

(a) *Sufficiency.* As

$$y(x) = \frac{u_1(x)}{d}\int_x^b u_2(t)f(t)\,dt + \frac{u_2(x)}{d}\int_a^x u_1(t)f(t)\,dt$$

the verification of the differential equation (at the points where f is continuous) and of the boundary conditions, reduces to routine computations of derivatives (and use of (8.7.3)).

(b) *Necessity.* Apply the identity (11.7.5) in both intervals $a \leqslant t \leqslant x$ and $x \leqslant t \leqslant b$, with $u(t) = y(t)$ and $v(t) = \mathrm{K}_x(t)$; the relation $y(x) = -\int_a^b \mathrm{K}(t, x) f(t)\, dt$ follows at once from the properties (11.7.6) of the Green function.

From (11.7.8) it follows that any solution of the Sturm–Liouville problem is a solution of the Fredholm integral equation with *hermitian* kernel:

(11.7.9)
$$y(x) - \lambda \int_a^b \mathrm{K}(t, x) y(t)\, dt = g(x),$$

where

$$g(x) = -\int_a^b \mathrm{K}(t, x) f(t)\, dt,$$

and conversely. The *inverses* λ_n of the eigenvalues $\neq 0$ of the operator U in the prehilbert space G defined in (11.2.8), corresponding to the kernel function K, are called the *eigenvalues* of the Sturm–Liouville problem. We can now state the following theorem which solves the Sturm–Liouville problem in every case:

(11.7.10) *For any real-valued continuous function $q(x)$ in the compact interval* $\mathrm{I} = [a, b]$*:*

(a) *The Sturm–Liouville problem has an infinite strictly increasing sequence of eigenvalues (λ_n) which are real numbers such that $\lim_{n \to \infty} \lambda_n = +\infty$ and that the series $\sum_n 1/\lambda_n^2$ is convergent.*

(b) *For each eigenvalue λ_n, the homogeneous Sturm–Liouville problem has a real valued solution $\varphi_n(x)$ such that $\int_a^b \varphi_n^2(x)\, dx = 1$, and every other solution is a constant multiple of φ_n.*

(c) *The sequence (φ_n) is a total orthonormal system in the prehilbert space* G (notation of Section 11.6).

(d) *Let w be a complex-valued continuous function in* I, *which is the primitive of a regulated function w', such that:* (i) *w' is continuous in* I *except at a finite number of interior points;* (ii) *w' has a continuous derivative w'' in each interval in which it is continuous;* (iii) *w satisfies the boundary conditions* (11.7.2). *Then, if $c_n = (w \mid \varphi_n) = \int_a^b w(t)\varphi_n(t)\, dt$, we have $w(x) = \sum_n c_n \varphi_n(x)$ where the series is absolutely and uniformly convergent in* I.

(e) *If λ is not one of the eigenvalues λ_n, for each regulated function f, continuous in* I *except at a finite number of points, the Sturm–Liouville problem has a unique solution w which is such that $c_n = (w \mid \varphi_n)$ is given by the formula $c_n = d_n/(\lambda - \lambda_n)$, where $d_n = \int_a^b f(t)\varphi_n(t)\, dt$.*

(f) *For $\lambda = \lambda_n$, a necessary and sufficient condition for the Sturm–Liouville problem to have a solution is that* $\int_a^b f(t)\varphi_n(t)\,dt = 0$. *Then, for any solution* w, $c_n = (w \mid \varphi_n)$ *is arbitrary, and for* $m \neq n$, c_m *is given by the same formula as in* (e).

The homogeneous Sturm–Liouville problem cannot have two linearly independent solutions, otherwise it would have solutions y for which $y(a)$ and $y'(a)$ are arbitrary, which is absurd; this proves (b). The fact that all eigenvalues λ_n are real follows from (11.7.7) and (11.5.7); moreover it follows from (11.7.4) that at most finitely many λ_n are negative. By Mercer's theorem ((11.6.7) and (11.6.8)), we have for the Green function

$$\text{(11.7.10.1)} \qquad K(t, x) = \sum_n \frac{1}{\lambda_n} \varphi_n(t)\varphi_n(x)$$

the series being absolutely and uniformly convergent in $I \times I$ (it is supposed, as we may, that 0 is not one of the λ_n). We observe that (d) follows from (11.6.3) and (11.7.8) when the additional assumption is made on w that w' is *continuous in* I. To prove (d) in general, let t_i $(1 \leqslant i \leqslant m)$ be the points of $\mathring{I}$ where w' has a discontinuity, and let $\alpha_i = w'(t_i+) - w'(t_i-)$. Then the function $v = w + \sum_{i=1}^{m} \alpha_i K_{t_i}$ satisfies all the conditions of (d) and in addition has a continuous derivative, by (11.7.6). Using (11.7.10.1) we conclude the proof of (d). From the fact that the identity mapping of $E = \mathscr{C}_{\mathbf{C}}(I)$ into G is continuous, it follows that for the functions w satisfying the conditions of (d), we can also write $w = \sum_n c_n \varphi_n$, the sequence being convergent *in the prehilbert space* G. To prove (c) it will then be enough to show that the set P of these functions w is *dense* in G. Now, for any function $u \in G$, consider the continuous function w_m equal to u in

$$\left[a + \frac{1}{m}, b - \frac{1}{m}\right],$$

to a linear function $x \to \alpha x + \beta$ satisfying the first (resp. second) boundary condition (11.7.2) in

$$\left[a, a + \frac{1}{2m}\right] \quad \left(\text{resp. } \left[b - \frac{1}{2m}, b\right]\right),$$

and to a linear function in each of the intervals

$$\left[a + \frac{1}{2m}, a + \frac{1}{m}\right], \quad \left[b - \frac{1}{m}, b - \frac{1}{2m}\right].$$

We can in addition suppose that at the points a, b, the value of w_m is 0 or 1; it is then clear that $|u(x) - w_m(x)| \leqslant \|u\| + 1$ in each of the intervals

$$\left[a, a + \frac{1}{m}\right] \quad \text{and} \quad \left[b - \frac{1}{m}, b\right],$$

and therefore $\|u - w_m\|_2$ is arbitrarily small by the mean value theorem; as w_m satisfies all conditions in (d), this proves our assertion. Once (c) is thus proved, it is clear that the total sequence (φ_n) must be infinite, and (applying (11.6.2)), (a) is also completely proved. Finally, (e) and (f) follow at once from (11.5.11).

Remark. It is possible to obtain much more precise information on the φ_n and λ_n, and to prove in particular that λ_n/n^2 tends to a finite limit (see Problems 3 and 4).

PROBLEMS

1. Let $\mathrm{I} = [a, b]$ be a compact interval in $\mathbf{R}$, and let H_0 be the real vector space of all real-valued continuously differentiable functions in I; H_0 is made into a real prehilbert space by the scalar product

$$(x \mid y) = \int_a^b (x'y' + xy)\, dt.$$

(a) Show that H_0 is separable (approximate the derivative of a function $x \in \mathrm{H}_0$ by polynomials (7.4.1)); H_0 is therefore a dense subspace of a separable Hilbert space H (6.6.2).

(b) If (x_n) is a Cauchy sequence in the prehilbert space H_0, show that the sequence (x_n) is uniformly convergent to a continuous function v in I, and that if (y_n) is a second Cauchy sequence in H_0 having the same limit in H, then (y_n) converges uniformly in I to the same function v; the elements of H can thus be identified to some continuous functions in I, which however need *not* be differentiable at every point of I. (Observe that for every function $x \in \mathrm{H}_0$, $|x(t) - x(a)| \leqslant (t-a)^{1/2}\left(\int_a^b x'^2\, dt\right)^{1/2}$ in I.) Show that, for any function $z \in \mathrm{H}_0$ which is twice continuously differentiable in I and such that $z'(a) = z'(b) = 0$, $(v \mid z) = -\int_a^b vz''\, dt + \int_a^b vz\, dt$.

(c) Let α, β be two real numbers, q a continuous function in I. Show that in H_0, the function $x \to \Phi(x) = \int_a^b (x'^2 + qx^2)\, dt - \alpha(x(a))^2 - \beta(x(b))^2$ is continuous. Let A be the subset of H consisting of the functions x such that $\int_a^b x^2\, dt = 1$ (observe that this is *not* a bounded set in the Hilbert space H). Show that in $\mathrm{A} \cap \mathrm{H}_0$, the g.l.b. of $\Phi(x)$ is *finite*. (One need only consider the case $\alpha > 0$, $\beta > 0$. Assume there is a sequence (x_n) in

$A \cap H_0$ such that $\lim_{n \to \infty} \Phi(x_n) = -\infty$, and, if $\gamma_n = \left(\int_a^b x_n'^2 \, dt \right)^{1/2}$, $\lim_{n \to \infty} \gamma_n = +\infty$; consider the sequence of the functions $y_n = x_n / \gamma_n$, and derive a contradiction from the fact that, on one hand $\lim_{n \to \infty} \int_a^b y_n^2 \, dt = 0$, and on the other hand, there is an interval $[a, c] \subset I$ and a number $\rho > 0$ such that $|y_n(t)| \geqslant \rho$ for every n and every point $t \in [a, c]$.)

(d) Let μ_1 be the g.l.b. of $\Phi(x)$ in $A \cap H_0$. Show that if (x_n) is a sequence in $A \cap H_0$ such that $\lim_{n \to \infty} \Phi(x_n) = \mu_1$, (x_n) is bounded in H (same method as in (c)). Deduce from that result that, by extracting a convenient subsequence, one may assume that the sequence (x_n) is uniformly convergent in I to a function u (which, however, need not *a priori* belong to H) (use Ascoli's theorem (7.5.7)).

(e) $\Phi(x)$ is a quadratic form in H_0, i.e. one has $\Phi(x + y) = \Phi(x) + \Phi(y) + 2\Psi(x, y)$, where Ψ is bilinear; for any function z which is twice continuously differentiable in I and such that $z'(a) = z'(b) = z(a) = z(b) = 0$, one has $\Psi(x, z) = -\int_a^b xz'' \, dt + \int_a^b qxz \, dt$; $\Psi(v, z)$ can be defined by the same formula for any function v continuous in I. Show that for any such function z and any real number ξ, one has

$$\lim_{n \to \infty} \left(\Phi(x_n + \xi z) \Big/ \int_a^b (x_n + \xi z)^2 \, dt \right) \geqslant \mu_1$$

and deduce from that result that one must have

$$\int_a^b (uz'' - quz + \mu_1 uz) \, dt = 0.$$

Hence, if w is a twice continuously differentiable function such that $w'' = qu - \mu_1 u$, one has $\int_a^b (u - w)z'' \, dt = 0$ by integration by parts; conclude that $u - w$ is a polynomial of degree $\leqslant 1$ (observe that by substracting from $u - w$ a suitable polynomial p of degree 1, there exists a function z such that $z'' = u - w - p$, $z(a) = z(b) = z'(a) = z'(b) = 0$). Hence u is twice continuously differentiable, satisfies the differential equation

$$u'' - qu + \mu_1 u = 0,$$

and is such that $\int_a^b u^2 \, dt = 1$; furthermore, $u'(a) = -\alpha u(a)$, $u'(b) = \beta u(b)$. (To prove the last statement, express that for *any* $z \in H_0$, $\Phi(u + \xi z) \geqslant \mu_1 \int_a^b (u + \xi z)^2 \, dt$, for any real number ξ.)

2. (a) With the notations of (11.7.10), suppose first that $k_1 k_2 \neq 0$, and let $\alpha = h_1/k_1$, $\beta = -h_2/k_2$. Show that the φ_n can be defined (up to sign) by the following conditions: (1) φ_1 is such that, on the sphere A: $(y \mid y) = 1$ in G, the function Φ (defined in Problem 1(c)) reaches its minimum for $y = \varphi_1$, and that minimum is equal to λ_1; (2) for $n > 1$, let A_n be the intersection of A and of the hyperplanes $(y \mid \varphi_k) = 0$ for $1 \leqslant k \leqslant n - 1$; then φ_n is such that on A_n, Φ reaches its minimum for $y = \varphi_n$, and that minimum is equal to λ_n. (The characterization of φ_1 follows at once from the results of Problem 1; use the same kind of argument to characterize φ_n.)

(b) If $k_1 = 0$, $k_2 \neq 0$, prove similar results, replacing α by 0 in Φ, but replacing the sphere A by its intersection with the hyperplane in G defined by $y(a) = 0$. Proceed similarly when $k_1 \neq 0$ and $k_2 = 0$, or when $k_1 = k_2 = 0$.

(c) Under the assumptions of (a), let $z_1, \ldots, z_{n-1}$ be $n-1$ arbitrary twice continuously differentiable functions in I, and let $B(z_1, \ldots, z_{n-1})$ be the intersection of A and of the $n-1$ hyperplanes $(y \mid z_k) = 0$ $(1 \leqslant k \leqslant n-1)$. Show that in $B(z_1, \ldots, z_{n-1})$, the function Φ reaches a minimum $\rho(z_1, \ldots, z_{n-1})$ at a point of $B(z_1, \ldots, z_{n-1})$, and that λ_n is the l.u.b. of $\rho(z_1, \ldots, z_{n-1})$ when the z_i vary over the set of twice continuously differentiable functions in I (the "maximinimal" principle; same method as in (a) to prove the existence of the minimum; the inequality is proved by the same method as in Section 11.5, Problem 8). Extend the result to the cases $k_1 k_2 = 0$.

3. (a) One considers in the same interval I two linear differential equations of the second order $y'' - q_1 y + \lambda y = 0$, $y'' - q_2 y + \lambda y = 0$, with the *same* boundary conditions (11.7.2); let $(\lambda_n^{(1)})$, $(\lambda_n^{(2)})$ be the two strictly increasing sequences of eigenvalues of these two Sturm–Liouville problems. Show that if $q_1 \leqslant q_2$, then $\lambda_n^{(1)} \leqslant \lambda_n^{(2)}$ for every n, and if $|q_1(t) - q_2(t)| \leqslant M$ in I, then $|\lambda_n^{(1)} - \lambda_n^{(2)}| \leqslant M$ for every n (use the maximinimal principle).

(b) Conclude from (a) that there is a constant c such that

$$\left| \lambda_n - \frac{n^2 \pi^2}{l^2} \right| \leqslant c$$

for every n, with $l = b - a$. (Study the Sturm–Liouville problem for the particular case in which q is a constant.)

4. (a) Let y be *any* solution of (11.7.3) in $I = [a, b]$ for $\lambda > 0$. Show that there are two constants A, ω such that y is a solution of the integral equation

$$(*) \qquad y(t) = A \sin \sqrt{\lambda}(t + \omega) + \frac{1}{\sqrt{\lambda}} \int_a^t q(s) y(s) \sin \sqrt{\lambda}(t - s)\, ds.$$

Show that there exists a constant B independent of λ, such that $A^2 \leqslant B(y \mid y)$ (use Cauchy–Schwarz in order to majorize the integral on the right-hand side of (*)).

(b) Deduce from (a) that if, in the Sturm–Liouville problem, $k_1 k_2 \neq 0$ or $k_1 = k_2 = 0$, then there are two constants C_0, C_1, such that, for every n, and every $t \in I$

$$|\varphi_n(t) - \sqrt{2/l} \sin \sqrt{\lambda_n}\, t| \leqslant C_0/n$$

and

$$|\varphi_n'(t) - \sqrt{2/l}\sqrt{\lambda_n} \cos \sqrt{\lambda_n}\, t| \leqslant C_1 \qquad \text{with} \quad l = b - a$$

(use (a), and the result of Problem 3(b)). What is the corresponding result when only one of the constants k_1, k_2 is 0?

APPENDIX

ELEMENTS OF LINEAR ALGEBRA

♠ Except for boolean algebra (Section 1.2) there is no theory more universally employed in mathematics than linear algebra; and there is hardly any theory which is more elementary, in spite of the fact that generations of professors and textbook writers have obscured its simplicity by preposterous calculations with matrices. We shall give a brief survey of the concepts and results of linear algebra which are used in this book. For a more complete account we refer the reader to the works of Halmos [11], Jacobson [13], or Bourbaki [4].

1. VECTOR SPACES

(A.1.1) Throughout this appendix, K is a fixed (commutative) field, whose elements are called *scalars*. A *vector space over* K (or simply *a vector space*, if there is no ambiguity about K) is a set E endowed with the structure defined by two mappings:

$(x, y) \to x + y$ of $E \times E$ into E	(called *addition*)
$(\lambda, x) \to \lambda x$ of $K \times E$ into E	(called *scalar multiplication*)

having the following properties:

(I.1) $x + (y + z) = (x + y) + z$ (written $x + y + z$)

(I.2) $x + y = y + x$

(I.3) there exists an element $0 \in E$ such that $x = 0 + x$ for all $x \in E$†

† Experience shows that, contrary to the opinion of some authors, there is no risk of confusion in using the same symbol 0 to denote the zero elements of all vector spaces (and of K in particular).

(I.4) for each $x \in \mathrm{E}$ there exists an element $-x \in \mathrm{E}$ such that $x + (-x) = 0$

(II.1) $(\lambda + \mu)x = \lambda x + \mu x$

(II.2) $\lambda(x + y) = \lambda x + \lambda y$

(II.3) $\lambda(\mu x) = (\lambda\mu)x$

(II.4) $1 \cdot x = x$

(in these conditions, x, y, z are arbitrary elements of E and λ, μ are arbitrary elements of K).

▲ Conditions (I.1) to (I.4) express that E is a *commutative group* with respect to addition. It follows that, if $(x_i)_{i \in \mathrm{H}}$ is any *finite* family of elements of E, the sum $\sum_{i \in \mathrm{H}} x_i$ is unambiguously defined. (We recall the convention that $\sum_{i \in \varnothing} x_i = 0$.)

▲ From (I.3) and (II.2) we deduce that $\lambda x = \lambda(x + 0) = \lambda x + \lambda 0$, and therefore $\lambda 0 = 0$ for all $\lambda \in \mathrm{K}$. From (II.1) it follows that $\lambda x = (\lambda + 0)x = \lambda x + 0x$, so that $0x = 0$ for all $x \in \mathrm{E}$. Finally, from these two relations and (I.4), (II.1), and (II.2) we deduce that $\lambda x + \lambda(-x) = \lambda 0 = 0$, and $\lambda x + (-\lambda)x = 0x = 0$, so that $(-\lambda)x = \lambda(-x) = -(\lambda x)$.

▲ The elements of E are often called *vectors*.

(A.1.2) An additive group consisting of the element 0 alone is a vector space: the scalar multiplication is the unique mapping of $\mathrm{K} \times \{0\}$ into $\{0\}$. The field K is a vector space over itself, the scalar multiplication being multiplication in K. If K′ is a *subfield* of K and if E is a vector space over K, then E is also a vector space over K′ if we define the scalar multiplication to be the restriction to $\mathrm{K}' \times \mathrm{E}$ of the mapping $(\lambda, x) \to \lambda x$.

(A.1.3) If E is a vector space, a *vector subspace* (or simply *subspace*) of E is defined to be any subset F of E such that the relations $x \in \mathrm{F}$, $y \in \mathrm{F}$ imply $\lambda x + \mu y \in \mathrm{F}$, for all scalars λ, μ.

▲ The restriction to $\mathrm{F} \times \mathrm{F}$ (resp. $\mathrm{K} \times \mathrm{F}$) of the addition (resp. scalar multiplication) in E is a mapping *into* F, and therefore F is a vector space with respect to these mappings. This justifies the terminology.

▲ If $(x_i)_{1 \leqslant i \leqslant n}$ is any finite family of vectors in F, and if $(\lambda_i)_{1 \leqslant i \leqslant n}$ is a family of scalars, then by induction on n we see that $\sum_{i=1}^{n} \lambda_i x_i \in \mathrm{F}$. A vector of the form $\sum_{i=1}^{n} \lambda_i x_i$ (where $x_i \in \mathrm{E}$ and $\lambda_i \in \mathrm{K}$) is called a *linear combination* of the x_i. (A linear combination is always a *finite* sum, even if E is, for example, a normed space (Section 5.1) in which certain infinite sums are defined (Section 5.3).)

▲ In any vector space E the subsets $\{0\}$ and E are vector subspaces (called the *trivial* subspaces). If $(M_\alpha)_{\alpha \in I}$ is any family of vector subspaces of E, the intersection $\bigcap_{\alpha \in I} M_\alpha$ is again a vector subspace. If A is any subset of E, the intersection M of the subspaces which contain A (such subspaces exist, for example E itself) is therefore the smallest subspace containing A. We say that M is *generated* by A, or that A is a *system of generators* of M.

(A.1.4) *The vector subspace* M *generated by* A *is the set of all linear combinations of finite families of elements of* A.

▲ It follows from above that such linear combinations belong to every vector subspace containing A, and therefore belong to M. Conversely, if $x = \sum_i \gamma_i x_i$ and $y = \sum_j \delta_j y_j$ are two linear combinations of elements of A, then so is $\lambda x + \mu y = \sum_i (\lambda\gamma_i)x_i + \sum_j (\mu\delta_j)y_j$. Hence the set of all such linear combinations is a vector subspace of E, which contains A (by (II.4)) and therefore coincides with M.

▲ In particular, take A to be the *union* of a family $(N_\beta)_{\beta \in J}$ of vector subspaces of E. Every linear combination of elements of A is then of the form $x_{\beta_1} + x_{\beta_2} + \cdots + x_{\beta_m}$, where $(\beta_j)_{1 \leqslant j \leqslant m}$ is any finite family of elements of J, and $x_{\beta_j} \in N_{\beta_j}$ for each j. The set of all these sums is therefore the smallest vector subspace containing all the N_β. It is called *the sum of the* N_β (not to be confused with their union!) and is denoted by $\sum_{\beta \in J} N_\beta$. When $J = \{1, 2\}$, the notation $N_1 + N_2$ is also used, and similarly for any finite set of indices. It is clear that $M + N = N + M$ and $M + (N + P) = (M + N) + P$ for any three subspaces M, N, P in E. The relation $M \subset N$ is equivalent to $M + N = N$.

▲ For every $x \in E$, the subspace of E generated by x is written Kx (and is sometimes called a "ray" when $x \neq 0$). If $(x_\alpha)_{\alpha \in A}$ is any family of vectors in E, the subspace generated by the family is therefore $\sum_{\alpha \in A} Kx_\alpha$.

(A.1.5) Let $(E_\alpha)_{\alpha \in I}$ be *any* family of vector spaces. We shall construct a new vector space E, called the *direct sum* (or *external direct sum*) of the family (E_α) and denoted by $\bigoplus_{\alpha \in I} E_\alpha$. The elements of E are the families $x = (x_\alpha)_{\alpha \in I}$, where $x_\alpha \in E_\alpha$ for all α *and* $x_\alpha = 0$ *for all except a finite number of indices*. The vector x_α is called the *component of index* α in x. Addition and scalar multiplication in E are defined by the formulas

$$(x_\alpha) + (y_\alpha) = (x_\alpha + y_\alpha)$$

$$\lambda(x_\alpha) = (\lambda x_\alpha)$$

((λx_α) belongs to E because $\lambda 0 = 0$). The conditions of (A.1.1) are immediately verified (the element 0 of E is the family (x_α) for which $x_\alpha = 0$ for *all* α). When $J = \{1, 2\}$, the notation $E_1 \oplus E_2$ is used, and similarly for any finite set of indices. When J is finite, the set E is equal to the product set $\prod_{\alpha \in J} E_\alpha$. If J is arbitrary and H is a subset of J (other than $\varnothing$ or J), the vector space $\bigoplus_{\alpha \in J} E_\alpha$ can be identified in an obvious way with $\left(\bigoplus_{\alpha \in H} E_\alpha\right) \oplus \left(\bigoplus_{\alpha \in J-H} E_\alpha\right)$.

▲ When all the E_α are equal to K, their direct sum is denoted by $K^{(I)}$. It is the set of all mappings $\alpha \to \lambda(\alpha)$ of I into K such that $\lambda(\alpha) = 0$ for all but a finite number of indices $\alpha \in I$.

2. LINEAR MAPPINGS

(A.2.1) Let E, F be two vector spaces over the *same* field K. A mapping $u : E \to F$ is said to be *linear* if it satisfies the condition

(A.2.1.1) $$u(\lambda x + \mu y) = \lambda u(x) + \mu u(y)$$

for all scalars λ, μ and all vectors x, y in E. In particular, we have $u(0) = 0$. By induction on n it follows from (A.2.1.1) that

(A.2.1.2) $$u\left(\sum_{i=1}^{n} \lambda_i x_i\right) = \sum_{i=1}^{n} \lambda_i u(x_i),$$

where $(x_i)_{1 \leqslant i \leqslant n}$ is any finite family of vectors in E, and $(\lambda_i)_{1 \leqslant i \leqslant n}$ is a family of scalars.

▲ A linear mapping of E into E is called an *endomorphism* of E. A linear mapping of E into K is called a *linear form* on E.

(A.2.2) Let $u : E \to F$ be a linear mapping. If M is any subspace of E, it is immediately verified that its image $u(M)$ is a subspace of F. If N is any subspace of F, then its inverse image $u^{-1}(N)$ is a subspace of E. If (M_α) is any family of subspaces of E, then $u\left(\sum_\alpha M_\alpha\right) = \sum_\alpha u(M_\alpha)$.

▲ In particular, $u(E)$ (which is called the *image of u* and is written $\text{im}(u)$) is a subspace of F, and $u^{-1}(0)$ (which is called the *kernel of u* and written $\ker(u)$) is a subspace of E. The mapping u is *injective* if and only if $u^{-1}(0) = \{0\}$, because the relation $u(x) = u(x')$ is equivalent to $u(x - x') = 0$.

▲ If u is *bijective*, it is called an *isomorphism* of E onto E. (If also F = E, then u is an *automorphism* of E). If u is bijective, it is clear that the inverse mapping $u^{-1} : F \to E$ is linear, and therefore an isomorphism of F onto E.

Two vector spaces E, F are said to be *isomorphic* if there exists an isomorphism of E onto F. In that case, any theorem proved for E, involving vectors and subspaces of E, immediately gives a corresponding theorem for F, involving the images of the vectors and subspaces in question.

▲ If $u : E \to F$ is an injective linear mapping, then u can be considered as an isomorphism of E onto its image $u(E)$.

Examples of linear mappings

(A.2.3) The identity mapping of a vector space E onto itself (often denoted by 1_E or I_E, or simply 1 or I) is linear. So is the unique mapping of E into a vector space consisting of 0 alone. For every $\lambda \in K$, the mapping $h_\lambda : x \to \lambda x$ is an endomorphism of E, called the *homothetic mapping with ratio* λ. If $\lambda = 0$, its image is the zero subspace $\{0\}$ of E. If $\lambda \neq 0$, then h_λ is *bijective* and its inverse automorphism is the homothetic mapping with ratio λ^{-1}, because we have $x = \lambda^{-1}(\lambda x)$ by (II.3). For each $x_0 \in E$, the mapping $\xi \to \xi x_0$ of K into E is linear. Its image is $\{0\}$ if $x_0 = 0$; otherwise, the mapping is *injective*, for if $\xi \neq 0$ we have $\xi^{-1}(\xi x_0) = x_0 \neq 0$ (by II.3 and II.4) and it follows that $\xi x_0 \neq 0$. Every "ray" Kx_0 in E (where $x_0 \neq 0$) is therefore isomorphic to K, and is equal to $K(\lambda x_0)$ for any nonzero scalar λ.

▲ If F is any vector subspace of E, the *canonical injection* $j : F \to E$ (1.6.1) is a linear mapping.

▲ Let $(E_\alpha)_{\alpha \in I}$ be a family of vector spaces and $E = \bigoplus_{\alpha \in I} E_\alpha$ their direct sum. For each $\alpha \in I$ we define a linear mapping $j_\alpha : E_\alpha \to E$ by the rule $j_\alpha(x_\alpha) = (y_\beta)_{\beta \in I}$, where $y_\beta = 0$ if $\beta \neq \alpha$, and $y_\alpha = x_\alpha$. It is clear that j_α is injective, and hence its image $j_\alpha(E_\alpha)$ is a subspace of E, isomorphic to E_α. This subspace is called the *component* subspace of index α in E, and is often identified with E_α. We also define linear mappings $p_\alpha : E \to E_\alpha$ (for each $\alpha \in I$) as follows: if $x = (x_\beta)_{\beta \in I}$ is an element of E, then $p_\alpha(x) = x_\alpha$. It is clear that p_α is surjective. If I is finite, p_α is the projection with index α (Section 1.3). For each $x \in E$, the set H of indices $\alpha \in I$ such that $p_\alpha(x) \neq 0$ is finite, and we have $x = \sum_{\alpha \in H} j_\alpha(p_\alpha(x))$.

(A.2.4) If $u : E \to F$ and $u' : E \to F$ are linear mappings, and if λ is a scalar, it is immediately verified that the mappings

$$x \to u(x) + u'(x)$$

and

$$x \to \lambda u(x)$$

are linear mappings of E into F. They are denoted by $u + u'$ and λu, respectively. It is then routine to check that the *set of linear mappings of* E *into* F (which is denoted by $\mathrm{Hom}_K(E, F)$, or simply by Hom(E, F)) is a *vector space* with respect to the addition $(u, u') \to u + u'$ and the scalar multiplication $(\lambda, u) \to \lambda u$. In other words, the eight conditions of (A.1.1) are satisfied.

▲ Let $u : E \to F$ and $v : F \to G$ be linear mappings. Then their *composition* $v \circ u : E \to G$ is linear. Furthermore, if $u' : E \to F$ and $v' : F \to G$ are linear mappings and λ is a scalar, then we have

(A.2.4.1) $$v \circ (u + u') = v \circ u + v \circ u',$$

(A.2.4.2) $$(v + v') \circ u = v \circ u + v' \circ u,$$

(A.2.4.3) $$v \circ (\lambda u) = (\lambda v) \circ u = \lambda(v \circ u).$$

(The verifications involved are trivial if one bears in mind the definition of equality of two mappings (Section 1.4).)

▲ The set Hom(E, E) of endomorphisms of E is also denoted by End(E) or $\mathrm{End}_K(E)$. This set, endowed with the addition $(u, v) \to u + v$ and the "multiplication" $(u, v) \to u \circ v$, is a *ring* (in general not commutative) whose *identity element* is 1_E. This follows from the formulas above and from Section 1.7. The property (A.2.4.3), which relates the ring structure of End(E) to its vector space structure, may be expressed by saying that End(E) is an *algebra* over K.

3. DIRECT SUMS OF SUBSPACES

(A.3.1) *Let $(E_\alpha)_{\alpha \in I}$ be a family of vector spaces, let F be a vector space, and for each $\alpha \in I$ let $u_\alpha : E_\alpha \to F$ be a linear mapping. Then there exists a unique linear mapping u of the direct sum $E = \bigoplus_{\alpha \in I} E_\alpha$ into F such that $u \circ j_\alpha = u_\alpha$ for all $\alpha \in I$ (where $j_\alpha : E_\alpha \to E$ is the canonical injection defined in* (A.2.3)).

▲ For each $x \in E$ we have $x = \sum_{\alpha \in H} j_\alpha(p_\alpha(x))$, where H is any finite subset of I containing all $\alpha \in I$ such that $p_\alpha(x) \neq 0$. Hence we must have $u(x) = \sum_{\alpha \in H} u(j_\alpha(p_\alpha(x))) = \sum_{\alpha \in H} u_\alpha(p_\alpha(x))$, from which the uniqueness of u follows. Conversely, if we *define* u by this formula, it is immediately verified that u is linear (by using the fact that, given x and y in E, we may take H to be a finite set containing all the indices $\alpha \in I$ for which either $p_\alpha(x) \neq 0$ or $p_\alpha(y) \neq 0$). This completes the proof.

(A.3.2) Now let E be a vector space, let $(M_\alpha)_{\alpha \in I}$ be a family of subspaces of E, and for each $\alpha \in I$ let $f_\alpha : M_\alpha \to E$ be the canonical injection. By (A.3.1) there exists a linear mapping f of $M = \bigoplus_{\alpha \in I} M_\alpha$ into E such that $f \circ j_\alpha = f_\alpha$ for all $\alpha \in I$. The image of f is the subspace $M' = \sum_{\alpha \in I} M_\alpha$ of E. If f is *injective*, the sum $\sum_{\alpha \in I} M_\alpha$ of subspaces of E is said to be *direct*. This therefore means that every vector x belonging to $\sum_{\alpha \in I} M_\alpha$ can be expressed *uniquely* in the form $\sum_{\alpha \in H} x_\alpha$, where H is a finite subset of I, and $x_\alpha \in E_\alpha$ and $x_\alpha \neq 0$ for all $\alpha \in H$. (If $x = 0$ we have to take $H = \varnothing$.)

▲ We shall usually identify $\sum_{\alpha \in I} M_\alpha$ and $\bigoplus_{\alpha \in I} M_\alpha$ by means of f.

(A.3.3) *The sum of a family* $(M_\alpha)_{\alpha \in I}$ *of subspaces of a vector space is direct if and only if* $M_\alpha \cap \sum_{\beta \neq \alpha} M_\beta = \{0\}$ *for all* $\alpha \in I$.

▲ For to say that the mapping f defined in (A.3.2) is not injective means that there exists a finite number of nonzero elements $x_{\alpha_i} \in M_{\alpha_i}$ $(1 \leqslant i \leqslant n)$ such that $\sum_i x_{\alpha_i} = 0$ (A.2.2). This equation can be written in the form $x_{\alpha_1} = \sum_{j>1} (-x_{\alpha_j})$, and expresses that x_{α_1} belongs to $M_{\alpha_1} \cap \sum_{\beta \neq \alpha_1} M_\beta$. Hence the result.

(A.3.4) If E is equal to the direct sum of two subspaces M and N, we say that M and N are *supplementary subspaces* of E (or that M (resp. N) is a *supplement* to N (resp. M)). This signifies that $M + N = E$ and $M \cap N = \{0\}$. Hence we have linear mappings $p : E \to M$ and $q : E \to N$, the "projections" of E onto M and N, such that $x = p(x) + q(x)$ for all $x \in E$. The kernel of p (resp. q) is N (resp. M), and $p(p(x)) = p(x)$, $q(q(x)) = q(x)$.

▲ We cannot speak of "the" supplementary subspace of a subspace M, because in general there is more than one. However, there is the following result:

(A.3.5) *Let* M, N, N′ *be subspaces of* E, *such that* M *and* N *are supplementary, and* M *and* N′ *are supplementary. Let* $q : E \to N$ *be the projection of* E *onto* N *corresponding to the direct sum decomposition* $E = M \oplus N$. *Then the restriction* $q' : x \to q(x)$ *of* q *to* N′ *is an isomorphism of* N′ *onto* N.

▲ For since the kernel of q is M, the kernel of q' is $\mathrm{M} \cap \mathrm{N}' = \{0\}$ and therefore q' is injective. On the other hand, if x is any element of N, there exist $y \in \mathrm{M}$ and $z \in \mathrm{N}'$ such that $x = y + z$, so that $q(z) = q(x) = x$, because $q(y) = 0$. Hence q' is surjective.

4. BASES. DIMENSION AND CODIMENSION

(A.4.1) A family $(x_\alpha)_{\alpha \in \mathrm{I}}$ of distinct vectors in a vector space E is said to be *free*, and the x_α are said to be *linearly independent*, if for each finite subset H of I the relation $\sum_{\alpha \in \mathrm{H}} \lambda_\alpha x_\alpha = 0$ implies that $\lambda_\alpha = 0$ for all $\alpha \in \mathrm{H}$. It follows that $x_\alpha \neq 0$ for all $\alpha \in \mathrm{I}$, and $x_\beta \neq x_\alpha$ if $\beta \neq \alpha$ (otherwise we should have $1 \cdot x_\alpha + (-1)x_\beta = 0$). The subspaces $\mathrm{K}x_\alpha$ are therefore "rays" isomorphic to K, and the linear independence of the x_α may be expressed by saying that *the x_α are all nonzero and the sum of the rays $\mathrm{K}x_\alpha$ is direct.*

(A.4.2) *The family $(x_\alpha)_{\alpha \in \mathrm{I}}$ is free if and only if, for each $\alpha \in \mathrm{I}$, the vector x_α does not belong to the subspace generated by the x_β with $\beta \neq \alpha$.*

▲ This follows from the remark above and (A.3.3).

(A.4.3) *Let $u : \mathrm{E} \to \mathrm{F}$ be a linear mapping, and let $(y_\alpha)_{\alpha \in \mathrm{I}}$ be a free family of elements of $u(\mathrm{E})$. For each $\alpha \in \mathrm{I}$, let $x_\alpha \in \mathrm{E}$ be such that $u(x_\alpha) = y_\alpha$. Then the family $(x_\alpha)_{\alpha \in \mathrm{I}}$ is free, and the sum of* $\ker(u)$ *and* $\sum_{\alpha \in \mathrm{I}} \mathrm{K}x_\alpha$ *is direct.*

▲ Suppose that, for some finite subset H of I, we have a relation of the form $\sum_{\alpha \in \mathrm{H}} \lambda_\alpha x_\alpha + y = 0$, where $y \in \ker(u)$. It follows that $\sum_{\alpha \in \mathrm{H}} \lambda_\alpha u(x_\alpha) = 0$, because $u(y) = 0$. Since the family $(u(x_\alpha))_{\alpha \in \mathrm{H}}$ is free, we deduce that $\lambda_\alpha = 0$ for all α, and hence that $y = 0$. Q.E.D.

(A.4.4) A family $(b_\alpha)_{\alpha \in \mathrm{I}}$ of vectors in E is said to be a *basis* of E if it is free and generates E; or, equivalently, if the sum $\sum_{\alpha \in \mathrm{I}} \mathrm{K}b_\alpha$ is *direct* and *equal* to E; or, equivalently again, if for each $x \in \mathrm{E}$ there exists *a unique finite family of scalars* $(\lambda_\alpha)_{\alpha \in \mathrm{H}}$ such that $\mathrm{H} \subset \mathrm{I}$ and $\lambda_\alpha \neq 0$ for all $\alpha \in \mathrm{H}$, and $x = \sum_{\alpha \in \mathrm{H}} \lambda_\alpha b_\alpha$.

▲ Every free family $(x_\alpha)_{\alpha \in \mathrm{I}}$ is therefore a *basis* of the vector subspace $\sum_{\alpha \in \mathrm{I}} \mathrm{K}x_\alpha$.

In the vector space $K^{(I)}$, we denote by e_α the vector $(\delta_{\beta\alpha})_{\beta \in I}$ such that $\delta_{\beta\alpha} = 0$ if $\beta \neq \alpha$, and $\delta_{\alpha\alpha} = 1$. Clearly the family $(e_\alpha)_{\alpha \in I}$ is a *basis* of $K^{(I)}$. This basis is called the *canonical basis* of $K^{(I)}$. If a vector space E has a basis $(b_\alpha)_{\alpha \in I}$, then there exists a unique isomorphism of $K^{(I)}$ onto E which maps e_α to b_α for each $\alpha \in I$ (A.3.1).

(A.4.5) *Let* V *be a vector subspace of a vector space* E, *and suppose that* E *is generated by the union of* V *and the set of vectors of a finite family* $(x_i)_{1 \leqslant i \leqslant n}$. *Then there exists a subfamily* $(x_{i_k})_{1 \leqslant k \leqslant r}$ *which is a basis of a subspace supplementary to* V *in* E.

▲ The integer r is defined to be the largest for which there exists a subfamily $(x_{i_k})_{1 \leqslant k \leqslant r}$ of $(x_i)_{1 \leqslant i \leqslant n}$ such that the sum E′ of V and the Kx_{i_k} is *direct*. It is enough to show that E′ = E.

Suppose that E′ ≠ E. Then there is an index j such that $1 \leqslant j \leqslant n$ and $x_j \notin E'$ (otherwise E′ would contain V and all the x_i, and therefore by hypothesis would be equal to E). Hence we shall arrive at a contradiction if we can show that the sum of V, the Kx_{i_k} and Kx_j is direct. So consider a relation of the form $\lambda x_j + \sum_k \mu_k x_{i_k} + y = 0$, with $y \in V$. First of all, this implies that $\lambda = 0$ (otherwise $x_j = -\sum_k (\lambda^{-1}\mu_k)x_{i_k} - \lambda^{-1}y$, which belongs to E′). Then the definition of $(x_{i_k})_{1 \leqslant k \leqslant r}$ shows that $\mu_k = 0$ for all k, and $y = 0$. Q.E.D.

(A.4.6) *Every vector space generated by a finite set of vectors has a basis consisting of vectors belonging to this set.*

Take V = {0} in A.4.5.

▲ These last two results remain valid without the finiteness conditions (see [4]), but we shall not need to use this generalization in this book.

(A.4.7) *Let* E *be a vector space with a finite basis* $(b_i)_{1 \leqslant i \leqslant n}$. *Then every basis of* E *has exactly* n *elements.*

▲ It is enough to show that every other basis of E has *at most* n elements, because we can then interchange the roles of the two bases. We proceed by induction on n, the result being trivial when $n = 0$. Let $(b'_\alpha)_{\alpha \in I}$ be a basis of E, and consider an element b'_γ of this basis and the ray $V = Kb'_\gamma$ of E. The subspace $V' = \sum_{\alpha \neq \gamma} Kb'_\alpha$ is supplementary to V in E. On the other hand,

E is generated by V and the b_i, hence there is a subfamily $(b_{i_k})_{1 \leqslant k \leqslant r}$ of $(b_i)_{1 \leqslant i \leqslant n}$ such that the i_k are all distinct and such that $V'' = \sum_k K b_{i_k}$ is supplementary to V in E (A.4.5). We cannot have $r = n$, otherwise we should have $V'' = E$, which is absurd. Hence V″ has a basis of $r \leqslant n - 1$ elements, and since V′ is isomorphic to V″ (A.3.5), it follows that V′ has a basis of $r \leqslant n - 1$ elements. Hence the inductive hypothesis shows that $I - \{\gamma\}$ has *at most* $n - 1$ elements, and so I has at most n elements. Q.E.D.

▲ A vector space E which has a finite basis is said to be *finite dimensional.* The integer n in (A.4.7), that is to say the number of elements in any basis of E, is called the *dimension* of E (over K) and is denoted by dim E or $\dim_K E$. If $\dim E = n$, then E is isomorphic to K^n. A vector space which is not of finite dimension is said to be *infinite dimensional.* The relation $\dim E = 0$ is equivalent to $E = \{0\}$.

(A.4.8) (i) *In a vector space* E *of finite dimension n, every system of generators contains a basis of* E *and has at least n elements. Any system of generators consisting of n elements is a basis.*

(ii) *In a vector space* E *of finite dimension n, every free system of vectors is contained in a basis of* E *and has at most n elements. Any free system consisting of n elements is a basis.*

If $(x_i)_{1 \leqslant i \leqslant m}$ is a free system, it follows from (A.4.5) applied to $V = \sum_{i=1}^{m} K x_i$ and a basis $(b_j)_{1 \leqslant j \leqslant n}$ of E that there exists a subfamily $(b_{j_h})_{1 \leqslant h \leqslant r}$ such that the x_i and the b_{j_h} form a basis of E. This proves (ii). The assertion (i) follows from (A.4.7) and (A.4.6) in the case of a finite system of generators. In the general case, it is enough to show that a system S of generators contains a free system of n elements. Suppose this is not the case, and that the greatest number of elements in a free system extracted from S is $m < n$. If $(y_i)_{1 \leqslant i \leqslant m}$ is such a free system, then $V = \sum_{i=1}^{m} K y_i$ cannot be equal to E, by (A.4.7), and hence there exists $z \in S$ not contained in V. Then the y_i and z form a basis of $V + Kz$ by virtue of (A.4.5), and hence form a free family of $m + 1$ elements. This contradiction completes the proof.

(A.4.9) A subspace V of a vector space E is said to be *of finite codimension* if V has a supplementary subspace in E which is finite dimensional. The dimension in question does not depend on the choice of the supplementary subspace (A.3.5), and is called the *codimension* of V in E. It is denoted by codim V or codim_E V. If V has no supplementary subspace of finite dimension, then V is said to be *of infinite codimension* in E. By (A.4.5), V is of finite codimension in E if and only if E is generated by the union of V and a finite set of vectors.

(A.4.10) *If* E *is a finite-dimensional vector space, every subspace* F *of* E *is finite dimensional and of finite codimension in* E, *and*

(A.4.10.1) $$\dim F + \operatorname{codim} F = \dim E.$$

For by applying (A.4.5) to F and a basis of E, it follows that there exists a supplementary subspace F′ of F in E, with dim F′ ⩽ dim E. Interchanging the roles of F and F′, and using (A.3.5), it follows that F is also finite dimensional. If $(x_i)_{1 \leqslant i \leqslant p}$ is a basis of F and if $(x'_j)_{1 \leqslant j \leqslant q}$ is a basis of F′, it is clear that the x_i and the x'_j together form a basis of E.

(A.4.11) *Let* E *be a finite-dimensional vector space and let* F *be a subspace of* E. *If* dim F = dim E, *then* F = E.

This follows immediately from (A.4.10.1).

(A.4.12) *Let* M *and* N *be two finite-dimensional subspaces of a vector space* E. *Then* M + N *is finite dimensional, and we have*

(A.4.12.1) $$\dim(M + N) + \dim(M \cap N) = \dim M + \dim N.$$

The set consisting of the elements of a basis of M and a basis of N will generate M + N, which is therefore of finite dimension (A.4.6). Let P (resp. Q) be a supplementary subspace of M ∩ N in M (resp. N). It is clear that M + N is the *direct* sum of M ∩ N, P, and Q (A.3.3), and therefore $\dim(M + N) = \dim(M \cap N) + \dim P + \dim Q$. But also (A.4.10) we have $\dim P = \dim M - \dim(M \cap N)$, and $\dim Q = \dim N - \dim(M \cap N)$. Hence the result.

(A.4.13) *Let* M *and* N *be two vector subspaces of finite codimension in a vector space* E. *Then* M ∩ N *is of finite codimension in* E, *and we have*

(A.4.13.1) $$\operatorname{codim}(M + N) + \operatorname{codim}(M \cap N) = \operatorname{codim} M + \operatorname{codim} N.$$

Let V be a supplementary subspace of M in E. Then V is finite dimensional. Let $p : E \to V$ be the projection of E onto V with kernel M (A.3.4). The subspace $p(N)$ is finite dimensional (A.4.10). Let $(b_i)_{1 \leqslant i \leqslant m}$ be a basis of $p(N)$, and for each i let $c_i \in N$ be such that $p(c_i) = b_i$. Then N is generated by $M \cap N$ and the c_i (A.4.3), hence $M \cap N$ is of finite codimension in N and therefore of finite codimension in E. Let P (resp. Q) be a supplementary subspace of $M \cap N$ in M (resp. N), and let R be a supplementary subspace of $M + N$ in E. Then E is the direct sum of $M \cap N$, P, Q, and R, so that we have $\operatorname{codim}(M \cap N) = \dim P + \dim Q + \dim R$, $\operatorname{codim} M = \dim Q + \dim R$, $\operatorname{codim} N = \dim P + \dim R$, and $\operatorname{codim}(M + N) = \dim R$. The result (A.4.13.1) follows immediately from these formulas.

(A.4.14) A subspace of codimension 1 in a vector space E is called *a hyperplane in E*. If E is of finite dimension n, every hyperplane in E is of dimension $n - 1$ (A.4.10.1).

(A.4.15) *If* H *is a hyperplane in* E, *there exists a linear form* $f \neq 0$ *on* E *such that* $f^{-1}(0) = H$. *If* f' *is another linear form on* E *such that* $f'^{-1}(0) = H$, *then there exists a scalar* $\gamma \neq 0$ *such that* $f' = \gamma f$. *Conversely, if* g *is any nonzero linear form on* E, *then* $g^{-1}(0)$ *is a hyperplane in* E.

▲ If H is a hyperplane, there exists a vector $a \notin H$ such that E is the direct sum of H and Ka, and every $x \in E$ can therefore be expressed uniquely in the form $x = y + f(x)a$, where $f(x) \in K$. Since $x \to f(x)a$ is linear (A.3.4), so is $x \to f(x)$ (A.2.3); hence f is a linear form, and H is its kernel (A.3.4). If f' is any linear form such that $f'^{-1}(0) = H$, and if we put $f(a) = \alpha$ and $f'(a) = \beta$, then we have $\alpha \neq 0$ and $\beta \neq 0$, and $\alpha f' - \beta f$ is a linear form on E which vanishes on H and at a, and therefore vanishes identically on $E = H + Ka$. This shows that $f' = \alpha^{-1}\beta f$. Finally, if $H' = g^{-1}(0)$, then there exists a vector $b \notin H'$, because $g \neq 0$. Let $\gamma = g(b) \neq 0$. Then for every $x \in E$ we have $g(x - \gamma^{-1}g(x)b) = 0$, so that $x = y + \gamma^{-1}g(x)b$ for some $y \in H'$. This shows that $E = Kb + H'$, and the sum is direct because $b \notin H'$. Hence H′ is a hyperplane.

(A.4.16) Let $u : E \to F$ be a linear mapping. We say that u is of *finite rank* if $u(E)$ is of finite dimension. The dimension of $u(E)$ is then called the *rank* of u, and is written rank(u). If $u(E)$ is infinite dimensional, then u is said to be of *infinite rank*.

(A.4.17) *The mapping u is of finite rank if and only if* $\ker(u)$ *is of finite codimension, and then*

(A.4.17.1) $$\operatorname{rank}(u) = \operatorname{codim}_E(\ker(u)).$$

If $\ker(u)$ has a supplementary subspace V of finite dimension, then the restriction of u to V is an isomorphism of V onto $u(E)$, so that $u(E)$ has finite dimension equal to dim V. Conversely, if $(b_i)_{1 \leqslant i \leqslant n}$ is a finite basis of $u(E)$, let a_i be a vector in E such that $u(a_i) = b_i$ $(1 \leqslant i \leqslant n)$. Then E is the direct sum of $\ker(u)$ and the Ka_i (A.4.3).

(A.4.18) *Let* E, F *be vector spaces and let* $u : E \to F$ *be a linear mapping.*

(i) *If* F *is finite dimensional, then* $\operatorname{rank}(u) \leqslant \dim F$, *and* $\operatorname{rank}(u) = \dim F$ *if and only if u is surjective.*
(ii) *If* E *is finite dimensional, then* $\operatorname{rank}(u) \leqslant \dim E$, *and* $\operatorname{rank}(u) = \dim E$ *if and only if u is injective.*

The first assertion is an immediate consequence of the definition of $\operatorname{rank}(u)$ and (A.4.11). To prove (ii) it is enough to observe that if $\dim E = n$, then $u^{-1}(0)$ is of dimension $n - \operatorname{rank}(u)$, by (A.4.17) and (A.4.10).

(A.4.19) *Let* E *be a finite-dimensional vector space and let u be an endomorphism of* E. *Then the following assertions are equivalent:*

(i) *u is bijective;*
(ii) *u is injective;*
(iii) *u is surjective;*
(iv) $\operatorname{rank}(u) = \dim E$.

This follows immediately from (A.4.18).

(A.4.20) Let E be a vector space over a field K, and let K′ be a subfield of K. Let $(b_\alpha)_{\alpha \in I}$ be a basis of E over K, and let $(\rho_\lambda)_{\lambda \in J}$ be a basis of K considered as a vector space over K′. Then the family $(\rho_\lambda b_\alpha)$, where (λ, α) runs through $J \times I$, is *a basis of* E *over* K′. For it is clear that E is generated (over K′) by the elements of this family. On the other hand, suppose we have $\sum_{\lambda,\alpha} \xi_{\lambda\alpha} \rho_\lambda b_\alpha = 0$ with scalars $\xi_{\lambda\alpha} \in K'$. This relation may be written in the form $\sum_\alpha \left(\sum_\lambda \xi_{\lambda\alpha} \rho_\lambda\right) b_\alpha = 0$. Since the b_α are linearly independent over K, it follows that $\sum_\lambda \xi_{\lambda\alpha} \rho_\lambda = 0$ for each index $\alpha \in I$, and then that $\xi_{\lambda\alpha} = 0$ for each $(\lambda, \alpha) \in J \times I$ because the

ρ_λ are linearly independent over K′. Hence the $\rho_\lambda b_\alpha$ are linearly independent over K′, and our assertion is proved. In particular:

(A.4.21) *If* E *is finite dimensional over* K, *and* K *is finite dimensional over* K′, *then* E *is finite dimensional over* K′ *and we have*

(A.4.21.1) $$\dim_{K'} E = \dim_K E \cdot \dim_{K'} K.$$

5. MATRICES

(A.5.1) Let E, F be vector spaces over a field K, and suppose that E is of *finite* dimension n. Let $(a_i)_{1 \leqslant i \leqslant n}$ be a basis of E, so that E is the direct sum of the Ka_i. By (A.3.1) there is a one-one correspondence between the linear mappings u of E into F and the families $(b_i)_{1 \leqslant i \leqslant n}$ of n vectors of F; this correspondence is defined by $b_i = u(a_i)$ $(1 \leqslant i \leqslant n)$. Thus the vector space Hom(E, F) is *isomorphic* to F^n.

(A.5.2) Suppose furthermore that F is of *finite* dimension m, and let $(b_j)_{1 \leqslant j \leqslant m}$ be a basis of F. Then there is a one-one correspondence between the vectors $y \in F$ and the families $(\eta_j)_{1 \leqslant j \leqslant m}$ of m elements of K, defined by $y = \sum_{j=1}^{m} \eta_j b_j$. Hence there is a one-one correspondence between the linear mappings $u : E \to F$ and the "double" families (α_{ji}) (with $1 \leqslant j \leqslant m$, $1 \leqslant i \leqslant n$) of elements of K, defined by the relations

(A.5.2.1) $$u(a_i) = \sum_{j=1}^{m} \alpha_{ji} b_j \qquad (1 \leqslant i \leqslant n).$$

▲ Such families are called *matrices with m rows and n columns* (or $m \times n$ *matrices*) over K. They form a vector space over K, isomorphic to K^{mn}. The subfamily $(\alpha_{ji})_{1 \leqslant i \leqslant n}$ is the jth *row*, and the subfamily $(\alpha_{ji})_{1 \leqslant j \leqslant m}$ is the ith *column*, of the matrix $(\alpha_{ji})_{1 \leqslant j \leqslant m, 1 \leqslant i \leqslant n}$. The matrix $M(u) = (\alpha_{ji})$ defined by (A.5.2.1) is called *the matrix of u with respect to the bases* (a_i) *and* (b_j). If u, u' are two linear mappings of E into F, and if λ is any scalar, then

$$M(u + u') = M(u) + M(u'),$$
$$M(\lambda u) = \lambda M(u),$$

the matrices being taken in each case with respect to the same bases (a_i) of E and (b_j) of F.

(A.5.3) Now let G be another finite-dimensional vector space over K, and let $(c_k)_{1 \leqslant k \leqslant p}$ be a basis of G. Let $u : \mathrm{E} \to \mathrm{F}$ and $v : \mathrm{F} \to \mathrm{G}$ be two linear mappings and let $w = v \circ u : \mathrm{E} \to \mathrm{G}$. Suppose that the matrix $M(u)$ of u with respect to (a_i) and (b_j), and the matrix $M(v)$ of v with respect to (b_j) and (c_k) are known, and let us calculate the matrix $M(w)$ of w with respect to (a_i) and (c_k). If $M(u) = (\alpha_{ji})$, $M(v) = (\beta_{kj})$, $M(w) = (\gamma_{ki})$, then by definition we have

$$w(a_i) = \sum_{k=1}^{p} \gamma_{ki} c_k = v\left(\sum_{j=1}^{m} \alpha_{ji} b_j\right) = \sum_{j=1}^{m} \alpha_{ji} v(b_j) = \sum_{j=1}^{m} \alpha_{ji}\left(\sum_{k=1}^{p} \beta_{kj} c_k\right)$$

from which it follows that

(A.5.3.1)
$$\gamma_{ki} = \sum_{j=1}^{m} \beta_{kj} \alpha_{ji}.$$

The $p \times n$ matrix $M(w)$ is said to be the *product* of the $p \times m$ matrix $M(v)$ and the $m \times n$ matrix $M(u)$, and we write

$$M(v \circ u) = M(v)M(u).$$

Thus the product of two matrices is calculated by "multiplying the rows of the first by the columns of the second."

▲ Having given these definitions, it is of course possible to translate into matrix language most of the results we have established for linear mappings. We shall not stop to do this: indeed, in practice it is almost always advantageous, when presented with a problem of matrix algebra, to reformulate it in the language, so much more flexible and appropriate, of linear mappings. For example, there is no simple interpretation, in terms of matrices, of the essential concepts of the *kernel* and the *image* of a linear mapping.

6. MULTILINEAR MAPPINGS. DETERMINANTS

(A.6.1) Let $\mathrm{E}_1, \ldots, \mathrm{E}_r$ and F be $r + 1$ vector spaces over a field K. A mapping $u : \mathrm{E}_1 \times \mathrm{E}_2 \times \cdots \times \mathrm{E}_r \to \mathrm{F}$ is said to be *r-linear* if it is "linear in each of its arguments": that is to say, for each $i = 1, 2, \ldots, r$ and each choice of elements $a_j \in \mathrm{E}_j$ $(j \neq i)$, the partial mapping

$$x_i \to u(a_1, \ldots, a_{i-1}, x_i, a_{i+1}, \ldots, a_r)$$

of E_i into F is *linear*. This implies in particular that

$$u(a_1, \ldots, a_{i-1}, 0, a_{i+1}, \ldots, a_r) = 0$$

for all choices of the a_j. By induction on n, it follows from the definition that

(A.6.1.1)
$$u\left(\sum_{j=1}^{n} \xi_{1j} x_{1j}, \sum_{j=1}^{n} \xi_{2j} x_{2j}, \ldots, \sum_{j=1}^{n} \xi_{rj} x_{rj}\right) = \sum_{(j_i)} \xi_{1j_1}, \xi_{2j_2}, \ldots, \xi_{rj_r} u(x_{1j_1}, x_{2j_2}, \ldots, x_{rj_r}),$$

where the sum on the right-hand side is over all systems $(j_1, \ldots, j_r)$ such that $1 \leqslant j_1 \leqslant n, \ldots, 1 \leqslant j_r \leqslant n$; the ξ_{ij} are scalars and the x_{ij} are elements of E_i $(1 \leqslant i \leqslant r, 1 \leqslant j \leqslant n)$.

▲ An r-linear mapping of $E_1 \times \cdots \times E_r$ into K is called an *r-linear form.*

(A.6.2) Suppose that each of the vector spaces E_i $(1 \leqslant i \leqslant r)$ has a *finite basis* $(b_{ij})_{1 \leqslant j \leqslant n_i}$. Then it follows from the formula (A.6.1.1) that an r-linear mapping u of $E_1 \times E_2 \times \cdots \times E_r$ into F is uniquely determined by the vectors $u(b_{1j_1}, b_{2j_2}, \ldots, b_{rj_r}) \in F$ $(1 \leqslant j_i \leqslant n_i$ for each $i = 1, 2, \ldots, r)$. Conversely, if we are given *any* system $(c_{j_1 j_2 \ldots j_r})$ of $n_1 n_2 \cdots n_r$ vectors in F, then there exists a unique r-linear mapping u of $E_1 \times E_2 \times \cdots \times E_r$ into F such that $u(b_{1j_1}, b_{2j_2}, \ldots, b_{rj_r}) = c_{j_1 j_2 \ldots j_r}$ for each system of indices $(j_1, j_2, \ldots, j_r)$. To see this it is enough to *define* u by the formula (A.6.1.1) (taking n there to be greater than all the n_i, with $x_{ij} = b_{ij}$ for $j \leqslant n_i$ and $x_{ij} = 0$ for $j > n_i$). It is immediately verified that the mapping u so defined is indeed r-linear.
or extend it to the whole space by linearity.

* (A.6.3) Consider the case where all the E_i are equal to the same vector space E. An r-linear mapping $u : E^r \to F$ is said to be *alternating* if $u(x_1, x_2, \ldots, x_r) = 0$ whenever there are two distinct indices $i < j$ such that $x_i = x_j$. It follows from this definition that

$$0 = u(x_1, \ldots, x_{i-1}, x_i + x_j, x_{i+1}, \ldots, x_{j-1}, x_i + x_j, x_{j+1}, \ldots, x_r)$$
$$= u(x_1, \ldots, x_i, \ldots, x_j, \ldots, x_r) + u(x_1, \ldots, x_j, \ldots, x_i, \ldots, x_r)$$

for all $x_i \in E$. In other words, if we interchange two of the arguments x_i, x_j in u, the value of u *changes sign*. Since every permutation σ of the set $\{1, 2, \ldots, r\}$ may be expressed as a product of transpositions, the following formula is an easy consequence:

(A.6.3.1)
$$u(x_{\sigma(1)}, x_{\sigma(2)}, \ldots, x_{\sigma(r)}) = \varepsilon_\sigma u(x_1, x_2, \ldots, x_r),$$

where ε_σ is the *signature* of the permutation σ.

• If E is finite dimensional and $(b_j)_{1 \leqslant j \leqslant n}$ is a basis of E, then the $u(b_{j_1}, b_{j_2}, \ldots, b_{j_r})$ are zero by definition whenever two of the indices $j_1, \ldots, j_r$ are equal. By virtue of (A.6.3.1), the values of $u(b_{j_1}, \ldots, b_{j_r})$ for sequences of distinct indices (j_i) are determined by those which correspond to *increasing* sequences $j_1 < j_2 < \cdots < j_r$. Conversely, if we assign an arbitrary element $c_{j_1 j_2 \ldots j_r}$ of F to each increasing sequence, then there exists a unique alternating r-linear mapping $u : \mathrm{E}^r \to \mathrm{F}$ such that $u(b_{j_1}, b_{j_2}, \ldots, b_{j_r}) = c_{j_1 j_2 \ldots j_r}$ whenever $j_1 < j_2 < \cdots < j_r$. The verification of this statement is left to the reader.

(A.6.4) Consider the particular case of *alternating n-linear forms* on E^n, where n is the *dimension* of E. The remarks above show that such a form f is completely determined by its value $f(b_1, b_2, \ldots, b_n)$, where (b_i) is any *basis* of E; and f is identically zero if and only if $f(b_1, \ldots, b_n) = 0$. It follows that, if f_0 is one of these nonzero forms, then *every other alternating n-linear forms on* E^n *can be written as* λf_0, *where* λ *is a scalar*. These hypotheses and notations will remain in force for the rest of this section.

(A.6.5) *Let u be an endomorphism of* E. *Then there exists a unique scalar* $\det(u)$ *such that, if f is any alternating n-linear form on* E^n, *we have:*

(A.6.5.1) $$f(u(x_1), u(x_2), \ldots, u(x_n)) = \det(u) \cdot f(x_1, x_2, \ldots, x_n)$$

for all choices of $x_i \in \mathrm{E}$ $(1 \leqslant i \leqslant n)$.

▲ It is enough to prove this for f_0, in which case the result follows from (A.6.4) and the fact that $(x_1, \ldots, x_n) \to f_0(u(x_1), \ldots, u(x_n))$ is an alternating n-linear form on E^n.

The scalar $\det(u)$ is called the *determinant* of u. Clearly we have

(A.6.5.2) $$\det(1_{\mathrm{E}}) = 1.$$

(A.6.6) *If* u, v *are two endomorphisms of* E, *then*

(A.6.6.1) $$\det(u \circ v) = \det(u) \det(v).$$

By applying (A.6.5) to the alternating n-linear form

$$(x_1, \ldots, x_n) \to f_0(u(x_1), \ldots, u(x_n))$$

and the endomorphism v, we obtain

$$\begin{aligned} f_0(u(v(x_1)), \ldots, u(v(x_n))) &= \det(v) f_0(u(x_1), \ldots, u(x_n)) \\ &= \det(v) \det(u) f_0(x_1, \ldots, x_n). \end{aligned}$$

Since f_0 is not zero, the formula (A.6.6.1) now follows from the definition of $\det(u \circ v)$.

(A.6.7) $\det(u) \neq 0$ *if and only if* u *is bijective.*

If u is bijective, it has an inverse u^{-1} such that $u \circ u^{-1} = 1_E$. Hence, by (A.6.6) and (A.6.5.2), we have $\det(u)\det(u^{-1}) = 1$, so that certainly $\det(u) \neq 0$. If u is not bijective, then it is not injective (A.4.19), hence there exists $b_1 \neq 0$ such that $u(b_1) = 0$. There exists a basis $(b_i)_{1 \leqslant i \leqslant n}$ of E containing b_1 (A.4.5), and we have $f_0(b_1, \ldots, b_n) \neq 0$, whereas $f_0(u(b_1), \ldots, u(b_n)) = 0$. Hence $\det(u) = 0$.

(A.6.8) Let $(b_i)_{1 \leqslant i \leqslant n}$ be a basis of E, and let $M(u) = (\alpha_{ji})$ be the matrix of u with respect to the two bases (b_i) and (b_i) of E (or, as is usually said, *the matrix of* u *with respect to the basis* (b_i)). Since $f_0(b_1, \ldots, b_n) \neq 0$, the formulas (A.6.1.1) and (A.6.5.1) give

(A.6.8.1) $$\det(u) = \sum_{\sigma} \varepsilon_\sigma \alpha_{\sigma(1)1}\alpha_{\sigma(2)2} \cdots \alpha_{\sigma(n)n},$$

where σ runs through the symmetric group $\mathfrak{S}_n$ of all *permutations* of $\{1, 2, \ldots, n\}$.

The *determinant of the matrix* $M(u)$ is by definition the determinant of u. This provides the link between our theory and the classical theory of determinants in its original form. We shall not need to use this latter theory, and we leave the task of transcribing our results into the old-fashioned notation to those readers who are interested in this type of calculation. In applications it is always much simpler to go back to the definition (A.6.5), as we shall illustrate by considering the *eigenvalues* of an endomorphism.

(A.6.9) The definition of the eigenvalues of an endomorphism u is that given in (11.1.1), except that the field **C** is now replaced by an arbitrary field K. It follows immediately from (A.6.7) that these eigenvalues are the *roots* of the equation (called the *characteristic equation* of u)

(A.6.9.1) $$\det(u - \lambda \cdot 1_E) = 0.$$

The formula (A.6.8.1) shows immediately that the left-hand side of this equation is a *polynomial of degree* n in λ, with leading coefficient $(-1)^n$. In what follows we shall *assume* that the field K is *algebraically closed*, so that $\det(u - \lambda \cdot 1_E)$ factorizes into *linear* factors $(\lambda_1 - \lambda)(\lambda_2 - \lambda) \cdots (\lambda_n - \lambda)$.

(A.6.10) *There exists a basis* $(b_1, \ldots, b_n)$ *of* E *such that*

(A.6.10.1) $$u(b_i) = \lambda_i b_i + \alpha_{i,i+1} b_{i+1} + \cdots + \alpha_{in} b_n \qquad (1 \leqslant i \leqslant n).$$

Conversely, if $(b_i)_{1 \leqslant i \leqslant n}$ *is a basis with this property, then*

$$\det(u - \lambda \cdot 1_E) = (\lambda_1 - \lambda)(\lambda_2 - \lambda) \cdots (\lambda_n - \lambda).$$

The proof is by induction on n. By hypothesis, there exists a vector $b_n \neq 0$ in E which is an eigenvector for the eigenvalue λ_n; in other words, $u(b_n) = \lambda_n b_n$. Let us split E into a direct sum $Kb_n + V$, and let $p : E \to V$ be the corresponding projection (A.3.4). The mapping $x \to p(u(x))$ is an endomorphism of V, and hence there exists a basis $(b_1, \ldots, b_{n-1})$ of V such that

$$p(u(b_i)) = \mu_i b_i + \alpha_{i,i+1} b_{i+1} + \cdots + \alpha_{i,n-1} b_{n-1} \qquad (1 \leqslant i \leqslant n-1)$$

and consequently

$$u(b_i) = \mu_i b_i + \alpha_{i,i+1} b_{i+1} + \cdots + \alpha_{i,n-1} b_{n-1} + \alpha_{i,n} b_n \qquad (1 \leqslant i \leqslant n-1)$$

for suitable scalars α_{in}. We now have

$$\begin{aligned} &f_0(u(b_1) - \lambda b_1, \ldots, u(b_n) - \lambda b_n) \\ &\quad = f_0((\mu_1 - \lambda)b_1 + \cdots + \alpha_{1n} b_n, (\mu_2 - \lambda)b_2 + \cdots + \alpha_{2n} b_n, \ldots, \\ &\qquad \ldots, (\mu_{n-1} - \lambda)b_{n-1} + \alpha_{n-1,n} b_n, (\lambda_n - \lambda)b_n). \end{aligned}$$

If we expand the right-hand side by means of (A.6.1.1) and use the definition of an alternating multilinear form, we see easily that the only term which does not vanish is

$$(\mu_1 - \lambda)(\mu_2 - \lambda) \cdots (\mu_{n-1} - \lambda)(\lambda_n - \lambda) f_0(b_1, \ldots, b_n),$$

and therefore $\det(u - \lambda \cdot 1_E) = (\mu_1 - \lambda)(\mu_2 - \lambda) \cdots (\mu_{n-1} - \lambda)(\lambda_n - \lambda)$. This proves that the μ_i are (except possibly for their order) the scalars $\lambda_1, \ldots, \lambda_{n-1}$, and the calculation above also establishes the second assertion of (A.6.10).

The matrix of u with respect to a basis satisfying the conditions of (A.6.10) is said to be *lower triangular*.

(A.6.11) *For each integer* $k > 0$, *we have*

(A.6.11.1) $$\det(u^k - \lambda \cdot 1_E) = (\lambda_1^k - \lambda)(\lambda_2^k - \lambda) \cdots (\lambda_n^k - \lambda).$$

For it follows from the formulas (A.6.10.1) that

$$u^k(b_i) = \lambda_i^k b_i + \alpha_{i,i+1}^{(k)} b_{i+1} + \cdots + \alpha_{in}^{(k)} b_n \qquad (1 \leqslant i \leqslant n)$$

and the result therefore follows from (A.6.10).

(A.6.12) *The endomorphism u is a nilpotent element of the ring* End(E) *if and only if all its eigenvalues are zero.*

If u is nilpotent, it follows from (A.6.11) that all the eigenvalues of u are zero. Conversely, if all the λ_i are zero, the formula (A.6.10.1) shows, by induction on k, that $u^k(\mathrm{E}) \subset \mathrm{K}b_{k+1} + \mathrm{K}b_{k+2} + \cdots + \mathrm{K}b_n$ if $k < n$, and finally that $u^n(\mathrm{E}) = \{0\}$, that is to say, $u^n = 0$.

7. MINORS OF A DETERMINANT

(A.7.1) Let E be a vector space of dimension n over K, and let $(b_i)_{1 \leqslant i \leqslant n}$ be a basis of E. For each subset I of the index set $\mathrm{A} = \{1, 2, \ldots, n\}$, let E(I) be the subspace of E generated by the b_i with $i \in \mathrm{I}$. Then E is the direct sum of E(I) and E(A − I). If $\mathrm{I} = \{i_1, i_2, \ldots, i_r\}$, where $i_1 < i_2 < \cdots < i_r$, let j_I be the bijection of K^r onto E(I) such that $j_\mathrm{I}(e_k) = b_{i_k}$ $(1 \leqslant k \leqslant r)$, where $(e_k)_{1 \leqslant k \leqslant r}$ is the canonical basis of K^r (A.4.4). Also let p_I be the linear mapping of E onto K^r such that $p_\mathrm{I}(b_{i_k}) = e_k$ for $1 \leqslant k \leqslant r$, and $p_\mathrm{I}(b_j) = 0$ if $j \notin \mathrm{I}$. The kernel of p_I is therefore E(A − I), and the restriction of p_I to E(I) is a *bijection* of E(I) onto K^r.

(A.7.2) Let u be an endomorphism of E and let $M(u) = (\alpha_{ji})$ be its matrix with respect to the basis (b_i) (A.6.8). If I, J are two subsets of the index set A, having the *same* number of elements r, consider the endomorphism $u_{\mathrm{JI}} = p_\mathrm{J} \circ u \circ j_\mathrm{I}$ of K^r. Its matrix with respect to the canonical basis (e_k) of K^r consists of those α_{ji} for which $i \in \mathrm{I}$ and $j \in \mathrm{J}$. The determinant of this matrix (that is to say, $\det(u_{\mathrm{JI}})$) is called the $r \times r$ *minor* of $\det(u)$, corresponding to the basis $(b_i)_{1 \leqslant i \leqslant n}$ of E and the subsets I, J of the index set A.

(A.7.3) *An endomorphism u of* E *is of rank r if and only if all the $s \times s$ minors (where $s > r$) in* $\det(u)$ *relative to (b_i) are zero and at least one of the $r \times r$ minors is nonzero.*

Let ρ be the rank of u. With the notation of (A.7.2), we have $u_{\mathrm{JI}}(\mathrm{K}^r) = p_\mathrm{J}(u(\mathrm{E(I)}))$, hence (A.4.18) $\mathrm{rank}(u_{\mathrm{JI}}) = \dim(u_{\mathrm{JI}}(\mathrm{K}^r)) \leqslant \dim(u(\mathrm{E(I)})) \leqslant \dim u(\mathrm{E}) = \mathrm{rank}(u) = \rho$. If $r > \rho$, we therefore have $\det(u_{\mathrm{JI}}) = 0$, by (A.4.19) and (A.6.7). On the other hand, there exists a subset I_0 of A, containing ρ elements, such that $\mathrm{E}(\mathrm{I}_0)$ is supplementary to $\ker(u)$, and a subset J_0 of A containing ρ elements, such that $\mathrm{E}(\mathrm{A} - \mathrm{J}_0)$ is supplementary to $u(\mathrm{E})$ (A.4.5).

It follows that u, restricted to $E(I_0)$, is a bijection of $E(I_0)$ onto $u(E)$ (A.4.19), and that p_{J_0} restricted to $u(E)$ is a bijection of $u(E)$ onto K^p (A.3.5). Hence $u_{J_0 I_0}$ is bijective and therefore $\det(u_{J_0 I_0}) \neq 0$ (A.6.7). The proposition follows immediately from these remarks.

(A.7.4) With the preceding notations let us now take $I = J = \{1, 2, \ldots, m\}$, hence $A - I = A - J = \{m+1, \ldots, n\}$, and let us suppose in addition that $u_{A-I, I} = 0$, in other words the matrix $M(u)$ has the form

$$\begin{pmatrix} X & Y \\ 0 & Z \end{pmatrix}$$

where $X = M(u_{II})$ is an $m \times m$ matrix, $Y = M(u_{I, A-I})$ an $m \times (n-m)$ matrix and $Z = M(u_{A-I, A-I})$ an $(n-m) \times (n-m)$ matrix (0 standing for the zero $(n-m) \times m$ matrix). Then we have

(A.7.4.1) $$\det(M(u)) = \det(X)\det(Z).$$

For if v is the endomorphism of $E(I)$ having X as matrix with respect to $(b_i)_{1 \leqslant i \leqslant m}$, we have, with the notations of (A.6.10),

$$f(u(b_1), \ldots, u(b_m), u(b_{m+1}), \ldots, u(b_n)) = f(v(b_1), \ldots, v(b_m), u(b_{m+1}), \ldots, u(b_n)).$$

But the mapping

$$(x_1, \ldots, x_m) \to f(x_1, \ldots, x_m, u(b_{m+1}), \ldots, u(b_n))$$

is an alternating m-linear form on $(E(I))^m$, hence, by (A.6.5),

$$f(v(b_1), \ldots, v(b_m), u(b_{m+1}), \ldots, u(b_n)) = (\det X) f(b_1, \ldots, b_m, u(b_{m+1}), \ldots, u(b_n)).$$

For each $j \geqslant m+1$, let us write $u(b_j) = c'_j + c''_j$, with $c'_j \in E(I)$, $c''_j \in E(A—I)$. By definition of an alternating multilinear form, we have

$$f(b_1, \ldots, b_m, u(b_{m+1}), \ldots, u(b_n)) = f(b_1, \ldots, b_m, c''_{m+1}, \ldots, c''_n).$$

Let w then be the endomorphism of $E(A - I)$ having Z as matrix with respect to $(b_j)_{m+1 \leqslant j \leqslant n}$; by definition $w(b_j) = c_j''$ for $j \in A - I$. The mapping

$$(x_{m+1}, \ldots, x_n) \to f(b_1, \ldots, b_m, x_{m+1}, \ldots, x_n)$$

is an alternating $(n-m)$-linear form on $(E(A - I))^{n-m}$, hence we get similarly

$$f(b_1, \ldots, b_m, w(b_{m+1}), \ldots, w(b_n)) = (\det Z) f(b_1, \ldots, b_n) = \det Z$$

which proves (A.7.4.1). By induction on r, we conclude that for any "triangular matrix of matrices"

$$U = \begin{pmatrix} X_{11} & X_{12} & \cdots & X_{1r} \\ 0 & X_{22} & \cdots & X_{2r} \\ & & \vdots & \\ 0 & 0 & \cdots & X_{rr} \end{pmatrix}$$

where X_{ij} is an $m_i \times m_j$ matrix, we have

(A.7.4.2) $$\det U = (\det X_{11})(\det X_{22}) \cdots (\det X_{rr})$$

("Computation of a determinant by blocks").

REFERENCES

[1] Ahlfors, L., "Complex Analysis." McGraw-Hill, New York, 1953.

[2] Bachmann, H., "Transfinite Zahlen" (Ergebnisse der Math., Neue Folge, Heft 1). Springer, Berlin, 1955.

[3] Bourbaki, N., "Eléments de Mathématique," Livre I, "Théorie des Ensembles" (Actual. Scient. Ind., Chaps. I, II, No. 1212; Chap. III, No. 1243). Hermann, Paris, 1954–1956.

[4] Bourbaki, N., "Eléments de Mathématique," Livre II, "Algèbre," Chap. II (Actual. Scient. Ind., Nos. 1032, 1236, 2nd ed.). Hermann, Paris, 1955.

[5] Bourbaki, N., "Eléments de Mathématique," Livre III, "Topologie générale" (Actual. Scient. Ind., Chaps. I, II, Nos. 858, 1142, 4th ed.; Chap. IX, No. 1045, 2nd ed.; Chap. X, No. 1084, 2nd ed.). Hermann, Paris, 1949–1958.

[6] Bourbaki, N., "Eléments de Mathématique," Livre V, "Espaces vectoriels topologiques" (Actual. Scient. Ind., Chap. I, II, No. 1189, 2nd ed.; Chaps. III–V, No. 1229). Hermann, Paris, 1953–1955.

[7] Cartan, H., "Séminaire de l'Ecole Normale Supérieure, 1951–1952: Fonctions analytiques et faisceaux analytiques."

[8] Cartan, H., "Théorie élémentaire des fonctions analytiques." Hermann, Paris, 1961.

[9] Coddington, E., and Levinson, N., "Theory of Ordinary Differential Equations." McGraw-Hill, New York, 1955.

[10] Courant, R., and Hilbert, D., "Methoden der mathematischen Physik," Vol. I, 2nd ed. Springer, Berlin, 1931.

[11] Halmos, P., "Finite Dimensional Vector Spaces," 2nd ed. Van Nostrand, Princeton, New Jersey, 1958.

[12] Ince, E., "Ordinary Differential Equations." Dover Publications, New York, 1949.

[13] Jacobson, N., "Lectures in Abstract Algebra," Vol. II, "Linear Algebra." Van Nostrand, Princeton, New Jersey, 1953.

[14] Kamke, E., "Differentialgleichungen reeller Funktionen." Akad. Verlag, Leipzig, 1930.

[15] Kelley, J., "General Topology." Van Nostrand, Princeton, New Jersey, 1955.

[16] Landau, E., "Foundations of Analysis." Chelsea, New York, 1951.

[17] Springer, G., "Introduction to Riemann Surfaces." Addison-Wesley, Reading, Massachusetts, 1957.

[18] Weil, A., "Introduction à l'étude des variétés kählériennes" (Actual. Scient. Ind., No. 1267). Hermann, Paris, 1958.

[19] Weyl, H., "Die Idee der Riemannschen Fläche," 3rd ed. Teubner, Stuttgart, 1955.

INDEX

In the following index the first reference number refers to the number of the chapter in which the subject may be found and the second to the section within the chapter.

D

E

F

G

H

I

O

P

Q

R

S

T

U

Pure and Applied Mathematics

A Series of Monographs and Textbooks

Editors

Paul A. Smith and Samuel Eilenberg

Columbia University, New York

1: ARNOLD SOMMERFELD. Partial Differential Equations in Physics. 1949 (Lectures on Theoretical Physics, Volume VI)

2: REINHOLD BAER. Linear Algebra and Projective Geometry. 1952

3: HERBERT BUSEMANN AND PAUL KELLY. Projective Geometry and Projective Metrics. 1953

4: STEFAN BERGMAN AND M. SCHIFFER. Kernel Functions and Elliptic Differential Equations in Mathematical Physics. 1953

5: RALPH PHILIP BOAS, JR. Entire Functions. 1954

6: HERBERT BUSEMANN. The Geometry of Geodesics. 1955

7: CLAUDE CHEVALLEY. Fundamental Concepts of Algebra. 1956

8: SZE-TSEN HU. Homotopy Theory. 1959

9: A. M. OSTROWSKI. Solution of Equations and Systems of Equations. Second Edition. 1966

10: J. DIEUDONNÉ. Treatise on Analysis. Volume I, Foundations of Modern Analysis, enlarged and corrected printing, 1969. Volume II, 1970.

11: S. I. GOLDBERG. Curvature and Homology. 1962.

12: SIGURDUR HELGASON. Differential Geometry and Symmetric Spaces. 1962

13: T. H. HILDEBRANDT. Introduction to the Theory of Integration. 1963.

14: SHREERAM ABHYANKAR. Local Analytic Geometry. 1964

15: RICHARD L. BISHOP AND RICHARD J. CRITTENDEN. Geometry of Manifolds. 1964

16: STEVEN A. GAAL. Point Set Topology. 1964

17: BARRY MITCHELL. Theory of Categories. 1965

18: ANTHONY P. MORSE. A Theory of Sets. 1965

Pure and Applied Mathematics

A Series of Monographs and Textbooks

19: Gustave Choquet. Topology. 1966

20: Z. I. Borevich and I. R. Shafarevich. Number Theory. 1966

21: José Luis Massera and Juan Jorge Schaffer. Linear Differential Equations and Function Spaces. 1966

22: Richard D. Schafer. An Introduction to Nonassociative Algebras. 1966

23: Martin Eichler. Introduction to the Theory of Algebraic Numbers and Functions. 1966

24: Shreeram Abhyankar. Resolution of Singularities of Embedded Algebraic Surfaces. 1966

25: François Treves. Topological Vector Spaces, Distributions, and Kernels. 1967

26: Peter D. Lax and Ralph S. Phillips. Scattering Theory. 1967

27: Oystein Ore. The Four Color Problem. 1967

28: Maurice Heins. Complex Function Theory. 1968

29: R. M. Blumenthal and R. K. Getoor. Markov Processes and Potential Theory. 1968

30: L. J. Mordell. Diophantine Equations. 1969

31: J. Barkley Rosser. Simplified Independence Proofs: Boolean Valued Models of Set Theory. 1969

32: William F. Donoghue, Jr. Distributions and Fourier Transforms. 1969

33: Marston Morse and Stewart S. Cairns. Critical Point Theory in Global Analysis and Differential Topology. 1969

34: Edwin Weiss. Cohomology of Groups. 1969

35: Hans Freudenthal and H. De Vries. Linear Lie Groups. 1969

36: Laszlo Fuchs. Infinite Abelian Groups: Volume I. 1970

In preparation

Keio Nagami. Dimension Theory.

Peter L. Duren. Theory of H^p Spaces.

Eduard Prugovecki. Quantum Mechanics in Hilbert Space.

Ex. 3.b. $x \in \bar{A} \Rightarrow x \notin \bar{B}$ i.e there exists an open nbhd of x which does not contain points of B i.e $x \in ext(B) \subset B^c$. Given $x \in fr(A) \subset \bar{A}$ and $x \in U_x$ the set $U_x \cap ext(B)$ is open and not empty $\subset B^c$ and contains points of A^c since $x \in fr(A)$.

Ex. III.10.5 (P.p 44).

Since E is separable there exists a countable subset $A = \{x_1, x_2, \ldots\}$ dense in E. We consider the open balls $B_{kn}(x_k, \frac{1}{n})$. If such a ball contains a point of the subspace F we call it y_{k_n} and all such points form a subset B of F.

B is dense in F. Proof: Consider $y \in F$ and the ball $B(y; \varepsilon)$. The ball $B(y; \varepsilon/2)$ contains a point $x_k \in A$. Hence $d(x_k, y) < \varepsilon/2$. We see that the ball $B(x_k; \varepsilon/2)$ contains points of F (at least y) i.e contains one $y_{km} \in B$. It is enough to prove that $y_{km} \in B(y; \varepsilon)$

$$d(y, y_{km}) \leq d(y, x_k) + d(x_k, y_{km}) \leq \varepsilon/2 + \varepsilon/2 = \varepsilon$$